Avian Physiology

SECOND EDITION

AVIAN
PHYSIOLOGY

Second Edition

By Paul D. Sturkie

PROFESSOR OF PHYSIOLOGY
RUTGERS UNIVERSITY
THE STATE UNIVERSITY OF NEW JERSEY

Comstock Publishing Associates

A DIVISION OF

Cornell University Press

ITHACA, NEW YORK

CORNELL UNIVERSITY PRESS

First edition 1954
Second edition 1965

Library of Congress Catalog Card Number: 65-24473

PRINTED IN THE UNITED STATES OF AMERICA

To my wife, Betty

Preface to First Edition

PHYSIOLOGY may be divided into three main categories: cellular, comparative, and special—i.e., the physiology of special groups of organisms. The physiology of special groups has received the most attention. In the animal field, interest has centered largely on mammalian physiology, with particular emphasis on human physiology and its relationship to medicine. By comparison, the physiology of birds has been neglected. Knowledge in certain areas of avian physiology is limited, fragmentary, and often confused, and little or no new research is being conducted. Much of the physiological research on the bird has been conducted from the comparative viewpoint, which is concerned more with broad functional relationships between groups of animals than with details of a special group. In some areas, however, these fundamental functions have not been definitely established. Even in certain fields, such as endocrinology, where there is considerably more research activity on the bird, there are wide gaps in our knowledge.

This book is the first one in any language devoted to the specialized physiology of birds. It deals mainly with the chicken, the duck, and the pigeon, because most of the research has been conducted on these species and they represent species of economic importance to man.

Inasmuch as physiology provides a rational basis for much of animal husbandry and veterinary medicine, this book should be of especial interest to teachers, students, and research workers in poultry science and husbandry and in veterinary medicine. More knowledge and research in avian physiology, particularly on the domestic species, should have important applications to the poultry industry, which is rapidly expanding in this country. Although few poultry departments at present offer course work on the physiology of birds, it is hoped that this book may be instrumental in increasing the number of institutions offering such work and in stimulating more research. It may serve, also, as a source of reference for the experimental physiologist and should provide pertinent physiological material for courses in comparative physiology, ecology, and ornithology.

The bibliography is extensive but not exhaustive. An attempt was made to select the most important and more recent references, with minor consideration given to priority. The references are cited at the end of each chapter and include the complete title.

The writer is indebted to investigators, journals, and books for many of the illustrations used. Separate acknowledgment is made in the legends to the authors and books or journals from which illustrations came. The original drawings and modifications of illustrations of others were prepared by my wife, to whom I am grateful.

Special thanks are extended to colleagues who read one or more chapters and made helpful suggestions. These are Drs. H. H. Dukes, J. A. Dye, F. B. Hutt, R. M. Fraps, C. S. Shaffner, A. V. Nalbandov, T. C. Byerly, J. H. Leathem, J. B. Allison, W. C. Russell, and H. J. Metzger.

PAUL D. STURKIE

New Brunswick, New Jersey
July 1953

Preface to Second Edition

SINCE the publication of the first edition in 1954 there has been a considerable increase in research activity in avian endocrinology and reproduction and a modest increase in research in other areas. Much work, however, remains to be done on such systems as respiration, muscle, nerve, and digestion.

New features of the second edition include a chapter on the nervous system by Dr. Jasper ten Cate, Professor of Comparative Physiology, University of Amsterdam, Holland, and contributions from other authors active in various fields. An expanded chapter on chemical constituents has been written, mainly by Dr. D. J. Bell, Head of Biochemistry Section, Poultry Research Center, Edinburgh, Scotland. The section on coagulation of blood was written by Dr. Paul Griminger, Associate Professor of Nutrition, Rutgers University.

Expanded chapters on temperature regulation and on energy metabolism have been contributed by Dr. G. C. Whittow, formerly physiologist at the Hannah Dairy Research Institute, and now Associate Professor of Physiology, Rutgers University.

The chapter on carbohydrate metabolism was completely revised by Dr. R. L. Hazelwood, Associate Professor of Physiology, University of Houston.

The chapter on sense organs was revised by Dr. M. R. Kare, Professor of Physiology, North Carolina State College. Chapter 19, "Thyroids," has been considerably expanded by Dr. Robert K. Ringer, Professor of Avian Physiology, Michigan State University.

Chapter 15, "Reproduction in the Female," has also been expanded. That part of it relating to calcium metabolism and egg laying was contributed by Dr. T. G. Taylor, Reader in Physiological Chemistry, University of Reading, England, and Dr. D. A. Stringer, Unilever Research Laboratory, Bedford, England.

Most of the chapters that I revised have also been enlarged. The revision has resulted in a substantial increase in the size of the book.

The authors are indebted to various investigators, journals, and books for many of the illustrations used. Individual acknowledgment is made in the legends.

P. D. S.

New Brunswick, New Jersey
May 1965

Contents

Chapter 2

Chemical Constituents of Blood, by D. J. Bell and Paul D. Sturkie   32

Chapter 3

Circulation, Blood Pressure, Blood Flow, and Body Fluids   85

Chapter 4

Contraction and Conduction in the Heart   118

Chapter 5

Electrocardiography   133

Chapter 6

Respiration 152

Chapter 7

Transport of the Blood Gases 177

Chapter 8

Regulation of Body Temperature, by G. C. Whittow   186

Chapter 9

Energy Metabolism, by G. C. Whittow   239

Contents

Chapter 10

Alimentary Canal: Anatomy, Prehension, Deglutition, Appetite, Passage of Ingesta, Motility 272

Chapter 11

Chapter 12

Chapter 13

Kidneys and Urine 372

Chapter 14

The Special Senses, by M. R. Kare   406

The Eye and Vision   406

The Ear and Hearing   419

The Chemical Senses   428

Chapter 15

Reproduction in the Female and Egg Formation   447

Chapter 16

Reproduction in the Male, Fertilization, and Early
Embryonic Development   515

Chapter 17
Hypophysis 534

Chapter 18
Gonadal Hormones 568

Chapter 19

Thyroids, by Robert K. Ringer   592

Contents

Chapter 20

Parathyroids, Thymus, Pineal, and Pancreas 649

Chapter 21
Adrenals 668

Chapter 22
The Nervous System of Birds, by Jasper ten Cate 697

Physiology of the Nervous System of Birds 707

Contents

Avian Physiology

SECOND EDITION

CHAPTER 1

Blood: Formed Elements, Physical Characteristics, and Coagulation

BLOOD has many functions. Some of these are (1) absorption and transport of nutrients from the alimentary canal to the tissues, (2) transport of the blood gases to and from the tissues, (3) removal of waste products of metabolism, (4) transportation of hormones produced by the endocrine glands, and (5) regulation of the water content of the body tissues. Blood is also important in the regulation and maintenance of body temperature.

Blood contains a fluid portion (the plasma), salts and other chemical constituents, and certain formed elements, the corpuscles. The corpuscles comprise the erythrocytes (red cells) and leucocytes (white cells).

ERYTHROCYTES

Erythrocytes of birds are oval-shaped, and unlike those of most mammals, are nucleated; they are also larger (Figure 1). The sizes of the erythrocytes of some avian species are presented in Table 1. These figures agree closely with the later results of Lucas and Jamroz (1961) for heavy breeds of chickens, but not for Leghorns. These authors reported that the length of the red cells was less in White Leghorns. Jaffe (1960) has reported differences in erythrocyte numbers of inbred lines of White Leghorns. Nice *et al.*

Table 1. Dimensions of bird erythrocytes in microns (mainly from Groebbels, 1932) ·

Species	Long diameter	Short diameter	Thickness	Author
Chicken (breed not given)				
3 days old	12.5	7.0	3.8	Lange
25 days old	13.0	7.2	3.5	Lange
70 days old	13.0	6.5	3.5	Lange
mature (♂ & ♀)	12.8	6.9	3.6	Lange
Chickens (White Leghorn)	10.7	6.8	—	Lucas & Jamroz (1961)
Pigeon				
1 day old	13.0	7.7	3.8	Lange
mature	12.7	7.5	3.7	Lange
Turkey				
male	15.5	7.5	—	Venzlaff
female	15.5	7.0	—	Venzlaff
Duck	12.8	6.6	—	Malassez

(1935) have reported red cell numbers for several wild species of birds.

Numbers

The number of erythrocytes is influenced by age, sex, and other factors. Values for a number of species are shown in Table 2.

Effects of hormones. Sexually mature males have a higher number of erythrocytes than females (Domm and Taber, 1946; Juhn and Domm, 1930; Newell and Shaffner, 1950; and others). Until sexual maturity there appears to be no significant difference in the counts and little variation due to age. Domm and Taber and others have reported that the number of erythrocytes in the castrate male is nearly the same as that in the female, suggesting that androgen, the male hormone, accounted for the difference. When these workers administered androgen to male castrates, erythrocyte numbers approached the level for normal males. Sturkie and

Table 2. Erythrocyte numbers in birds in millions per cubic millimeter

Species	Age	Sex Male	Sex Female	Sex not given	Investigator
Chicken	Adult	3.8	3.0		Lucas & Jamroz (1961)
"	"	3.24	2.77		Dukes (1947)
"	"	3.32	2.72		Olson (1937)
"	"	3.26	2.72		Lange (Groebbels, 1932)
"	3 hours			1.84	"
"	3 days			2.23	"
"	12 days			2.65	"
"	26 days			2.77	Cook (1937)
"	32–47 days			2.83	Twisselmann (1939)
"	50 days			2.34	Lange
"	70 days			2.39	"
"	82 days			2.79	Cook
Chicken (W. Leghorn)	42 days		3.02		Lucas & Jamroz (1961)
" "	84 days		3.02		"
Pigeon	Adult	4.00	3.07		Wastl & Leiner (Groebbels)
"	"	3.23	3.09		Riddle & Braucher (1934)
Dove	"	3.04	2.99		"
Goose (domestic)	"			2.71	Wastl & Leiner (Groebbels)
Duck (domestic)	"			2.80	Malassez (Groebbels)
Turkey (domestic)	"	2.24	2.37		Venzlaff (Groebbels)
Ostrich	"		1.89*		De Villiers (1938)
Red-tailed Hawk	Immature			3.2	Bond & Gilbert (1958)
Quail				3.4	"
Great horned owl				2.2	"
Diving duck				3.2	"
Dabbling duck				3.6	"
Red-throated loon				3.1	"

* Males and females

Textor (1960), however, found the erythrocyte numbers in White Leghorn male castrates to be intermediate between those in normal males and females. Female castrates (poulards) have the same number of red cells as normal females, indicating that estrogen does not influence cell count. Androgen administration increased the numbers to the normal male level.

That the thyroid hormone (thyroxine) exerts a control over erythrocyte numbers in the male chicken was shown by Domm and Taber (1946) in their experiments on thyroidectomy, as follows:

	Males	*Females*
Completely thyroidectomized	2.43*	2.60
Incompletely thyroidectomized	2.62	2.65
Normal individuals	3.25	2.61

* Millions per cubic centimeter.

The operation had no effect upon numbers in the female.

Thiouracil (a goitrogen or antithyroid drug) is considered to have an effect similar to thyroidectomy, but when administered to chickens it depressed the erythrocyte numbers significantly in males, females, and capons (Domm and Taber, 1946).

Season. According to Domm and Taber, the number of erythrocytes in hens is greater in the fall than in the winter and spring, when rate of laying is usually higher. Domm and Taber also observed a diurnal variation in erythrocytes, with high values at midnight and the lowest values at noon. The data of Olson (1937) suggest a seasonal variation in red cell count, with values higher in the winter, and recent data by Vogel (1961) show higher erythrocyte volumes for males and females in winter.

Other factors. The concentration of erythrocytes in the blood may be influenced by certain minerals, vitamins, and drugs. Deficiencies in iron and copper produce anemia and a decrease in hemoglobin (Hart, Elvehjem, and Kemmerer, 1930).

Cobalt is not usually considered essential for normal erythropoiesis, but when excessive amounts are administered to certain mammals and to ducks, an increase in the number of erythrocytes (polycythemia) occurs. When cobalt chloride (1 to 4 mg. daily for 14 days) is injected into ducks, the red cell count increases from 2.6 to 3.1 million (Davis, McCullough, and Rigdon, 1945). Davis *et al.* suggest that the initial rise in count following the administration of cobalt is due to erythropoietic stimulation, but that the maintenance of the elevated number may be due to a decreased rate of destruction of erythrocytes.

High altitude and anoxia stimulate erythropoiesis and increase erythrocyte numbers in chicken as they do in mammals (Vezzani, 1939; Smith, personal communication). Whole body X-radiation of chickens of various ages has been reported and reviewed by

Lucas and Denington (1957). There was no significant effect on erythrocyte numbers except with dosages above 600–800 r units.

Corpuscular Volume (Hematocrit)

The corpuscles may be separated from the plasma by centrifugation. A sample of blood is placed in a hematocrit tube and centrifuged for 15 to 20 minutes at 3,000 or more r.p.m. The tube is graduated so that volume of the cells can be read off. The cell volume is composed largely of erythrocytes, but includes leucocytes as well. The method is subject to an error of about 5 percent because of the trapping of some plasma with the cells as they settle out. The estimation includes the leucocytes. Values for cell volume in percentages are shown as follows:

Species, Age and Condition	No Sex	Male	Female	Author
Chicken, sexually immature		29	29	Newell & Shaffner (1950)
" " mature		45	29	"
" " "		40	31	Lucas & Jamroz (1961)
" 6 weeks			31	"
" 12 "			30	"
" sexually mature				
(W. Leghorn)		48	31	Sturkie & Textor (1960)
" " " (capon)		38		"
Turkey			35.9	McCartney (1952)
" 9 months (Bronze)		45.1	36.4	Ringer (unpublished)
Pigeon		58.5	56.4	Kaplan (1954)
"	52			Bond & Gilbert (1958)
Pheasant (Ring-necked)		33	34	"
Red-tailed hawk, immature	43			"
Great horned owl	32			"
Quail	38			"
Red-throated loon	54			"
Diving ducks	37			"
Dabbling ducks (mallard)	43			"
Coot	46			"

It is apparent from the table that there is no appreciable sex difference in hematocrits among some species, whereas in others, such as the chicken and turkey, the difference is considerable. Androgen is known to increase the numbers and volume of red cells in the chicken (Newell and Shaffner, 1950; Sturkie and Newman, 1951; and others).

Changes in cell volume may occur or be induced, without influencing the absolute number of cells, by an increase in plasma water (hemodilution) or by a decrease (hemoconcentration). The act of sampling may cause hemodilution (Sturkie and Newman, 1951). Hemoconcentration may be induced by the administration of epinephrine (Tapper and Kare, 1959) or by hypothermia (see Chapter 8).

Resistance of Erythrocytes

Hemolysis is the discharging of hemoglobin from the corpuscles into the plasma. A number of factors, such as freezing, thawing, and changes in osmotic pressure of the blood, produce hemolysis. Solutions that have the same osmotic pressure as blood and that do not cause hemolysis are isotonic. Solutions with lower osmotic pressures than blood are hypotonic, and those with higher pressure are hypertonic. Hypotonic solutions cause hemolysis and bursting by increasing the water content of the cells, and hypertonic solutions cause a shrinking of the corpuscles, because water is lost from the cells. The fragility of red cells is measured by their resistance to solutions of known concentrations and osmotic pressures, usually NaCl solutions. The point at which hemolysis begins is termed minimum resistance, and the point at which all cells are hemolyzed is termed maximum resistance. Figures for the resistance of bird erythrocytes are as follows:

Species	Minimum resistance Percent NaCl	Maximum resistance Percent NaCl	Author
Chicken	0.4 or 4.7	—	Kleineberger & Carl (from De Villiers, 1938)
"	0.44	0.28	Demmel (from Dukes, 1947)
Ostrich, males	0.47	0.27	De Villiers (1938)
Ostrich, females	0.48	0.28	"

Hunter (1953) has studied the permeability of chicken erythrocytes to hypotonic and hypertonic solutions, employing a photoelectric method, by which it is possible to measure swelling and shrinking of cells before actual hemolysis occurs. His results indicate that erythrocytes in chicken, as in man, behave as perfect osmometers in slightly hypotonic and slightly hypertonic solutions, but that in markedly hypertonic solutions they shrink less than would be expected if they were behaving as perfect osmometers. Hunter introduces the term "frailty" to indicate the tendency of cells to hemolyze following volume changes in a solution which at equilibrium is isosmotic, and "fragility" to indicate the hemolyzing tendency to solutions of varying tonicities.

The blood of birds contains relatively more potassium and less sodium than mammalian blood (see Chapter 2).

A physiological saline (Ringer's solution) for birds, formulated by Benzinger and Krebs, takes into account the difference in electrolyte content of bird blood, in grams per liter of solution as follows (Prosser and Brown, 1961):

$NaCl$	KCl	$CaCl$	$NaHCO_3$	$MgSO_4$	pH
6.8	1.73	0.64	2.45	0.25	7.4

Details concerning the exchange of Na and K in bird erythrocytes have been reported by Hunter *et al.* (1956), Orskov (1954), Toteson and Robertson (1956), and others.

Formation and Destruction of the Corpuscles

Two theories on the origin of the blood cells have been evolved; one is the monophyletic and the other the polyphyletic theory. The proponents of the monophyletic theory maintain that there is one specific stem cell developing from the mesenchyme which gives rise to both of two main types of blood cells, the white and the red. The proponents of the polyphyletic theory of blood cell formation believe that erythrocytes and leucocytes develop from two originally distinct cell types, the erythrocytes from the vascular endothelium of the bone marrow, and the leucocytes from reticular connective tissue cells.

Jordan (1939), an adherent of the monophyletic view, regarded the bone marrow as the chief hematopoietic center in birds and consequently believed it could give rise to all of the different cell types. Krumbhaar (1928) believed that although the bone marrow is the chief site of hematopoiesis in birds, the liver may also be such a site. Lucas (1959) and Lucas and Jamroz (1961), who have reviewed and discussed the origin of the various blood cell types, state that most hematologists subscribe to the polyphyletic view.

Erythrocyte series. Lucas (1959) discussed the nomenclature applied to cells of this series in avian and mammalian blood, and has proposed terminology applicable to all vertebrates, as follows:

Avian	Mammalian	Proposed Vertebrate Terminology
Early erythroblast	Rubriblast	Early rubriblast
Late erythroblast	Prorubricyte	Late rubriblast
Early polychromatic erythrocyte	Rubricyte	Prorubricyte
Mid polychromatic erythrocyte	Metarubricyte	Mesorubricyte
Late polychromatic erythrocyte		Metarubricyte
Reticulocyte	Reticulocyte	Reticulocyte
Mature erythrocyte	Erythrocyte	Erythrocyte

Thrombocytes. The thrombocyte or platelet of mammalian blood has its origin from the giant cells, megakaryocytes, of the lungs and bone marrow. The megakaryocyte is lacking in avian bone marrow and the thrombocytes arise from antecedent mono-nucleated cells that have a blast stage like other cells (Lucas and Jamroz, 1961). Evidence from a number of sources suggests that they are cells belonging to the erythrocyte series. Blount (1939) states that a thrombocyte is an erythrocyte in which the process of hemoglobinization of the cell did not proceed to maturity. All stages of the erythroblast-thrombocyte series can be detected in smears prepared from the bone marrow.

The thrombocytes show considerable variation in size, and their shape may vary from oval to round (Figure 1). The typical thrombocyte is oval, with a round nucleus in the center of a clear cytoplasm. A constant feature is the one or more brightly red-stained granules present at the poles of the cell. The chromatin of the nucleus is dense and is clumped into relatively large masses which are distinctly separated by the parachromatin.

Life span of erythrocyte. The length of life of the erythrocyte in

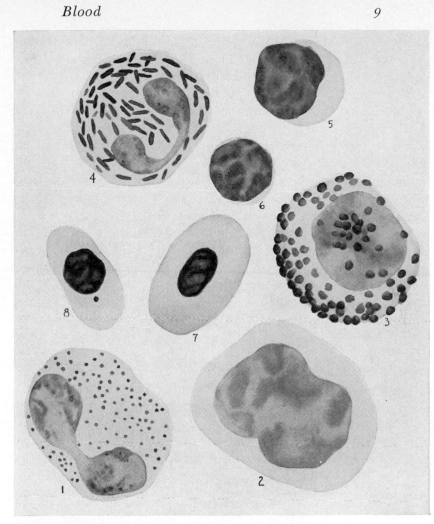

Figure 1. Drawing of mature blood cells of the bird.

1, eosinophil; 2, monocyte; 3, basophil; 4, heterophil; 5 and 6 large and small lymphocytes; 7, erythrocyte; 8, thrombocyte.

mammals is estimated to be from 28 to 100 days, and in the chicken, 28 days (Hevesy and Ottesen, 1945). Brace and Atland (1956), who tagged the red cells with C^{-14}, reported a mean life span of 20 days and 39 days for chicken cells and duck cells respectively. Rodnan, Ebaugh, and Fox (1957), employing radioactive chromium, reported the maximum life span of red cells as 35 days for the chicken, 42 days for the duck, and 35 to 45 days for the pigeon. The life span of erythrocytes in birds and certain mammals was inversely related to energy metabolism.

According to Rous's conception of erythrocyte destruction, the red corpuscles break up in the blood stream into smaller and smaller pieces, still retaining their hemoglobin. When in a very fine state of division these fragments are taken out by cells of the reticuloendothelial system, by which the hemoglobin is split into its iron-containing part and its protein fraction. Another way in which the red corpuscles are destroyed is through phagocytosis by the cells of the reticuloendothelial system. In the dog, the main seat of bilirubin formation is the red bone marrow. It is reasonable to suppose, therefore, that this is the principal site of erythrocyte destruction. In man, the spleen is probably of great importance in the process, but in the rabbit and guinea pig it is probably less important; in birds, the main site is the liver, according to Krumbhaar (1928).

Storage of Erythrocytes in the Spleen

Barcroft (1925) demonstrated that the spleen of mammals serves as a reservoir of erythrocytes and in times of emergency expels the reserve cells into the general circulation. This function was also ascribed to the spleen of the chicken by Harmon, Ogden, and Cook (1932), who reported that asphyxia, induced in normal chickens, increased hemoglobin, but not in splenectomized ones. Sturkie (1943), using a more reliable method of hemoglobin determination and a larger number of birds, could not confirm their findings. His results showed that although asphyxia in the intact bird appeared to increase the hemoglobin slightly, none of the differences was significant. This would indicate that asphyxia does not stimulate the spleen of the fowl to expel erythrocytes into the general circulation as it does the spleen of mammals. It is known that the high degree of contractility of the mammalian spleen plays an important role in the expulsion of blood into the main circulating channels (Barcroft, 1925; Klemperer, 1938) and is dependent upon the thick muscular capsule and prominent trabeculae of the organ. The spleen of birds has a thin capsule with few muscle fibers and no true trabeculae (Klemperer) and is capable of contraction to only a slight extent (for details on hemoglobin, see Chapter 2).

LEUCOCYTES

Counting. Leucocyte counts in the blood of chickens and other bird species have been made by many investigators. Olson (1937 and 1952), Twisselmann (1939), Lucas and Jamroz (1961, and De Villiers (1938) have discussed and summarized the reports of various authors, including their own work. There is considerable variation in the numbers of the various cell types. In part, these discrepancies may be attributed to the method of making the count and, in many cases, to the small numbers of birds used (see Lucas and Jamroz for details of methods).

Total leucocytes include all of the white cells, and counts upon these are made in a counting chamber as described for erythrocytes, except that the blood is usually diluted 1–100 instead of 1–200 before it is placed in the counting chamber. Determining the total white cell count is attended by difficulty because the red cells are nucleated. Diluting fluids containing acetic acid that are ordinarily used to dissolve the red cells of mammalian blood are unsatisfactory for bird blood because the stroma of the red cells contract about the nuclei, making it impossible to distinguish these from some of the leucocytes. If a fluid such as Toisson's solution is used which preserves the red and white cells, then again it is difficult to distinguish with certainty between the thrombocytes and the small lymphocytes under the powers of magnification that can be used in conjunction with the counting chamber (De Villiers, 1938). Natt and Herrick (1952) described a new leucocyte diluent which contained methyl violet and which, according to Chubb and Rowell (1959), was the best of the several diluents tried. Another new diluent was described by Hairston (1955).

De Villiers, working with ostrich blood, and Olson (1937 and 1952), working with chicken blood, found Wiseman's stain to be satisfactory for making total leucocyte counts. This solution stains the granulocytes a bright red—in contrast with the other cells, which stain much less brilliantly.

For the differential count, a number of stains are available, such as the May-Grunewald, Giemsa, Leishman's, Jenner's, Wright's, and supra-vital techniques as used by Twisselmann. According to Twisselmann (1939), the supra-vital techniques are more reliable because there are no unidentifiable, degenerated cells present, as occurs with Wright's stain. The monocytes can be unmistakably differentiated, and the staining of the cells is always of the same intensity.

De Villiers (1938) states that staining with Wright's stain entails little work, and that the smear is usually ready for examination within 10 minutes. Olson (1952) seems to prefer this stain for normal chicken blood, but states that the May-Grunewald and Giemsa combinations have been found useful, especially with pathological blood.

Olson has shown that in differential counts, the error in terms of coefficients of variability are: lymphocytes, 8.6 percent; heterophils, 27.9 percent; eosinophils, 58.8 percent; basophils, 62.6 percent; and monocytes, 22.2 percent. The coefficient of variability for total leucocytes was 34.2 percent, using phloxine as the stain. Because of the great variability in counts, Lucas and Jamroz have suggested that a large number of determinations on different birds be made.

Description of Cell Types

The description of the cell types which follows is that of Olson (1937) (see Figure 1).

Heterophils. This type of leucocyte in the blood of the fowl is sometimes designated polymorphonuclear-pseudoeosinophilic granulocyte, but for the sake of brevity such cells are designated as heterophils. The designation is also made for the sake of clarity, in order to avoid the confusion associated with use of the term "pseudo-eosinophil." In man and in certain mammals, such as the dog, these leucocytes possess neutral-staining granules. In rabbits and birds, the granules of these leucocytes are acid in reaction. The term heterophil then would imply the variableness of the staining reaction of this group of cells in the various species of animals.

The heterophils in the blood of the children are usually round and have a diameter of approximately 10 to 15 microns (μ). The characteristic feature of these cells is the presence of many rod-shaped or spindle-shaped acidophilic crystalline bodies in the cytoplasm. Frequently, in routinely stained smears, these cytoplasmic bodies are distorted, and they may then be variable in shape. In cases of such distortion, the color reaction must be used as a criterion for distinguishing them. The bodies are of a distinct and sometimes brilliant red, against a background of colorless cytoplasm. The nucleus is polymorphic with varying degrees of lobulation.

Eosinophils. Polymorphonuclear eosinophilic granulocytes are of about the same size as the heterophils. The granules are spherical and relatively large. Their color is dull red as compared to the brilliant red of the heterophil when stained with Wright's stain. The cytoplasm has a faint yet distinct bluish-gray tint. The nucleus is often bilobed and is of a richer blue than that of the heterophil, thus giving the impression of a sharper differentiation between chromatin and parachromatin than in the nucleus of the latter.

The question has arisen as to the correctness of distinguishing between the heterophil and eosinophil of avian blood. Some workers believe that the two cell types represent modified forms of the same group, but Olson (1957 and 1952) thinks that the heterophil and eosinophil have different cell lineages. (See Lucas and Jamroz concerning the effects of various treatments [artifacts] on the appearance of eosinophils and heterophils.)

Basophils. Polymorphonuclear basophilic granulocytes are of about the same size and shape as the heterophils. The nucleus is weakly basophilic in reaction and round or oval in shape; at times it may be lobulated. The cytoplasm is abundant and devoid of color. Deeply basophilic granules abound in the cytoplasm.

Lymphocytes. The lymphocytes constitute the majority of the leucocytes in the blood of the fowl. There is a wide range in the size and shape of these cells. The cytoplasm is usually weakly basophilic. It may consist of a narrow rim bordering one side of the nucleus, as in the small lymphocytes, or it may constitute the major portion of the cell, as in the larger lymphocytes. The nucleus is usually round and may have a small indentation. There is usually a fairly coarse pattern of chromatin. In some instances, however, the chromatin is fine and is not distinctly separated by the parachromatin. Sometimes a few nonspecific azure granules are noted in the cytoplasm.

Monocytes. The monocytes in the blood of the fowl are sometimes difficult to identify or to distinguish from large lymphocytes because there are transitional forms between the two. In general, the monocytes are large cells with relatively more cytoplasm than the large lymphocytes. The cytoplasm of these cells have a blue-gray tint. The nucleus is usually irregular in outline. The nuclear pattern in the monocyte is of a more delicate composition than in the lymphocyte. Chromatin appears in monocytes in strands rather than in blocks.

Number of Leucocytes

Numbers of leucocytes and thrombocytes for different species of birds are shown in Table 3. In most cases, the smears for the differential counts were stained with Wright's stain. Twisselmann (1939) showed that the supravital technique is more reliable, for reasons previously given, and that the number of lymphocytes is higher and that of heterophils lower with Wright's stain. In most species the percentage of lymphocytes is higher than for any other cell type, comprising 40 to 70 percent of the total count, and the heterophils are the second most numerous group. In the ostrich and pheasant the opposite is true, with the heterophils comprising over half of the total count. The significance of this difference is not known.

Sex and age differences. Most workers have not found a consistent sex difference in leucocytes. Olson (1937) did report a sex difference in adult chickens, but not in young chickens; Twisselmann (1939) likewise reported no sex difference in the latter. Cook (1937) reported little variation in the count attributable to sex in chickens from 26 to 183 days of age.

Glick (1960) has reported a diurnal variation in the leucocyte count of 3-week-old New Hampshire chicks. The leucocyte num-

Table 3. Number of leucocytes and thrombocytes in bird blood

Species, Age and Sex	Numbers in thousands			Differential count (percent)				Author
	Leuco-cytes	Throm-bocytes	Lympho-cytes	Hetero-phils	Eosino-phils	Baso-phils	Mono-cytes	
Chicken, adult male	19.8	25.4	59.1	27.2	1.9	1.7	10.2	Olson, 1937
" (nonlaying) female	19.8	26.5	64.6	22.8	1.9	1.7	8.9	"
" (young, 2–21 weeks, males and females	29.4	32.7	66.0	20.9	1.9	3.1	8.1	"
Chicken, White Leghorn, 6 weeks to maturity, males and females								Twisselmann, 1939
supravital stain	32.6	—	40.9	35.6	2.7	4.3	16.5	
Wright's stain	—	—	54.0	27.8	1.5	2.7	13.7	
Chicken, average, all ages	30.4	—	73.3	15.1		2.7	6.3	Cook, 1937
Chicken, 5–10 weeks, males	28.6	—	69.5	20.4	1.3	3.3	3.7	Goff et al., 1953
" 6 weeks, female (W.L.)	30.6	30.4	81.5	10.1	1.5	2.3	4.5	Lucas & Jamroz, 1961
" 12 " " (W.L.)	29.4	26.2	77.8	11.7	3.9	1.7	4.9	"
" adult female (W.L.)	16.6	30.8	76.1	13.3	2.5	2.4	5.7	"
" " male "	28.8	27.6	64.0	25.8	1.4	2.4	6.4	"
" " female (farmstock W.L.)	35.8	37.2	71.7	23.7	1.4	2.1	1.1	"
" " " (R.I.R.)		60.3	58.1	35.1	1.2	3.1	2.5	"
Duck, male (Mallard)	23.4	30.7	32.0	48.0	7.0	5.0	8.0	Lucas & Jamroz, 1961
Duck	—	—	61.7	24.3	2.1	1.5	10.8	Magath & Higgins, 1934
Turkey	—	—	50.6	43.4	0.9	3.2	1.9	Johnson & Lange, 1939
Canada goose, male	—	—	46.0	39.0	7.0	2.0	6.0	Lucas & Jamroz, 1961
Pheasant, male (ringneck)	—	—	34.0	48.0	1.0	10.0	8.0	"
Pigeon	13.0	—	32.0	49.0	0.5	3.0	15.0	Shaw, 1933
Pigeon A.M.	18.5	—	65.6	23.0	2.2	2.6	6.6	"
Pigeon P.M.		—	47.8	42.8	1.9	2.4	5.1	"
Ostrich, males and females	21.05	10.5	26.8	59.1	6.3	4.7	3.0	De Villiers, 1938

bers were highest from 2 P.M. to 4 P.M. and the relative number of heterophils was lowest and that of lymphocytes highest at this time.

Effects of diet on leucocytes. Although the work of Cook (1937) suggested that diet might influence the leucocyte count, the data are not conclusive. Work by Goff *et al.* (1953) demonstrates conclusively that a deficiency of riboflavin significantly increases the heterophils and decreases the lymphocytes. Similar results were obtained with vitamin B_1 deficiency.

Lance and Hogan (1948) showed that turkey poults fed a diet deficient in folic acid were anemic and had decreased leucocyte counts, including a decrease in lymphocytes, heterophils, basophils, monocytes, and thrombocytes. When the diet was deficient in inositol, the total leucocyte count was likewise decreased.

Effects of environment. Very little experimental work has been conducted upon the effects of changes in environment exclusive of ration upon leucocyte count. Olson's studies indicate that more work should be conducted along these lines. He showed that when adult birds were reared in batteries within a building where there was little or no exposure to the elements, their total leucocyte counts were lower than for chickens reared outside. For the birds raised indoors the leucocyte count was 17,000, and for those raised outside, 23,600.

It is known that changes in environment may induce stress, with the consequent release of adrenal corticoids, and with changes in leucocyte numbers, in mammals and birds. Newcomer (1958) has shown that in chickens physical restraint, and the use of ACTH, cortical hormones, and other stressing agents produce a relative increase in number of heterophils. In mammals such treatments produce a decrease in the eosinophils. The mechanism is unknown.

Effects of hormones, drugs, and other factors. Shapiro and Schechtman (1949) reported that a single injection of adrenal cortical extract in the adult fowl caused a transient lymphopenia and leucocytosis. The increase was mainly in the heterophils. Weller and Schechtman (1949) also found that when ACE was injected in chick embryos (0.2 to 0.6 cc.) at 13 to 15 days of incubation, the number of lymphocytes was not changed significantly, but there was a marked increase (about 3 times) in the number of polymorphonuclear cells. There was no effect upon the red cells.

Later work by Newcomer (1958), Glick (1961), and Huble (1955) demonstrates conclusively that ACTH and cortical hormones increase heterophils and cause a relative decrease in lymphocytes. Cortisone and acetate (2.5 mg.) increased the total count from 13,000 to 18,000 cells, $3\frac{1}{2}$ hours after injection. Desoxycorticosterone acetate had a similar effect (Glick). Growth hormone alone did not influence the differential or the total leucocyte count.

Compound 48/80, which liberates histamine in mammals and birds, decreases considerably the number of basophils in chicken blood and increases the lymphocytes (Hunt and Hunt, 1959).

Denning, Meschan, Keith, and Day (1950) demonstrated that X-radiation decreased the leucocyte count in hens from 29,500 to 13,000. When urethane was injected, the count dropped to 9,400.

A detailed study of the effects of X-ray on blood cells of the chicken has been conducted by Lucas and Denington (1957). Total body irradiation with dosages from 50 to 300 r. units in chicks and hens decreased the total leucocyte count significantly, and the low level persisted for about 12 days after the treatment. There was likewise a decrease in lymphocytes, but an increase in heterophils. With dosages 200 r. and above, the effect on the latter cells was greater in adult birds. The number of eosinophils and basophils was also depressed. There was no consistent effect of X-ray on the number of monocytes. Usually, by 15 days after the treatment there was some recovery in cell numbers, and younger birds recovered sooner than older ones.

Leucocytosis and disease. There is considerable variation in the blood picture of normal birds, and caution should be exercised before attributing changes in the blood picture to disease. Olson (1952 and later) has reviewed the hematological changes associated with certain diseases. It is known that various disorders in mammals cause an increase in number of leucocytes (leucocytosis). Leukemia of chickens is characterized by an increase in lymphocytes and abnormal cells of the lymphocyte series. Pullorum and typhoid produce leucocytosis (Olson, 1952), and blue comb or pullet disease increases leucocytes and particularly monocytes (Jungherr, 1948). Certain parasitic infestations cause leucocytosis, and principally an increase in the heterophils. However, the results of different investigators are not always in agreement.

PHYSICAL CHARACTERISTICS

Sedimentation rate. Sedimentation rate of erythrocytes is dependent on two main forces: (1) the force of gravity, causing cells to settle, and (2) the frictional resistance of the surrounding plasma, which holds the cells in suspension. The role played by each of these forces is related to a number of factors, such as cell size and shape, the specific gravity of cells and plasma, and the chemical composition of plasma. The sedimentation rate in human beings may be increased during infections and in diseases associated with tissue injury.

Less is known about the sedimentation rate in birds, because few reports are available, and in most cases the effects of disease, age, and sex have not been ascertained. Mean sedimentation rates ranging from 0.5 to 9 mm. per hour, with most falling between 1.5 and 4, have been reported (Albritton, 1952; Swenson, 1951; Gray *et al.*, 1954; Sturkie and Textor, 1958). These values were determined in the usual way, with the sedimentation tube held vertically, and are considerably lower than those reported for man.

It has been demonstrated that the sedimentation rate of human blood can be increased considerably by positioning the tube at 45° (Washburn and Meyers, 1957), and similar results have been obtained with chicken blood (Sturkie and Textor, 1958). The sedimentation rate of erythrocytes in adult males, capons, and female chickens with the Wintrobe tube filled and held at 45°, at a temperature of 80°F., appear in tabular form on the following page. It is apparent that the sedimentation rate is lowest for males, intermediate for capons, and highest for females. It was also found (Sturkie and Textor, 1960) that erythrocyte numbers were highest in the male, intermediate in the capon, and lowest in the female. The same investigators showed that the sedimentation rate (1958)

Time in minutes	Male mean*	Capon mean*	Female mean**
10	0.80	0.73	1.35
20	1.33	2.13	3.48
30	2.06	2.87	5.30
40	2.53	4.00	6.84
50	3.00	5.47	8.51
60	3.86	6.47	10.46
70	4.13	7.60	11.89
80	4.67	8.40	13.32
90	4.93	9.67	14.78
100	5.93	10.67	16.03
110	6.66	11.87	16.92
120	7.00	12.93	18.05
Mean	3.91	6.90	10.58

* Mean of 15 individuals.
** Mean of 37.

in the three sex groups was linear with time during a period of 10 to 120 minutes.

Other factors. Hyperlipemia produced by the drug nicarbazine (Sturkie and Textor, 1960) or by estrogen (Gilbert, 1962) decreases the sedimentation rate significantly. Evidence was presented which indicates that the number of cells and their total volume have the greatest influence on the sedimentation rate, and that cell size affects it to a much lesser degree (Sturkie and Textor, 1960).

Viscosity. Viscosity of whole blood is most influenced by number of cells, and one would expect it to be higher in males (Table 4). Viscosity of the plasma is influenced considerably by plasma proteins and is significantly higher in females or estrogenized males, since in each of the latter plasma proteins are higher than in normal males.

Osmotic Pressure and Specific Gravity

The colloid osmotic pressure of avian plasma is considerably lower than for most mammals because plasma albumen, which is relatively lower in birds, has more influence on colloid osmotic pressure than do globulins. Values for colloid osmotic pressure in

Table 4. Physical properties of avian blood

Specific gravity

Species	Whole blood	Plasma	Serum	Reference
Chicken (female)	1.050	1.099		Sturkie & Textor (1960)
" "	—	1.0180 (Very lipemic)		"
" "	1.0439	1.0177		Medway & Kare (1959)
" (male)	—	1.0210		Sturkie & Textor (1960)
" "	1.054		1.023	Wirth (1931)
Goose	1.050		1.021	"
Duck	1.056		1.020	"
Guinea Fowl	1.057		1.021	"
Ostrich	1.063	1.022	—	De Villiers (1938)

Viscosity (in relation to water at given temperatures)

Species	Whole blood	Plasma	Temperature	Reference
Chicken (male)	3.67	1.42	42°C.	Vogel (1961)
" (capon)	2.47	1.28	"	"
" (female)	3.08	1.51	"	"
Duck	4.0	1.5	14–20°C.	Spector (1956)
Goose	4.6	1.5	14–20°C.	"
Ostrich	4.5	—	—	De Villiers (1938)

chickens and doves are 150 and 110 mm. H_2O respectively (Albritton, 1952).

The specific gravity of blood of various avain species is shown in Table 4. The figure for the plasma of female chickens is significantly lower than for that of males. This is surprising, since the plasma proteins that supposedly most influence specific gravity are significantly higher in females. However, female plasma is lipemic, and this condition tends to depress specific gravity. The plasma of laying female chickens made hyperlipemic by administration of nicarbazine had a lower specific gravity than plasma of untreated females (Sturkie and Textor, 1960). These results demonstrate that plasma specific gravity is not a good measure of plasma protein in birds having lipemic plasma.

BLOOD COAGULATION

BY PAUL GRIMINGER

The classical theory of blood coagulation developed by Schmidt and his contemporaries toward the end of the 19th century (see Bethell, 1958) has been the point of departure for modern studies in this field. The decisive step in this theory is the transformation of fibrinogen, a soluble protein, into the insoluble fibrin, through the enzymatic activity of thrombin. Thrombin, also a protein, is derived from prothrombin by the proteolytic breakdown of the prothrombin molecule, and the reaction is catalyzed by thromboplastin, calcium ions, and several accessory factors (see Figure 2). Thromboplastin may be derived from tissue juices or from blood platelets, and the active elements appear to be phospholipid in character. In the more carefully studied human clotting system at least seven accessory factors have been designated (factors V and VII through XII; see Table 5). They are mainly protein in character, and in electrophoresis they migrate with the plasma globulin fractions. The mode of interaction of these factors is not perfectly understood; for more details and a discussion of the various theories, one of the specialized works should be consulted (Biggs and Macfarlane, 1962; Kugelmass, 1959; and others).

In 1929 Dam, while studying the biosynthesis of cholesterol in the hen, observed subcutaneous and intramuscular hemorrhages, resembling those of scurvy, in experimental birds fed certain purified diets (McCollum, 1957). This chance observation later led to the discovery of the role of vitamin K in prothrombin synthesis in the liver. To date there is considerable evidence that vi-

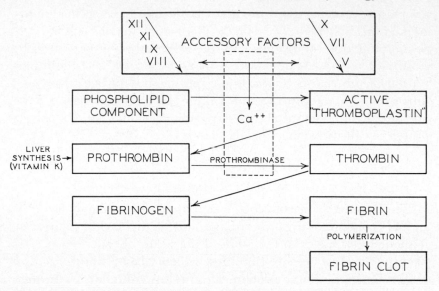

Figure 2. A scheme of blood coagulation.

tamin K is involved not only in prothrombin synthesis but also in the function of certain of the accessory factors mentioned previously (Brinkhous, 1959).

Although most clotting factors do not exhibit absolute species specificity, there are nevertheless pronounced differences between

Table 5. Synonyms for blood coagulation factors

Factor	Synonyms
V	Labile factor, proaccelerin, accelerator globulin
VII	Stable factor, proconvertin, serum prothrombin conversion accelerator (SPCA)
VIII	Antihemophilic factor A, antihemophilic globulin (AHG), platelet cofactor I, thromboplastinogen A
IX	Antihemophilic factor B, plasma thromboplastin component (PTC), platelet cofactor II, Christmas factor (CF)
X	Stuart (Prower) factor
XI	Antihemophilic factor C, plasma thromboplastin antecedent (PTA)
XII	Hageman factor

the clotting systems of different classes of animals, and perhaps even between different species of the same class. The absence of platelets from avian blood raises the question whether the nucleated thrombocytes could act as a source of thromboplastin in the chicken, or whether activation of avian hemostasis depends entirely on tissue thromboplastin. Although the major factors involved in avian blood coagulation are apparently similar to those observed in mammals, avian plasma lacks the thromboplastin component (factor IX) and another activating factor, the so-called "Hageman factor" (Didisheim *et al.*, 1959). According to Wartelle (1957) however, these factors are present, but in very small amounts. Certain factors recently shown to exist in chicken blood might very well play a role similar to the above-mentioned factors in avian blood coagulation. Indeed, at least one of these factors seems to be vitamin K–dependent, as has been indicated for factor IX in mammals (Sorby and Kruse, 1960).

Certainly a partial species specificity exists for brain tissue thromboplastin, so that thromboplastin extract, a requirement for the determination of avian prothrombin, must necessarily be prepared from birds (Hecht, 1955; Chubb and Long, 1957; Bigland and Triantaphyllopoulos, 1961). Experimentation with ducks and turkeys (Didisheim *et al.*, 1959; Griminger, 1957) has indicated that in assay work it might possibly even be advantageous to use the brain of the same rather than another avian species.

Prothrombin time. Vitamin K, essential for normal blood coagulation, can be supplied both in the food and by intestinal bacterial synthesis; the chicken, however, appears to be particularly dependent upon an exogenous source for this vitamin, and growing chickens will become severely hypoprothrombinemic after a short time on a K–deficient diet. This fact has led to the widespread use of the species in experiments for the bioassay of vitamin K. In this assay, varying amounts of the material to be assayed are fed to small groups of vitamin K–deficient chicks, and known amounts of the vitamin to others. A comparison of plasma prothrombin times, usually by the one-stage method of Quick (1957), indicates the amount of vitamin K–active material in the assayed samples. For the determination of prothrombin times, blood is drawn, and the calcium is bound by the addition of oxalate or citrate, thus preventing coagulation. The blood is then centrifuged, and calcium and a thromboplastin extract are added to the plasma. The time required for a clot to be formed is called the prothrombin time.

Prothrombin times below 12 seconds can be obtained in growing chicks with the one-stage method of Quick (1957) if a carefully prepared chick brain thromboplastin extract is employed. However, comparable results can be obtained with other extracts that promote slower clotting (Griminger, 1962). Prothrombin times similar to those of chicks have been observed in this laboratory for adult males, whereas those for adult females tend to be slightly longer. The adult male chicken appears to be relatively resistant to hypoprothrombinemia as a result of vitamin K deprivation, although an equivalent condition will produce severe intramuscular and subcutaneous hemorrhages in growing chicks, and will initiate a more moderate hypoprothrombinemia in laying hens.

Whole blood clotting times are much more variable than prothrombin time. From 2 to 10 minutes appears to be the normal range for nonhypoprothrombinemic birds, although longer clotting times are not infrequently recorded. (Bigland, 1964).

A functional clotting system in the chicken embryo can be detected during the second half of the incubation period. Kane and Sizer (1953) found clotted material after 12 to 13 days of embryonic development, but no clotting was demonstrable at 11 days.

Anticoagulants. Chickens are more resistant than mammals, to oral anticoagulants of the coumarin type, but will succumb as a consequence of massive internal hemorrhages when given large doses of anticoagulants. When 1600 mg. of dicumoral per kg. of feed were given in our laboratory to day-old chicks, 70 percent mortality ensued within two weeks. The mortality of chicks one or two weeks older, administered the same dose, was 50 percent within the same period. The reaction to lower doses is shown in Table 6. The anticoagulant effect of dicumarol can be overcome by feeding increased amounts of vitamin K: 1,600 mg. K_1/kg. diet were required to obtain normal prothrombin times in chickens fed 400 mg. dicumarol/kg. diet (Griminger and Donis, 1960), whereas not more than 1 mg. K_1/kg. diet is required in the absence of antivitamins or other stress factors.

Table 6. Response of chicks to the feeding of dicumarol for one week when receiving 5 mg. of menadione (vitamin K_3) per kg. of diet

Dicumarol added (mg./kg. diet)	0	50	100	200	400	800
Average prothrombin times[1] (seconds)		13.7	14.3	14.7	17.8	27.0	59.9

[1] Averages on the basis of reciprocals of individual plasma prothrombin times.

The question has been raised whether the hemorrhages which seem to be the cause of death in hypoprothrombinemia are precipitated by a simultaneous decrease in capillary strength. Increased capillary fragility in hypoprothrombinemia has indeed been demonstrated in the rat (Pastorova, 1957) by the use of the negative-pressure method. This method is based upon the production of pinpoint hemorrhages by the application of negative pressure to a specific area of skin with the aid of a suction cup, varying either the pressure or the application time. Used on the chicken, this method produces bruises in the underlying flesh ("vascular faults") which obscure the usual observation of petechiae in the skin (Morrissette, 1956). Preliminary observations made in this laboratory indicate that in the chicken dicumarol will also reduce capillary strength. It is not impossible, however, that the phenomenon in both rat and chicken is an indirect effect of low coagulability on an ever-changing capillary bed rather than a direct effect on the capillary fragility.

It has been shown that blood also contains natural anticoagulants in the form of antithrombin, heparin, and perhaps an antithromboplastin. It is possible that heparin acts in conjunction with antithrombin (Kugelmass, 1959). When a clot is formed, thrombin is also inactivated by the absorptive action of fibrin, thus localizing clot formation.

The shrinking of a blood coagulum, with the simultaneous expression of a serum, is called clot retraction. In chicken blood, clot retraction occurs appreciably slower than in human blood, according to Bigland (1960), and is negligible, according to Didisheim *et al.* (1959).

Hemorrhagic syndrome. The so-called "hemorrhagic syndrome"

observed in growing chickens is characterized by subcutaneous hemorrhages; frequently anemia and a pale bone marrow have also been observed. Although several factors have been implicated as causative agents, the etiology of the syndrome has not yet been satisfactorily explained (Morrissette, 1956; Marthedal and Velling, 1961). Some of the early field cases of the syndrome were probably due to a deficiency of vitamin K, since the formulation of poultry rations had reduced the amount of the vitamin in practical rations without a compensatory addition of synthetic vitamin K. Another contributory factor in the etiology of the hemorrhagic syndrome may be the injudicious use of the coccidiostatic drug sulfaquinoxaline. Although sulfa drugs will, in general, influence intestinal synthesis of vitamin K by virtue of their bacteriostatic action, such synthesis plays a minor role in the genesis of this vitamin in the growing chicken. Furthermore, a positive correlation exists between the dose of sulfaquinoxaline and the amount of vitamin K necessary to overcome the hypoprothrombinemia induced by the former (Griminger, 1957). It must therefore be concluded that in addition to having a bacteriostatic effect sulfaquinoxaline acts as an antagonist of vitamin K. Finally, molds have recently been implicated, and Schumaier *et al.* (1961) have been able to produce symptoms typical of this syndrome by providing growing chickens with feed samples contaminated with either of two species of aspergilli.

REFERENCES

Albritton, E. C.   1952   Standard Values in Blood. W. B. Saunders Co., Philadelphia.

Barcroft, J.   1925   The significance of hemoglobin in sub-mammalian forms of life. Physiol. Rev. 5:596.

Bethell, Frank H.   1958   The Chemistry of Blood Coagulation. Charles C. Thomas, Springfield, Ill.

Biggs, R., and R. G. Macfarlane   1962   Human Blood Coagulation. F. A. Davis Co., Philadelphia.

Bigland, C. H.   1960   Studies on avian blood coagulation. Thesis, University of Alberta, Edmonton, Canada.

Bigland, C. H.   1964   Blood clotting time of five avian species. Poultry Sci. 43:1035.

Bigland, C. H., and D. C. Triantaphyllopoulos 1961 Chicken pro-thrombin, thrombin and fibrinogen. Am. J. Physiol. 200:1013.

Blount, W. P. 1939 Thrombocyte formation in the domestic hen. Vet. J. 95:195.

Bond, C. F., and P. W. Gilbert 1958 Comparative study of blood volume in representative aquatic and nonaquatic birds. Am. J. Physiol. 194:519.

Brace, K., and P. D. Atland 1956 Life span of the duck and chicken erythrocyte as determined with C14. Proc. Soc. Exp. Biol. & Med. 92:615.

Brinkhous, K. M. 1959 Blood clotting: The plasma procoagulants. Am. Rev. Physiol. 21:271.

Chubb, L. G., and P. L. Long 1957 The estimation of prothrom-bin in chicken blood. Brit. Vet. J. 113:3.

Chubb, L. G., and J. G. Rowell 1959 Counting blood cells of chickens. J. Agric. Sci. 52:263.

Cook, S. F. 1937 A study of blood picture of poultry and its diag-nostic significance. Poultry Sci. 16:291.

Davis, J. E., A. W. McCullough, and R. II. Rigdon 1945 Polycy-themia produced by cobalt in duck: A hematologic and pathologic study. J. Lab. Clin. Med. 30:327.

Denning, J. S., I. Meschan, C. K. Keith, and P. L. Day 1950 Effects of X-irradiation and urethane treatment on chicken bone marrow. Proc. Soc. Exp. Biol. & Med. 74:776.

De Villiers, O. T. 1938 Blood of ostrich. Onderstepoort J. Vet. Sci. 11:419.

Didisheim, P., K. Hattori, and J. H. Lewis 1959 Hematologic and coagulation studies in various animal species. J. Lab. Clin. Med. 53:866.

Domm, L. V., and E. Taber 1946 Endocrine factors controlling erythrocyte concentration on the blood of the domestic fowl. Physiol. Zool. 19:258.

Dukes, H. H. 1947 The Physiology of Domestic Animals. Comstock Publishing Associates, Ithaca, N.Y.

Gilbert, A. B. 1962 Sedimentation rate of erythrocytes in the domes-ticated cock. Poultry Sci. 41:784.

Glick, B. 1960 Leucocyte count variation in young chicks during an 18-hour period. J. Appl. Physiol. 15:965.

Glick, B. 1961 The effect of bovine growth hormone desoxycorti-costerone acetate, and cortisone acetate on the white blood cell counts of 2-week-old chickens. Poultry Sci. 40:1537.

Goff, S., W. C. Russell, and M. W. Taylor 1953 Hematology of the chick in vitamin deficiencies. I:Riboflavin. Poultry Sci. 32:54.

Gray, J. E., G. H. Snoeyenbos, and I. M. Reynolds 1954 The hemorrhagic syndrome of chickens. J. Am. Vet. Med. Assoc. 125:144.

Griminger, P. 1957 On the vitamin K requirements of turkey poults. Poultry Sci. 36:1227.

Griminger, P. 1962 Prothrombin bioassay for vitamin K with different thromboplastin preparations. Internat. J. Vit. Res. 32:405.

Griminger, P., and O. Donis 1960 Potency of vitamin K_1 and two analogues in counteracting the effects of dicumarol and sulfaquinoxaline in the chick. J. Nutr. 70:361.

Groebbels, F. 1932 Der Vogel. Erster Band: Atmungswelt und Nahrungswelt. Verlag von Gebrüder Borntraeger, Berlin.

Hairston, M. A. 1955 One-solution stain for enumeration of avian leucocytes. Stain Technology 30:148.

Harmon, I. W., E. Ogden, and S. F. Cook 1932 The reservoir function of the spleen in fowls. Am. J. Physiol. 11:99.

Hart, E. B., C. A. Elvehjem, and A. R. Kemmerer 1930 Does the practical chick ration need iron and copper additions to insure normal hemoglobin building? Poultry Sci. 9:92.

Hecht, E. 1955 Zur Kenntnis der Thrombokinasen. Biochem. Zeitschr. 326:325.

Hevesy, G., and J. Ottesen 1945 Life-cycle of the red corpuscles of the hen. Nature 156:534.

Huble, J. 1955 Hematological changes in cockerels after ACTH and cortisone-acetate treatment. Poultry Sci. 34:1357.

Hunt, T. E., and E. A. Hunt 1959 Blood basophils of cockerels before and after intravenous ingestion of compound 48/80. Anat. Rec. 132:19.

Hunter, F. R. 1953 An analysis of the photoelectric method for studying osmotic changes in chicken erythrocytes. J. Cell. Comp. Physiol. 41:387.

Hunter, F. R., D. Chalfin, F. J. Finamore, and M. L. Sweetland 1956 Sodium and potassium exchange in chicken erythrocytes. J. Cell. Comp. Physiol. 47:37.

Jaffe, P. 1960 Differences in numbers of erythrocytes between inbred lines of chickens. Nature 186:978.

Johnson, E. P., and C. J. Lange 1939 Blood alterations and typhlohepatitis of turkeys with notes on the disease. J. Parasit. 25:157.

Jordan, H. E. 1939 The lymphocytes in relation to erythrocyte production. Anat. Rec. 73:227.

Juhn, M., and L. V. Domm 1930 The relation of gonadal condition to erythrocyte number in fowls. Am. J. Physiol. 94:656.

Jungherr, E. 1948 Avian monocytosis, Chapter 29 in Biester and Schwarte, Diseases of Poultry. 2nd ed. Iowa State College Press, Ames.

Kane, R. E., and I. W. Sizer 1953 Some studies on the developing blood clotting system of chick embryo. Anatomical Record 117: 614.

Kaplan, H. M. 1954 Sex differences in the packed cell volume of vertebrate blood. Science 120:1044.

Klemperer, P. 1938 Handbook of Hematology. III. Paul B. Hoeber, Inc., New York.

Krumbhaar, E. B. 1928 The erythrocyte. Cowdry's Special Cytology 1:275. Paul B. Hoeber, Inc., New York.

Kugelmass, I. 1959 Biochemistry of Blood in Health and Disease. Charles C Thomas, Springfield, Ill.

Lance, B. G., and A. G. Hogan 1948 Inositol and nicotinic acid in the nutrition of the turkey. J. Nutrition 36:369.

Lucas, A. M. 1959 A discussion of synonymy in avian and mammalian hematological nomenclature. Am. J. Vet. Res. 20:887.

Lucas, A. M., and E. M. Denington 1957 Effect of total body X-ray irradiation on the blood of female single comb White Leghorn chickens. Poultry Sci. 36:1290.

Lucas, A. M., and C. Jamroz 1961 Atlas of Avian Hematology. U.S. Department of Agriculture.

McCartney, M. C. 1952 Total blood and corpuscular volume in turkey hens. Poultry Sci. 31:184.

McCollum, E. V. 1957 A History of Nutrition. Houghton Mifflin Co., Boston.

Magath, T. B., and G. M. Higgins 1934 The blood of the normal duck. Folia Haematol. 51:230.

Marthedal, H. E., and G. Velling 1961 Haemorrhagic syndrome in poultry. Brit. Vet. J. 117:357.

Medway, W., and M. R. Kare 1959 Blood and plasma volume, hematocrit blood specific gravity and serum protein electrophoresis of the chicken. Poultry Sci. 38:624.

Morrissette, M. C. 1956 The hematology of broilers in the presence of mild stress, with reference to the hemorrhagic syndrome. Thesis, Oklahoma A. and M. College, Stillwater.

Natt, M. P., and C. A. Herrick 1952 A new blood diluent for counting the erythrocytes and leucocytes of the chicken. Poultry Sci. 31:735.

Newcomer, W. S. 1958 Physiologic factors which influence acidophilia induced by stressors in the chicken. Am. J. Physiol. 194:251.

Newell, G. W., and C. S. Shaffner 1950 Blood volume determinations in chickens. Poultry Sci. 29:78.

Nice, L. B., M. M. Nice, and R. M. Kraft 1935 Erythrocytes and hemoglobin in blood of some American birds. Wilson Bull. 47:120.

Olson, C. 1937 Variation in the cells and hemoglobin content in the blood of the normal domestic chicken. Cornell Vet. 27:235.

Olson, C. 1952 Avian hematology, in Biester and Schwarte, Diseases of Poultry, 3rd ed., pp. 71-91. Iowa State College Press, Ames.

Orskov, S. L. 1954 The potassium absorption by pigeon blood cells. Acta Physiol. Scand. 31:221.

Pastorova, V. E. 1957 Tzmenenie protsihnosti kapilljornych sosudov pris K-avitaminose i spetsiftschnost' diestvija vitmina K na protschnost' kapilljarov. Doklady Akad. Nauk SSSR 113:1379.

Prosser, C. L., and F. A. Brown, Jr. 1961 Comparative Animal Physiology. W. B. Saunders Co., Philadelphia.

Quick, A. J. 1957 (1959) Hemorrhagic Diseases. Lea & Febiger, Philadelphia.

Riddle, O., and P. F. Braucher 1934 Hemoglobin and erythrocyte differences according to sex and season in doves and pigeons. Am. J. Physiol. 108:554.

Rodnan, G. P., F. G. Ebaugh, Jr., and M. R. S. Fox 1957 The life span of the red blood cell and the red blood cell volume in the chicken, pigeon and duck as estimated by the use of $Na_2C_1{}^{51}O_4$ with observations on red cell turnover rate in the mammal, bird and reptile. Blood, J. Hematol. 12:355.

Schumaier, G., B. Panda, H. M. DeVolt, N. C. Laffer, and R. D. Creek 1961 Hemorrhagic lesions in chickens resembling naturally occurring "hemorrhagic syndrome" produced experimentally by mycotoxins. Poultry Sci. 40:1132.

Shapiro, A. B., and A. M. Schechtman 1949 Effect of adrenal cortical extract on the blood picture and serum proteins of fowl. Proc. Soc. Exp. Biol. & Med. 70:440.

Shaw, A. F. B. 1933 The leucocytes of pigeons with special reference to diurnal rhythm. J. Path. & Bacteriol. 37:411.

Sørby, O., and I. Kruse 1960 Studies on the coagulation of chicken blood. I. Factors which limit plasma coagulation rate during vitamin K deficiency and treatment with coumarin drugs. Act. Chem. Scand. 14:2177.

Spector, W. S. 1956 Handbook of Biological Data. W. B. Saunders Co., Philadelphia.

Sturkie, P. D. 1943 Reputed reservoir function of the spleen of the domestic fowl. Am. J. Physiol. 138:599.

Sturkie, P. D., and H. J. Newman 1951 Plasma proteins of chickens as influenced by time of laying, ovulation, number of blood samples taken and plasma volume. Poultry Sci. 30:240.

Sturkie, P. D., and K. Textor 1958 Sedimentation rate of erythrocytes in chickens as influenced by method and sex. Poultry Sci. 37:60.

Sturkie, P. D., and K. Textor 1960 Further studies on sedimentation rate of erythrocytes in chickens. Poultry Sci. 39:444.

Swenson, M. J. 1951 Effect of a vitamin B_{12} concentrate and liver meal on the histopathology of chicks fed on all-plant protein ration. Am. J. Vet. Res. 12:224.

Tapper, D. N., and M. R. Kare 1959 Epinephrine induced hemoconcentration in the domestic fowl. Am. J. Physiol. 196:1322.

Toteson, D. C., and J. S. Robertson 1956 Potassium transport in duck red cells. J. Cellular & Comp. Physiol. 47:147.

Twisselmann, N. M. 1939 A study of the cell content of blood of normal chickens with supra-vital stains. Poultry Sci. 18:151.

Vezzani, V. 1939 Influence of a sojourn on the mountains on blood composition, body development, and egg production of White Leghorn pullets. Proc. World's Poultry Congress Exposition 7:117.

Vogel, J. 1961 Studies on cardiac output in the chicken. Thesis, Rutgers University, New Brunswick, N.J.

Wartelle, O. 1957 Mécanisme de la coagulation chez la poule. I: Étude des éléments du complexe prothomique et de la thrombo-plastino-formation. Revue d'hémat. 12:351.

Washburn, A. H., and A. J. Meyers 1957 The sedimentation of erythrocytes at an angle of 45 degrees. J. Clin. Lab. Med. 49:318.

Weller, E. M., and A. M. Schechtman 1949 Effect of adrenal cortex on blood cells of embryonic chick. Proc. Soc. Exp. Biol. & Med. 72:370.

Wirth, D. 1931 Grundlage einer klinischen Haematologie der Haustiere. Urban & Schwarzenberg, Berlin.

CHAPTER 2

Chemical Constituents of Blood

BY D. J. BELL AND PAUL D. STURKIE

MANY of the blood components of small molecular dimensions are unequally distributed between the formed and the unformed elements. For example, urate is not detected within the erythrocytes and glucose is likewise virtually confined to the plasma. On the other hand, the erythrocytes carry all the glutathione, all the ergothioneine, and various phosphoric acid esters which are probably absent from the plasma. Citrate is unequally distributed between cells and plasma. Urea and creatine are both equally distributed between the water of the cells and that of the plasma.

Age, sex, and physiological state influence the plasma-erythrocyte ratio of the blood; therefore, analyses made upon whole blood for substances such as urate or glutathione may lead to false deductions if the relative volumes of the cells and plasma are not taken into account. Less is known about the composition of avian blood than that of mammals, especially man. Most of the available information relates to the domestic fowl, but even for this readily available animal it is only within recent years that attempts have been made to discover by means of reliable methods what chemical substances are present in the formed and unformed elements of the circulating blood in health and in disease. It must be emphasized that the concentrations of many substances show considerable variation, both within and between individuals.

THE COMPOSITION OF THE ERYTHROCYTE

The erythrocytes of all animals carry components markedly different from those of the plasma in which they circulate. The cell "walls" or boundaries not only are impermeable to large molecules such as proteins, but can maintain considerable differences of concentration between intra- and extracellular ions and various small molecules. Besides the anaerobic glycolytic metabolism of the non-nucleated erythrocytes of mammals, the nucleated cells of the other animal classes possess a notable aerobic metabolism. Moreover, their components are not inert toward changes in the physiological and pathological state of the bird (Bell, McIndoe, and Gross, 1959). Considerable evidence now available indicates marked differences between birds and mammals with respect not only to hemoglobins but to certain other components as well. Most birds examined have been shown to contain more than one hemoglobin.

Avian Hemoglobins

Very little information is directly available about the structures of avian hemoglobins, which, like their better-known mammalian analogues, are obviously of considerable molecular size. The sedimentation constants of hen, pigeon, and duck hemoglobins (regarded at the time as single chemical entities) have been measured respectively as 4.2, 4.4, and 4.4 cm $\times$ 10^{-3}/sec/dyne (Svedberg and Pederson, 1940); the constant for man is 4.48, and the isoelectric pH's of the avian substances are all more alkaline than the human material. Circumstantial evidence suggests that the chromogen, heme, is probably the same as in mammals; but the protein moieties, the globins, are certainly different, since the avian hemoglobins migrate electrophoretically at speeds different from those of the mammalian pigments.

At present there is no reason to suppose that avian hemoglobins do not contain the 4 heme units characteristic of mammalia. The iron-containing heme (probably $C_{34}H_{32}C_4N_4Fe$, as in mammals) is synthesized through addition of iron to a protoporphyrin molecule, the enzymic synthesis of which from the simple precursor $NH_2CH_2COCH_2CH_2CO_2H$ (5-amino-4-oxopentanoic acid or 8-aminolevulinic acid) has been exhaustively studied in ducks and chickens (e.g. by Gibson, Neuberger, and Scott, 1954; Dresel and Falk, 1954; Granick, 1954; Shemin, Russell, and Abramsky, 1955, and subsequent papers by these groups of authors). The intact avian erythrocyte can synthesize hemoglobin *in vitro* (Dresel and Falk, 1956).

Avian oxyhemoglobins and carboxyhemoglobins are easily crystallized. Among the different species studied, the hemoglobins exhibit considerable variation in crystalline structure (Reichert and Brown, 1909; Franz, 1957). Hilgert and Vojlskova (1959) and Ramakrishnan and Barnabas (1962) found distinctive rates of alkaline denaturation of avian hemoglobins according to race, and Franz (1957) observed differences in catalase and peroxidase activities.

Using electrophoretic separations, numerous workers have demonstrated that avian erythrocytes usually contain more than one type of hemoglobin. It is important to note, in chickens at least, the absence from the plasma of hemoglobin-binding proteins, "haptoglobins," which might give false-positive results (Riou *et al.*, 1962). Two hemoglobins have been demonstrated in 20 races, including the chicken, by Johnson and Dunlap (1955), and by Dunlap, Johnson, and Farner (1956); at pH 8.7 the two chromoproteins separated usually in the ratio of 1 part faster-running ("alpha") to 3 to 4 slower ("beta"). Adults contain a higher proportion of the beta component than do embryos or young chicks. Van der Helm and Huisman (1958) separated hemoglobins of pooled chicken blood on columns of Amberlite IRC-50 and reported proportions of 85 and 15 percent respectively for the slow ("I") and fast ("II") fractions, which were analyzed for their amino acid components and found to differ from one another, especially as regards aspartate, serine, glutamate, tyrosine, lysine, histidine, and arginine (Table 7). The same authors noted that the composition of these globin moieties differed markedly from those of cattle, sheep, and man. Unfortunately they did not present evidence regarding the purity of their preparations. Matsuda and Takei (1963) have studied the purification of chicken hemoglobin by column chromatography. Rodman and Ebaugh (1957) reported 2 components (fast and slow) in White Leghorn chickens, ducks, and robins, and 3 components in New Hampshire

Table 7. Differences in amino acid composition (g./100 g.) of the two hemoglobins of the fowl (from Van der Helm and Huisman, 1958)

Amino acid	Hemoglobin I (slow-moving)	Hemoglobin II (Fast-moving)
Aspartic acid	8.80	11.50
Threonine	4.50	4.10
Serine	3.15	5.15
Glutamic acid	6.80	11.50
Proline	3.20	3.00
Glycine	3.05	2.95
Alanine	8.95	7.55
Methionine	0.00	0.00
Isoleucine	5.00	3.75
Leucine	13.20	15.00
Tyrosine	3.10	1.15
Phenylalanine	6.50	6.80
Lysine	14.55	11.80
Histidine	11.80	7.70
Arginine	7.55	4.95

chickens. The pigeon and penguin exhibited only one component, a finding confirmed by Fine and Uriel (1958) for the pigeon. D'Amelio and Salvo (1959), employing electrophoresis on starch gel at a pH of 8.6, reported 3 hemoglobin components in New Hampshire and White Leghorn chickens. The slow-moving components had serological characteristics specifically different from the others. Saha, Dutta, and Ghosh (1957) have reported two components in blood of *Columba livia,* duck, guinea fowl, chicken, and crow, and one component in blood of the koel (Cuculidae) and the parakeet.

Amounts of Hemoglobin

The amount of hemoglobin in chicken blood, as observed from the literature, is highly variable. Recent work has demonstrated that much of this variation may be attributed to the methods of determination. Many of the earlier workers used the Newcomer

acid hematin method, but since the erythrocytes of birds are nucleated, the consequent turbidity of the solution following treatment with acid produces readings that usually are too high. A
modification of the Newcomer acid hematin method, by which the
blood is first hemolyzed with NH_4OH, gives more reliable figures,
since the turbidity of the solution is eliminated or minimized
(Schultze and Elvehjem, 1934). Hunter, Stringer, and Weiss
(1940) showed that in slightly acid solutions there is a retention of
hemoglobin during osmotic hemolysis of erythrocytes.

The reliability of a number of different methods of determining
hemoglobin in the chicken was tested by Bankowski (1942). He
worked with chickens 42 to 56 days of age. The amount of hemoglobin in grams per 100 ml. of blood as determined by the various
methods was as follows: (1) Dare, 7.7; (2) Haden-Hauser, 7.8; (3)
modified Newcomer, 9.7; (4) photelometric acid hematin, 9.8; (5)
alkaline hematin, 12.1; and (6) Sheard-Sanford, 8.91. Bankowski
stated that methods 3 and 4 were the most reliable.

Rostorfer (1949) has shown that there is considerable variation
in the density readings of acid hematin of duck blood. Readings at
450 mμ showed much greater variation than at 410 mμ. The density
of acid hematin at 450 mμ is quite variable, and this may account
for some of the variation in results obtained.

It is noted from Table 8 that as early as 21 days of age the hemoglobin of chickens has almost reached the normal adult value.

The hemoglobin values for normal small White Holland turkeys are shown in grams percent (Wolterink, Davidson, and Reineke, 1947) as follows:

Age (weeks)	1	4	8	12	16	20	24	28	32	40
Hb. (g./ 100 ml.)	7.77	8.11	8.56	9.01	9.46	9.91	10.37	10.82	11.27	12.17

Hemoglobin determinations have been made on a number of
other avian species (see De Villiers, 1938; Olson, 1937; Groebbels,
1932), but in many cases, because of unreliable methods, the values are too high. For example, the figures reported by different
investigators for pigeon blood are 10.6, 16.1, 15.2, 13.7, and 15.97
mg./100 ml.

Table 8. Hemoglobin values (grams percent) of whole blood of birds

Species	Age	Male	Female	Method	Investigator
Chicken	21 days	9.16	9.30	Modified Sahli (acid as hemolyzing agent)	Holmes *et al.* (1933)
"	42 "	9.70	9.60	"	"
"	63 "	9.70	9.70	"	"
"	84 "	10.10	9.70	"	"
"	Adult	13.50	9.80*	Acid hematin (corrected for turbidity)	Dukes & Schwarte (1931)
"	"	—	9.71*	Modified Newcomer	Bankowski (1942)
"	"	—	8.90*	"	Sturkie (1943)
"	"	—	8.90*	"	Schultze & Elvehjem (1934)
"	"	—	7.44*	Dare	Harmon (1936)
"	"	—	10.95**	"	"
"	"	11.76	9.11	Not given	Olson (1937)
"	"	—	8.00*	Determined Fe in blood	Winters (1936)
"	"	—	8.10**	"	"
Turkey		—	10.6*	Alkali hematin	Paulsen *et al.* (1950)
"		12.5–14.0	13.2**		"
Pigeon		16–20	19–20		Rodnan *et al.* (1957; see Chapter 1)

* Laying.
** Nonlaying.

Effect of rate of egg production on hemoglobin. Hemoglobin in nonlaying hens is higher than that in laying ones, according to Harmon (1936), Maughan (1935), and Tanaka and Rosenberg (1954); but Winters (1936) and Jaffe (1960) reported no difference in the hemoglobin of laying and nonlaying birds. Schultze *et al.* (1936) stated that most of their birds were laying when the determinations were made, but some of them stopped laying and the hemoglobin did not change.

Since the sex hormones influence erythrocyte numbers, it is to be expected that they would affect hemoglobin levels, as Tanaka and Rosenberg (1955) have demonstrated. Androgen increased the hemoglobin level in castrate males to near the normal male level; estrogen did not influence the level appreciably. It is known that erythrocyte numbers in the capon may be intermediate between that of males and females, or may approach the level of normal females.

The mean corpuscular hemoglobin concentration (MCHC) expresses the mean content of hemoglobin in g./100 ml. of erythrocytes; it is usually calculated from the packed cell volume (PCV) and the hemoglobin measured in the whole blood. Its primary importance lies in diagnosis of anemic conditions and reflects the capacity of the bone marrow to produce erythrocytes of normal size, metabolic capacity, and hemoglobin content. Bell *et al.* (1964) found, in every hen examined, that highly significant alterations in the MCHC took place, as follows: At the end of a laying period the MCHC was low; it rose to a relatively high level during the subsequent pause, and reached a peak around the time when the bird returned to laying. At the end of the laying period the MCHC fell once more. The lowest values found (in Brown Leghorns) at the end of laying were 30–31 grams percent and the highest, around the return to laying were 40–41 grams percent. That the MCHC does not appear to be controlled by the estrogen-androgen balance is deduced from its independence of the erythrocyte numbers and the stages in the physiological cycle when the changes become obvious. The MCHC of cocks lies around the upper levels found in the nonlaying hens.

Electrolytes

With the exception of free sugars and neutral fats, virtually all the small molecular components of cells, including erythrocytes, are ionizable. For clarity these electrolytes are divided into cations and anions. At the pH of tissue fluids, the amino acids, the phosphates, and their derivates can be regarded as anions. The cations include sodium, potassium, calcium, and magnesium.

Table 9a. Electrolyte content of erythrocytes (in milliequivalents per liter)

	Age	Sex	Sodi-um	Potas-sium	Chlo-rides	Phos-phate (inor-ganic)	Reference
Chicken							
R. I. Red	—	Female	25.6	92.8	—	—	Morgan & Chichester (1935)
"	—	—	6.7	121.0	—	—	Hunter
"	—	—	—	—	53.4	2.2	Morgan & Chichester (1935)
"	—	L. female	—	—	49–50	—	Heller & Pursell (1937)
New Hampshire	—	Male	10.7	89.0	—	—	Ketz & Assman (1960)
"	—	Mixed	—	—	—	0.9	Gourlay (1957)
White Leghorn	—	Female	—	—	—	1.5	Heller *et al.* (1932)
Goose	—	—	10.8	99.6	—	—	Ketz & Assman (1960)
Duck, Pekin	Adult	Male	7.3	112.0	—	—	Tosteson & Robertson (1956)

Electrolytes of erythrocytes are reported for certain avian species in Table 9a. The chlorides, and phosphate and calcium, are lower in cells than in the plasma, but the concentration of potassium is higher in the cells.

Nonprotein Nitrogen and Amino Acids

Amino acids are present in quantity within the erythrocytes of laying hens (Bell, McIndoe, and Gross, 1959) as compared with nonlayers. The following amino acids have been detected in chicken erythrocytes by Bell *et al.* (1959) and by Chubb (1960):

glycine, alanine, serine, valine, methionine, leucine and isoleucine, aspartate, glutamate, arginine, lysine, cystine and cysteine, tyrosine, histidine, proline, hydroxyproline, and 4-amino-butyrate. Values for nonprotein nitrogen and amino nitrogen of erythrocytes are shown in Table 9b.

Organic Phosphates

The bulk of the phosphate in the erythrocytes is organically bound. Some of this must be associated with lipids of the cellular membranes, but the major portion (90–120 mg.) is soluble in dilute acid (Kutas and Stutzel, 1958). The role of inositol hexaphosphate in the cell's metabolism is not known; Gerlach, Fleckenstein, and Freundt (1957) have shown that phytic acid in the pigeon erythrocyte exchanges with $P^{32}O_4$ 600–800 times more slowly than does the terminal pyrophosphate unit of adenosine triphosphate. Oshima and Taylor (1963) have shown that the concentration of phytate phosphorus rises from about 20 mg./100 ml. at hatching to the adult level of 76 mg./100 ml. at about 10 weeks, and that phytate is synthesized in the chicken fed on an inositol-free diet.

The main fractions of the acid-soluble phosphate of the red cells are the pyrophosphate derivatives and phytate. In the pigeon, Gerlach, Fleckenstein, and Freundt (1957) showed that of the acid soluble phosphate, adenosine triphosphate (27.6 percent), adenosine diphosphate (2.3 percent), adenosine monophosphate (0.9 percent), guanosine triphosphate (3 percent), and guanosine diphosphate (1.5

Table 9b. Nonprotein nitrogen in erythrocytes of chicken
(mg./100 ml.)

Physiological state	Sex	Total NPN	Amino N	Reference
Laying	Female	109	—	Bell, McIndoe, & Gross (1959)
"	"	113	31.9	"
Nonlaying	"	105	43.0	"
	Male	114	—	"
Immature	Female	144	50.5	"

percent) together account for 35.3 percent of the total. The total acid-soluble phosphate-phosphorus of erythrocytes in chickens is 90–105 mg./100 ml. of cells, and the values in turkeys, ducks, geese, pigeons, and others range from 98–130 mg./ml. (Heller *et al.*, 1932; Rapoport and Guest, 1941; Kutas and Stutzel, 1958).

The levels of pyrophosphate P— in all species examined ranged from 10 to 50 mg./100 ml. of cells, and those of phytate phosphorus from 49 to 77 mg./100 ml.

Enzymes in Erythrocytes

A list of enzymes and enzymic systems detected in erythrocytes of birds is collated in Table 10.

Miscellaneous Components

Proteins of the erythrocyte of the fowl have been studied by Mauritzen and Stedtman (1952), Engbring and Laskowski (1953), Mauritzen and Stedtman (1959), Neelin and Connell (1959), and Neelin and Butler (1961). A number of assays of the DNA and RNA contents of the erythrocyte nucleus have been reported. In the fowl, Mauritzen and Stedtman (1952) assessed the RNA content of the dried erythrocyte nucleus as 0.7–0.9 percent, while McIndoe and Davidson (1952) found 0.20–0.25 μg. $\times$ 10^{-6} per nucleus. More data are available for DNA. The dry weight proportion of DNA in the fowl erythrocyte nucleus has been given as 34–38 percent (Mauritzen and Stedtman, 1952), and 40–44 percent (Mirsky and Ris, 1949). Assessed in weight per nucleus, 2.22–2.49 μg. $\times$ 10^{-6} have been found by Davidson *et al.* (1950) and McIndoe and Davidson (1952). Similar ranges (1.9–2.3 μg. $\times$ 10^{-6} per nucleus) have been observed by others for erythrocytes from the duck, goose, turkey, pheasant, pigeon, and sparrow.

The pigments protoporphyrin and coproporphyrin-III have been detected in the red cells of the fowl by Schwartz and Wickoff (1952)

CONSTITUENTS OF PLASMA

Glucose

Evidence was presented in 1901, and confirmed by Bell (1957a), that the blood sugar of birds is in the form of D-glucose, as in

Table 10. Erythrocyte enzymes (other than those involved in
hemoglobin synthesis)

Enzyme	Species in which enzyme was detected	Reference
Adenyl cyclase	Chicken, pigeon	Davoren & Sutherland (1963); Klainer *et al.* (1962)
Carbonic anhydrase	Chicken	Common (1941); Gutowska & Mitchell (1945)
Peptidases	Chicken, goose	Salvidio & Urbani (1954)
Phosphatase, alkaline	Chicken, goose	Rapoport, Leva, & Guest (1942)
Phosphatase, acid	Chicken	Dounce & Seibel (1943)
Phosphatase, ATP-ase	Pigeon	Venkstern & Engelhardt (1955); Frank, Lipshitz, & Barth (1950)
Phytase	Chicken, goose, pigeon	Rapoport, Leva, & Guest (1942)
Estradiol 17-B dehydrogenase	Chicken, pigeon	Portius & Repke (1960)
Catalase	Chicken	Foulkes & Lemberg (1949–1950)
Tricarboxylic acid cycle	Chicken	Rubinstein & Denstedt (1953, 1954); Hunter & Hunter (1957)
Glycolysis system	Chicken	Dische (1946)
Glucose 6-phosphate and gluconic acid 6-phosphate dehydrogenases	Pigeon	Salvidio *et al.* (1963)

mammals but that the levels are generally higher than for mammals (see Chapter 12 for details). Sturkie (1954) compiled the literature on glucose of whole blood of birds, and such figures showed
considerable variation, apparently related to differences in methods and physiological state. Since virtually all of the glucose in
blood is confined to the plasma, whole blood analyses do not take

into account sex differences in relative amounts of plasma and cells, and therefore are in error. For example, glucose in whole blood of chickens is significantly lower than for females (Sturkie, 1955), but there is no sex difference in plasma glucose (Tapper and Kare, 1956, Bell, 1957a). Erlenbach (1938) reported whole blood glucose values in 41 species of birds, and concluded that aquatic birds had lower values than terrestrial birds.

Blood sugar level is influenced markedly by certain hormones, such as insulin, glucagon, and corticoids; this subject is discussed in detail in Chapter 12. Likewise, whether the animal is fed or starved influences the level, as shown in Table 11. Plasma glucose level is evidently not influenced by state of reproduction, since

Table 11. Plasma reducing sugar (glucose) in domestic fowls mg./100 ml.)

Breed	Age	Sex	Physiological state	Range	Mean	Reference
White Leghorn	Newly hatched	Mixed	—	—	227	Tapper & Kare (1960)
	3 days	M	Fed	—	282	Bernstein *et al.* (1956)
	3 days	M	Starved	—	253	"
	7 weeks	F	Starved 12 hrs.	—	229	Tapper & Kare (1960)
	4½ mo.	M	"	—	250	"
	6½ mo.	M	Starved 16 hrs.	—	300	"
	12 mo.	M	Starved 18 hrs.	—	287	"
	Adult	F	"	—	245	"
	Adult	F	Starved 16 hrs.	—	233	Tapper & Kare (1956)
Brown Leghorn	15–18 mo.	F	Laying, fed	225–305	251	Bell (1957a)
	"	F	Nonlaying, fed	247–286	267	"
	28–29 mo.	F	Laying, fed	227–273	246	"
	"	F	Nonlaying, fed	225–262	244	"
	36–60 mo.	F	Laying, fed	213–262	243	"
	"	F	Nonlaying, fed	221–273	231	"
Rhode Island Red	2 weeks	Mixed	Starved 12 hrs.	—	227	Tapper & Kare (1960)
	3 weeks	Mixed	"	—	242	"
	4 weeks	Mixed	"	—	265	"

there were no significant differences between layers and nonlayers (see Table 11).

Nonprotein Nitrogen (NPN)

When the proteins of plasma are precipitated, the protein-free fluid contains a number of nitrogenous substances. These include amino acids and urates as the major components, and urea and creatine as minor ones. There appear to be no definitely detectable amounts of creatine in avian blood, as there are in that of mammals. The bulk of NPN in mammals is in the form of urea. Avian erythrocytes contain about 6 times as much NPN as the plasma, volume for volume; therefore whole blood NPN determinations are of little value unless the plasma-cell ratio is known. This is also true of urate determinations because all of the urate is found in the plasma. Figures for NPN are shown in Table 12. Although few age groups are included, NPN appears to be slightly higher in fed adult birds than in immature ones. Starved males exhibit lower values than those fed. Hens, whether fed or starved, have less NPN in their plasma than males. NPN is lower in laying than in nonlaying birds, and this suggested to Bell, McIndoe, and Gross (1959) that nitrogenous substances accumulate in the plasma when eggs are not laid, as holds also for uric acid.

Table 12. The partition of chicken plasma nonprotein nitrogen into amino-N (amino acids and small peptides) and residual-N, including substances of unknown constitution (Bell, McIndoe, and Gross, 1959)

Sex	Physiological state	Total NPN (mg./100 ml.)	Amino N (mg./100 ml.)	Residual N (mg./100 ml.)			
				Total	Urate-N	Urea N	Unknown
Hens	Laying	15.4*	7.8	7.5**	0.76	1.12	5.6
"	Nonlaying	18.9*	8.3	11.5**	1.80	2.40	7.3
Both sexes	Immature	19.4	9.1	8.2	1.46	2.20	6.5
Cocks	Fed	26.7	—	—	—	—	—
"	Starved 36 hrs.	22.0	—	—	—	—	—

* P < 0.02 > 0.01.
** P < 0.01 > 0.001.

Effects of diet, breed, and disease on NPN. Shimer (1937) reported no difference in nonprotein nitrogen and uric acid of the blood of chickens fed high and low protein diets, and Hermann (1946) found no difference in these constituents between young birds and old hens. Shimer reported no difference in the chemical constituents of blood of normal birds and of those afflicted with paralysis and cannibalism, nor among the different breeds he studied, namely White Leghorn, Barred Plymouth Rock, New Hampshire, and crossbreeds.

Chickens suffering from blue comb or pullet disease have higher than average amounts of nonprotein nitrogen (26.8 mg. percent) and of uric acid (18.9 mg.) in the blood, according to Jungherr (1948). The values for phosphorus, magnesium, and glucose were normal. The values for calcium and chlorides were low. In birds severely affected, serum potassium was subnormal but the amount in whole blood was high.

Uric acid. Until the advent of the specific enzymatic determination of urate by uricase, the accurate measurement of uric acid presented technical difficulties; hence, much of the older work reported by Sturkie (1954) involved questionable methods, and only recent data are included here (Tables 12 and 13). Bell, McIndoe, and Gross (1959), Pudelkiewicz *et al.* (1959), and Sturkie (1961) have shown that plasma uric acid varies considerably under standard conditions and appears to be influenced by sex and reproductive state; nonlayers had higher levels. A high-protein diet increases plasma urate (Siller, 1959). Starvation depresses the level significantly. The results reported by Sturkie (1961) and by Bell *et al.* suggest that the level of circulating estrogens may influence plasma uric acid levels in chickens and should be studied.

Although uric acid is the end product of protein metabolism in birds and represents the bulk of waste nitrogen eliminated by the bird, the levels of uric acid in birds are not much different from those reported in man. The low solubility of uric acid in blood (about 10 percent) has long caused investigators to be puzzled as to its mode of transport. Abnormalities in the elimination of uric acid produce an abnormal increase in uric acid in the blood (uricemia), which may be fatal (see Chapter 13).

Avian Physiology

Table 13. Plasma urate (mg./100 ml.) enzymatically measured, in fowls

| Breed | Sex* | Age | Condition | Uric acid | | | Reference |
				Range	Mean	S.D.	
Brown	F	10 wks.	Fed	2.2–6.3	4.38	1.35	Bell *et al.* (1959)
Leghorn	F	Adult	"	2.2–9.9	5.40	2.44	"
	F	"	Starved	0.8–2.1	1.50	0.42	"
	LF	"	Fed	0.8–5.3	2.27	1.28	"
	LF	"	Starved	0.3–2.2	1.41	0.76	"
	M	"	Fed	1.1–5.3	2.86	0.93	"
	M	"	Starved	1.4–2.7	2.26	0.55	"
	Mixed	22–29 wks.	Normal diet (18% protein)	—	5.0	—	McIndoe, quoted by Siller (1959)
	Mixed	26 wks.	High nitrogen diet (30%)	—	7.3	—	"
	"	29 wks.	High nitrogen diet (60%)	—	9.0	—	"
New Hampshire	M	5 wks.		—	1.8	—	Pudelkiewicz *et al.* (1959)
	F	5 wks.		—	1.7	—	"
	M	28 wks.		—	5.6	—	"
	F	28 wks.		—	4.9	—	"
White	F	10–26 mo.	Fed	1.87–5.64	3.90	2.10	Sturkie (1961)
Leghorn	LF	10–26 mo.	Fed	—	2.54	1.17	"

* F, female; LF, female in lay; M, male.

Urea. This substance is equally distributed between plasma and cell water. Howell (1939) and Bell (1957b) have pointed out that most of the older determinations were inaccurate (with values usually too high) because of faulty methods. Bell (1957b) and Bell *et al.* (1959) presented plasma urea values determined in normal chickens of various ages, fed and starved, laying and nonlaying, and in both sexes. None of these differences appeared to influence urea level appreciably. The values in mg. urea per 100 ml. blood for (1) laying females, fed and starved, were 2.23 and 2.5, and for (2) nonlaying females, mg./100 ml. fed and starved, were 2.80 and 2.83. Values of 4.9 and 4.7 mg./100 ml. have been reported for turkey hens and toms (Kirshner *et al.*, 1951). Since urea contributes so small a part to total plasma NPN, it is not surprising that Bell (1957b) found no significant alteration in the levels of this substance in fowls suffering from glomerulonephritis. In mammals, where urea is the major NPN component, increased plasma urea levels are the rule. Howell (1939) reported that birds suffering from paralysis, tumors, respiratory disorders, and parasites had increased plasma urea level.

It seems probable that free plasma urea in birds arises, as suggested by Hunter and Dauphinee (1920), not by hydrolysis of arginine but by transfer of its ornithine moiety to benzoic or other aromatic acids to form dibenzoyl ornithine. Bell (1957b) suggested that plasma urea of the fowl arises by diffusion from the kidney.

Creatine. Creatine is equally distributed between the water of plasma and of corpuscles. The determination of creatine often presents difficulties when the Jaffe method is employed because other chromogens are present. A more specific method, however, is available. Salander and Fisher (1956) have measured the plasma creatine content in 5-week-old cocks and laying hens; the former showed a range of 1.58–0.50 mg./100 ml. with a mean of 0.97 mg., while the latter showed a range of 1.83–0.74 mg./100 ml. with a mean of 1.17 mg. In turkeys, Kirshner *et al.* (1951) found 2.5 mg. and 2.8 mg. respectively for female and male plasma.

Ammonia. The amount of free ammonia (or properly, ammonium ion) in the blood of birds and mammals is very small when the blood is freshly shed; indeed, ammonia may be virtually absent (Conway and Cooke, 1939). Enzymes in blood rapidly deaminate amino purine and pyrimidine derivatives, present mainly in the cells.

Free Amino Acids—Residual Nitrogen. "Total free amino acids" can be assessed by the use of several methods, none of which is entirely satisfactory, because they usually tend to include at least one terminal amino acid residue in a peptide. Attempts to measure individual free amino acids by microbiological assay are open to the criticism that the microorganism employed may possess a peptidase capable of liberating the amino acid in question from its combination in a peptide structure. At least 22 free amino acids have been detected in avian plasma (Richardson *et al.*, 1953; Owings and Balloun, 1961; Bell *et al.*, 1959; and others).

Total free amino acids, expressed as aminonitrogen have been determined under known conditions and are presented in Table 12. Residual nitrogen values are obtained by subtracting total amino nitrogen from TPN, and they are by no means negligible. Little is known concerning the nature of residual nitrogen.

PLASMA PROTEINS

The plasma of the bird, like that of other vertebrates, contains a variety of proteins, which can be arbitrarily grouped by conventional methods into pre-albumins, albumins, post-albumins, and globulins. The latter can be divided into alpha-, beta-, and gamma-fractions, and each of these can be further subdivided. Fibrinogen is also present, but it does not behave identically with mammalian fibrinogen (Bigland and Triantaphyllopoulos, 1961). The classical separation of plasma proteins into "albumins" and "globulins" by fractional precipitation, is merely an imperfect separation of the whole into two analytically complex and overlapping parts. It is not always fully appreciated that all of the quantitative methods of protein analysis commonly employed, either directly or by comparison, are based on measurement of the total amino- and imino-nitrogen which is converted into "protein" by multiplying by a factor (usually 6.25) under the assumption that the "protein" is a long-chain polypeptide derived entirely from amino acids. This is not true, especially in the instance of the globulin fractions. Many proteins contain not inconsiderable amounts of such nonpeptide components as carbohydrates or lipids, in which the nitrogen content is low or even zero. These components are integral parts of the molecule and therefore contribute appreciably to molecular weight (Stacey, 1946; Ewing, 1947; Kent and Whitehouse, 1955). Schjeide and Ragan (1957) have measured the total serum-bound polysaccharide and seromucoid polysaccharide in chicks up to 14 days old; the former varied from 65 to 89 mg./100 ml. and the latter from 16 to 23 mg./100 ml. (see also Schjeide and Simons, 1961). Kloker and Micheel (1959) have found that duck gamma-globulins contain 0.8 percent hexose, 0.2 percent fructose, 1.2 percent N-acetyl-glucosamine, and 0.21 percent N-acetyl neuraminic acid. The serum lipoproteins which accumulate in stilbestrol-treated cockerels contain galactose, mannose, glucosamine, and sialic acid (Abrahams, Hillyard, and Chaikoff, 1960). Williams (1962) found fowl plasma transferring contained 2.8 percent hexose, 1.4 percent hexosamine, and 0.35 percent sialic acid.

Methods of Analysis

A complex mixture of proteins such as is found in blood plasma may theoretically be separated into groups of molecules, according to differences either in molecular weight or in ionic mobility. Only very small amounts of material are required. Separation on the basis of particle-weight can be accomplished by the enhanced gravitational force of the ultracentrifuge. Differences in ionic mobility allow separations under the influence of an applied electric potential, in the process known as electrophoresis or ionophoresis. Electrophoretic separation, as devised by Tiselius, is carried out in solution in an appropriate buffer, and the analysis is derived from observations of the changes in refractive index of the solution manifested as the ionized proteins migrate at different rates. In this "free" electrophoresis the only large molecules present are the proteins themselves, and only these large molecules can interfere with each other's speed of migration. In zone electrophoresis, migration is also induced in a buffer solution; but this solution is held in the interstices of a rigid system such as filter paper or a starch gel. Extra resolution may be possible through intermolecular forces between the proteins and the stationary carbohydrate, and also by filtration effects. The proteins are thus separated into more or less discrete bands. The positions occupied by these bands are revealed by a suitable stain which will dye the protein but not the support. In paper or starch electrophoretic separation, it is frequently possible by the use of appropriate dyes to detect lipoproteins, enzymes, and sometimes carbohydrates.

The separation of total plasma proteins into two fractions, albumins and globulins, is accomplished by precipitating the globu-

lins having no higher molecular weight by a suitable agent of
known concentration (i.e. salting out). It is not surprising that the
electrophoretic and salting-out methods do not always reveal the
same quantitative results.

Nomenclature of Protein Fractions

The resolutions effected by the ultracentrifuge, and by "free"
and paper electrophoreses, are greatly inferior to those carried out
in gels. Whereas the former methods separate the plasma proteins
into but 5 main components, starch gel electrophoresis reveals the
presence of at least 14 distinct individual proteins (Lush, 1959,
unpublished; Riou *et al.*, 1962). McIndoe (1962) has thus demonstrated the occurrence of two genetically distinct plasma albumins
in the Brown Leghorn.

Both free and paper electrophoresis reveal five main fractions,
corresponding   to   the   so-called   albumin,   alpha$_1$-globulin,

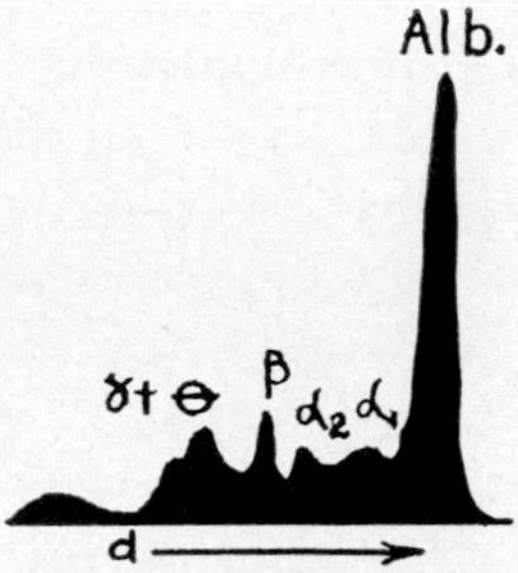

Alb.

Figure 3. Electrophoretic pattern (descending,
d) of chicken plasma.

Alb., albumin; α_1 and α_2, alpha$_1$ and alpha$_2$
globulins; β, beta globulin; θ, fibrinogen; γ,
gamma globulin. (Modified from Sanders, Huddle-
son, and Schaible, *J. Biol. Chem.*, 1944.)

alpha$_2$-globulin, beta-globulin and gamma-globulin of mammalian plasma analyzed in the same way (Figure 3). These fractions
are somewhat arbitrarily defined. Some workers prefer to number
their fractions serially (Lush, 1963), whereas others use the mammalian type designations. Vanstone, Maw and Common (1955)
have suggested a scheme for correlating the observations made by
free and paper electrophoresis. Urist, Schjeide, and McLean
(1958), and Schjeide and Urist (1960), employed ultracentrifugal
analysis for plasma proteins and calcium of laying hens, males, and
estrogenized males. They showed that in the laying females or estrogenized males, there are three new components not present in
males, namely (1) a phosphoprotein, X$_1$, designated phospovitin

by Common and Mok (1959), (2) a lipoglycoprotein, X_2, designated lipovitellin by the same workers, and (3) a light lipoprotein. It is mainly the phosphoprotein that is responsible for the binding of calcium, which is also elevated in laying females or estrogenized males. Based upon calculations by Urist and Schjeide (1961), the mixed serum proteins of chicken blood have a calcium-binding capacity of, respectively, 3.0 mg. and 50 mg. of calcium per gram of protein for nonestrogenized and for estrogenized chickens. The calcium-binding capacity is likewise high in estrogenized amphibia and reptiles, but not mammals. The molecular weights of the serum X_1 and X_2 protein fractions are 144,000 and 400,000 respectively. In the passage of these complex proteins across the membranes between blood and the yolk sac, their molecular weights are decreased by exactly one half (Urist and Schjeide).

Further work by Mok, Martin, and Common (1961), and by Heald and McLachlan (1963), has dealt with phophovitin in plasma of estrogenized and laying hens. Both plasma and yolk phosovitins were shown to have identical chromatographic patterns with average molecular weights of 4.2×10^4; but this finding is not in agreement with the ultracentrifugal analysis of Urist and Schjeide (1961). Although the two phosphovitins are probably identical chemically, the complexes in which they exist are different.

Pre-albumins. Common and his co-workers (in Vanstone, Maw, and Common, 1955 and later), and Heim and Schechtman (1954), reported two small but distinct pre-albumin fractions in chicken blood; an "alpha$_1$-globulin" tended to disappear with the onset of laying, and a slow lipoprotein fraction ("PP") was present only in the plasma of the laying hen.

Lush (1963), applying starch gel electrophoresis, has shown that certain pre-albumins are present in nonlaying hens, whereas other components are characteristic of layers. A "post-albumin" or "pre-globulin" appears in quantity when the hen goes off laying and disappears at some time before laying is resumed. Association of pre-albumin fractions with laying hens has also been reported by Kristjansson *et al.* 1963.

Schjeide and Urist (1960) have suggested that some of the proteins observed following biochemical manipulations or zone elec-

trophoresis are derived fractions, and that the smaller number revealed by free electrophoresis or ultracentrifugation may more
nearly represent physiological entities; but this idea has been
strongly criticized by Cook (1961), who has emphasized that ultracentrifugation separates materials only on the basis of weight.

The Total Protein Level in Plasma

The usual method of measuring total plasma proteins is to precipitate them by means of trichloroacetic acid, tungstic acid, etc.
Such reagents do not always precipitate acidic proteins with large
prosthetic groups of carbohydrates—which, in fact, are not usually
present in quantity. It is generally accepted that the level of the
plasma proteins is lower in adult cocks than in adult hens (Rochlina, 1934; Sturkie and Newman, 1951; Brandt, Clegg, and Andrews, 1951). This difference also exists between the immature
cock and the pullet (Table 14). Sturkie and Newman (1951) were
unable to show any significant difference between the total plas-
ma-protein levels of laying and nonlaying White Leghorn hens;
they measured the plasma proteins on the days when the hens (a)
laid but did not ovulate, (b) both laid and ovulated, and (c) neither laid nor ovulated. These authors noted considerable variation among individuals in the different groups; the plasma proteins of some laying hens were found to be as high as in some
birds that had been out of production for about two months. A
progressive decrease in the amount of plasma protein with successive blood samples was considered to be due to hemodilution rather
than to a change in rate of formation or destruction of protein.
Such a fall in plasma protein concentration is, however, not invariably observed, and is probably related to the amount of blood
removed in relation to the blood volume of the bird.

Bell and McIndoe (1962) found a peak in the amount of protein in the plasma of 2-year-old hens during the 10-day period before laying recommenced. A similar peak has been observed in
pullets beginning to lay for the first time by Greenberg, Larson,
Pearson, and Burmester (1936) and by Vanstone, Maw, and Common (1955). Pigeons show a similar prelaying rise in plasma protein (McDonald and Riddle, 1945; Sendroy *et al.*, 1961). This

Table 14. Some measurements of total plasma (or serum) proteins, "albumins," "globulins" and "A/G" ratio expressed in g./100 ml. (P indicates measurement made on plasma.)

	Age	Total protein	"Alb."	"Glob."	A/G	Reference
Cocks						
Brown Leghorn	8 wks.	P 4.0	2.00	1.98	1.01	Bell (unpublished)
"	12 wks.	P 3.33	1.79	1.53	1.17	"
White Leghorn	12 wks.	3.93	2.22	1.71	1.32	Perk *et al.* (1960)
"	12 wks.	4.00	2.10	1.90	1.10	"
Kansas W. Rock	16 wks.	4.63	1.75	3.31	0.56	Brandt *et al.* (1951)
White Leghorn	18 mos.	P 4.00	1.66	2.33	0.71	Sturkie & Newman (1951)
Females, immature						
New Ham. Red	4–7 wks.	3.36	1.75	2.14	0.82	Brandt *et al.* (1951)
Brown Leghorn	8 wks.	P 4.49	2.80	2.19	1.05	Bell (unpublished)
White Leghorn	12 wks.	4.00	2.31	1.68	1.40	Perk *et al.* (1960)
Brown Leghorn	16 wks.	P 4.13	2.05	2.10	0.98	Bell (unpublished)
New Ham. Red	16 wks.	4.49	1.30	3.58	0.36	Brandt *et al.* (1951)
Females, mature, not laying						
White Leghorn		5.14	1.94	3.20	0.60	Sturkie & Newman (1951)
"		5.34	2.00	3.34	0.60	"
Brown Leghorn		P 4.69	1.38	3.31	0.42	Bell (unpublished)
Females, mature, laying						
New Ham. Red		5.40	1.75	4.08	0.43	Brandt *et al.* (1951)
White Leghorn		5.45	2.50	2.94	0.85	Sturkie (1951)
"		4.64	2.15	2.48	0.86	"
"		5.32	2.53	2.79	0.90	"
"		5.18	2.50	2.67	0.90	"
Brown Leghorn		P 4.48	1.86	2.62	0.71	Bell (unpublished)
Pigeon (sex and condition not stated)						
		2.30	1.38	0.95	1.50	Mandel *et al.* (1947)
Turkey						
		3.96–	2.85–	1.11–	2.57–	Lynch & Stafseth (1953 1954)
		4.91	3.04	1.86	1.63	"

Total serum proteins have been reported by Defalco (1942) for the following birds: guinea fowl (*Numida meleagris*), 2.82; goose (*Anser anser*), 3.50; turkey, 3.95; duck (*Anas platyrhyncus*), 3.50; pheasant (*Phasianus colchicus*), 2.80; turkey buzzard, 2.94; pelican, 3.20. Werner (1944) found total proteins of 6.44 g./100 ml. in ducks (both sexes) and 8.47 in geese (both sexes).

peak is certainly due to the presence of phosphoprotein (Bell and McIndoe, 1962; Heald and Badman, 1963).

Reznichenko (1961) reported that, in hens laying down egg albumen, the plasma protein is at a higher level than at other times. Although Bell and McIndoe (1962) did not pay attention to the position of eggs in the oviduct, their results are in general agreement with those of Sturkie and Newman (1951).

The ratio of albumin to globulin (A/G ratio) for a number of avian species is shown in Table 14. It is observed that the A/G ratio seems to fall with the approach of maturity, largely as a result of a progressive increase in the globulin fraction, and that laying hens have relatively more globulin than nonlayers. The globulin fraction is the one that is most increased with estrogen (Urist, Schjeide, and McLean, 1958).

The lipophosphoprotein complex ("PLP") in the plasma of laying hens. Laskowski (1934) obtained a phosphoprotein fraction by dilution of hen plasma, and Roepke and Bushnell (1936) observed the precipitation of a phosphoprotein with concomitant precipitation of lipoprotein. McKinley *et al.* (1953 and 1954) presented evidence for the occurrence of phosphoprotein in the material precipitated on dilution of the serum of estrogen-treated pullets. McIndoe (1957 and 1959) has examined PLP in detail. About 7 or 8 days before the first ovulation in hens, dilution of the plasma with 9 to 11 volumes of water results in the precipitation of PLP. PLP increases to a maximum amount at about 3 days before the first ovulation; thereafter it decreased toward a relatively constant level. About the day of the last ovulation before a hen stops laying, PLP begins to disappear, and it is not present 4 days later.

PLP is not detectable in the plasma of nonlaying hens or of cocks. The concentration is about 2 g./100 ml. of plasma and is very variable. The precipitate contains about 20 percent protein and 80 percent lipid. The protein fraction contains approximately 0.75 percent phosphorus, of which 80 percent can be demonstrated to originate in phosphoprotein. The lipid moiety comprises 25 percent phospholipid and 4 percent cholesterol (mainly free); the remainder is probably triglyceride.

Formation of Plasma Proteins

The liver is considered a site of formation of plasma proteins in mammals, at least for albumin. Mandel, Clavert, and Mandel (1947) presented evidence that albumin is formed by the liver of pigeon. They ligated the hepatic blood vessels and found that albumin was decreased but that there was no appreciable change in globulin. Vanstone, Dale, Oliver, and Common (1957) demonstrated by functional hepatectomy that all of the phosphoprotein is formed in the liver of the chicken.

Estrogen administered at high levels increases the proteins of blood and liver and causes hypertrophy of the latter organ in the chicken and pigeon. These effects can be counteracted or prevented by administration of thyroxine (Common, Rutledge, and Bolton, 1947; Common, Bolton, and Rutledge, 1948; Fleischmann and Fried, 1945; Sturkie, 1951; McDonald and Riddle, 1945). Thus it has been suggested that excess thyroxine either inhibits the synthesis of plasma proteins in the liver or increases the oxidative destruction of them.

It is interesting to note that the plasma protein level of laying hens remains fairly constant and is not related to time of ovulation, formation of albumin in the egg, or laying. Yet the amount of protein which must be mobilized and stored in the yolk and albumen of a single egg (approximately 6 grams) is equivalent to the total circulating plasma proteins of the hen. This suggests that rate of formation and turnover of plasma proteins is indeed rapid in the fowl, as has been demonstrated by Vanstone, Oliver, Maw, and Common (1957).

Functions of Plasma Proteins

Fibrinogen in mammals when converted into fibrin constitutes the main part of the blood clot. Presumably it has a similar function in the chicken.

One of the chief functions of the plasma proteins is the maintenance of normal blood volume and water content in the tissues. The molecules of the proteins are of such dimensions that they do not normally diffuse through the wall of the blood vessel as do crystalloids. Hence they exert a colloidal osmotic pressure, which tends to hold a certain volume of water in the blood. Any upset in this mechanism may upset the normal water balance between the blood and tissues. Albumin in mammalian blood accounts for about 80 percent of the total osmotic pressure of the plasma proteins, because such blood contains more albumin than globulin, and the albumin molecule is smaller than that of globulin. In avian blood, which contains more globulin than albumin, the osmotic pressure exerted by the proteins is considerably less than that for mammals, averaging 150 and 110 mm. of H_2O for the hen and dove (Albritton, 1952). Changes in body temperature and other factors may upset the balance of water between the blood and tissues, so that more than normal amounts of fluid diffuse from the blood into the tissues, thus concentrating the plasma proteins, or from the tissues to the blood, causing hemodilution. This has been demonstrated in mammals, and in chickens by Sturkie (1947) and by Sturkie and Newman (1951).

Globulins are associated with the production of antibodies in mammals and birds. Chickens are good producers of antibodies, and this is related to the higher ratio of globulins to albumin in chicken blood (Wolfe *et al.,* 1957).

"Carrier" or "binding" proteins of plasma. I. E. Lush and W. N. M. Ramsay (unpublished) have found that iron in the laying hen can be carried by a protein which electrophoresed just behind the main albumin band (Lush, 1963); this fraction is therefore quite distinct from the known iron-binding transferrins. W. M. McIndoe (unpublished) has obtained evidence that Lush's fraction 8 (from the "globulin" region) binds the xanthophyll which gives the color to the plasma of the nonlaying bird.

Plasma proteins bind some of the circulating steroids in mammalian and reptilian blood, and this is also true of avian blood (Seal and Doe, 1963).

Plasma iodine compounds exist in two forms, as protein-bound iodine (PBI) and in the unbound condition. Their measurement is important in relation to thyroid function (see Chapter 19).

Balfour and Tunnicliffe (1960) have reported that a pre-albumin isolated from duck serum is able to bind thyroxine. Tata and

Shellabarger (1959) had previously shown that only small amounts, if any, of the thyroxine-binding proteins were present in chicken and duck sera, but that each would bind equally thyroxine and 3, 5, 3-triiodo-thyronine. This may explain why birds, as compared to mammals, do not respond differently to thyroxine and triiodothyronine.

PLASMA LIPIDS

The lipid fractions of avian blood plasma are a complex mixture. They have been roughly classified as "free fatty acids," "neutral fat," "phospholipid" (or "phosphatide"), "cholesterol esters," and so forth. The fatty acids, whether free or combined, differ from one another only by one or two of $-CH_2-$ groups among many, by one or two double bonds, or in the position in the carbon chain of these bonds.

The plasma lipids of various avian species are presented in Table 15. The levels of all of those fractions are probably affected by the physiological and nutritional states of the birds. For example, the level of total plasma lipids for the laying hen is higher than for the nonlayer, the male, or the immature bird. It has been amply demonstrated that the rise in plasma lipids with the onset of sexual maturity in the female is caused by the secretion of estrogen by the maturing ovary. This is particularly true of the phospholipids, fatty acids, and neutral fats. Heald and Badman (1963) have shown that, although the onset of lay in the chicken is preceded by large increases in free fatty acids and total lipids as well as phosphoproteins, the quantities of these components decrease markedly when laying commences. When intermittent laying was induced by decreasing the "day-length" provided by artificial light, a cyclical rise and fall of the plasma lipid components was observed to be associated with oviposition. Cholesterol levels do not appear to be influenced appreciably by endogenous estrogen, since the differences between adult males and laying and nonlaying famales are not consistent. Exogenous estrogen, however, does increase plasma cholesterol (Stamler, Katz, Pick, and Rodbard, 1955), although it increases the other lipid fractions still more (see also Chapter 18).

Table 15. Plasma lipids in birds (mg./100 ml.)

Species and breed	Age (weeks)	Sex	Condition	Total lipid	Total cholesterol	Total fatty acid	Phospho-lipid	Reference
Chicken, White Leghorn	5	Male		279	86		—	Diller et al. (1960)
"	12	"			100–113		174–225	Caldwell & Suydam (1960)
"	8, 12, 16	"			143			Weiss (1957)
"	23	"			134			"
"	45	"			209			"
"	8–14	Female			189			"
"	26–29, 57	"			209, 198			Weiss (1960)
"	24–72	"	L		159–211		155	Urist & Deutsch (1960)
"	Adult	Male	L	450			402	"
"	"	Female	L	1500			373	Walker et al. (1951)
"	"	"	NL	1253	101	989	219	Greenberg et al. (1936)
"	"	"		550			642	Lorenz et al. (1938)
"	"	"	L	1689	125	1569	155	Urist & Deutsch (1960b)
"	Capon			875				
Turkey, bronze	3–5	Male			100–129		164–266	Waibel et al. (1960)
"	20	No Sex			81–102	365–517		Heller & Thayer (1948)
Pigeon	Adult	Male			407			Lofland & Clarkson (1960)
"	"	Female			468			"
"	Young	"			133		450	McDonald et al. (1945)
Duck, Pekin	Adult	Male			114			Landauer et al. (1941)
Mallard	"	"			450–500			"
					730			

In recent years a considerable mass of data has accumulate... lating to the effects of changes in composition of the diet, particularly in the lipids, on plasma lipids and atherosclerosis. No attempt will be made here to review these data, but it can be stated that excess cholesterol added to the diet of chickens increases plasma cholesterol particularly, and some other lipids as well. The effect of dietary cholesterol on plasma cholesterol is influenced by the level of saturated and unsaturated fats in the diet. There is some evidence that certain polyunsaturated fats tend to depress plasma cholesterol in cholesterol-fed chickens. A few pertinent references on the effects of diet on plasma lipids are: Stamler, Pick, and Katz (1959); Bieri, Pollard, and Briggs (1957); Fisher *et al.* (1950 and 1960); Feigenbaum *et al.* (1961). Data by Fisher *et al.* (1961) indicate that the sterol fraction of the unsaturated fats may be the effective component.

The effect of dietary changes upon plasma unsaturated fatty acids is shown in Table 16.

Genetic differences in plasma cholesterol levels of chickens up to 16 weeks of age have been developed by selective breeding (Hardy, Auger, and Wilcox, 1962).

METALLIC ELEMENTS IN PLASMA

It is customary to refer to the sodium, potassium, calcium, and magnesium present in the plasma of animals as "cations" or "electrolytes." This is incorrect for the last two elements, since some of the magnesium and often the majority of the calcium is firmly bound by covalent links ("chelated") to large molecules. Iron, copper, and trace elements are probably similarly chelated. The calcium and magnesium protein complexes can be separated from the remainder of the elements because of their size, which renders them unable to pass an ultrafiltering barrier. Sodium and potassium, on the other hand, are probably completely ultrafilterable, and there is at present no reason to suspect that they exist in plasma in any state other than the ionic.

The presence in ultrafiltrates of polybasic anions, mainly phosphate with a little citrate, poses the problem of whether in practice these anions may chelate some of the calcium and magnesium

Table 16. Unsaturated fatty acids (mono and polyenoic) in chicken plasma

Breed	Sex	Age	Diet	Enoic acids, in percent of total fatty acid (A) or total fat (F)						Reference
				Monenoic	Dienoic	Trienoic	Tetra- enoic	Penta- enoic	Hexa- enoic	
New Hampshire	F	8 wks.	I	A —	2.3	10.1	2.7	+	+	Bieri et al. (1957)
			II	A —	19.9	0	21.1	++	+	"
Crosses	F	Pullets and hens	III	F —	1.3	1.3	0.9	0.4	0.8	Fisher et al. (1959)
Columbia and New Hampshire	M	5–20 wks.	IV	F —	4.3		0.9			Feigenbaum et al. (1961)
			V	F —	1.14		2.9			"
White Leghorn	F	3 yrs	VI	F 39.3	9.9	1.3	1.9	0.2	0.7	Fisher et al. (1960)
			VII	F 38.2	15.7	1.2	1.0	0.2	0.6	"
			VIII	F 49.7	6.9	0.9	1.6	0.2	0.7	"

Diets:

I   Fat free (Protein, Casein 20 pts. gelatin 9 pts.)
II 4% corn oil (Protein as I)
III No fat added to diet (8% and 20% protein levels)
IV 5% coconut oil (10% protein)
V   5% corn oil (10% protein)
VI No fat supplement
VII 10% corn oil supplement
VIII 10% animal fat supplement

and thus withdraw them from the ionic state. At present we
no definite information as to the real state of the entire
ultrafilterable calcium and magnesium.

Sodium and Potassium

Na+ and K+ form the bulk of the "fixed base" of the plasma. A
fair number of measurements have been made on fowls, mainly
without reference to their physiological state (Table 17). As in
mammals, the quantity of sodium in the plasma greatly exceeds that
of potassium. Kravis and Kare (1960) measured the plasma sodium and potassium of White Leghorns from 1 to 463 days of age.
From hatching to 12 days there was great variation and
fluctuation in the levels of both ions, but thereafter both were
much more stable. There were no differences attributable to sex.
The role of adrenal steroids in the control of electrolyte levels is
discussed in Chapter 21. It should be noted that Kravis and Kare
(1960) have also studied the Na+ and K+ levels in the brain, skin,
muscle, and liver.

Plasma Iron, Copper, and Molybdenum

Plasma of the laying hen and the estrogenized bird contains
considerably more iron than the nonlayer or than males (Ramsay
and Campbell, 1954; Campbell, 1960). Values in micrograms per
100 ml. are as follows: nonlaying hen, 100–250; laying hen
500–900. Similar values (in micrograms) have been reported by
Planas *et al.* (1961) as follows: laying hen, 500; laying goose, 1,260;
laying duck, 1,065. The values for the males were 103 to 164 micrograms.

Copper in the *whole blood* of fowls and turkeys (Beck, 1956),
and molybdenum in the *whole blood* of New Hampshire chicks
(Kurnick *et al.*, 1957), have been assessed at 23 μg./100 ml. and 3.2
μg./100 ml. respectively.

Total Calcium in Plasma

It was early realized that the actively ovulating female bird had
a total calcium level 2 or 3 times that observed in the male and
sexually immature female (Table 18). The elevation accompany-

Table 17. Plasma sodium and potassium contents, in milliequivalents
per liter; some typical findings

Species and breed	Sex	Age	Sodium	Potas-sium	References
Chicken					
White Leghorn	Mixed	1 day	147.6	6.7	Kravis & Kare (1960)
"	"	5 days	145.5	3.5	"
"	"	19 days	143.0	3.0	"
"	"	42 days	131.6	4.0	"
"	"	125 days	151.6	3.8	"
"	"	463 days	138.6	3.6	"
Brown Leghorn	Male	28 weeks	171.0	4.9	Lake *et al.* (1958)
New Hampshire	Male and Female	5 weeks	170	7.3	Pudelkiewicz *et al.* (1959)
	"	28 weeks	148	6.4	
Turkey	Female	28 weeks	149	6.0	Kirshner *et al.* (1951)
	Male	28 weeks	155	6.4	
Duck					
Pekin	Male	9–12 weeks	138	3.4	Phillips, Holmes, & Butler (1961)
Gull (*L. glaucescens*)	*	12 weeks	151	5.71	"
	**	12 weeks	152.8	4.8	"

* Drinking fresh water.
** Drinking sea water.

ing the laying state is considered to be controlled by the endogenous estrogens, which stimulate the appearance in the plasma of
phosphoproteins with a high calcium-binding capacity (Greenberg, Larson, Pearson, and Burmester, 1936; Clegg, Ericson,
Hein, McFarland, and Leonard, 1956; Schjeide and Urist, 1956;
Winget and Smith, 1959; see also Chapters 18 and 20).

During active shell deposition, calcium is withdrawn from the blood at the rate of 25–30 mg. every 15 minutes, or in an amount roughly equivalent to the total circulating plasma calcium of the hen; the plasma calcium level, however, does not vary appreciably during the reproductive cycle (see Chapter 15).

Ultrafilterable (diffusible) calcium. Some observations have been made on the partition of avian plasma (or serum) calcium into ultrafilterable and "bound" fractions (Table 18). The warning of Dillman and Visscher (1933) and subsequently of others, e.g. Toribara, Terepka, and Dewey (1957), on the importance of maintaining the pH of the system at its physiological level has often been disregarded. Exposure of plasma to the atmosphere leads to loss of CO_2, rise in pH, and a concomitant fall in ultrafilterable Ca^{2+} and Mg^{2+}. Taylor and Hertelendy (1961) have shown that the pH of the plasma of laying hens increases by approximately 0.3 units when exposed to air for three hours, and that the ultrafilterable calcium falls by about 1–2 mg./100 ml. Taylor and Hertelendy (1961) found shell deposition often to be associated with a fall in ultrafilterable calcium of from 0.2 to 2.6 mg./100 ml.; however, this had not been observed by some others. The matter is discussed in Chapter 15. The effect of the parathyroid hormone on diffusible calcium is considered in Chapter 20.

Magnesium

Part of the magnesium, like calcium, is nonfilterable and is presumably bound to protein; the amounts are also pH-dependent. Few determinations have been made on avian blood, but the work of Taylor and Hertelendy (1961) indicates that both fractions of magnesium may be decreased when the hen is depositing shell on the egg. Typical values in mg./100 ml. are as follows:

	Total	Ultrafilterable	Author
White Leghorn, laying	3.88	2.20	Taylor & Hertelendy (1961)
Rhode Island Red, laying	3.0 – 3.05	1.8 – 2.3	"
Brown Leghorn, laying	3.11±0.17	—	J. Filshie (unpublished)
Brown Leghorn, immature	1.88±0.04	1.88±0.04	"

Table 18. Plasma calcium of normal birds

Breed	Sex	Age	Total Ca mg./100 ml.	Ultrafilterable Ca mg./100 ml.	m. equiv./l.	Reference
White Leghorn	Capon	—	10.1	6.0	3.0	Urist & Deutsch (1960a)
	Female	Immature	9.8–11.8	5.2–7.4	2.6–3.7	Urist & Deutsch (1960b)
	Female	L-pullets	12.5–35.5	6.3–8.6	3.2–4.3	Urist & Deutsch (1960a)
	Female	Hens	7.6–11.0	4.8–5.2	2.4–2.6	"
	Male	Adults	9.6–11.0	6.8–7.2	2.4–3.6	"
	Female	L. Pullets	23.5–29.1	—	—	Hertelendy & Taylor (1961)
	Female	L. Hens	21.5–28.1	8.7–13.2	4.4–6.6	Winget & Smith (1958)
	Female	L. Hens	23.9	9.45[1]	4.73[2]	Taylor & Hertelendy (1961)
	Female	L. Pullets	21.5	7.2	—	Polin & Sturkie (1959)
	Female	L. Pullets (starved 24 hrs.)	16.5	5.9	—	"
Brown Leghorn	Mixed	15 weeks	10.0–10.8	5.6–6.0	2.8–3.0	Bell & Campbell (1961)
	Male	7 months	10.2–11.0	—	—	Lake et al. (1958)
	Male	15–29 months	10.8–11.2	—	—	"
Rhode Island Red	Female	L-Hens	19.5–30	7.5–8.7[1]	3.8–4.4	Taylor & Hertelendy (1961)

Table 18 (Continued)

Breed	Sex	Age	Total Ca mg./100 ml.	Ultrafilterable Ca mg./ml.	m. equiv./l.	Reference
Turkey	Male		11.7	—		Scott et al. (1933)
	Female		11.1	—		"
	Female	L.	25.2	—		Rhian et al. (1944)
	Female	L.	16.1–38.7	—		Paulsen et al. (1950)
Ducks, Pekin	Male		9.0–9.6	6.0–6.8	3.0–3.4	Mandel et al. (1952)
Ducks, Mallard	Male		9.9–10.4	—	—	Landauer et al. (1941)
Pigeon	Mixed		9.7–11.7			McDonald et al. (1945)
	Female		9.4–10.4[2]	4.4–8.2	2.2–4.1	Sendroy, et al. (1961)
	Female		22.6[3]			"
Ring Dove	Male		8.1–9.8			Riddle & Reinhart (1926)
	L. Female		19.9			"
Quail, Bobwhite	Male	14.1–15.4				Baldini & Zarrow (1952)
	Female	14.0–14.8				"
	L. Female	23.0–40.0				"

L. = laying.

[1] Ultrafiltration conducted in atmosphere of 5 percent CO_2.

[2] Several days after laying egg.

[3] Immediately before laying egg.

Citrate

The physiological significance of citrate in avian blood is not understood. Young, immature chickens have higher plasma citrate levels than adults. Typical values are shown as follows:

	Citrate (*mg./100 ml.*)	*Author*
White Leghorn, female, 1–5 months	6.8–11.2	Taylor *et al.* (1960)
White Leghorn, female, laying	2.7–2.9	"
R.I. Red cross, female, laying	2.64	Hertelendy & Taylor (1960)

Taylor and Hertelendy (personal communication) found that citrate was unequally distributed between the cells and plasma. In males and sexually immature females the amount in the plasma (8.05 mg./100 ml.) was higher than in the cells (2.9–4.0 mg./100 ml.). In laying females the amount in cells (5.8–6.0 mg./100 ml.) was higher than in the plasma (2.7–3.5 mg./100 ml.).

Inorganic Phosphate

This exists in animal tissue in equimolar amounts of HPO_4^{2-} and $H_2PO_4^{-}$ (Morgan and Chichester, 1935). Its level in the plasma, apart from added ions originating in the food (Heller, Hunter, and Thompson, 1932; Elvehjem and Kline, 1932) appears to be largely under the control of the kidney. This organ is stimulated by parathyroid hormone to excrete phosphate in the urine (Levinsky and Davidson, 1957; see Chapter 20). T. G. Taylor (unpublished) and D. J. Bell (unpublished) noted independently that the inorganic phosphate in individual laying hens can vary between 2 and 12 mg./100 ml. of plasma. There appeared to be no relation to shell production, although several workers have found that the levels of plasma inorganic phosphate increase during shell calcification (Feinberg *et al.,* 1937; Peterson and Parrish, 1939; Hunsaker, 1959), and others found no change or a decrease (Sturkie, 1954). An increase during shell deposition may be related to bone calcium phosphate mobilization, if the rate at which calcium is removed from the circulation by the uterus is greater than the rate at which phosphate is excreted by

Table 19. Inorganic phosphorus in the plasma of adult birds

Breed	Sex	Phosphate (mg./100 ml.)	Reference
Chicken, White Leghorn	Female	8.0	Urist & Deutsch (1960a)
"	Male	6.0	"
"	Capon	6.1	"
Greenleg	L. female	4.5	Laskowski (1933)
"		2.9	"
Rhode Island Red	L. female	7.1–8.0	Hayden & Sampson
"		5.9–10.3	"
Wyandotte	"	3.0–7.1	Common (1936)
Turkey	L. female	5.4–7.09	Paulsen *et al.* (1950)
Pigeons	Mixed	4.3	McDonald, Riddle, & Smith (1945)

L. = laying.

the kidney. Typical values for several avian species are given in Table 19.

Chloride and Bicarbonate

Very few determinations have been made of these anions. Plasma bicarbonate in White Leghorn females 4 weeks of age ranged from 21 to 28 milliequivalents per liter (Ackerson, Blish, and Mussehl, 1925), and similar figures were reported by Shimer (1937). Inorganic chloride in plasma of adult chickens, sex unspecified, ranged from 75 to 110 mg./liter (Dyer and Roe, 1934; Heller and Pursell, 1937).

PLASMA ENZYMES

The acid phosphatase activity in plasma of fowl (Bell, 1961) and of geese and pigeons (Rapoport, Leva, and Guest, 1942) has been studied. Adenosine triphosphatase (ATP-ase, apyrase) has been found in plasma of fowls by Frank, Lipshitz, and Barth (1950). Phytase is present in plasmas from fowls, pigeons, ducks, and geese (Rapoport, Leva, and Guest, 1942). It is not certain to what extent the various phosphate esters are hydrolyzed by one and the same enzyme, nor whether a collection of highly specific phosphatases occur in avian plasma.

Amylase activity has been detected in fowl plasma by Squibb, Braham, Guzman, and Scrimshaw (1955) and by McGeachin, Gleason, and Adams (1958). It appears to be much greater in young birds than in adult hens.

Aldolase and glutamic-oxalacetic transferase have been reported in avian plasma by Cornelius, Bishop, Switzer, and Rhode (1959), and by Cornelius, Law, Julian, and Asmundsen (1959). The latter enzyme, along with glutamic-pyruvic transaminase, lactic dehydrogenase, and malic dehydrogenase, has been exhaustively studied in White Rocks and White Leghorns by McDaniel and Chute (1961). An inhibitor of elastase is present (Walford and Schneider, 1959), and the slow destruction of glucagon by fowl plasma has been noted by Mirsky, Perisuttie, and Davis (1959); see also Beekman, 1958, and Chapter 12). Both true cholinesterases and pseudocholinesterases have been detected in avian plasma (fowl, duck, and pigeon) by Mendel, Mundel, and Rudney (1943); Caridroit, Kaswin, and Polonorski (1945), and Augustinsson (1959). Multiple aryl esterases have been detected in fowl plasma by Paul and Fottrell (1961), and by I. E. Lush (1962, unpublished), employing starch-gel electrophoresis. On the other hand, Augustinsson (1959), using separation of plasma proteins by cellulose-column electrophoresis, was unable to find such esterases in the fowl and duck. Lush's evidence points to variability in the occurrence of the enzymes between lines and breeds. Some of the enzymes present in blood cells (see Table 10) are also present in plasma.

Alkaline phosphatase in growing chickens. Elevated levels of plasma phosphatase can be correlated with increased cellular activity in various organs and tissues, and particularly in the bone. Plasma of young chicks up to 4 weeks of age has high levels of enzyme activity, which in general decrease thereafter and reach a low point at 14 to 18 weeks (Tanabe and Wilcox, 1960). These authors also showed that phosphatase level is heritable. Similar observations have been made by McDaniel and Chute (1961), and by D. J. Bell (unpublished); however, the levels of activity reported by the later authors were lower than those of Tanabe and Wilcox. Common (1936) also reported high alkaline phosphatase in young White Wyandotte chicks.

Phosphatase levels in mature birds. All investigators have agreed that the phosphatase level in blood is lower in adults than in growing birds, but the relation of phosphatase level to egg production is not clear. Bell (1960) reports that preceding the onset of laying there is a rise in phosphatase activity, and that the level drops when the hen is not laying. However, after continued laying for 3 or 4 months the level that was high at the onset of laying tends to drop also. Common (1936), and Stutts, Briles, and Kunkel (1957), found no differences in phosphatase levels in laying and nonlaying birds; but the latter workers did find differences between inbred lines. The plasma phosphatase activity of hens on calcium-deficient diets is significantly elevated (Hurwitz and Griminger, 1961).

Acid phosphatase. The plasma levels of acid phosphatase have been determined in chickens from 5 to 18 weeks of age (Bell and Campbell, 1961; McDaniel and Chute, 1961). The levels were much lower than reported for alkaline phophatase. The values are quite variable. Bell (1961) has reported an increase in phosphatase level in birds suffering from osteoporosis.

REFERENCES

Abrahams, S., L. A. Hillyard, and I. L. Chaikoff 1960 Components of serum and egg yolk lipoproteins: Galactose, mannose and sialic acid. Arch. Biochem. Biophys. 89:74.

Ackerson, C. W., M. J. Blish, and F. E. Mussehl 1925 A study of the phosphorus, calcium, and alkaline reserve of the blood sera of normal and rachitic chick. J. Biol. Chem. 63:75.

Albritton, E. C. 1952 Standard Values in Blood. W. B. Saunders Co., Philadelphia.

Augustinsson, K. B. 1959 Electrophoresis studies on blood plasma esterases. II: Avian, reptilian, amphibian, piscine plasmata. Acta Chem. Scand. 13:1081.

Baldini, J. T., and M. X. Zarrow 1952 Estrogen and serum calcium levels in the bobwhite quail. Poultry Sci. 31:800.

Balfour, W. E., and H. E. Tunnicliffe 1960 Thyroxine bindings by serum proteins. J. Physiol. 153:179.

Bankowski, R. A. 1942 Studies of the hemoglobin content of chicken's blood and evaluation of methods for its determination. Am. J. Vet. Res. 3:373.

Beck, A. B. 1956 The copper content of the liver and blood of some vertebrates. Australian J. Zoology 4:1.

Beekman, B. E. 1958 A bioassay for glucagon based on the hyperglycemic response of the fowl. Poultry Sci. 37:595.

Bell, D. J. 1957a The distribution of glucose between the plasma water and the erythrocyte water in hen's blood. Quart. J. Exp. Physiol. 42:410.

Bell, D. J. 1957b Tissue components of the domestic fowl. 2: Blood urea. Biochem. J. 67:33.

Bell, D. J. 1960 Tissue components of the domestic fowl. 4: Plasma-alkaline-phosphatase activity. Biochem. J. 75:224.

Bell, D. J. 1961 Plasma acid phosphatase activity and bone dystrophies in the domestic fowl. Biochem. J. 80:44P.

Bell, D. J., T. P. Bird, and W. M. McIndoe 1964 Changes in mean corpuscular hemoglobin concentration with physiological state in the domestic fowl. Quart. J. Exp. Physiol. (in press).

Bell, D. J., and J. G. Campbell 1961 Pathological and biochemical observations on virus-induced osteopetrosis gallinarum. J. Comp. Path. 71:85.

Bell, D. J., and W. M. McIndoe 1962 Plasma protein levels and physiological state in Brown Leghorn hens. Proc. XII World's Poultry Congress, p. 101.

Bell, D. J., W. M. McIndoe, and D. Gross 1959 Tissue components of the domestic fowl. 3: The non-protein nitrogen of plasma and erythrocytes. Biochem. J. 71:355.

Bernstein, E. K., S. P. Stearner, and A. M. Brues 1956 Liver function in the chick following X-irradiation. Plasma amino acids and plasma glucose. Am. J. Physiol. 186:543.

Bieri, J. G., C. J. Pollard, and G. M. Briggs 1957 Essential fatty acid in the chick. II: Polyunsaturated fatty acid composition of blood of heart and liver. Arch. Biochem. Biophys. 68:300.

Bigland, C. H., and O. C. Triantaphyllopoulos 1961 Chicken prothrombin, thrombin, and fibrinogen. Am. J. Physiol. 200:1013.

Brandt, L. W., R. E. Clegg, and A. C. Andrews 1951 The effect of age and degree of maturity on the serum proteins of the chicken. J. Biol. Chem. 191:105.

Caldwell, C. T., and D. E. Suydam 1960 Comparison of cholesterol and estrogen-induced atherosclerosis in cockerels. Proc. Soc. Exp. Biol. & Med. 104:133.

Campbell, E. A. 1960 Changes in plasma iron, hemoglobin and plasma proteins in immature pullets, resulting from simultaneous administration of (A) estrogen and thyroxine, (B) estrogen and sulphamethazine. Poultry Sci. 39:140.

Caridroit, F., A. Kaswin, and M. Polonorski 1945 Cholinesterase activity of blood plasma of domestic cocks and hens. Compt. Rend. Soc. Biol. 139:1028.

Chubb, L. G. 1960 The distribution of free amino acids between erythrocytes and plasma in the fowl. Res. Vet. Sci. 1:321.

Clegg, R. E., A. T. Ericson, R. E. Hein, R. H. McFarland, and G. W. Leonard 1956 An electrophoretic component responsible for calcium bindings in the blood sera of chickens. J. Biol. Chem. 219:447.

Common, R. H. 1936 Serum phosphatase in the domestic fowl. J. Agr. Sci. 26:492.

Common, R. H. 1941 The carbonic anhydrase activity of the hen's oviduct. J. Agr. Sci. 31:412.

Common, R. H., W. Bolton, and W. A. Rutledge 1948 The influence of gonadal hormones on the composition of the blood and liver of the domestic fowl. J. Endocrinol. 5:263.

Common, R. H., and C. Mok 1959 Phosvitin in the serum of the hen. Nature 183:1811.

Common, R. H., W. A. Rutledge, and W. Bolton 1947 The influence of gonadal hormones on the serum riboflavin and certain other properties of blood and tissues in the domestic fowl. J. Endocrinol. 5:121.

Conway, E. J., and R. Cooke 1939 Blood ammonia. Biochem. J. 33:457.

Cook, W. H. 1961 Proteins of hen's egg yolk. Nature 190:1173.

Cornelius, C. E., J. Bishop, J. Switzer, and E. A. Rhode 1959 Serum and tissue transaminase activities in domestic animals. Cornell Vet. 49:116.

Cornelius, C. E., G. R. J. Law, L. M. Julian, and V. S. Asmundsen 1959 Plasma aldolase and glutamic-oxaloacetic transaminase activities in inherited muscular dystrophy of domestic chickens. Proc. Soc. Exp. Biol. & Med. 101:41.

D'Amelio, V., and A. M. Salvo 1959 The serological specificity of chicken hemoglobin fractions. Z. Naturforsch. 14:455.

Davidson, J. N., I. Leslie, R. M. S. Smellie, and R. Y. Thompson 1950 Chemical changes in the developing chick embryo related to desoxyribonucleic content of the nucleus. Biochem. J. 46:11.

Davoren, P. R., and E. W. Sutherland 1963 The effect of L-epinephrine and other agents on synthesis and release of adenosine 3', 5'-phosphate by whole pigeon erythrocytes. J. Biol. Chem. 238:3009.

Defalco, A. J. 1942 A serological study of some avian relationships. Biol. Bull. 82:205.

De Villiers, O. T. 1938 Blood of ostrich. Onderstepoort J. Vet. Sci. 11:419.

Diller, E. R., C. L. Rose, and O. A. Harvey 1960 Effect of beta-sitesterol on regression of hyperlipemia and increased plasma coagulability in the chicken. Proc. Soc. Exp. Biol. & Med. 104:173.

Dillman, L. M., and M. B. Visscher 1933 The calcium content of ultrafiltrates of plasma and the influence of changes in hydrogen and bicarbonate ion concentrations upon it. J. Biol. Chem. 103: 791.

Dische, Z. 1946 The aerobic glycolysis of avian red blood cells and its control by intracellular ions in physiological concentration. J. Biol. Chem. 163:575.

Dounce, A. L. 1950 The Enzymes, edited by J. D. Sumner and K. Myrback, p. 217. Academic Press, New York.

Dounce, A. L., and D. Seibel 1943 Acid phosphatase content of nuclei of chicken erythrocytes. Proc. Soc. Exp. Biol. & Med. 54:22.

Dresel, E. I. B., and J. E. Falk 1954 Studies on the biosynthesis of blood pigments. 1: Heme synthesis in hemolyzed erythrocytes of chicken blood. Biochem. J. 56:156.

Dresel, E. I. B., and J. E. Falk 1956 Studies on the biosynthesis of blood pigments. 2: Heme and porphyrin formation in intact chicken erythrocytes. Biochem. J. 63:72.

Dukes, H. H., and L. H. Schwarte 1931 The hemoglobin content of the blood of fowls. Am. J. Physiol. 96:89.

Dunlap, J. S., V. L. Johnson, and D. S. Farner 1956 Multiple hemoglobins in birds. Experientia 12:352.

Dyer, H. M., and J. H. Roe 1934 The chemistry of the blood of normal chickens. J. Nutr. 7:623.

Elvehjem, C. A., and B. E. Kline 1932 Calcium and phosphorus studies in the chick. J. Biol. Chem. 103:733.

Engbring, V. K., and M. Laskowski 1953 Protein components of chicken erythrocyte nuclei. Biochim. Biophys. Acta 2:224.

Erlenbach, F. 1938 Experimentelle Untersuchungen über den Blutzucker der Vögel. Z. Vergl. Physiol. 26:121.

Ewing. W. R. 1947 Poultry Nutrition, 3rd ed. Ewing Publishing Co., Pasadena, California.

Feigenbaum, A. S., H. Fisher, G. A. Leveille, H. S. Weiss, and P. Griminger 1961 The polyunsaturated fatty acid and cholesterol concentrations of plasma and aorta and their relationship to avian atherosclerosis. J. Am. Oil Chemists Soc. 38:93.

Feinberg, J. G., J. S. Hughes, and H. M. Scott 1937 Fluctuation of calcium and inorganic phosphorus in the blood of the laying hen during the cycle of one egg. Poultry Sci. 16:132.

Fine, J. M., and J. Uriel 1958 L'electrophorèse en gélose des hémoglobines animales. Sem. Hôpital Paris Path. Biol. 6:1553.

Fisher, H., A. Feigenbaum, G. A. Leveille, H. S. Weiss, and P. Griminger 1959 Biochemical observations on aortas of chickens. Effect of different fats and varying levels of protein, fat and cholesterol. J. Nutr. 69:163.

Fisher, H., H. S. Weiss, and P. Griminger 1961 Influences of fatty acids on sterols on atherosclerosis in the avian abdominal aorta. Proc. Soc. Exp. Biol. & Med. 106:61.

Fisher, H., H. S. Weiss, G. A. Leveille, A. S. Feigenbaum, S. Hurwitz, O. Donis, and H. Lutz 1960 Effect of prolonged feeding of differently saturated fats to laying hens on performance of blood pressure, plasma lipids and changes in the aorta. Brit. J. Nutr. 14:433.

Fleischmann, W., and I. A. Fried 1945 Studies on mechanism of the hypercholesterolemia and hypercalcemia induced by estrogen in immature chicks. Endocrinol. 36:406.

Foulkes, E. C., and R. Lemberg 1949-1950 Formation of choleglobin and the role of catalase in the erythrocyte. Proc. Royal Soc. London, B, 136:435.

Frank, S., R. Lipshitz, and L. G. Barth 1950 Properties of water extractable apyrases from different tissue sources. Arch. Biochem. 28:207.

Franz, R. D. 1957 Untersuchungen über die katalytische Wirksamkeit des Pferdeoxyhämoglobins und über die Peroxydaseaktivität verschiedener Vögeloxyhämoglobine. Wiss. Z. Univ. Halle Math. Nat. 6:823.

Gerlach, E., A. Fleckenstein, and K. J. Freundt 1957 Konzentration und Turnover der Adenosin- und Guanosinphosphate sowie anderer säureloslicher Phosphorverbindungen in Taubenerythrocyten. Studien mit 32p- markiertem Orthophosphat. Arch. ges. Physiol. (Pflügers) 263:682.

Gibson, K. D., A. Neuberger, and J. J. Scott 1954 The enzyme conversion of delta aminolaevulic acid to porphobilinogen. Biochem. J. 58:41.

Gourlay, D. R. H. 1957 Phosphate transfer in chicken erythrocytes. Am. J. Physiol. 190:536.

Granick, S. 1954 Enzymatic conversion of delta-amino levulinic acid to porphobilinogen. Science 120:1105.

Greenberg, D. M., C. E. Larson, P. B. Pearson, and B. R. Burmester 1936 The state and partition of the calcium and inorganic phosphorus in the serum of the fowl: Effect of growth and ovulation. Poultry Sci. 15:483.

Groebbels, F. 1932 Der Vogel. Erster Band: Atmungswelt Nahrungswelt. Verlag von Gebrüder Borntraeger, Berlin.

Gutowska, M. S., and C. A. Mitchell 1945 Carbonic anhydrase in the calcification of egg shell. Poultry Sci. 24:159.

Hardy, L. B., H. V. Auger, and F. H. Wilcox 1962 Genetic differences in serum cholesterol in chickens. Am. J. Physiol. 202:997.

Harmon, I. W. 1936 Hemoglobin regulation in chickens. Poultry Sci. 15:53.

Heald, P. J., and H. G. Badman 1963 Lipid metabolism in the laying hen. I: Plasma free fatty acid and the onset of laying in the domestic fowl. Biochim. Biophys. Acta 70:381.

Heald, P. J., and P. M. McLachlan 1963 Isolation of phosvitin from the plasma of the laying hen. Biochem. J. 87:571.

Heim, W. G., and A. M. Schechtman 1954 Electrophoretic analysis of the serum of the chicken during development. J. Biol. Chem. 209:241.

Heller, V. G., K. R. Hunter, and R. B. Thompson 1932 Phosphorus distribution in chicken blood as affected by the diet. J. Biol. Chem. 97:127.

Heller, V. G., and L. Pursell 1937 Chemical composition of the blood of the hen during its life cycle. J. Biol. Chem. 118:549.

Heller, V. G., and R. H. Thayer 1948 Chemical changes in the blood composition of chickens and turkeys fed synthetic estrogens. Endocrinol. 42:161.

Hermann, G. R. 1946 Blood and tissue chemical studies in fowl. Proc. Soc. Exp. Biol. & Med. 61:229.

Hertelendy, F., and T. G. Taylor 1960 On the interaction between vitamin D and parathyroid hormone in the domestic fowl. Biochim. Biophys. Acta 44:200.

Hertelendy, F., and T. G. Taylor 1961 Changes in blood calcium associated with egg shell calcification in the domestic fowl. I: Changes in the total calcium. Poultry Sci. 40:108.

Hilgert, I., and M. Vojlskova 1959 Species haemoglobin in guinea fowl hen–domestic cock hybrids. Folia Biologica 5:317.

Holmes, A. D., M. G. Piggot, and P. A. Campbell 1933 The hemoglobin content of chicken blood. J. Biol. Chem. 103:657.

Howell, S. F. 1939 The determination of urea in chicken blood. J. Biol. Chem. 128:573.

Hunsaker, W. G. 1959 Blood flow and calcium transfer through the uterus of the chicken. Thesis, Rutgers University, New Brunswick, N. J.

Hunter, A., and J. A. Dauphinee 1924 The distribution of arginase in fishes and other animals. Proc. Royal Soc. London, B, 97:227.

Hunter, A. S., and F. R. Hunter 1957 A comparative study of erythrocyte metabolism. J. Cell. Comp. Physiol. 49:479.

Hunter, F. R., L. D. Stringer, and H. D. Weiss 1940 Partial retention of hemoglobin by chicken erythrocytes. J. Cell. Comp. Physiol. 16:123.

Hurwitz, S., and Paul Griminger 1961 The response of plasma alkaline phosphatase, parathyroids and blood and bone minerals to calcium intake in the fowl. J. Nutr. 73:177.

Jaffe, P. 1960 Differences in numbers of erythrocytes between inbred lines of chickens. Nature 186:978.

Johnson, V. L., and J. S. Dunlap 1955 Electrophoretic separation of hemoglobin from chicken. Science 122:1186.

Jungherr, E. 1948 Avian monocytosis, Chapter 29 in Biester and Schwarte, Diseases in Poultry. 2d ed. Iowa State College Press, Ames.

Kent, P. W., and M. W. Whitehouse 1955 Biochemistry of the Amino Sugars. Butterworth, London.

Ketz, H. A., and G. Assman 1960 Der Natrium-, Kalium und Glukosegehalt im Serum und Erythrozyten von Vögeln und Fischen. Acta Biol. & Med. Germanica 4:598.

Kirshner, N., G. H. Pritham, G. O. Bressler, and S. Gordeuk, Jr. 1951 Composition of normal turkey blood. Poultry Sci. 30:875.

Klainer, L. M., Y-M Chi, S. L. Freidberg, T. W. Rall, and E. W. Sutherland 1962 Adenyl cyclase: Effects of neurohormones on formation of adenosine 3', 5'-phosphate by preparations from brain and other tissues. J. Biol. Chem. 237:1239.

Kloker, W., and F. Micheel 1959 Über die Kohlenhydratkomponenten von Gamma Globulinen. Z. Physiol. Chem. (Hoppe-Seyler's) 315:261.

Kravis, E. M., and M. R. Kare 1960 Changes with age in tissue levels of sodium and potassium in the fowl. Poultry Sci. 39:13.

Kristjansson, F. K., A. C. Taneja, and R. S. Gowe 1963 Variations in a serum protein of the hen during egg formation. British Poultry Sci. 4:239.

Kurnick, A. A., B. L. Reid, R. N. Burroughs, H. O. Stelzner, and J. R. Couch 1957 Effect of distillers' dried solubles and molybdenum on the growing chick. Proc. Soc. Exp. Biol. & Med. 95:353.

Kutas, F., and M. Stutzel 1958 The organic acid soluble phosphate content of mammalian and avian erythrocytes at the beginning of post natal life. Experientia 14:214.

Lake, P. E., E. J. Butler, J. W. McCallum, and I. J. MacIntyre 1958 A chemical analysis of the seminal and blood plasmas of the cock. Quart. J. Exp. Physiol. 43:309.

Landauer, W., C. A. Pfeiffer, W. U. Gardner, and J. C. Shaw 1941 Blood serum and skeletal changes in two breeds of ducks receiving estrogens. Endocrinol. 28:458.

Laskowski, M. 1933 Über den Calciumzustand im Blutplasma der Henne. Biochem. Z. 260:230.

Laskowski, M. 1934 Über die Phosphorverbindungen im Blutplasma der Legehenne. Biochem. Z. 275:293.

Levinsky, N. G., and D. G. Davidson 1957 Renal action of parathyroid extract in the chicken. Am. J. Physiol. 191:530.

Lofland, H. B., and T. B. Clarkson 1960 Serum lipoproteins in atherosclerosis- susceptible and resistant pigeons. Proc. Soc. Exp. Biol. & Med. 103:238.

Lorenz, F. W., C. Entenman, and I. L. Chaikoff 1938 The influence of age, sex, and ovarian activity on the blood lipids of the domestic fowl. J. Biol. Chem. 122:619.

Lush, I. E. 1963 The relationship of egg laying to changes in the plasma proteins of the domestic fowl. Brit. Poult. Sci. 4:255.

Lynch, J. E., and H. F. Stafseth 1953 Electrophoretic studies on the serum proteins of turkeys. I: The composition of normal turkey serum. Poultry Sci. 32:1068.

Lynch, J. E. and H. F. Stafseth 1954 Electrophoretic studies on the serum proteins of turkeys. II: The composition of pullorum immune turkey serum. Poultry Sci. 33:54.

McDaniel, L. S., and H. L. Chute 1961 Enzyme activity levels in chicken plasma. Am. J. Vet. Res. 22:99.

McDonald, M. R., and O. Riddle 1945 Effect of reproduction and estrogen administration on partition of calcium, phosphorus and nitrogen in pigeon plasma. J. Biol. Chem. 159:445.

McDonald, M. R., O. Riddle, and G. C. Smith 1945 Action of thyroxine on estrogen induced changes in blood chemistry and endosteal bone. Endocrinol. 37:23.

McGeachin, R. L., J. R. Gleason, and M. R. Adams 1958 Amylase distribution in extrapancreatic extrasalivary tissues. Arch. Biochem. Biophys. 75:403.

McIndoe, W. M. 1957 A lipophosphoprotein complex in the plasma of the domestic fowl. Biochem. J. 67:19.

McIndoe, W. M. 1959 A lipophosphoprotein complex in the hen plasma associated with yolk production. Biochem. J. 72:153.

McIndoe, W. M. 1962 Occurrence of two plasma albumins in the domestic fowl. Nature 195:353.

McIndoe, W. M., and J. N. Davidson 1952 The phosphorus compounds of the cell nucleus. Brit. J. Cancer 6:200.

McKinley, W. P., W. A. Maw, W. F. Oliver, and R. H. Common 1954 The determination of serum protein fractions on filter paper electrophorograms by the biuret reaction, and some observations on the serum proteins of the estrogenized immature pullet. Can. J. Biochem. Physiol. 32:189.

McKinley, W. P., W. F. Oliver, W. A. Maw, and R. H. Common 1953 Filter paper electrophoresis of serum proteins of the domestic fowl. Proc. Soc. Exp. Biol. & Med. 84:346.

Mandel, L., J. Clavert, and P. Mandel 1952 Action de la parathyroidectomie sur l'hypercalcémie d'origine folliculinique chez le canard: Calcium ultrafilterable. Comp. Rend. Soc. Biol. 146: 1805.

Mandel, P., J. Clavert, and L. Mandel 1947 Modifications des proteins du serum après ligature des vaisseaux hépatiques chez le pigeon soumis à l'action de la folliculine. Comp. Rend. Soc. Biol. 141:913.

Matsuda, G., and H. Takei 1963 Studies on the structure of chicken hemoglobin. I: Chromatographic purification of chicken hemoglobin. J. Biochem. (Japan) 54:156.

Maughan, G. H. 1935 Hemoglobin studies in chickens. Am. J. Physiol. 113:96.

Mauritzen, C. M., and E. Stedtman 1959 Cell specificity of B-histones in the domestic fowl. Proc. Royal Soc. London, B, 150:299.

Mauritzen, Roy, and E. Stedtman 1952 Ribose nucleic acid content of isolated cell nuclei. Proc. Royal Soc. London, B, 140:18.

Mendel, V., D. B. Mundel, and H. Rudney 1943 Studies on cholinesterase. 3: Specific tests for true cholinesterase and pseudo-cholinesterase. Biochem. J. 37:473.

Mirsky, A. E., and H. E. Ris 1949 Variable and constant components of chromosomes. Nature 163:666.

Mirsky, I. A., G. Perisuttie, and N. C. Davis 1959 The destruction of glucagon by the blood plasma from various species. Endocrinol. 64:992.

Mok, Chi-Ching, W. G. Martin, and R. H. Common 1961 A comparison of phosvitins prepared from hen's serum and from hen's egg yolk. Can. J. Biochem. Physiol. 39:109.

Morgan, V. E., and D. F. Chichester 1935 Properties of the blood of the domestic fowl. J. Biol. Chem. 110:285.

Neelin, J., and G. C. Butler 1961 A comparison of histones from chicken uterus by zone electrophoresis in starch gel. Canad. J. Biochem. Physiol. 39:485.

Neelin, J., and A. E. Connell 1959 Zone electrophoresis of chicken-erythrocyte histone in starch gel. Biochim. Biophys. Acta 31:539.

Olson, C. 1937 Variations in the cells and hemoglobin content in the blood of the normal chicken. Cornell Vet. 27:235.

Oshima, M., and T. G. Taylor 1963 Phytic acid in chicken erythrocytes. Biochem. J. 86:13P.

Owings, W. J., and S. L. Balloun 1961 Effect of protein sources and amino acid supplementation on intestinal microflora and plasma amino acids of the chick. Poultry Sci. 40:1718.

Paul, J., and P. Fottrell 1961 Tissue-specific and species esterase. Biochem. J. 78:418.

Paulsen, T. M., A. L. Moxon, and W. O. Wilson 1950 Blood composition of broad-breasted bronze breeding turkeys. Poultry Sci. 29:15.

Perk, K., M. Perek, K. Loebl, and D. Allalouf 1960 Chemical and electrophoretic analysis of young chickens' serum following sex hormones administration. Poultry Sci. 39:775.

Peterson, W. J., and D. B. Parish 1939 Fluctuations of phosphatase and inorganic phosphorus in the blood or laying hen during the period of egg formation. Poultry Sci. 18:54.

Phillips, J. F., W. N. Holmes, and D. G. Butler 1961 The effect of total and subtotal adrenalectomy on the renal and extra-renal response of the domestic duck (Anas platyrhynchus) to saline loading. Endocrinol. 69:958.

Planas, J., S. DeCastro, and J. M. Recio 1961 Serum iron and its transport mechanism in the fowl. Nature 189:668.

Polin, D., and P. D. Sturkie 1959 The decreases of plasma non-diffusible calcium levels in starved laying hens in relationship to shell deposition and estrogen. Poultry Sci. 38:166.

Portius, H. J., and K. Repke 1960 Über stereospezifität und Aktivität der Oestradiol Dehydrogenasen in der Erythrozyten von Mensch und Tier. Arch. exp. Path. Pharmak. 239:184.

Pudelkiewicz, W. J., R. V. Boucher, E. W. Callenbach, and R. C. Miller 1959 Some physiological responses of New Hampshire chickens to a mixture of penta- and hexachloronaphthalenes. Poultry Sci. 38:424.

Ramakrishnan, P., and J. Barnabas 1962 Investigations on the heterogeneity of the vertebrate haemoglobins. Acta physiol. pharmacol. Neerl. 11:328.

Ramsay, W. N. M., and A. E. Campbell 1954 Iron metabolism in the laying hen. Biochem. J. 58:313.

Rapoport, S., and G. M. Guest 1941 Distribution of acid-soluble phosphorus in the blood cells of various vertebrates. J. Biol. Chem. 138:269.

Rapoport, S., E. Leva, and G. M. Guest 1942 Acid and alkaline phosphatase and nucleophosphatase in the erythrocytes of some lower vertebrates. J. Cell. Comp. Physiol. 19:103.

Reichert, E. T., and A. P. Brown 1909 The crystallography of the hemoglobin. Carnegie Inst. Wash. Publ. No. 116.

Reznichenko, L. P. 1961 Vmist fraktsiy asotistikh rechovin v krovi ta yaysteprovodi kurey na risnikh stadiyakh for muvannya yaytsya. Ukrainskiy Biok. J. 33:727.

Rhian, M., W. O. Wilson, and A. L. Moxon 1944 Composition of blood of normal turkeys. Poultry Sci. 23:224.

Richardson, L. R., L. G. Blaylock, and C. M. Lyman 1953 Influence of the level of vitamins in the diet of the concentration of free acids in the plasma of chicks. J. Nutr. 49:21.

Riddle, O., and W. H. Reinhart 1926 Studies on the physiology of reproduction in birds. XXI: Blood calcium changes in the reproductive cycle. Am. J. Physiol. 76:660.

Riou, G., C. Paoletti, and R. Truhaut 1962 Fractionnement par electrophorèse sur gel d'amidon de protéines plasmatiques des différentes espèces animales. Bull. Soc. Chem. Biol. 44:149.

Rochlina, M. 1934 Les proteines du sang et la ponte des poules. Bull. Soc. Chim. Biol. 16:1645.

Rodnan, G. P. and F. G. Ebaugh, Jr. 1957 Paper electrophoresis of animal hemoglobins. Proc. Soc. Exp. Biol. & Med. 95:397.

Roepke, R. R., and L. D. Bushnell 1936 A serological comparison of the phosphoprotein of the serum of the laying hen and the vitellin of the egg yolk. J. Immunol. 30:109.

Rostorfer, H. H. 1949 Comparison of methods of measurement of avian hemoglobin. J. Biol. Chem. 190:90.

Rubinstein, D., and O. F. Denstedt 1953 The metabolism of the erythrocyte. III: The tricarboxylic acid cycle in the avian erythrocyte. J. Biol. Chem. 204:623.

Rubinstein, D., and O. F. Denstedt 1954 Cytochrome oxidase activity of cell nuclei. Canad. J. Biochem. Physiol. 32:548.

Saha, A., R. Dutta, and J. Ghosh 1957 Paper electrophoresis of avian and mammalian hemoglobins. Science 125:447.

Salander, R. C., and Hans Fisher 1956 Plasma amino nitrogen and creatine values of growing chick and laying hen. Proc. Soc. Exp. Biol. & Med. 92:538.

Salvidio, E., I. Pannacciulli and A. Tizanello 1963 Glucose 6-phosphate and gluconic acid 6-phosphate dehydrogenases in erythrocytes of mammals and pigeon. Nature 200:372.

Salvidio, E., and E. Urbani 1954 The influences of the nucleus and of heat regulation on the dipeptidase activity of the nucleated and anucleated erythrocytes of vertebrates. Experientia 10:25.

Schjeide, O. A., and N. Ragan 1957 Studies of the New Hampshire chicken embryo. VIII Glycoproteins of serum. J. Biol. Chem. 227:1035.

Schjeide, O. A., and S. Simons 1961 Effects of estrogen on protein-bound carbohydrates of embryo and chick serum. Growth 25:35.

Schjeide, O. A., and M. R. Urist 1956 Proteins and calcium in serums of estrogen-treated roosters. Science 124:1242.

Schjeide, O. A., and M. R. Urist 1960 Proteins induced in plasma by estrogens. Nature 188:291.

Schultze, M. O., and C. A. Elvehjem 1934 An improved method for the determination of hemoglobin in chicken blood. J. Biol. Chem. 105:253.

Schultze, M. O., C. A. Elvehjem, E. B. Hart, and J. C. Halpin 1936 The hemoglobin content of blood of laying hens on practical poultry rations. Poultry Sci. 15:9.

Schwartz, S., and H. M. Wickoff 1952 The relation of erythrocyte coproporphyrin and protoporphyrin to erythropoiesis. J. Biol. Chem. 194:563.

Scott, H. M., P. J. Serfontein, and D. H. Sieling 1933 Blood analyses of normal Bronze turkeys. Poultry Sci. 12:17.

Seal, U. S., and R. P. Doe 1963 Corticosteroid binding globulin: species distribution and small-scale purification. Endocrinology 73:371.

Sendroy, J., Jr., M. Mackenzie, and H. A. Collison 1961 Serum protein and calcium of pigeons during the reproductive cycle. Proc. Soc. Exp. Biol. & Med. 108:641.

Shemin, D., C. S. Russell, and T. Abramsky 1955 The succinate-glycine cycle. I: The mechanism of pyrrole synthesis. J. Biol. Chem. 215:613.

Shimer, S. R. 1937 Chemical studies on chicken blood. Univ. New Hampshire Tech. Bull. 69.

Siller, W. G. 1959 Avian nephritis and visceral gout. Lab. Investig. 8:1319.

Squibb, R. L., J. E. Braham, M. Guzman, and N. S. Scrimshaw 1955 Blood serum total proteins, riboflavin, ascorbic acid, carotenoids and vitamin A of New Hampshire chickens infected with coryza, cholera or Newcastle disease. Poultry Sci. 34:1054.

Stacey, M. 1946 The chemistry of mucopolysaccharides and mucoproteins. Adv. Carbohydrate Chem. 2:161.

Stamler, J., L. N. Katz, R. Pick, and S. Rodbard 1955 Dietary and hormonal factors in experimental atherogenesis and blood pressure regulation. Recent Prog. Hormone Res. 11:401.

Stamler, J., R. Pick, and L. N. Katz 1959 Saturated and unsaturated fats. Effects on cholesterolemia and atherogenesis in chicks on high-cholesterol diets, Circulation Res. 7:398.

Sturkie, P. D. 1943 Reputed reservoir function of the spleen of the domestic fowl. Am. J. Physiol. 138:599.

Sturkie, P. D. 1947 Effects of hypothermia upon the specific gravity and proteins of the blood of chickens. Am. J. Physiol. 148:610.

Sturkie, P. D. 1951 Effects of estrogen and thyroxine upon plasma proteins and blood volume in the fowl. Endocrinol. 49:565.

Sturkie, P. D. Avian Physiology (1st ed., 1954) Cornell University Press, Ithaca, N.Y.

Sturkie, P. D. 1955 Effects of gonadal hormones on blood sugar of the chicken. Endocrinol. 56:575.

Sturkie, P. D. 1961 The effects of age and reproductive state on plasma uric acid levels in chickens. Poultry Sci. 40:1650.

Sturkie, P. D., and H. J. Newman 1951 Plasma proteins of chickens as influenced by time of laying, ovulation, number of blood samples taken and plasma volume. Poultry Sci. 30:240.

Stutts, E. C., W. E. Briles, and H. O. Kunkel 1957 Plasma alkaline phosphatase activity in mature inbred chickens. Poultry Sci. 36:269.

Svedberg, T., and K. O. Pederson 1940 The Ultracentrifuge. Oxford University Press, New York; (1959) Johnson Reprint Corporation.

Tanabe, Y., and F. H. Wilcox 1960 Effects of age, sex and line on serum alkaline phosphatase of the chicken. Proc. Soc. Exp. Biol. & Med. 103:68.

Tanaka, T., and M. M. Rosenberg 1954 Relationship between hemoglobin levels in chickens and certain characters of economic importance. Poultry Sci. 33:821.

Tanaka, T., and M. M. Rosenberg 1955 Effect of testosterone and dienestrol diacetate on hemoglobin levels of cockerels and capons. Poultry Sci. 34:1429.

Tapper, D. N., and M. R. Kare 1956 Distribution of glucose in blood of the chicken. Proc. Soc. Exp. Biol. & Med. 92:120.

Tapper, D. N., and M. R. Kare 1960 Blood glucose distribution in the domestic fowl. Proc. Soc. Exp. Biol. & Med. 103:789.

Tata, V. R., and C. J. Shellabarger 1959 An explanation for the differences between the responses of mammals and birds to thyroxine and the triiodothyronine. Biochem. J. 72:608.

Taylor, T. G., and F. Hertelendy 1961 Changes in the blood calcium associated with egg shell calcification in the domestic fowl. 2: Changes in the diffusible calcium. Poultry Sci. 40:115.

Taylor, T. G., J. H. Moore, and F. Hertelendy 1960 Variations in the mineral composition of individual bones of the skeleton of the domestic fowl. Brit. J. Nutr. 14:49.

Toribara, T. Y., A. R. Terepka, and P. A. Dewey 1957 The ultrafilterable calcium of human serum. I: Ultrafiltration methods and normal values. J. Clin. Invest. 36:738.

Tosteson, D. C., and J. S. Robertson 1956 Potassium transport in duck red cells. J. Cell. Comp. Physiol. 47:147.

Urist, M. R., and N. M. Deutsch 1960a Effects of cortisone upon blood, adrenal cortex, gonads, and the development of osteoporosis in birds. Endocrinol. 66:807.

Urist, M. R. and N. M. Deutsch 1960b Osteoporosis in the laying hen. Endocrinol. 66:377.

Urist, M. R., and O. A. Schjeide 1961 The partition of calcium and protein in the blood of oviparous vertebrates during estrus. J. Gen. Physiol. 44:743.

Urist, M. R., O. A. Schjeide, and F. C. McLean 1958 The partition and binding of calcium in the serum of the laying hen and of the estrogenized rooster. Endocrinol. 65:570.

Van der Helm, H. J. and T. H. J. Huisman 1958 The two hemoglobin components of the chicken. Science 127:762.

Vanstone, W. E., D. G. Dale, W. F. Oliver, and R. H. Common 1957 Sites of formation of plasma phosphoprotein and phospholipid in the estrogenized cockerel. Canad. J. Biochem. Physiol. 35:659.

Vanstone, W. E., W. A. Maw, and R. H. Common 1955 Levels and partition of the fowl's serum proteins in relation to age and egg production. Canad. J. Biochem. Physiol. 33:891.

Vanstone, W. E., W. F. Oliver, W. A. Maw, and R. H. Common 1957 Observations on the physiological half-life of serum proteins in the cockerel and the laying pullet. Canad. J. Biochem. Physiol. 35:281.

Venkstern, T. V., and V. A. Engelhardt 1955 Surface localized adenosine polyphosphatase of nuclear erythrocytes. Doklady Akad. USSR 102:133.

Waibel, P. E., R. E. Burger, R. A. Bell, J. H. Sautter, I. E. Liener, and B. S. Pomeroy 1960 Effect of triparanol on beta-aminopropionitrile-induced dissecting aneurysm and blood lipid levels in the turkey. Proc. Soc. Exp. Biol. & Med. 104:673.

Walford, R. L., and R. Schneider 1959 Serum elastase inhibitor: Levels in animal and human sera, including selected disease states. Proc. Soc. Exp. Biol. & Med. 101:31.

Walker, A. E., M. W. Taylor, and W. C. Russell 1951 The level and interrelationship of the plasma lipids of the laying hen. Poultry Sci. 30:525.

Weiss, H. S. 1957 Age related changes in plasma cholesterol of the chicken. Proc. Soc. Exp. Biol. & Med. 95:487.

Weiss, H. S. 1960 Nicarbazine induced hypercholesterolemia in the hen. Proc. Soc. Exp. Biol. & Med. 103:49.

Werner, H. 1944 Vergleichende Blutuntersuchungen. Untersuchung des Ratten-, Enten- und Gänseblutes. Arch. ges. Physiol. (Pflügers) 248:426.

Williams, J. 1962 A comparison of conalbumin and transferrin in the domestic fowl. Biochem. J. 83:355.

Winget, C. M., and A. H. Smith 1958 Changes in plasma calcium concentration during egg formation. Poultry Sci. 37:509.

Winget, C. M., and A. H. Smith 1959 Dissociation of the calcium-protein complex of laying hen's plasma. Am. J. Physiol. 196:371.

Winters, A. R. 1936 Influence of egg production and other factors on iron content of chicken blood. Poultry Sci. 15:252.

Wolfe, H. R., A. Mueller, J. Neess, and C. Tempelis 1957 Precipitin production in chickens. XVI: The relationship of age to antibody production. J. Immunol. 79:142.

Wolterink, L. F., J. A. Davidson, and E. P. Reineke 1947 Hemoglobin levels in the blood of Beltsville small white poults. Poultry Sci. 26:559 (abs.).

CHAPTER 3

Circulation, Blood Pressure, Blood Flow, and Body Fluids

DURING ventricular contraction, oxygenated blood from the left ventricle is forced through the aortic valve into the aorta and into the branches of the arterial system, and venous blood is forced from the right ventricle through the pulmonary valve into the pulmonary artery, which carries blood to the lungs, where it is oxygenated. Oxygenated blood leaves the lungs via the pulmonary veins and enters the left atrium. Venous blood from the systemic circulation enters the right atrium through the venae cavae. After the blood is ejected, the pressure in the ventricles drops below that in the aorta, the pulmonary arteries, and the atria, and the valves of these arteries close and the atrioventricular valves open. Blood then flows from the atria into the ventricles (diastole and diastasis).

Circulation Time

The time required for the blood to make a complete circuit is considered the circulation time. It is determined, for example, by injecting dye or other substances into a blood vessel in one limb, and measuring the time required for the substance to reach the corresponding vessel in the opposite limb. The injected substance may also be one, such as acetylcholine, that causes a drop in blood pressure and slowing of the heart. The time required for the drug to reach the heart does not represent complete circulation time, but the latter may be estimated from it. Acetylcholine has been used to determine the time required for the drug to cause a drop in blood pressure when injected into the femoral vein of the chicken (Rodbard and Fink, 1948). The average time reported by these authors for White Leghorn chickens (sex and age not given) was 2.8 seconds. A 1-mg. dose of acetylcholine injected intravenously into the fowl causes a momentary arrest or slowing of the heart, which can be detected with the electrocardiogram (Sturkie, unpublished).

The circulation time from the right atrium to the base of the aorta is 2 to 3 seconds in nondiving ducks, and increases to 9 seconds when the birds are submerged (Johansen and Aakhus, 1963).

BLOOD PRESSURE

The pressure in the heart and arteries reaches its peak during systole (systolic pressure), and its minimum during diastole (diastolic pressure). The difference between these two pressures is known as the pulse pressure (PP). Mean blood pressure (MBP) is equal to one-half the area under the pressure curve. In the chicken, MBP = DBP + 3/8 PP. The pulse pressure decreases in the small arteries and disappears in the arterioles. In the large arteries of man, for example, mean pressure may be 100, and in the arterioles it may be as low as 30 mm. Hg. In the venules the pressure may drop to 12 mm. Hg, and will continue to fall in the veins; in the large central veins it may become negative, as a result of the negative pressure in the thorax. The positive pressure at the peripheral end and the negative pressure at the central end of the venous system, plus muscular activity, force the venous blood to the heart.

Changes in heart rate, output of the heart, elasticity and resistance of the arteries all influence blood pressure. Any factor which increases or decreases the distention of the system will cause changes in blood pressure. An increase in stroke volume ordinarily increases blood pressure, if resistance is unchanged, and this output is influenced by the amount of blood returned to the heart from the veins. Also, an increase in heart rate may increase pressure, provided the output of the heart is not decreased. It is possible to have a decreased output with an increased rate, resulting in no change in blood pressure.

As the blood flows through the arteries, it meets resistance, particularly in the small arteries and arterioles. Constriction of these vessels resulting from the stimulation of vasoconstrictor nerves, and from the action of certain chemicals and drugs increases blood pressure. Vasodilation, such as occurs after stimulation of vasodilator nerves or the action of certain chemicals, decreases blood pressure.

The elasticity of the blood vessels tends to decrease the work of the heart and to provide for a continuous flow of blood. It dampens blood pressure and thereby protects the capillaries from sudden fluctuations in pressure. Decreased elasticity resulting from arteriosclerosis may also increase blood pressure.

Methods of Determining Blood Pressure

The methods may be classified as direct and indirect. The most direct method is to insert a glass tube vertically into the vessel and observe the height to which the blood rises in it (Stephen Hales). This is a cumbersome method and is not ordinarily employed. In all of the commonly used direct methods, a cannula or needle is inserted into the artery or vein, and pressure of the blood is exerted against a tube of liquid (containing an anticoagulant) which is attached to the manometer. Where a mercury manometer is used, the liquid is in contact with the mercury, which rises and falls in the U tube with heartbeat.

Because of the inertia of mercury, systolic and diastolic pressures are not recorded accurately. At slow heart rates the mercury overshoots, and systolic pressure is recorded too high and diastolic pressure too low. At very rapid heart rates, full systolic and diastolic pressure are not reached, so that the systolic pressures recorded are too low and the diastolic pressures too high. If the mercury system can be so damped that only minute oscillations occur, a reasonable approximation of mean pressure may be obtained.

The membrane manometer is more sensitive than the mercury

manometer and records sudden pressure changes more accurately. Here the pressure exerted against the column of liquid is transmitted to a thin rubber membrane. The membrane moves up and down with changes in pressure, and these movements can be made to activate a recording lever.

There are other types of manometers, where the pressure is exerted against a relatively rigid membrane. These are more sensitive than the membrane or mercury manometers. Examples of these are the Hamilton manometer, in which the recording is done optically, and also the various strain gages and capacitance manometers. With the strain gage, the blood pressure and pressure pulses can be recorded by a direct-writing electrocardiograph, an oscillograph, and other recording devices. Weiss and Sturkie (1951) used a Statham strain gage for determining blood pressure in the chicken. The gage is attached to rigid tubing (M) which is filled with an anticoagulant. Either a hypodermic needle attached to the end of the tubing, or the tubing itself, is inserted into the blood vessel. Changes in pressure create an electrical imbalance in the gage or Wheatstone bridge, and this is picked up, amplified, and recorded (see Figure 4, upper part).

Indirect methods. An apparatus which is commonly used clinically for measuring blood pressure is the sphygmomanometer. It consists essentially of a compressing cuff, a manometer, and an air-inflating bulb. The cuff is applied to the upper arm and is inflated enough to obliterate the pulse. Then the cuff is deflated slowly, and when the pulse reappears, as may be determined by auscultation or palpation, the reading of the pressure of the manometer is taken. Indirect methods have been used on some species of animals, notably the horse, cow, dog, and rat. In the rat, the pressure cuff is applied to the tail (see Sobin, 1946, for details). Olmsted, Corcoran, Glasser, and Page (1948) have reported an indirect method of taking blood pressure in the rat, which involves the use of a miniature cuff and an inelastic cloth band attached to the foot. The cloth contains an electric displacement unit (strain gage), which records electrically the changes in volume of blood in the foot before and after inflation of the cuff.

An indirect method for chickens was first developed by Weiss

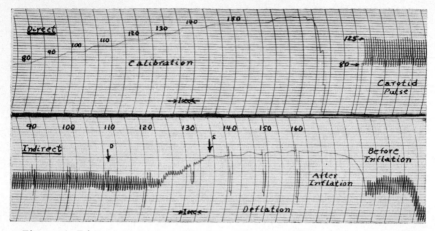

Figure 4. Direct (upper) and indirect (lower) blood pressure recordings from White Leghorn hens, taken with a Statham strain gage pickup and amplified and recorded with Brush equipment.

Systolic and diastolic pressures in upper tracing, 125 and 80 respectively, and in lower tracing, 135 and 110 mm. Hg. Read from right to left. (From Weiss and Sturkie, *Poultry Sci.,* 30:587 [1951].)

and Sturkie (1951) and later modified and improved by Sturkie, Durfee, and Sheahan (1957). . . . A cuff, one inch in diameter for adult chickens, and made to fit the lower thigh, is inflated well above the point where pulse disappears. It is then deflated, and the pressure at the point where pulse reappears represents systolic pressure. The improved method involves the use of a capacitance pulse pickup, which is small and easily attached to the shank of the bird in an upright position, and a control box (Infraton). The output from the latter is fed to the input of an ECG amplifier and recorded on a suitable oscillograph.

Normal Values

Chickens. Values for normal arterial blood pressures of chickens are shown in Table 20. The values obtained with the more reliable direct methods, Hamilton manometer and strain gage, indicate that the systolic pressure of the adult nonanesthetized male is approximately 190 mm. Hg and the diastolic pressure about 150, with a pulse pressure of 40 mm. Hg. Systolic pressures for adult females range from about 140 to 160 mm. Hg with a pulse pressure

Table 20. Blood pressure of the chicken in mm. Hg

Breed	Age	Body weight	Sex	Blood pressure			Method	Anesthetic	Artery	Reference
				Mean	Sys.	Dias.				
Mixed	Adult	2190	M	196	—	—	Hg man.	None	Carotid	Stubel (1910)
	"	1770	F	164	—	—	"	"	"	"
	"	—	F	170	180	160	Membrane	"	"	"
Mixed	"	—	?	108	130	85	Hamilton man.	Barbital, ether	Femoral	Woodbury & Abreu (1944)
Mixed	6–10 wks.	—	?	128	125	120	"	None	Ischiatic	Rodbard & Tolpin (1947)
W. Leg.	10–14 mos.	Adult	F	—	131	—	Indirect	None	1″ cuff on femur	Sturkie et al. (1953)
"	19–26 "	"	F	—	139	—	"	"	"	"
"	30–38 "	"	F	—	155	—	"	"	"	"
"	42–54 "	"	F	—	163	—	"	"	"	"
"	10–14 "	"	M	—	164	—	"	"	"	"
"	22–54 "	"	M	—	189	—	"	"	"	"
W. Leg.	7 wks.	—	Male	—	151	128	Direct; strain gage	None	Carotid	Ringer et al. (1957)
"	"	—	Capon	—	159	134	"	"	"	"
"	"	—	Female	—	150	131	"	"	"	"
"	"	—	Poulard	—	136	121	"	"	"	"
W. Leg.	13 wks.		Male	—	166	142	Direct; strain gage	"	"	"
"	"		Capon	—	157	135	"	"	"	"
"	"		Female	—	156	131	"	"	"	"
"	"		Poulard	—	162	135	"	"	"	"
W. Leg.	26 wks.	Adult	Male	—	191	154	Indirect	None	1″ cuff on femur	"
"	"	"	Capon	—	180	149	"	"	"	"
"	"	"	Female	—	162	133	"	"	"	"
"	"	"	Poulard	—	189	152	"	"	"	"

of about 25 mm. Hg. There is an important sex difference in the blood pressure of chickens, which becomes evident at about 10 to 13 weeks of age (Ringer, Sturkie, and Weiss, 1957; Weiss, Ringer, and Sturkie, 1957).

Blood pressure tends to increase with age after sexual maturity (see table), and so does atherosclerosis (see Chapter 2), but there is no significant correlation between blood pressure level and plasma cholesterol, nor between blood pressure and cholesterol in the thoracic aorta. There is, however, a statistically significant correlation between systolic pressure—but not diastolic pressure—and cholesterol in the abdominal aorta (Weiss, Ringer, and Sturkie, 1957). A similar relation exists in the turkey (Speckmann and Ringer, 1962).

Other avian species (Table 21). There is a significant sex difference in blood pressure levels of New Jersey Buff turkeys and Bronze turkeys. The pressure level is very high in turkeys (up to 400 mm. Hg), and Ringer and Rood (1959) have suggested that this very high level may be a predisposing cause of aortic aneurysms and ruptures, which have been reported in the turkey. Speckmann and Ringer (1962) reported that reserpine at low levels in the feed lowered blood pressure of the turkey and might minimize the incidence of aortic ruptures.

There is no sex difference in the blood pressure of pigeons and ducks.

Ventricular and Pulmonary Pressure

Bredeck (1960) measured the systolic and diastolic intraventricular pressures of chickens. His results follow:

	Systolic	Diastolic	Heart Rate
Left ventricular pressure (mm. Hg)	145	0	331
Right ventricular pressure (mm. Hg)	27	−.3 to −2.0	—

Respiratory movements caused fluctuations ranging from 2 to 10 mm. Hg, and averaging 8.8 for left ventricular pressures and 3.6 mm. Hg for right ventricular pressure. Bredeck found a

Table 21. Blood pressure of birds other than the chicken. Direct determinations were made from carotid artery (C), brachial artery (B), or from ventricle (V) with Hamilton manometer or Strain gauge. Local anesthesia was used.

Species	Age or weight	Sex	Blood pressure			Reference
			Mean	Systolic	Diastolic	
Turkey, C	8750	—	193	—	—	Stubel (1910)
Turkey, N.J. Buff, C	6–7 wks.	Male	—	197	154	Weiss & Sheahan (1958)
"	"	Female	—	190–	146	"
"	8–9 mos.	Male	—	226	152	"
"	"	Female	—	212	157	"
Turkey, Bronze, C	8 wks.	Male		198	164	Ringer & Rood (1959)
	8 wks.	Female		189	158	"
	12 wks.	Male		219	185	"
	12 wks.	Female		226	185f	"
	16 wks.	Male		241	190	"
	16 wks.	Female		248	194	"
	22 wks.	Male		297	222	"
	22 wks.	Female		257	200	"
Duck, Pekin, C	4–5 mos.	(immature M)		185	158	Ringer et al. (1955)
	4–5 mos.	(immature F)		181	159	"
	12–13 mos.	(mature M)		179	134	"
	12–13 mos.	(mature F)		182	134	"
Pigeon, White King, C	Adult	Male		182	136	"
		Female		178	132	"
Pigeon, B	Adult	—		135	105	Woodbury & Hamilton (1937)
Starling, C	Adult	—		180	130	"
Robin, V	"			118	80	"
Canary, C	"			130	carotid	"
" V	"			220	154	"
Sparrow, C	"			180	140	"
" V	Young			108	—	"

significant positive correlation between heart rate and left ventricular pressure. However, this does not necessarily mean that birds with higher heart rates have higher arterial blood pressures. The various compensatory reflexes may nullify any correlation between ventricular pressure and heart rate.

Actually a comparison of the heart rates and blood pressures of many avian species suggests that there is little correlation between heart rate and blood pressure level. Even among the same species (chicken or turkey) considerable variation and differences can exist without much change in heart rate. The male chicken has a higher blood pressure and lower heart rate than the female.

Sturkie, Vogel, and Textor (1962), who reported differences of 20 or more mm. Hg in the mean blood pressure of genetically selected hypotensive and hypertensive chickens, found no difference in the heart rates.

The right ventricular systolic pressure of 27 mm. Hg reported by Bredeck is of the same magnitude as that reported for the pulmonary artery of chickens by Rodbard, Brown, and Katz (1949). Their results follow:

		Systolic	Diastolic	Heart rate	Respiratory Rate
Pressure in pulmonary artery	Mean	24	12	293	49
	Range	17–32	7–20	240–318	36–60

Injection of epinephrine had no appreciable effect on pulmonary arterial pressure even though it increased systemic arterial pressure 40–80 mm. Hg. The pressures in the pulmonary arteries of most vertebrates are of similar magnitude (Rodbard *et al.,* 1949).

Respiratory Influence

Little is known about the nature of the respiratory influences on blood pressure in birds, but recent experiments in this laboratory shed some light on this problem (Durfee, 1963; Sturkie, unpublished). At the peak of normal inspiration in birds, the intrathoracic pressure is lowest (negative) and blood pressure is normally highest at this point. At the peak of expiration the intrathoracic pressure is positive, and blood pressure is at its lowest. Actually blood pressure begins to rise about one second after the initiation of inspiration, and to fall about one second after expiration has begun. When artificial respiration is provided by means of a reciprocating pump, intrathoracic pressure is greatest on inspiration (positive pressure breathing) and lowest on expiration (negative). The blood pressure changes, however, are still correlated with intrathoracic pressure changes as in normal breathing.

The respiratory apparatus of birds is such that the lungs may be ventilated artificially in one direction, thus eliminating the cyclic changes in ventilation that occur normally in respiration, or in artificial respiration with a reciprocating pump. Under these conditions there is no cyclic variation in blood pressure. Hypoxia, produced in the curarized bird by decreasing ventilation rate with the "one-way" pump causes a reflex rise in heart rate and a significant drop in blood pressure, which, however, lags considerably behind the rise in heart rate. The rise in heart rate immediately follows the beginning of asphyxia, but the blood pressure begins to drop after about one minute and reaches its maximum sometime later, depending on the degree of hypoxia. After vagotomy the heart rate response is abolished, but not the drop in blood pressure which is still evident even after transection of the spinal cord.

The drop in blood pressure following hypoxia, rather than a rise such as may occur in mammals and is then attributable to stimulation of chemoreceptors, appears to be a direct effect of the hypoxia on the blood vessel. Chemoreceptor reflexes apparently are not involved in the blood pressure changes in birds.

The oscillations in blood pressure of birds associated with respiration appear to be caused solely by changes in intrathoracic pressure, and are not influenced by cyclic discharges from vasomotor centers, as has been reported in mammals. Harvey *et al.* (1954) reported that asphyxia in the normal breathing chicken usually elicited a rise in blood pressure, but in some instances elicited a fall. All asphyxial pressor responses were preceded by a depressor phase. Thus a need for considerably more research is indicated.

Effects of Anesthesia

Anesthesia may lower blood pressure in birds, as in mammals, depending upon the type, the dose, and the time after administration. Pentobarbital sodium (25–30 mg./kg.) injected intravenously into the adult chicken depresses blood pressure 30 mm. Hg within a few minutes after injection (Weiss and Sturkie, 1951). Harvey *et al.* (1954) induced anesthesia in chickens with urethane, 1.4 gm./kg. body weight; sodium barbital, 180 mg./kg.; and sodium phenobarbital, 200 mg./kg., in each instance administered intraperitoneally. The authors do not report blood pressure levels on unanesthetized birds, but it is apparent from their data that blood pressure levels were depressed, since the basal levels reported by them were quite low.

Dial, a commercial preparation containing urethane, has been used extensively by Durfee (1963) in dosages ranging from 0.50 to .75 ml./kg. At the lower level the birds were lightly anesthetized, but this dosage depressed blood pressure significantly.

Drugs and Hormones

Epinephrine. Most of the drugs and hormones that are pressor and depressor in mammals have the same effect in birds. Some of the pressor substances are epinephrine, benzedrine, ephedrine, and neosynephrine (Thompson and Coon, 1948). A detailed study of the effects of a number of drugs and adrenergic blockers on the blood pressure of chickens was made by Harvey *et al.* (1954). Isopropyl norepinephrine had a depressor effect, and considerable variation occurred in the responses to epinephrine and norepinephrine. The minimal pressor doses of both drugs varies from 0.02 to 1.5 micrograms/kg., and the maximal doses range from 4 to 10 micrograms/kg. In most hens the two sympathomimetics were about equipotent, although occasionally norepinephrine was 4 times as potent (pressor-wise) as epinephrine; but the latter exhibited greater cardioaccelerator activity. Epinephrine and norepinephrine (1 gamma/kg.) increased diastolic pressures 39 and 20 mm. Hg respectively in anesthetized chickens (Akers and Peiss,

1963). The increases in pulse pressure were 58 and 26 respectively. Heart rate was not appreciably influenced.

A number of ergot alkaloids (such as ergotamine and ergonovine) were tested, and most of them were consistently pressor at dosages lower than 200 micrograms/kg.

Serotonin. Serotonin (5-hydroxytryptamine) or angiotonin can be a pressor or a depressor in the fowl (Harvey *et al.*, 1954); normally it is a depressor (Bunag and Walaszek, 1962a and 1962b), because it releases histamine which is depressor. When the tissues of chickens were depleted of histamine by continued administration of 48/80, serotonin and tryptamine were pressor. The workers cited had previously reported that the histamine blood levels in the chicken were very high and that histamine may be quite readily released in this species. In their studies on the effects of indolealkylamines on blood pressure of the chicken and other species, Bunag and Walaszek (1962b) reported that dimethyltryptamine, bufotenine, psilocin, and psilocybin are strongly pressor in the chicken. The depressor response to serotonin can be blocked by certain lysergic acid derivatives (Bunag and Walaszek, 1962c).

Reserpine. Reserpine when injected intravenously in doses from 0.10 to 0.750 mg./kg., has a significant depressor effect in the chicken (Sturkie, Durfee, and Sheahan, 1958), and also in the turkey (Speckmann and Ringer, 1962). Since reserpine is known to cause release of serotonin in other species it may have a similar effect on birds, and since serotonin causes histamine release in birds, the depressor effect of reserpine may be attributable in part at least to the release of histamine.

Adrenergic blockade. Pressor responses can be blocked in the fowl by dibenzyline at dosages of 20 to 60 mg./kg. (Harvey *et al.*, 1954). Other adrenergic blockers, dibenamine and priscoline, are less effective. Pressor responses to epinephrine could also be blocked with ergot alkaloids, but higher dosages were required than for mammals.

Acetylcholine. Acetylcholine, methacholine, and other parasympathomimetic agents depress blood pressure in birds as they do in mammals. An injection of 0.2 mg of acetylcholine into chicks 6 to 12 weeks old depresses blood pressure 40–60 mm. Hg within 3 seconds (Rodbard and Fink, 1948). Intramuscular injections of 5 mg. into adult fowls similarly decreases blood pressure and heart rate, but the latter returns to normal shortly thereafter. Methacholine, whose effect is of longer duration than that of acetylcholine, produces significant depressor effects at levels as low as 0.15 mg./kg. subcutaneously (Durfee, unpublished).

Sex hormones. The existence of a sex difference in blood pressure of chickens suggests the influence of sex hormones. It was shown (Sturkie, and Ringer, 1955) that the higher blood pressure level of adult males and capons could be depressed by administration of estrogen. Later it was shown (see Table 20) that the blood pressure level of the castrate female was about the same as the adult, and that this level could likewise be depressed to near the level of a normal female by estrogen. Since exogenous estrogen at the level administered is known to suppress the output or utilization of pituitary gonadotrophins, the results suggested that the pituitary hormones might be involved in the control of blood pressure level. Accordingly, experiments were designed to test this possibility. Blood pressure levels of males and capons were depressed by administration of estrogen, and then the birds received pregnant-mare serum (gonadin) containing pituitary gonadotrophins. We were able to elevate the blood pressure of estrogen-treated birds with the pregnant-mare serum. In later work, more purified gonadotrophins were used, and also dried avian pituitaries, but these did not influence blood pressure level. It was concluded that the original pregnant-mare serum preparation may have contained a pressor substance. The effect of estrogen on blood pressure is not immediate, but requires from about 10 to 14 days. The mechanism of its action is not known; there is some evidence to suggest that it may have a direct vasodilating effect on the blood vessels, and it may also exert some effect on the medullary centers. As evidence for the direct effect of estrogen on the blood vessels it is reported by Malinow and Moguilevsky (1961) that estrogen increases the oxygen consumption of chicken arteries.

Oxytocin and vasopressin. The oxytocic fraction of posterior pituitary preparations, and synthetic oxytocin, depress blood pressure in the fowl within a few seconds (Woodbury and Abreu, 1944; Sawyer, 1961; Lloyd and Pickford, 1961). The drop is attributable not to changes in cardiac weakness or in heart rate, but to vasodilatation. Lloyd and Pickford found oxytocin always to be depressor in the chicken, but not always in mammals. This was true even after decapitation, decerebration, and the administration of atropine, bretylium, tetraethylammonium, and other drugs and hormones. The depressor effect was augmented by these drugs. The administration of estrogen may also have augmented the depressor effect, but the data are not conclusive. Dibenamine and dihydroergotamine reduced the depressor response to oxytocin.

Vasotocin is depressor in birds (Sawyer). Breneman *et al.* (1959) reported that the avian depressor effect of oxytocin could be prevented by extracts from the plant *Lithospermum ruderale*. The response of the chicken to vasopressin is variable (Lloyd and Pickford, 1961). In some instances a pure pressor response is obtained, in others a transient depressor response, which may or may not be followed by a pressor response. In most instances, 40 to 80 mu (i.e. milliunits) of vasopressin are required to change blood pressure level. The pressor action of vasopressin was reduced by all drugs and procedures employed to study the effects of oxytocin, except tetraethylammonium.

Renin and angiotensin. It has long been known that injections of kidney extracts are capable of producing an increase in blood pressure. The pressor principal is renin, a proteolytic enzyme which acts upon angiotensinogen to produce angiotensin, also known as hypertension or angiotonin. Angiotensinogen has been demonstrated in chicken plasma, where its concentration approaches that reported for plasmas of the dog, cat, and rat (Schaffenburg, Haass, and Goldblatt, 1960).

Oviposition and Blood Pressure

Immediately preceding contraction of the uterus and expulsion of the egg, according to Tanake and Nakajo (see Chapter 17), there is a release of oxytocin and vasotocin from the posterior pituitary, which these authors believe initiates oviposition. One might therefore expect, since both of these hormones have a depressor effect, that blood pressure would drop just prior to oviposition. Hunsaker and Sturkie (1962) recorded blood pressure of unrestrained hens before, during, and after oviposition. Blood pressure level did not change until after the egg was laid; the slight drop was transient and was not believed to be attributable to oxytocin.

Pressor Substances Released by Intracranial Compression

Acute compression of the brain causes an increase in blood pressure of mammals and birds (Rodbard, Reyes, Mininni, and Saiki, 1954). The rise in pressure could be blocked or prevented by administration of adrenergic blockers (dibenamine and benzo-dioxane). Tetraethylammonium, a ganglionic blocker, had no effect on the pressor response. These results suggest that a humoral substance is released following intracranial compression akin to norepinephrine. The pressor substance appears not to be released in the brain, because transection of cervical spinal cord prevents its release.

Effects of Body Temperature and Ambient Temperature on Blood Pressure

Sturkie and co-workers had observed seasonal change in blood pressure in chickens, with the pressure tending to drop with the advent of warm weather. The seasonal changes were studied in detail by Weiss, Fisher, and Griminger (1961). There was some question whether the seasonal changes were associated with changes in amount of light or with ambient temperature. Later work demonstrated conclusively that ambient temperature was largely responsible for the seasonal changes observed. Chickens acclimatized to high temperature had a significantly lower blood pressure level than those acclimatized to cold (see data on cardiac output).

Chickens exposed to acute heating (40.5°C.) and exhibiting hyperthermia experience a decrease in blood pressure, particularly after body temperatures reach 45°C. Above this temperature there was a precipitous drop in blood pressure (Frankel, Hollands, and Weiss, 1962). Similar results were obtained by Whittow, Sturkie, and Stein (1964), except that the birds were heated in a heating pad and they develop hyperthermia more rapidly; the decline in blood pressure began soon after the start of heating. Hypothermia likewise depresses blood pressure in the fowl, and the decrease is proportional to the degree of hypothermia (Rodbard and Tolpin, 1947; Whittow, Sturkie, and Stein (1964). Rewarming of the fowl after hypothermia produced an immediate rise in blood pressure and body temperature until normal body temperature was obtained; then, with further heating and hyperthermia, a decrease in pressure was observed. The hyperthermic and hypothermic birds responded normally to epinephrine and acetylcholine, indicating, according to Rodbard and Tolpin (1947), that contractility of the blood vessels was not impaired.

Nervous Control of Blood Pressure

Rodbard and Tolpin (1947) suggest that there is a direct central control of blood pressure in the chicken, such as they also report in the turtle. The center in the turtle is at the level of the third ventricle. The body of evidence indicates that the primary vasomotor centers of mammals are located in the medulla, and it is presumed that these centers in the bird are also located there, although no conclusive experiments have been conducted on this matter. There is some evidence that the thalamus influences blood pressure level, based upon crude experiments by Dijk (1932), who reported that stimulation of this area produced changes in blood pressure.

The vasomotor center of mammals influences blood pressure through the vasoconstrictor and vasodilator nerves. The constrictors cause contraction of the muscular elements of anterioles by liberating adrenergic substances. The vasodilators produce their effect by releasing an acetylcholine-like substance, and are said to be cholinergic. Although these nerve fibers are present in birds, relatively little research concerning them has been conducted.

Reflex control of blood pressure. The carotid sinus of birds is situated not high in the neck where the external and internal carotids diverge, as it is in mammals (Adams, 1958), but much lower, just behind the parathyroid glands near the origin of the common carotid arteries, and rostral to the root of the subclavian arteries (see figure, Adams). More recent studies by DeKock (1958) and Malinovsky (1962) confirm this. The carotid body is located in the same area (Figure 5), and is quite small. The dimensions of the gland are 0.8×0.5 mm. in the chicken (Chowdhary, 1953) and the gland is even smaller in several other species (Adams). The carotid body receives its blood supply from the carotid artery or a branch of it. It is drained by several veins. The innervation of the body is from the vagus nerve by way of the ganglion nodosum. Apparently the glassopharyngeal nerve does not contribute fibers to the carotid body, at least not in the fowl (Chowdhary), although Terni (see Adams) asserts that the body may receive fibers from the recurrent laryngeal nerve.

Reflexes. Attempts to elicit reflex effects on blood pressure by means of occlusion or stimulation in the region high in the neck of the bird corresponding to the sinus area in mammals have been unsuccessful (see Adams; also Heymans and Neil, 1958, and Lagerstedt, 1941). Stimulation of the carotid body or carotid sinus area in the thorax gave variable and unconvincing results (Heymans and Neil). According to the latter authors, Ara obtained sinus reflex responses by occluding the common carotid artery caudal to the site of the baroreceptor area. Durfee (1963) was unable to elicit reflex responses by occlusion either of the common carotid in the sinus region of chicken or of the brachiocephalic artery.

Upon the basis of studies involving various drugs, Harvey *et al.* (1954) concluded that pressor reflexes of significant magnitude are difficult to elicit in the chicken. Drug-induced vasopression was usually accompanied by bradycardia (similar results have been observed by Durfee, 1963; and see Chapter 4). The latter has shown that vasodepression induced by drugs is usually followed by tachycardia. These results suggest that baroreceptors are operative in the chicken, although their sites are unknown (see Chapter 4).

CARDIAC OUTPUT

Cardiac output is the amount of blood ejected from the ventricles in a given time, and is usually referred to as the minute volume, i.e., the amount ejected in one minute. The amount ejected

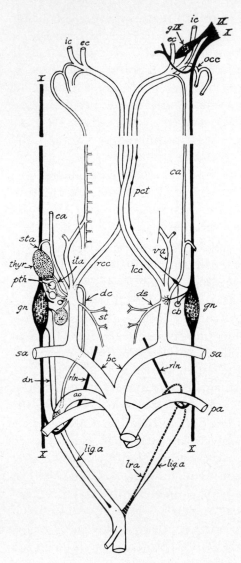

Figure 5. Innervation of the carotid sinus complex and aortic arch of birds, according to Adams (1958) based upon work of others.

Abbreviations: *ca,* anterior cervical artery; *cb,* carotid body; *dc,* ductus caroticus; *dn,* depressor nerve (or vagus); *ec,* external carotid; *gn,* ganglion nodosum of vagus; *gIX,* glossopharyngeal ganglion; *ita,* inferior thyroid artery; *lcc,* left common carotid; *occ,* occipital artery; *pa,* pulmonary artery; *pct,* prevertebral-precarotid nerve trunk; *pth,* parathyroids III and IV; *rcc,* right common carotid; *rln,* recurrent laryngeal nerve; *sa,* subclavian artery; *st,* syringotracheal artery; *sta,* superior thyroid artery; *thyr,* thyroid gland; *u,* ultimobranchial body; *va,* vetebral artery.

from the right and left ventricles is the same, and is influenced by heart rate, stroke volume, and the amount of venous blood returned to the heart. Minute volume equals stroke volume times heart rate. Details concerning the relation of these parameters to cardiac output may be found in any good textbook on mammalian physiology. Cardiac output or flow is directly proportional to pressure head and inversely proportional to resistance in peripheral blood vessels, and the latter varies inversely with the total cross sectional area (TSA) of capillary beds. Since an individual arteriole has a larger diameter than an individual capillary and branches into several capillaries, the result is that the TSA of the capillary bed is increased, and resistance is accordingly decreased. Obviously the resistance to flow in a single capillary would be greater than in a larger arteriole.

Cardiac output has been determined by a number of methods, including the direct Fick method and various dilution methods involving the use of dyes, radioactive substances, or heat (thermodilution). With the Stewart-Hamilton dye dilution method, a known quantity of dye is injected in a vein or right heart, where it is mixed with blood. Blood from an artery, such as the aorta, carotid, or femoral, is sampled. The concentration of the dye in the blood passing the sampling point changes with time, and forms a concentration curve (Figure 6). By calculating the area under the curve or average concentration ($\overline{C}$), and knowing the concentration of dye injected, cardiac output can be determined:

$$\text{C. O.} = \frac{\text{mg. dye injected}}{\overline{C} \times \text{time under curve}}$$

Normal values in birds. The few studies on cardiac output in birds have been conducted only in recent years (Sapirstein and Hartman, 1959; Sturkie and Vogel, 1959; Speckmann, Ringer, and Wolterink, 1961). Data are presented in Table 22.

The total cardiac output is higher in adult males than in females, but when it is calculated on a given weight basis, the output in females is usually higher. The variation in output from time to time can be considerable, although it is no greater than that reported in mammals when comparable methods are employed. Values obtained by the direct Fick method usually exhibit less variation, but they are calculated from data on oxygen consumption collected over a longer period of time than is involved in dilution curves, which are completed within a matter of seconds.

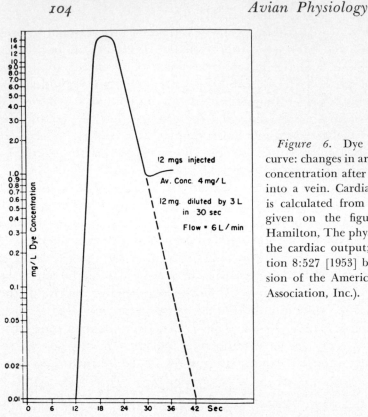

Figure 6. Dye dilution curve: changes in arterial dye concentration after injection into a vein. Cardiac output is calculated from the data given on the figure (from Hamilton, The physiology of the cardiac output; Circulation 8:527 [1953] by permission of the American Heart Association, Inc.).

Factors affecting cardiac output. It is known that cardiac output in mammals is influenced by exercise, environmental temperature, metabolic state, and various other factors. Starvation or withholding of food tends to decrease cardiac output, and this may account for some of the variation shown in the table. It is observed that the outputs for birds starved for 24 hours was lower than for those not starved. Moreover, Vogel and Sturkie (1963) have demonstrated that prolonged starvation decreases output considerably.

The effects on cardiac output of short-term heating of non-adapted mammals have received considerable attention; in general the results show an initial increase in cardiac output, with vasodilation and a slight increase in plasma volume (see Brooks *et al.,* 1955; Koroxenidis *et al.,* 1961). Acute heating in birds produces

Table 22. Cardiac output, blood pressure, and total peripheral resistance in chickens (means and standard errors)

Breed	Sex, age, condition	Body wt. (kg.)	Cardiac output per minute		Mean blood pressure	Peripheral resistance (units/kg.)	Heart rate	Stroke volume
			Per bird	Per kg.				
W. Leghorn	Male 16 mos, starved 24 hrs.	2.39	340±18	143±7	166±3	1.23±.06	307±14	1.17±.10[1]
"	Female	1.79	308±17	173±9	142±4	0.88±.08	378±6	0.82±.05[1]
"	Male 12–14 mos. winter	2.59	444±22	173±9	181±4.7	1.11±.07	303±8	1.50±.06[2]
"	" " summer	2.95	359±11	135±7	177±5	1.41±.10	289±10	1.20±.06[2]
"	Female 18 mo. winter	1.95	345±15	181±12	153±4	0.91±.13	336±24	1.04±.06[2]
"	" " summer	1.96	234±7	121±5	147±3	1.25±.07	347±9	0.68±.03[2]
Mixed	Female, Uncertain	1.6	—	218[3]	—			—

[1] Sturkie & Vogel (1959).
[2] Vogel & Sturkie (1963).
[3] Sapirstein & Hartman (1959); nembutal anesthesia, Male bronze turkeys, cardiac output = 231 ml./kg. 0.73 (Speckman *et al.* 1961).

similar results (Whittow, Sturkie, and Stein, 1964). Few studies have been conducted on cardiac output of heat-adapted mammals, and the findings are inconclusive. Recent studies in this laboratory on chickens (see Table 22) show that the heat-adapted chicken (in summertime) has a significantly lower cardiac output than the bird adapted to winter temperature (Vogel and Sturkie, 1963). Moreover when chickens are placed in a room with a controlled high temperature, their cardiac outputs are likewise lower than those adapted to low temperature. Not only is minute volume lower in the heat-adapted birds, but also the total peripheral resistance (mean blood pressure/cardiac output) is higher, and blood pressure is usually lower. In the acutely heated birds there is a drop in blood pressure and an increase in cardiac output with a resulting decrease in peripheral resistance.

In the adult female chicken, which has a lower blood pressure than the male, cardiac output tends to be higher per unit of body weight, and peripheral resistance lower. This is true also of hypotensive chickens developed by selective breeding (Sturkie, Vogel and Textor, 1962).

Regional blood flow. Sapirstein and Hartman (1959) determined the distribution of cardiac output in the chicken. The percentages of the total cardiac output flowing to the various organs are as follows: (1) heart 4.9, (2) kidney 15.2, (3) liver 6.7, (4) gut 8.6, (5) gizzard 1.6, and (6) spleen 0.47. The flow to the kidney, which represents only arterial flow and not renal portal flow, amounts to 33 ml./kg./minute.

It is known that in diving birds and mammals that there is a redistribution of blood flow, with a decrease in flow to the peripheral organs, particularly the legs (Johansen and Krog, 1959).

BODY FLUIDS

The total water of the body is distributed into intracellular and extracellular compartments. The latter may be partitioned into plasma and interstitial fluids.

Methods of estimating. Total body water may be estimated directly by desiccation, and indirectly by measuring the dilution of some substance that will come to equilibrium with all water compartments. Antipyrine is such a substance, and has been used by a number of investigators in mammals and in chickens by Weiss (1958), and by Medway and Kare (1959). Extracellular fluid volume is determined also by the dilution principle, employing a substance which is injected and which enters the extracellular but not the intracellular compartment. Thiocyanate ion has been most commonly used; manitol, inulin, and other substances have also been employed. These substances are taken up mainly by the extracellular fluids, but not completely; at least some thiocyanate may enter the cells. The extracellular fluid volume, determined by employing thiocyanate, is often referred to as thiocyanate space. The interstitial fluid is calculated, and is equal to thiocyanate space minus plasma volume. Intracellular space or fluid is equal to total body water minus thiocyanate space.

Blood volume includes the plasma and the cells. It may be determined directly by bleeding out and measuring the residual volume, or indirectly by the dilution principle. The latter may involve labeling red cells by injection with radioactive iron, chromium, or phosphorus, or labeling the plasma with a dye such as Evan's blue (T-1824; see Gregersen and Rawson, 1959).

The dye technique is probably the one most commonly used. A known amount of T-1824 is injected intravenously and allowed to mix completely with the blood. Since the circulation in birds is more rapid than in larger mammals, the time required for mixing is less—approximately 2 or 3 minutes (Pino *et al.*, 1951). The rate of disappearance of the dye from the blood of birds is also more rapid than in mammals, averaging about 1 percent per minute.

The concentration of the dye in the plasma is a measure of the total circulating volume of plasma. Total blood volume is calculated by adding to the plasma volume that of the corpuscles (hematocrit).

$$\text{Blood volume} = \frac{\text{Plasma volume} \times 100}{\text{Percent plasma}}$$

Table 23a. Distribution of body fluids in white leghorn chickens
(Medway and Kare, 1959)

Age (weeks)	Weight (gm.)	Percent of body weight				
		Total body water	Intra-cellular water	Extracellular water		
				Interstitial	Plasma	Total
1	55.1	72.4	11.4	52.3	8.7	61.0
2	108.4	71.6	21.0	42.3	7.3	50.6
3	175.3	70.5	24.6	39.1	6.8	45.9
4	241.8	68.4	24.1	38.3	6.0	44.3
6	372.3	—	—	36.8	5.9	42.7
8	527.3	68.7	26.6	36.1	6.1	42.2
16	1137.3	64.8	34.8	24.8	5.2	30.0
32	1759.5	57.3	31.1	21.7	4.6	26.2

Table 23b. Body water (percent of body weight) in White Leghorn
females (Weiss, 1958)

Age in weeks	26	30	36	42	55	61
Body weight (gm.)	1773	1996	1919	2032	2054	2035
Body water (percent)	66.0	61.2	56.7	53.3	52.9	53.4

Total Body Water

The distribution of body fluids of chickens of various ages is shown in Table 23a and 23b . Total body water is highest in the first 2 weeks of life, and decreases—though not appreciably—until 16 weeks of age. At 32 weeks of age, when the bird has reached full sexual maturity, body water is lowest (57.3 percent of body weight, according to Medway and Kare, 1959). Weiss (1958) studied body water in hens from 26 to 61 weeks of age (see Table 23b). The amount of water decreased from 26 weeks up to 42 weeks of age, and did not change appreciably thereafter. This decrease of body water in relation to body weight is a reflection of the increase in body fat with aging in the hen; it is known that adipose tissue contains less water than lean tissue. The figures for adult chickens are similar to those for human adults. Body water determined by antipyrine compares favorably with that determined directly (by desiccation) except for birds at 1, 6, and 16 weeks of age, where values obtained directly are somewhat higher (Medway and Kare, 1959).

Extracellular and intracellular water. It may be observed from the table that as total body water decreases with age up to sexual maturity, the greatest decrease is in extracellular water (both interstitial and plasma fractions). At the same time there is an increase in intracellular water, ranging from 11.4 percent at one week of age to above 30 percent at from 16 to 32 weeks of age.

Among the factors that produce changes in the compartments of the body waters are decreased water consumption and exposure to high and low environmental temperatures. Rodbard *et al.* (1951) have demonstrated that acute hyperthermia increases the volume of extracellular water and plasma, and that hypothermia decreases these fractions considerably.

Blood Volume

Crude blood volume (by bleeding but not washing out the blood vessels) has been determined in the chicken by Common, Bolton, and Rutledge (1948), Turner (1948), and others. The crude volumes, which average about 4 percent of body weight, amount to approximately two-thirds of those obtained with the dye technique. Earlier work on birds by Welcher and Brandt (1903) and others, who used the exsanguination technique, show blood volumes of about the same order, suggesting that the authors measured only the amount of blood drained out, not that washed out.

Normal values. The dye technique has been used by a number of workers, and in some of the older work the values reported are too high because the mixing time was too long (Pappenheimer, Goettsch, and Jungherr, 1939; Newell and Shaffner, 1950). Studies by Pino *et al.* (1951), Sturkie and Newman (1951), and Medway and Kare (1959), employing a mixing time of 3 minutes, reveal blood volumes ranging from 8.7 percent of body weight at one week of age to 4.6 percent at sexual maturity (see Table 24). Gilbert (1963), working with Brown Leghorn cocks 30 weeks of age

Table 24. Blood volume of female White Leghorn chickens
(Medway and Kare, 1959)

Age (weeks)	Body weight (gms.)	Mean blood volume (percent of body weight)	Mean plasma volume (percent of body weight)
1	61.8	12.0	8.7
2	115.0	10.4	7.3
3	163.3	9.7	6.8
4	249.9	8.7	6.0
6	398.7	8.3	5.9
8	571.6	8.4	6.1
16	1310.0	7.6	5.2
32	1789.0	6.5	4.6

and with a weight of 1,851 grams, obtained a mean blood volume
of 7.8 percent and a mean plasma volume of 4.65 percent. Sturkie
and Newman (1951 reported blood volumes of 15 laying White
Leghorn females, ranging in weight from 1.7 to 2 kg. as follows:

Plasma volume (ml)	Cell volume (gm./100 ml.)	Blood volume (ml).
93.5	28.5	130.8

Blood volumes for species other than the chicken are shown in
Table 25.

Effects of hormones. Common, Bolton, and Rutledge (1948) reported that estrogen administered to chickens greatly increased the
crude blood volume, but Sturkie (1951), using the dye technique,
found no change in blood volume following massive doses of estrogen or thyroxine to hens. Estrogen causes dilatation of blood
vessels, which may account for the increased "bleeding out" reported by Common *et al.* Estrogen produces hyperlipemia in
birds, and consequently a turbidity of the plasma which will interfere with the colorimetric determination of dye concentration
unless the blood is diluted sufficiently or the fat is extracted.
Campbell (1959) reported increased blood volumes in estrogenized immature chickens. Close examination of his data indicates

Table 25. Blood volume of avian species other than chicken

Species	Body weight (gm.)	Sex	Total blood volume (ml./100 gm.)	Plasma volume (ml./100 gm.)	Reference
Ducks, Mallard & dabbling	980		11.3	6.4	Bond & Gilbert (1958)
Coot	550		9.5	5.1	"
Pigeon	310		9.2	4.4	"
Pheasant	1190	Male	6.7	4.5	"
"	1110	Female	4.8	3.2	"
Hawk, red-tailed	925		6.2	3.5	"
Owl, great horned	1495		6.4	3.4	"
Turkey, adult White Holland			410 ml. per bird	—	McCartney (1952)

that much of the increase is related to the increased body weight of the treated birds, and that probably some of the increase is an artifact, resulting from interference by lipemia. Sturkie (unpublished) has repeated his work with estrogen on adult females after the fat was extracted from the plasma, and still found no increase in volume attributable to estrogen. Actually there is no increase, but rather a relative decrease, in plasma volume in females with the onset of sexual maturity (Medway and Kare, 1959).

Gilbert (1963) reports, however, that estrogen significantly increases plasma volume in cocks. Sturkie (unpublished) determined blood volume in males after extraction of lipids from plasma, and found that the blood volume of White Leghorn males was likewise increased by estrogen.

Effects of hypothermia and hyperthermia. In previous work, Rodbard had shown that changes in body temperature produced marked changes in plasma volume of chickens. Later, Williams and Rodbard (1960) reported that hypothermia decreased total circulating blood volume by 29 percent, and that this decrease could be prevented or minimized by injecting 15 mg./kg. dibenzyline, an adrenergic blocker. Moreover, the drug also increased blood volume in normothermic chicks.

Since dibenzyline blocks the effectors of postganglionic sympathetic fibers, the results suggest that these fibers may contribute to the control of regulation of plasma volume. A decrease in constrictor tone of certain blood vessels by dibenzyline apparently releases into the circulation pools of blood which normally are not reached by the dye (T-1824) used to determine blood volume. That the volumes of plasma and blood cells do not always change proportionately following hypothermia or injection of dibenzyline, suggests that blood cells may be shut off from the general circulation in certain vascular beds, and the plasma from others. Dibenzyline caused a slight depression in blood pressure (Williams and Rodbard).

REFERENCES

Adams, W. R. 1958 Comparative Morphology of the Carotid Body and Carotid Sinus. Charles C Thomas, Springfield, Ill.

Akers, T. K., and C. N. Peiss 1963 Comparative study of effect of epinephrine and norepinephrine on cardiovascular system of turtle, alligator, chicken and opossum. Proc. Soc. Exp. Biol. Med. 112:396.

Bond, C. F., and P. W. Gilbert 1958 Comparative study of blood volume in representative aquatic and nonaquatic birds. Am. J. Physiol. 194:519.

Bredeck, H. E. 1960 Intraventricular blood pressure in chickens. Am. J. Physiol. 198:153.

Breneman, W. R., M. Carmack, D. Overack, and R. Shaw 1959 Lithosperm inhibition of the blood pressure depressor effect of oxytocin in the fowl. Endocrine Soc., 41st Meeting, p. 46.

Brooks, C. McC., B. F. Hoffman, E. E. Suckling, and O. Orias 1955 Excitability of the Heart. Grune and Stratton, New York.

Bunag, R. D., and E. J. Walaszek 1962a The mechanism of serotonin and tryptamine induced vasodepression in the chicken. J. Pharma. and Exp. Therapeutics 134:151.

Bunag, R. D., and E. J. Walaszek 1962b Differential antagonism by bas-phenol of responses to the indolealkylamines. J. Pharma. Exp. Thera. 136:59.

Bunag, R. D., and E. J. Walaszek 1962c Blockade of depressor responses to serotonin and tryptamine by lysergic acid derivatives in the chicken. Arch. Int. Pharmacodyn. 135:1.

Campbell, E. A. 1959 Effects of estrogen on blood volume and hemoglobin in immature pullets. Am. J. Physiol. 197:1181.

Chowdhary, D. S. 1953 A comparative study of the carotid sinus of vertebrates. II: The carotid body and carotid sinus of the fowl (Gallus domesticus). Ph.D. Thesis, University of Edinburgh.

Common, R. H., W. Bolton, and W. A. Rutledge 1948 The influence of gonadal hormones on the composition of the blood and liver of the domestic fowl. J. Endocrinol. 5:263.

DeKock, L. L. 1958 On the carotid body of certain birds. Acta Anat. 35:161.

Dijk, J. A. 1932 Arch. Neerl. Physiol. 17:495. Cited from Chapter 23, Comparative Animal Physiology, Prosser, Brown, Bishop, Jahn, and Wulff, W. B. Saunders Co., Philadelphia (1950).

Durfee, W. 1963 Cardiovascular reflex mechanism in the fowl. Thesis, Rutgers University, New Brunswick, N.J.

Frankel, H., K. G. Hollands, and H. S. Weiss 1962 Respiratory and circulatory responses of hyperthermic chickens. Arch. Int. Physiol. Biochim. 70:555.

Gilbert, A. B. 1963 The effect of estrogen and thyroxine on blood volume of the domestic cock. J. Endocrinol. 25:41.

Gregersen, M. I., and R. A. Rawson 1959 Blood volume. Physiol. Rev. 39:307.

Hamilton, W. F. 1953 The physiology of the cardiac output. Circulation 8:527.

Harvey, S. C., E. G. Copen, D. W. Eskelson, S. R. Graff, L. D. Poulsen, and D. L. Rasmussen 1954 Autonomic pharmacology of the chicken with particular reference to adrenergic blockade. J. Pharm. Exp. Thera. 112:8.

Heymans, C., and E. Neil 1958 Reflexogenic Areas of the Cardiovascular System. Little, Brown & Co., Boston.

Hunsaker, W. G., and P. D. Sturkie 1962 Blood pressure before, during and after oviposition in the hen. Canad. J. Biochem. & Physiol. 40:177.

Johansen, Kjell, and Trygve Aakhus 1963 Central cardiovascular responses to submersion asphyxia in the duck. Am. J. Physiol. 205:1167.

Johansen, Kjell, and John Krog 1959 Peripheral circulatory response to submersion asphyxia in the duck. Acta Physiol. Scand. 46:194.

Koroxenidis, G. T., J. T. Shepherd, and R. J. Marshall 1961 Cardiovascular response to acute heat stress. J. Appl. Physiol. 16:869.

Lagerstedt, S.   1941   Beitrag zur Kenntnis der Pressoreceptoren bei Vögeln. Kugl. Fysiografiska Sallskapets I Lund forhandlingan 11:157.

Lloyd, S., and M. Pickford   1961   The persistence of a depressor response to oxytocin in the fowl after denervation and blocking agents. Brit. J. Pharm. & Chemothera. 16:129.

McCartney, M. G.   1952   Total blood and corpuscular volume in turkey hens. Poultry Sci. 31:184.

Malinovsky, L.   1962   Contributions to the anatomy of the vegetative nervous system in the neck and thorax of the domestic pigeon. Acta Anat. 50:326.

Malinow, M. R., and J. A. Moguilevsky   1961   Effect of estrogens on atherosclerosis. Nature 190:422.

Medway, W., and M. R. Kare   1959   Water metabolism of the grow-ing domestic fowl with special reference to water balance. Poultry Sci. 38:631.

Newell, G. W., and C. S. Shaffner   1950   Blood volume determina-tions in chickens. Poultry Sci. 29:78.

Olmsted, F., A. C. Corcoran, O. Glasser, and I. H. Page   1948   Systolic pressure in intact unanesthetized rat. Fed. Proc. 7:88.

Pappenheimer, A. M., M. Goettsch, and E. Jungherr   1939   Nutri-tional encephalomalacia in chicks and certain related disorders of domestic birds. Univ. Conn. (Storrs) Agr. Exp. Sta. Bull. 229.

Pino, J. A., H. S. Weiss, P. D. Sturkie, and R. J. Defalco   1951   Blood volume determinations in the fowl using diphtheria antitoxoid. Proc. IX World's Poultry Cong. 3:102.

Ringer, R. K., and K. Rood   1959   Hemodynamic changes associated with aging in the broad-breasted Bronze turkey. Poultry Sci. 38:395.

Ringer, R. K., P. D. Sturkie, and H. S. Weiss   1957   Role of the gonads in control of blood pressure in chickens. Am. J. Physiol. 190:54.

Ringer, R. K., H. S. Weiss, and P. D. Sturkie   1955   Effect of sex and age on blood pressure in the duck and pigeon. Am. J. Physiol. 183:141.

Rodbard, S., F. Brown, and L. N. Katz   1949   The pulmonary arterial pressure. Am. Heart J. 38:863.

Rodbard, S., and A. Fink   1948   Effects of body temperature changes on the circulation time in the chicken. Am. J. Physiol. 152:383.

Rodbard, S., M. Reyes, G. Mininni, and H. Saiki   1954   Neurohumoral transmission of the pressor response to intracranial compression. Am. J. Physiol. 176:455.

Rodbard, S., H. Saiki, A. Malin, and C. Young 1951 Significance of changes in plasma and extracellular volumes in induced hyperthermia and hypothermia. Am. J. Physiol. 167:485.

Rodbard, S., and M. Tolpin 1947 A relationship between the body temperature and the blood pressure in the chicken. Am. J. Physiol. 151:509.

Sapirstein, L. A., and F. A. Hartman 1959 Cardiac output and its distribution in the chicken. Am. J. Physiol. 196:751.

Sawyer, W. H. 1961 Neurohypophysial hormones. Pharma. Rev. 13:225.

Schaffenburg, C., E. Haas, and H. Goldblatt 1960 Concentration of renin and angiotensinogen in serum of various species. Am. J. Physiol. 199:788.

Sobin, S. S. 1946 Accuracy of indirect determinations of blood pressure in the rat: Relation of temperature of plethysmograph and width of cuff. Am. J. Physiol. 146:179.

Speckmann, E. W., and R. K. Ringer 1962 The influence of reserpine on plasma cholesterol, hemodynamics and arteriosclerotic lesions in the broad-breasted Bronze turkey. Poultry Sci. 41:40.

Speckmann, E. W., R. K. Ringer, and L. F. Wolterink 1961 The cardiac output of the broad-breasted Bronze turkey. Poultry Sci. 40:1460 (Abs.).

Stein, G., Jr., P. D. Sturkie, and G. C. Whittow 1964 Changes in the cardiac output, blood pressure and heart rate of the chicken during hyperthermia. Jour. Physiol. 61:170.

Stubel, H. S. 1910 Beiträge zur Kenntnis der Physiologie des Blutkreislaufes der verschiedenen Vogelarten. Arch. ges. Physiol. (Pflügers) 135:249.

Sturkie, P. D. 1951 The effects of estrogen and thyroxine upon plasma proteins and blood volume of chickens. Endocrinol. 49:565.

Sturkie, P. D., W. K. Durfee, and M. Sheahan 1957 Demonstration of an improved method for taking blood pressure in chickens. Poultry Sci. 36:1160.

Sturkie, P. D., W. K. Durfee, and M. Sheahan 1958 Effects of reserpine on the fowl. Am. J. Physiol. 194:184.

Sturkie, P. D., and H. J. Newman 1951 Plasma proteins of chickens as influenced by time of laying, ovulation, number of blood samples taken, and plasma volume. Poultry Sci. 30:240.

Sturkie, P. D., and R. K. Ringer 1955 Effects of suppression of pituitary gonadotrophins on blood pressure in the fowl. Am. J. Physiol. 180:53.

Sturkie, P. D., and J. A. Vogel 1959 Cardiac output, central blood volume and peripheral resistance in chickens. Am. J. Physiol. 197:1165.

Sturkie, P. D., J. A. Vogel, and K. Textor 1962 Cardiovascular differences between high and low blood pressure chickens. Poultry Sci. 41:1619.

Sturkie, P. D., H. S. Weiss, and R. K. Ringer 1953 The effects of age on blood pressure in the fowl. Am. J. Physiol. 174:405.

Thompson, R. M., and J. M. Coon 1948 Effects of adrenolytic agents on the response to pressor substances in the domestic fowl. Fed. Proc. 7:259.

Turner, C. W. 1948 Effects of thyroprotein-feeding on the glands and organ weights of two-year-old White Leghorn hens. Poultry Sci. 27:155.

Vogel, J. A., and P. D. Sturkie 1963 Cardiovascular responses of the chicken to seasonal and induced temperature changes. Science 140: 1404.

Vogel, J. A., and P. D. Sturkie 1963 Effects of starvation on the cardiovascular system of the chicken. Proc. Soc. Exp. Biol. & Med. 112:111.

Weiss, H. S. 1958 Application to the fowl of the antipyrine dilution technique for the estimation of body composition. Poultry Sci. 37:484.

Weiss, H. S., H. Fisher, and P. Griminger 1961 Seasonal variation in avian blood pressure. Fed. Proc. 2:115 (Abs.).

Weiss, H. S., R. K. Ringer, and P. D. Sturkie 1957 Development of the sex difference in blood pressure of the chick. Am. J. Physiol. 188:383.

Weiss, H. S., and M. Sheahan 1958 The influence of maturity and sex on the blood pressure of the turkey. Am. J. Vet. Res. 19:209.

Weiss, H. S., and P. D. Sturkie 1951 An indirect method for measuring blood pressure in the fowl. Poultry Sci. 30:587.

Welcher, H., and A. Brandt 1903 Gewichtswerte der Körperorgane bei dem Menschen und den Tieren. Arch. für Anthropologie 28:1.

Whittow, G. C., P. D. Sturkie, and G. Stein, Jr. 1964 Cardiovascular changes associated with thermal polypnea in the chicken. Amer. J. Physiol. 207:1349.

Whittow, G. C., P. D. Sturkie, and G. Stein, Jr. Cardiovascular effects of hypothermia in the chicken. Nature (in press) 1965.

Williams, F. I., and S. Rodbard 1960 Increased circulating plasma volume following dibenzyline. Am. J. Physiol. 198:169.

Woodbury, R. A., and B. E. Abreu 1944 Influence of oxytocin (pitocin) upon the heart and blood pressure of the chicken, rabbit, cat, dog, and turtle. Am. J. Physiol. 142:114.

Woodbury, R. A., and W. F. Hamilton 1937 Blood pressure studies in small animals. Am. J. Physiol. 119:663.

CHAPTER 4

Contraction and Conduction
in the Heart

ANATOMY OF THE HEART AND
CONDUCTING SYSTEM

IN birds the heart is located in the thorax slightly to the left of
the median line, and is ventral to the lungs, with the apex resting
in the median fissure of the liver (Kaupp, 1918). The heart of the
chicken is almost parallel to the long axis of the body except that
the apex may be bent to the right, according to Lewis (1915). In
most of the chicken hearts studied by Kisch (1951), the long axis
was directed toward the right wing, whereas the duck heart was
more nearly in and parallel to the median line. The heart is surrounded by the pericardial sac, which contains serous fluid.

The bird heart, like that of mammals, has four chambers: two
atria and two ventricles. The right atrium of the chicken heart is
larger than the left. The mass of the left ventricle is three times
that of the right ventricle (Lewis). The atria have openings into
the ventricles which are closed by the atrioventricular valves. The
left valve is thin, membranous, and bicuspid, like that of mammals, but the right valve is simply a muscular flap. The valves of
the aorta and pulmonary arteries are like those in mammals.

The interior of the heart is lined with a thin serous membrane,
the endocardium. The main mass of the heart wall, the myocardium, consists of cardiac muscle like that in mammals. The muscle
is thickest in the ventricles, particularly the left one. The outer
surface of the heart is termed the epicardium.

The heart muscle is supplied with arterial blood through the coronary arteries, and venous blood is returned to the venous circulation through the coronary veins, which course through the heart wall near the surface. Most birds have 2 main coronary arteries, but some may have 3 or 4. Petren (1926) showed that among chicken and pigeon hearts studied, 28 and 38 percent respectively had 3 coronary arteries.

The right coronary artery is larger than the left in chickens and is located on the ventral surface of the heart. It branches from the ventral side of the aorta at the point where the latter enters the heart. The left coronary artery originates from the dorsal side of the aorta and courses mainly over the dorsal surface of the heart. The ends and branches of the right and left coronary arteries anastomose freely, and many of them are located deep in the myocardium.

The size or weight of the bird heart varies considerably with body size. In proportion to body weight, smaller birds usually have larger hearts. The heart and body weights of some species are as follows (see Groebbels, 1932):

Species	Body weight gm.	Heart weight in gm./kg. of body weight
Goose	4405	8.00
Duck	1685	7.44
Chicken	3120	4.40
Pigeon	297	13.80

For more details, see Hartman (1955), who recorded heart weights of over 200 species of birds.

Specialized Conducting System

The existence of a specialized conducting system in bird hearts was doubted for a number of years. Earlier work by Mackenzie indicated that sino-atrial nodal tissue was absent. Work by Aschoff, however, indicated the presence of an S-A node. See Eyster and Meek (1921) for review.

Later work by Drennan (1927) on the ostrich, and by Davies

(1930), leaves little doubt as to the existence of a specialized conducting system in the heart of birds. Davies, who worked with swans and pigeons, made detailed histochemical studies on the hearts of these species. A diagram of the system as described by him is shown in Figure 7.

The system consists of (1) the sino-atrial node, (2) the atrio-ventricular node and branches, and (3) the right A-V ring of Purkinje fibers. The S-A node is located near the entrance of the vena cava to the right atrium.

The A-V node. The A-V node (pigeon) is embedded in connective tissue in the lower and posterior part of the atrial septum, a short distance in front and to the left of the opening of the left superior vena cava, a position similar to that occupied by the mammalian node. It is ovoid in shape, and its lower and anterior parts narrow into the commencement of the A-V bundle. The lower part of the node consists of cells which are larger than the atrial myocardial cells proper, and are frequently multinucleated, the nuclei being rounded in shape and central in position.

The A-V bundle. Beginning as a narrow, rounded bundle continuous with the lower and anterior end of the A-V node, the A-V bundle soon broadens out and runs forward and to the left in the ventricular septum. It then passes downward, forward, and to the left, to a point slightly below and to the right of the anterior septal attachment of the muscular right A-V valve. This site is about one-quarter of the distance from the base to the apex of the ventricular system, and here the bundle divides into the right and left limbs. The right limb runs downward and slightly forward. It passes in front of and close to the main septal artery, but no fibers appear to pass directly from the right limb to the collection of Purkinje fibers around the artery. The limb then reaches the subendocardial connective tissue on the right side of the septum, where it spreads out and becomes continuous with the subendocardial network of Purkinje fibers. The cells of the limbs are like those of the bundle.

The right limb also gives off a branch which runs up and around the right A-V valve. It suggests, according to Davies, that the right valve actively contracts early in the ventricular systole,

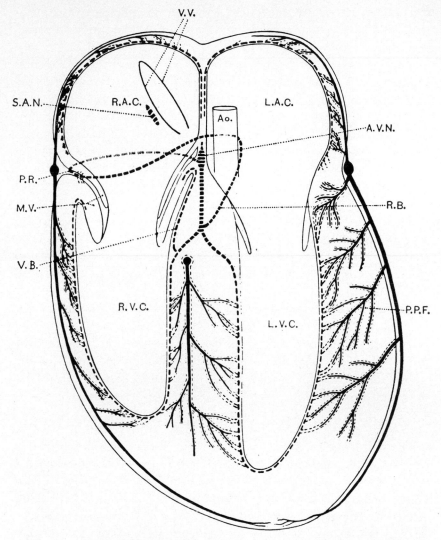

Figure 7. Diagram of the conducting system in the avian heart (pigeon).
Ao., aorta; A.V.N., atrioventricular node; L.A.C., left atrial cavity; M.V.,
muscular right A-V valve; P.P.F., periarterial Purkinje fibers; P.R., ring of
Purkinje fibers about right A-V orifice; R.A.C., right atrial cavity; R.V.C.,
right ventricle cavity; R.B., left recurrent branch of A-V bundle; S.A.N.,
sinoatrial node; V.B., branch of right limb of A-V bundle to muscular valve;
V.V., venous valves, right and left. (From Davies, *J. Anat.*, 1930.)

thus allowing exit for the blood from the greater part of the systole. This, he says, represents an example of adaptation of structure to function.

The left limb branches at the point where the right one branches and passes posteriorly and to the left, in the manner described for the right limb. The left branch, at its beginning, gives rise to another, the recurrent branch, which runs upward, forward, and to the left in the ventricular septum. Finally, it passes backward in the connective tissue on the left side of the root of the aorta and ends by joining the aortic end of the bundle of Purkinje fibers, which passes from the A-V node around the right A-V orifice, behind the root of the aorta.

The absence in birds of a fibrous sheath around the A-V bundle is correlated with the rapidity of the heart rate (according to Davies), the necessity having arisen for early and widespread diffusion of the impulse from the atrium along the bundle to all parts of the ventricles.

No nerve cells were observed in the A-V node with the stain used, but abundant nerve fibers penetrate the connective tissue surrounding the node. Likewise, no nerve fibers were observed in the S-A node, but small ganglia and fibers were plentiful in the epicardial tissue in the region of the node, and these could be traced to the node.

THE CARDIAC CYCLE

The sequence of events occurring in a complete heartbeat, a cardiac cycle, has been determined in the mammalian heart (for details, see any good textbook on mammalian physiology). These events include mechanical contraction of the atria and ventricles, or systole, and relaxation of the heart muscle, or diastole. This sequence is followed by filling of the ventricles (diastasis). Accompanying these changes are changes in volume and pressure in the atria and ventricles. Apparently no measurements upon intracardiac pressure, volume changes, and output as related to the cardiac cycle in birds have been made.

Kisch (1951 and 1953), who made records of the heart sounds of birds (phonocardiograms), reported that usually two sounds per cycle can be registered when the heart rates are below 500 per minute (see Figure 13).

INITIATION OF THE HEARTBEAT

The wave of contraction originates in the sinoatrial (S-A) node and spreads through the atria, thence through the atrioventricular (A-V) node, the A-V bundle, and its branches to all parts of the heart. The rhythm and initiation of the heartbeat is normally controlled by the S-A node (the pacemaker); but under certain conditions, for example when the S-A node is discharging abnormally, the A-V node or ventricles may initiate the beat (ectopic impulses), and may continue to do so (ectopic rhythm). This may occur in S-A block, where the impulse does not leave the S-A node, or when the S-A node discharges very slowly or arrhythmically, and in A-V block, where the impulse does not pass through the A-V node or bundles. These conditions have been reported in the bird and will be described later (Chapter 5). Complete atrioventricular block has been produced in the chicken by ligating the heart in the A-V groove, and also by transecting both right and left bundles. Cutting either right or left bundle alone does not produce complete block (Mangold and Kato, 1914).

FACTORS AFFECTING HEART RATE

Smaller birds and mammals usually have higher heart rates than large ones, but there are exceptions. The high heart rate of most birds cannot be accurately counted without resorting to the use of the electrocardiograph, cardiotachtometer, and other electronic devices.

The heart rates of several species are shown in Table 26. It is not known to what extent handling and restraint of the bird influences heart rate, but recent work by Sturkie (1963) employing telemetry indicates that the rates observed under these conditions with the bird unrestrained and undisturbed are very similar to those reported for the restrained bird. It was observed that the heart rate at night was lower than in the daytime, and also that activity such as walking or eating elevated the heart rate as much as 50 beats per minute. It may be observed from the table that

Table 26. Heart rate of birds

Species	Age	Sex	Body weight gm.	Mean heart rate	Reference
Chicken, W. Leghorn	1 day	—		286	Ringer, Weiss, & Sturkie (1957)
"	1 wk.	—		474	"
"	7 wks.	Male		422	"
"	"	Female		435	"
"	"	Capon		425	"
"	"	Poulard		452	"
"	13 wks.	Male		367	"
"	"	Female		391	"
"	22 wks.	Male		302	"
"	"	Female		357	"
"	"	Capon		350	"
"	"	Poulard		354	"
R. I. Red		Male	2,190	243	McNally (1941)
"		Female	1,980	279	"
Turkey, Bronze	Adult		8,750	93	Stubel (1910)
"	8 wks.	Male		288	Ringer and Rood (1959)
"	"	Female		283	"
"	12 wks.	Male		234	"
"	"	Female		230	"
"	18 wks.	Male		198	"
"	"	Female		212	"
"	22 wks.	Male		198	"
"	"	Female		232	"
Duck, Pekin	4 mo.	Male		194	Ringer, Weiss, & Sturkie (1955)
"	"	Female		190	"
"	12–13 mo.	Male		189	"
"	"	Female		175	"
Pigeon, White King	Adult	Male		202	Ringer, Weiss, & Sturkie (1955)
"	"	Female		208	"
Robin	Adult			570	Woodbury & Hamilton (1937)
Canary	Adult			795	Woodbury & Hamilton (1937)
"	"			1,000	Tigerstedt (1921)

heart rates of adult male chickens and turkeys are lower than for females, and that this sex difference develops at about the age when the gonads begin producing gonadotrophic hormones. The heart rate is lower in adult males than it is in castrate males, castrate females, or normal females. This difference might suggest that androgen influences heart rate; however, administration of androgen to capons and to females did not decrease heart rate (Ringer, unpublished). Likewise the administration of estrogen to the male did not change heart rate (Sturkie and Hunsaker, 1957). Whether the slower rate in males is attributable to increased vagal tone has not been tested. There is no sex difference in the heart rates of ducks and pigeons.

The heart of the chick embryo exhibits rhythmic contractions after about 30 hours of incubation (Barry, 1940), but the complete vascular circuit is not completed until the 40th hour (Patten and Kramer, 1933). The heart rate after 40 hours of incubation is 90 to 100 per minute; it increases gradually until it reaches a peak of 220 on the 8th or 9th day (Romanoff, 1944), and then decreases to about 200 per minute just before hatching. The heart rate of the day-old chick is 286; then the rate rises rapidly and reaches a peak at 1 week of age, remains high until about 13 weeks, when the gonads are developing, and then decreases somewhat, after the sex difference is first manifested.

Effects of Drugs and Hormones

Sympathetic nerves, when stimulated, release norepinephrine, whereas parasympathetic nerves release acetylcholine. The former are known as adrenergic and the latter as cholinergic nerves. Sympathomimetic drugs are those that mimic the effects of sympathetic nerve stimulation. Norepinephrine, epinephrine, ephedrine, and neosynephrin are some examples of these. Some of the parasympathomimetic drugs are acetylcholine, methacholine, and pilocarpine. The effects of such drugs on the chicken heart have received little attention. From the meager data available, however, the effects appear to be similar to those in the mammal. Epinephrine in smaller doses increases, whereas larger doses (1 mg. or more, intravenously) may slow the heart rate (Sturkie, unpub-

lished). Epinephrine, at the latter level, when injected intravenously into hens weighing 2 kg., not only slowed the heart, but
also produced premature systoles and other cardiac arrhythmias.
Minimal doses of norepinephrine (0.4 microgram/kg.), which have
a pressor effect, tend to decrease heart rate (reflexively), whereas
large doses may increase heart rate and produce arrhythmias.

Acetylcholine (0.2 to 1 mg., or more) injected intravenously into
chickens causes a momentary slowing or arrest in heart rate, after
which the rate increases rapidly. Methacholine administered at
minimal levels (0.15 mg./kg. subcutaneously) depresses blood pressure and causes a reflex rise in heart rate (Durfee, 1963).

Atropine blocks the effects of acetylcholine released from the
vagus nerve and releases the heart from vagal control; levels ranging from 0.13 to 12 mg./kg. have been used (Bunag and Walaszek,
1962; see Chapter 3). As little as 0.15 to 0.20 mg./kg. of atropine
injected subcutaneously will block the effects of an effective dose
of methacholine (Durfee, 1963). However, if methacholine or acetylcholine is administered intravenously, much larger doses of
atropine are required.

The heart of chickens on a diet deficient in potassium is usually
slowed, and the rate reverts to normal after the administration of
atropine (Sturkie, 1950).

Reserpine. When administered intravenously at dosages from
0.01 mg. to 0.75 mg. per kg. of body weight, reserpine significantly
reduced heart rate in chickens, and the log dose response was linear. Heart rate response was shown to be a sensitive assay technique for reserpinelike compounds (Sturkie, Durfee, and Sheahan,
1958). Similar results have been obtained in turkeys by Speckmann and Ringer (1961). The mechanism of the action of reserpine on the heart rate in birds is unknown. Effects of drugs and
other factors on the heartbeat of chick embryos are reviewed by
Romanoff (1960).

Nervous Control of the Heart

The heart of birds is supplied by sympathetic and parasympathetic nerves. The anatomy of these nerves has been studied ex-

tensively in a number of avian species, including ducks, geese, pigeons, chickens and the crow (Ssinelnikow, 1928), and in the pigeon by Malinovsky (1962).

The cardiac (sympathetic) nerve arises from the first thoracic ganglion between the first and second rib, in close apposition with the last branch of the brachial nerve plexus. It courses backward and downward and joins with fibers from the vagus nerve to form several cardiac plexuses (see Figure 8). According to Ssinelnikow, there are six of these; the right and left anterior cardiac plexuses, the right and left posterior plexuses, and the anterior and posterior atrial plexuses. All plexuses connect directly or indirectly with each other, and each receives contributions from the cardiac and vagus nerves.

Vagal control. The vagi in mammals and birds exert a tonic effect on the heart. The degree of vagal control varies considerably with the species and size of the bird. Stubel (1910) found that in birds with large hearts in relation to body size (pigeon, duck, sea gull, and hawk) the vagus had a powerful cardio-inhibitory effect, whereas in birds such as the chicken, rook, and jackdaw, it exerted little control over heart rate. For example, when both vagi were sectioned in pigeons and chickens, the following results were obtained:

	Heart rate, nerves intact	Heart rate, vagi sectioned
Pigeon	120	300
Chicken	288	312

The degree of vagal control appears to be influenced by respiration, according to Paton (1912) and Jurgens (1909), who reported that vagotomy in the duck does not increase heart rate if artificial respiration is supplied. Bilateral vagotomy in the chicken, however, tends to increase heart rate with or without artificial respiration (Durfee, 1963). The degree of increase after vagotomy depends on the basal rate before sectioning. For example, curare, which paralyzes skeletal muscle and makes artificial respiration necessary, tends to slow heart rate mainly by increasing vagal

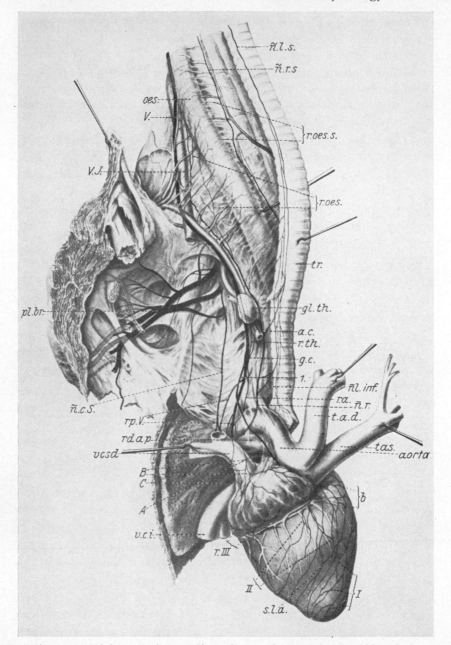

Figure 8. Right anterior cardiac plexus of goose heart. Abbreviations:
oes., oesophagus: *V.*, right vagus nerve; *V.J.* jugular vein; *pl. br.*, brachial

tone; following bilateral vagotomy the rate increases (Durfee and Sturkie, unpublished.). Starvation for 7 days decreases heart rate to less than half of normal, apparently by increasing vagal tone, since administration of atropine, a parasympathetic blocker, increases heart rate considerably (Vogel and Sturkie, 1963). Stimulation of the peripheral end of the vagus in the pigeon, chicken, and duck slows the heart and may arrest it momentarily in the pigeon and chicken, and for a longer period in the duck (Jurgens, Paton). It also diminishes the amplitude of contraction of the atria (Clark, 1927), and sometimes that of the ventricles (Jurgens, Paton). Stimulation of peripheral end of the right vagus of the chicken has a greater effect than the left vagus in slowing heart.

Heart rate in diving birds. It is well known that diving birds and mammals, including man, (Scholander *et al.,* 1962) exhibit bradycardia. This has been demonstrated in a number of wild species by Eliassen (1957), and in aquatic and nonaquatic birds by Bond, Douglas, and Gilbert (1961) and others (Johansen and Krog, 1959). Submersion of head and neck induces reflex slowing of the heart, and the effect is evidently mediated by the vagus, since when the latter are cut, heart rate is normal (Artom, 1927). When terrestrial birds such as the chicken, pigeon, and quail are submerged, the heart rate increases at the moment of submersion; the birds develop mild bradycardia after submersion for 10 seconds, although this was not as pronounced as in diving birds (Bond, Douglas, and Gilbert).

---

plexus; *n.c.S.,* sympathetic cardiac nerve; *rp.V.,* pulmonary rami of vagus; *vcsd,* right superior vena cava; *B,* little trunks of the anterior medial group of the cardiac sympathetic nerve; *C,* little trunks of the posterior lateral group of the cardiac sympathetic nerve; *A,* anastomosing trunk of the sympathetic cardiac nerve to the right superior cardiac nerve, *v.c.i.,* superior vena cava; *r. III,* cardiac rami; *II,* anterior right cardiac plexus; *s.l.a.,* anterior longitudinal sulcus; *ñ.l.s.,* superior laryngeal nerve; *ñ.r.s.,* left recurrent nerve; *r.oes.s.,* oesophageal ramus; *tr.,* trachea; *gl.th.,* thyroid gland; *a.c.,* carotid artery; *r.th.,* thyroid rami of vagus; *g.c.,* ganglion Couvrieur; *l.,* little trunk of left cardiac plexus; *nl.inf.,* inferior laryngeal nerve; *r.a.,* vagus branch to aorta; *n.r.,* recurrent nerve; *t.a.d.,* right innominate trunk; *tas.,* left innominate trunk; *I,* anterior left cardiac plexus. (From Ssinelnikow, 1928.)

Evidence has accumulated to suggest that heart rate in birds, at least in the chicken, is controlled mainly by the vagus nerves, and that the cardiac nerves do not influence it appreciably. For example, an adrenergic blocking agent (dibenzyline), administered at a level high enough to depress blood pressure significantly, does not influence heart rate (Sturkie, unpublished). Reflex changes in heart rate likewise appear to be mediated solely through the vagi. Minimal doses of norepinephrine, which elevate blood pressure, cause a transient reflex slowing of heart rate, which can be abolished by bilateral vagotomy. Depressing blood pressure with acetylcholine or methacholine produces a reflex increase in heart rate, which is also abolished by vagotomy (Durfee and Sturkie, 1963, Durfee, 1963).

Finally, the isolation and stimulation of the cardiac nerve in 8 chickens had no effect on heart rate in any except one bird, which had a slow basal rate (Sturkie, Vogel, and Freedman, unpublished). According to Bogdanov (1961), nervous control of the heart of the chick does not appear until about the 16th day of incubation. Transection of spinal cord prior to the 16th day does not influence the heart rate, but after this time the operation decreases it.

REFERENCES

Artom, C. 1927 Sur les rapports entre le rythme de la respiration et le rythme du coeur chez les oiseaux. Arch. Neerl. Physiol. 10:362.

Barry, A. 1940 Age changes in the pulsation frequency of the embryonic chick heart. J. Exp. Zool. 85:157.

Bogdanov, O. V. 1961 Effect of damage to different parts of the central nervous system on the cardiac activity of the chick embryo. Bull. Exp. Biol. & Med. 50:889. Trans. from Byulleten' Eksperimental'noi Biologii i Meditsiny 50:21 (1960).

Bond, C. F., S. D. Douglas, and P. W. Gilbert 1961 Effects of submergence on cardiac cycle and rate in aquatic and terrestrial birds. Am. J. Physiol 200:723.

Clark, A. J. 1927 Comparative Physiology of the Heart. The Macmillan Co., New York.

Davies, F. 1930 The conducting system of the bird's heart. J. Anat. 64:9.

Drennan, M. R. 1927 The auriculo-ventricular bundle in the bird's heart. Brit. Med. J. Part 1:321.

Durfee, W. K. 1963 Cardiovascular reflex mechanisms in the fowl. Thesis, Rutgers University.

Durfee, W. K., and P. D. Sturkie 1963 Some cardiovascular responses to anoxia in the fowl. Fed. Proc. 22:182.

Eliassen, E. 1957 Right-ventricle pressures and heart-rate in diving birds. Nature 180:512.

Eyster, J. A. E., and W. J. Meek 1921 The origin and conduction of the heart beat. Physiol. Rev. 1:1.

Groebbels, F. 1932 Der Vogel. Erster Band: Atmungswelt und Nahrungswelt. Verlag von Gebrüder Borntraeger, Berlin.

Hartman, F. A. 1955 Heart weight in birds. Condor 57:221.

Johansen, K., and J. Krog 1959 Peripheral circulatory response to submersion asphyxia in the duck. Acta Physiol. Scand. 46:194.

Jurgens, H. 1909 Über die Wirkung des Nervus Vagus auf das Herz der Vögel. Arch. ges. Physiol. (Pflügers) 129:506.

Kaupp, B. F. 1918 The Anatomy of the Domestic Fowl. W. B. Saunders Co., Philadelphia.

Kisch, B. 1951 The electrocardiogram of birds (chicken, duck, pigeon). Exp. Med. & Surg. 9:103.

Kisch, B. 1953 Heart sounds in tachycardia. Trans. Am. College of Cardiology II.

Lewis, T. 1915 The spread of the excitatory process in the vertebrate heart. V: The bird's heart. Phil. Trans. Royal Soc. London 207:298.

McNally, E. H. 1941 Heart rate of the domestic fowl. Poultry Sci. 20:266.

Malinovsky, L. 1962 Contribution to the anatomy of the vegetative nervous system in the neck and thorax of the domestic pigeon. Acta Anat. 50:326.

Mangold, E., and T. Kato 1914 Zur vergleichenden Physiologie des His'schen Bundels. III: Mitteilung: Die atrioventrikulare Erregungsleitung im Vogelherzen. Arch. ges. Physiol. (Pflügers) 160:91.

Paton, N. D. 1912 On the extrinsic nerves of the heart of the bird. J. Physiol. 45:106.

Patten, B. M., and T. C. Kramer 1933 The initiation of contraction in the embryonic chick heart. Am. J. Anat. 53:349.

Petren, T. 1926 Die Coronararterien des Vogelherzens. Morph. Jahrb. 56:239.

Ringer, R. K., and K. Rood 1959 Hemodynamic changes associated with aging in the broad-breasted Bronze turkey. Poultry Sci. 38:395.

Ringer, R. K., H. S. Weiss, and P. D. Sturkie 1955 Effect of sex and age on blood pressure in the duck and pigeon. Am. J. Physiol. 183:141.

Ringer, R. K., H. S. Weiss, and P. D. Sturkie 1957 Heart rate of chickens as influenced by age and gonadal hormones. Am. J. Physiol. 191:145.

Romanoff, A. L. 1944 The heartbeat of avian embryos. Anat. Rec. 89:313.

Romanoff, A. L. 1960 The Avian Embryo. The Macmillan Co., New York.

Scholander, P. F., H. T. Hammel, H. L. Messurier, E. Hemmingsen, and W. Garey 1962 Circulatory adjustment in pearl divers. J. Appl. Physiol. 17:184.

Speckman, E. W., and R. K. Ringer 1961 Hemodynamic responses following reserpine feeding to turkeys. Poultry Sci. 40:1292.

Ssinelnikow, R. 1928 Die Herznerven der Vögel. Z. f. Anat. u. Entwickl. 86:540.

Stubel, H. S. 1910 Beiträge zur Kenntnis der Physiologie des Blutkreislaufes bei verschiedenen Vogelarten. Arch. ges. Physiol. (Pflügers) 135:240.

Sturkie, P. D. 1950 Abnormal electrocardiograms of chickens produced by potassium deficiency and effects of certain drugs on the abnormalities. Am. J. Physiol. 162:538.

Sturkie, P. D. 1963 Heart rate of chickens determined by radio telemetry during light and dark periods. Poultry Sci. 42:797.

Sturkie, P. D., W. K. Durfee, and M. Sheahan 1958 Effects of reserpine on the fowl. Am. J. Physiol. 194:184.

Sturkie, P. D., and W. G. Hunsaker 1957 Role of estrogen in sex difference of the electrocardiogram of the chicken. Proc. Soc. Exp. Biol. & Med. 94:731.

Tigerstedt, R. 1921 Physiologie des Kreislaufes. Vol. II. Berlin and Leipzig.

Vogel, J. A., and P. D. Sturkie 1963 Effects of starvation on the cardiovascular system of the chicken. Proc. Soc. Exp. Biol. & Med. 112:111.

Woodbury, R. A., and W. F. Hamilton 1937 Blood pressure studies in small animals. Am. J. Physiol. 119:663.

CHAPTER 5

Electrocardiography

ACTION POTENTIALS

ACTIVE muscle or nerve exhibits electrical activity. If two electrodes, A and B, are attached, some distance apart, to a strip of muscle, and the muscle is stimulated, it depolarizes or becomes electrically negative at the electrode nearest the point of stimulation, for example at A; muscle at B is still in the resting stage, and a difference in potential is produced between the electrodes. When the electrodes are attached to a suitable recording instrument (galvanometer), the potential difference is registered as an initial upward deflection. As the excitation wave spreads to electrode B, the difference in potential decreases and finally reaches zero, and the curve returns to the base, or isoelectric line.

The muscle which depolarized first at A now begins recovery or repolarization ahead of the muscle at B, and there is now a new potential difference, but in the opposite direction. The curve is now downward, and as the repolarization process passes to B, the potential difference continues to decrease and the curve returns to the isoelectric line. The upward and downward (positive and negative) deflections constitute a diphasic record.

SPREAD OF THE ELECTRICAL EXCITATION
WAVE IN THE BIRD HEART

The electrical excitation wave precedes mechanical contraction slightly and spreads from the S-A node through the other branches of the conducting system. The paths and speed of conduction of this wave may be determined by placing electrodes at different areas of the heart and determining the change in potential at the electrodes (method of relative negativity).

Lewis (1915), Mangold (1919), and Kisch (1949 and 1951) used this method on the bird heart. Lewis and Mangold used bipolar leads. Lewis placed the exploring electrode on the heart and the other on the chest wall; Mangold placed both electrodes on the heart. Kisch used, for the most part, unipolar leads (chest, direct, and endocavity). Mangold and Lewis reported that the impulse started in the region of the S-A node and spread to the left side of the right atrium, thence to the left atrium and then to the septum.

The order of depolarization in the different areas of the ventricles (chicken) according to Lewis, Mangold, and Kisch is as follows:

Kisch 1951	Lewis 1915	Mangold 1919	Region of Heart
1	1	1	Apex of right ventricle
3	3	2	Base of left ventricle
2	4	3	Base of right ventricle
4	2	4	Apex of left ventricle

The time required for the impulse to spread from the region of the septum to other parts of the ventricle's surface, according to Lewis, is shown in Figure 9. Lewis found that the rate of conduction across the surfaces of the right and left ventricles was of the same magnitude but variable, averaging 1,119 and 1,087 mm. per second respectively. The rate across the septum was much lower, 740 mm. per second.

Based upon the distribution of surface potentials and studies of electrocardiograms, Lewis concluded that the impulse spreads (see Figure 9) downward through the septum, then upward through the septum, and later upward through the free walls, almost in line with the latter rather than at right angles to them. The very rapid spread of the impulse downward (electrical axis, $+90°$; see Figure 10) corresponds to the small upright R wave of the electrocardiogram. The depolarization wave then shifts abruptly upwards (electrical axis approximately $-90°$), and its duration is relatively long (Figure 9). This produces the S wave of the electrocardiogram (Lewis, 1915).

Neither Mangold nor Lewis determined which of the endocardial and epicardial surfaces was activated first. Kisch (1951) made such studies on the bird heart, using direct leads with the electrodes placed respectively in the interior and on the exterior surfaces of the atria or ventricles. The leads were taken simultaneously. He showed that the epicardial surfaces of the ventricles

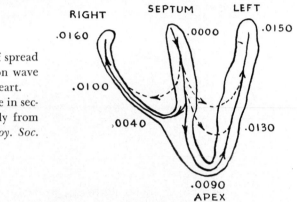

Figure 9. Diagram of spread of impulse or excitation wave in ventricles of bird heart.

Coronal section: time in seconds. (Modified slightly from Lewis, *Phil. Trans. Roy. Soc. London, B,* 1915.)

are activated or depolarized before the endocardial surfaces in the chicken, pigeon, duck, and sea gull. Depolarization on the surface of the right ventricles of the chicken heart begins about 0.02 to 0.03 seconds earlier than inside the right ventricle, but on the left ventricle it starts about 0.01 second earlier than on the inside. Depolarization in the interior of the left and right ventricles occurs at approximately the same time. When the exploring electrode was placed on the ventricular surface (right or left), the resulting electrogram (EG) resembled the normal electrocardiogram (ECG). Leads from the interior of the ventricle produce EG's with the configuration of waves in the opposite direction, similar to the normal ECG of man and dog, in which the endocardial surfaces are depolarized before the epicardial surfaces.

THE ELECTROCARDIOGRAM

The electrocardiogram (ECG) is a record of the electrical activity of the heart, picked up from electrodes attached to parts of the body other than the heart itself (leads). For details concerning the essentials and methods of taking and recording electrocardiograms, consult textbooks on the subject. Leads taken directly from the heart produce records termed electrograms (EG's). Records from any two electrodes constitute a lead. The standard bipolar

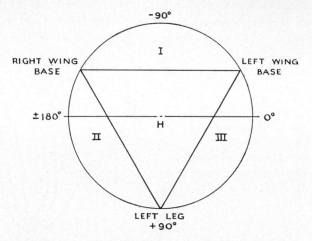

Figure 10. Limb leads for the ECG of the bird, with heart in center (H).

limb leads for man are: lead I, right arm and left arm; lead II, right arm and left leg; and III, left arm and left leg. The limb leads for the bird heart are the same as for man, except that the electrodes (usually needles) are attached to, or inserted in, the bases of the wings. The three limb leads form roughly an equilateral triangle with the heart located near the center (Figure 10). This is more nearly true for the bird heart than for man.

The conventional chest leads, CR, CL, and CF, have been recorded also in birds (Sturkie, unpublished; Kisch, 1951; Douglas, 1960). The exploring electrodes are placed on the right arm, left arm, and left leg or foot, and the chest electrode is the indifferent electrode.

It is impossible with bipolar leads to record the true potential at any one point because of the influence of the other electrode. Wilson devised a method of unipolar leads so that one of the electrodes was zero (see Lamb, 1957). Thus the positive exploring electrode records only the potential received at the point desired. Such electrodes placed on the right arm (VR), left arm (VL), and left leg or foot (VF) constitute the V leads. Because one lead is zero, the potential recorded in V leads is only half that of bipolar leads. Goldberger augmented (amplified) the potential of unipolar leads by removing the negative electrode from VL when the positive electrode was on the left arm, and in a like manner on the other extremities; such leads are designated as aVR, aVL and aVF, or augmented unipolar leads. Even with the augmentation, the amplitude obtained is only about 86 percent of that measured by bipolar leads (Lamb, 1957).

Method for Determining

The standard speed for the paper of the electrocardiogram for human beings is 25 mm. per second. The vertical lines 1 mm. apart on the paper represent units of time (0.04 second), at standard speeds. The horizontal lines, also 1 mm. apart, represent amplitude or voltage. For work with human beings, the instrument is usually standardized at 1 millivolt. When 1 millivolt is impressed upon the instrument, it causes a deflection of 10 mm. Since the heart rate of the chicken is considerably faster than that of man, the standard chart speed in most cases is not fast enough to record all waves faithfully. Usually, if the heart rate is 300 or more per minute, the P and T waves may be fused together, and the P wave is not always discernible (particularly in leads II and III). However, the P wave of the chicken may not, in some cases, be discernible even when the chart speed is increased to 50 or 75 mm. per second (Sturkie, 1948 and 1949; Kisch, 1951), and when the frequency response of the instrument is increased to 500 cycles per second, which is more than adequate (Sturkie, 1953, unpublished; see Figure 11) It appears that the P and T waves are fused because the atria begin depolarizing before the ventricles are completely repolarized.

Normal Electrocardiogram of the Bird

The normal ECG of man shows P, Q, R, S, and T waves in the limb leads. The bird ECG exhibits P, S, and T waves and usually

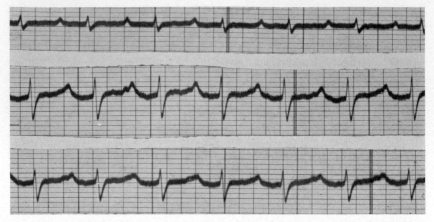

Figure 11. Electrocardiogram of female chicken taken on a high frequency instrument (500 cycles per second) showing the limb leads (I, II, and III from top downward). Standardization, 1 millivolt equals 1.5 cm. Chart speed 75 mm. per second. Note that P and T waves are fused; compare with Figure 12, where they are not.

a small, abortive R in some leads, but no Q wave. The P wave, as in man (Figures 12 and 13 represents the depolarization of atrial muscle and precedes slightly atrial contraction. There is no recognizable wave of repolarization. R and S waves represent the depolarization of ventricular muscle, which signals the onset of ventricular systole. The T wave represents repolarization of the ventricles.

The P wave when observed is usually upright (positive) in all leads in the chicken, duck, and pigeon (Sturkie, Kisch), although Douglas (1960), based on studies of a small number of birds, claims that the P wave is usually biphasic in leads I and III, and Kisch reported negative P III in the sea gull.

The P wave is observed most frequently in lead I in the chicken, even though the amplitude is less than in II or III, because the T wave in I is usually flat or isoelectric. P and T may be fused in II and III. T is positive in II and III. A small upright R is usually (Sturkie, 1949 and unpublished) or always (Kisch, 1951) present in lead II of the chicken and pigeon respectively, but is of lower amplitude or absent in III. Occasionally the R wave is prominent in II and III of the duck (Kisch).

Lead I is the most variable of the limb leads. The amplitude of all the complexes except the P wave is usually low. With respect to the configuration of R, S, and T in lead I, the three main types are described as follows (Sturkie, 1948 and 1949):

(a) Relatively prominent S and no R or a small R. The T is usually isoelectric or slightly positive.

(b) A relatively prominent R and no S or a small S. T is isoelectric or slightly negative.

(c) R's and S's of about equal prominence. Type *b* is the most prevalent.

The electrocardiogram of the chicken showing limb leads, chest leads, and augmented unipolar leads is reproduced in Figure 12. In leads CR and CL, the configurations of the waves are similar to those in II and III. In CF the P wave is usually biphasic and the amplitude of all waves is low.

In leads aVR and aVL the QRS complex is inverted when compared to lead II or III. The P wave is inverted in aVR and biphasic in aVL. The configuration of the waves in aVF is similar to those in II and III.

Sex Difference

There is a sex difference in the ECG of chickens characterized by a greater tendency toward fusion of P and T waves in II and III of females, and the greater amplitude of all waves in the male ECG. The mean amplitude in millimeters of the RS complex in lead II is 5.30 for males and 2.47 for females (Sturkie and Hunsaker, 1957). The female sex hormone, estrogen, plays a role in this difference. Administration of estrogen to males over a 2- or 3-week period depresses the amplitude of all waves significantly (approximately 35 percent).

V Leads Taken at Different Levels of Body

Douglas employed Wilson central terminal electrodes to explore different areas of the body dorsally and ventrally with respect to the heart. For example, leads were taken ventrally at the level of the sternum on both right and left sides of the body

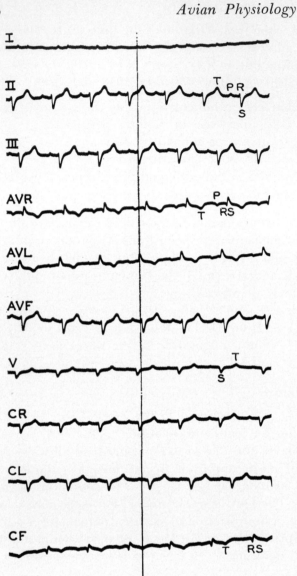

Figure 12. Electrocardiograms of male chicken showing limb leads (I, II, III), augmented unipolar leads (aVR, aVL, and aVF), V lead, and chest leads (CR, CL, and CF). Standardization, 1 millivolt equals 1.5 cm. Chart speed 50 mm. per second. Record taken on high frequency instrument. P, RS, and T waves clearly observed. From Sturkie (unpublished).

(chest), and dorsally at the level of clavicles. The results are shown in Figure 14 (Douglas). It is interesting to note that the ECG's taken at ventral right and dorsal left side are mirror images of each other, and so are those recorded at the dorsal right and ventral left sides. Unipolar limb leads VR, VL, and VF have been recorded in the duck, pigeon, and chicken by Kisch (1951), and in

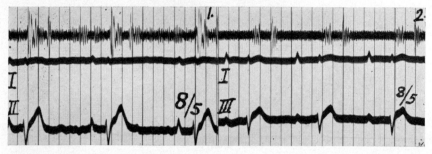

Figure 13. Phonocardiogram (upper tracing) and electrocardiogram of pigeon (leads I, II, and III).
Standardization, 1 millivolt equals 1.6 cm.; chart speed, 75 mm. per second. Photographic method of recording. (From Kisch, *Exp. Med. & Surg.*, 1951.)

the chicken by Douglas (1960) and Sturkie (unpublished). In leads VR and VL of the chicken and pigeon there is a prominent R, no S, and an inverted T, like the endocavity leads; but in the duck these leads show an S, a QS, or a small R and a prominent S. Kisch attributes this difference to the position of the heart, which according to the same author is more vertical in the duck. In VF of all birds studied by Kisch, there was a QS or a small R and prominent S.

Electrograms of Explanted Hearts

Electrograms of embryonic chicken hearts explanted and grown *in vitro* show two or three components of complexes, depending on the type and amount of heart tissue present (Szepsenwol, 1946; Bonsdorff, 1950). If portions of both atria and ventricles are explanted, P, QRS, and T waves are recorded. If only the atrium is explanted, two main complexes, a QRS (mainly positive) and a T wave, are recorded. Similar complexes are recorded in ventricular

Avian Physiology

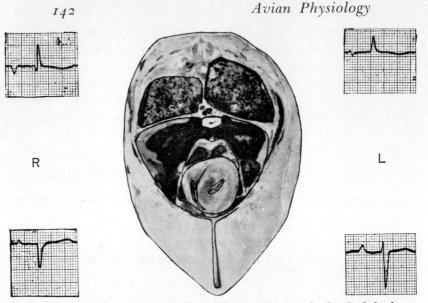

R   L

Figure 14. Cross section of White Leghorn rooster at the level of the heart. Posterior thoracic air sacs are shown injected with blue vinylite. Representative electrocardiograms are shown for each quadrant, retouched to facilitate reproduction. (After Douglas, *Am. J. Physiol.* 199:355 [1960].)

explants. The heart rate in ventricular explants is about one-half or less that of the atrial and compound explants (atrial and ventricular tissue). The rate is higher in the atrial explants when more S-A nodal tissue is present. The rate is highest when both atrial and ventricular tissues are present.

Intervals of the Electrocardiogram. The duration in seconds of the various waves of the avian ECG cannot always be determined, because of the fusion of P and T waves; therefore the work that has been reported is on selected ECG's where P and T are clearly discernible (Sturkie, 1949; Kisch, 1951). Duration of P, S, and T and intervals from the beginning of P to the start of S, and from the beginning of S to the end of T, have been determined for leads II and III in the chicken. The R wave in II and III is usually small or absent, and when present its starting point is difficult to locate. For this reason the P-S instead of the P-R interval is determined. In many cases there is no S-T segment. T usually begins where S ends, and that point is used as the starting point for T. S-

T represents the interval from the beginning of S to the end of T, or the time required for depolarization and repolarization of the ventricles.

The P-S interval is the time required for the impulse, beginning in the right atrium, to reach the ventricles. The intervals presented in Table 27 are based upon studies of selected ECG's in which both the beginning and end of all waves were discernible.

In general, as heart rate increases, the intervals for all complexes except S decrease; this was demonstrated also by Kisch in the chicken, pigeon, duck, and sea gull with direct leads. The intervals determined with direct leads on the chicken by Kisch (1951) are in close agreement with those determined with limb leads by Sturkie, except that for the ventricular complex. The duration of this interval is 0.037 second according to Kisch, and 0.024 according to Sturkie.

Amplitude. The amplitude of all waves of the bird ECG is relatively low and is considerably less than that of the human ECG. In lead I it is so low that accurate measurements with the usual standardization are difficult or impossible. An estimate of average amplitude in I can be deduced from the differences in mean amplitude for the various waves in leads II and III, in accordance with Einthoven's law, which states that the amplitude of a given wave in I and III should equal that in II. This is true provided the three leads are run simultaneously or, if they are not, provid-

Table 27. Intervals of the chicken electrocardiogram, in seconds
(Sturkie, 1949)

Waves	Heart rates	221 240	241 260	261 280	281 300	301 340
P	Mean	0.0408	0.0429	0.0421	0.0410	0.0374
S	Mean	0.0242	0.0247	0.0234	0.0233	0.0235
T	Mean	0.1161	0.1095	0.1048	0.1042	0.0925
P-S	Mean	0.0812	0.0847	0.0849	0.0790	0.0723
S-T	Mean	0.1402	0.1342	0.1281	0.1270	0.1164
	No. of ECG's	7–9	9–12	16	14–16	12–14

Table 28. Amplitude in millivolts of P, R, S, and T in leads II and III of chicken

	ECG's (No.)	II Mean	Stand. error	ECG's (No.)	III Mean	Stand. error
P	40	0.0602	0.0026	40	0.0421	0.0016
R	56	0.0346	0.0021	56	0.0221	0.0013
S (S in lead I)	18	0.2193	0.0135	18	0.01787*	0.0150
S (R in lead I)	43	0.1241	0.0067	44	0.1430*	0.0071
T (II>III)	46	0.1095	0.0056	46	0.0900	0.0050
T II<III)	15	0.0716	0.0046	15	0.0901	0.0062

* Difference statistically significant.

ed there is no appreciable change in heart rate and amplitude. Thus the amplitude in millivolts of S in lead I and S in III (added algebraically) should equal that in SII, as it does. Where S in I is the main ventricular wave (type a, lead I), SII is greater than SIII. When R is predominant in I, then the amplitude of SII is less than SIII. If SII and SIII are equal, then R or S waves are absent in I.

The amplitudes of P, R, S, and T for leads II and III of the chicken are shown in Table 28. These figures were derived from selected records, but they are subject to error because of the limitations of the instrument used, whose sensitivity to low voltages and response to high frequencies were not optimum for the bird heart: that is, they were calculated on records obtained at chart speeds of 25 mm. per second, which is not fast enough. Douglas (1960) used also a direct-writing electrocardiograph, but with chart speeds of 100 mm. per second. No really satisfactory data on amplitudes of avian ECG's are available. The P and T waves are not always clearly delineated, and the values for these, particularly for P, represent rough estimates. Chickens have ECG's of lower voltage than pigeons, swans, or ducks (Lewis, Kisch; see also Lepeschkin, 1951).

The relative amplitude of the waves in the limb leads is dependent upon the direction and magnitude of the electromotive force (electrical axis) of the heart in relation to the electrodes, and also upon the degree to which this force is conducted to the limbs of the body. It is known that certain organs of the body are good and others poor conductors of this force. If the heart of the bird is exposed by removing the sternum, sternal ribs, coracoids, and clavicle, and the tissues attached thereto, the amplitude of all waves in the limb leads is increased anywhere from twofold to threefold (Sturkie, 1948). This suggests that the sternum and pectoral muscles influence the spread of cardioelectro potentials, and Douglas (1960) has suggested that the air sacs of avian species likewise influence the spread.

Electrical Axis

The electrical axis represents the mean or average electromotive force (magnitude) of depolarization and repolarization, acting in an average direction during the period of electrical activity of the heart. It is a vector quantity in that it has direction, magnitude, and sense. Axes for any of the waves may be determined by measuring the amplitude of complexes in any two of the limb leads and plotting these values (for details see Lamb, 1957). Leads I and III are usually used for human ECG's, and II and III for the chicken since in the latter the amplitude for all waves in I is too low for accurate measurement. Electrical axes for chicken ECG's taken in the frontal plane are shown in Table 29. An RS axis of $-90°$ (see Figure 10) means that the mean electromotive force is directed upward and parallel to the long axis of the body. This would mean that the amplitudes of R and of S were equal in leads II and III and zero in I. It may be observed from the table that 74 percent of the chickens studied had RS axes averaging $-74.04°$. Thus, the axis is directed anteriorly and to the left of the long axis of the body (almost halfway between 12 and 1 o'clock). In these ECG's the amplitude of S III exceeds S II, and either the amplitude of R in I exceeds S, or S is absent. Twenty-six percent had RS axes averaging $-102.11°$ (between 11 and 12 o'clock). Thus, S II is greater than S III, and S I exceeds R I or R is absent. The normal RS axis in birds differs markedly from that in the normal human electrocardiogram (which ranges from 0 to $+90°$) and in that of a number of other animals.

Table 29. Electrical axes of chicken hearts (female) in relation to
type of lead I (Sturkie, 1949)

Type of ECG in I	No. of birds	ECG's		RS axes in degrees	
		No.	Percent	Range	Average
S present	15	17	25.8	−91 to −120	−102.11
R present	30	46	74.2	−26 to −103*	− 74.04
	2	3		+10 to + 30	

* Only one ECG above −90 degrees.

Direction of T wave in I	No. of birds	ECG's		T Axes in degrees	
		No.	Percent	Range	Average
Positive	34	43	70.49	+68 to + 89	+ 81.8
Negative	10	12	19.67	+95 to +115	+100.3
Isoelectric	6	6	9.83	+88 to + 91	+ 89.6

The electrical axes for T are grouped according to the direction of T in lead I (Table 29). In 70 percent of the ECG's studied, T I was positive and the axis averaged +81.8° (axis directed posteriorly between 5 and 6 o'clock). In 20 percent, with negative T I's, the axis was +100.3°; in those remaining, with isoelectric T waves, the axes averaged 89.6° or approximately 90°, as is to be expected in accordance with Einthoven's law. Thus, the more nearly the electrical axis parallels a given lead line, the higher the amplitude of the waves, and when it runs almost perpendicular to the lead line (as in lead I of the chicken), the amplitude is low. This can be demonstrated experimentally by rotating the heart on its anterioposterior axis to the left or right (Sturkie, 1948). When the heart is rotated to the left, so that the apex of the left ventricle is directly perpendicular to the lead III line and more nearly parallel to lead I, there is a pronounced decrease in amplitude of all the ventricular complexes in III, a slight decrease in II, and a great increase in lead I; and the change is proportional to the degree of rotation. There is, moreover, a change in direction or configuration of the waves in I. Normally, if an R and an inverted T are present in lead I, the R may be replaced after rotation to the left by an S, and the T wave becomes positive. If an S is normally present in I, its amplitude is decreased relatively, and an R wave appears after rotation to the left. Thus, the RS electrical axes for all birds increase after rotation, from an average normal of $-87°$ to $-98.7°$ after rotation to the left.

Conversely, when the heart is rotated to the right, there is a significant decrease in amplitude of all ventricular waves in II, a slight decrease in III, and a great increase in I. The RS electrical axis decreases from a normal of $-87°$ to $-68.6°$. Rotation to the right increases the height of R in lead I and the negativity of the T waves. When an S wave is normally present in I, it is replaced by an R after rotation.

Electrical axes in horizontal and sagittal planes. Douglas (1960) has made a vector analysis of the chicken ECG in the frontal, horizontal, and sagittal planes. The resultant spatial vector based on the projections from the three planes is longitudinal in direction. The resulting QRS-T angle is oblique and approximates 190 degrees. The area of the vectors for QRS and T in the frontal and horizontal planes is relatively narrow.

ABNORMAL ELECTROCARDIOGRAMS

Heart disorders as revealed by the electrocardiogram appear to cause few deaths in chickens during the first year of life. Serial ECG's were made on 72 adult females (White Leghorns) from 5 months (maturity) to 18 months of age (Sturkie, 1949). Although 27 of the birds died during this period, only 5 percent of these exhibited heart abnormalities that might have caused death. In studies involving approximately 1,000 ECG's of normal chickens of various ages, very few irregularities were observed. Four cases revealed inverted T waves in leads II or III, but these changes were transient. A few cases of premature systoles were also observed. Respiratory diseases, such as Newcastle and coryza, have no effect on the ECG. Phasic sinus arrhythmia, a variation in the discharge of the S-A node associated with respiration, has been reported in the pigeon (Kisch, 1951), but it is rare in the normal chicken (Sturkie).

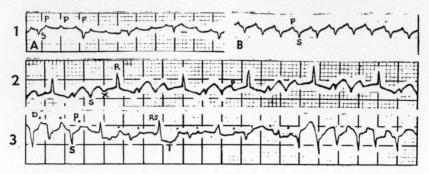

Figure 15. Partial and complete atrioventricular block in the chicken, produced by potassium deficiency in the diet.

1-A, three atrial beats (P's) to 1 ventricular beat (S), or two blocked ventricular beats. The ventricular and auricular rates are approximately 125 and 375 per minute respectively. 1-B, normal ECG of same bird. P and T are fused in these records.

2, one blocked ventricular beat (X) followed by an ectopic beat (R), initiated by the A-V node or ventricules.

3, complete A-V block with idioventricular rhythm. The atria and ventricles are beating independently at rates of approximately 300 and 200 per minute respectively. Since all of the impulses originating in the S-A node do not pass through the A-V node, the ectopic beats from the ventricle constitute a protective mechanism. Black dots indicate P waves. Chart speed, 25 mm. per second. (From Sturkie, *Am. J. Physiol.,* 1950.)

Effects of Mineral and Vitamin Deficiencies on the ECG

Acute potassium deficiency in growing chicks produces a high percentage of abnormal ECG's (70 percent) and 100 percent mortality within 2 to 4 weeks (Sturkie, 1950 and 1952). Most of these disorders are concerned with the rhythm and conduction of the heartbeat. They include, among others, partial and complete atrioventricular block, partial and complete sinoatrial block, sinus arrhythmia and marked sinus slowing, and premature nodal and ventricular systoles. Some examples are shown in Figures 15, 16, and 17. For further details concerning the physiology of such abnormalities, consult textbooks on electrocardiography.

Pathological lesions in the A-V node or bundle or in the S-A node may cause A-V and S-A block. Gross lesions were not observed in the hearts of potassium-deficient chickens, and it appears that the blocks result from a functional rather than a pathological disturbance in conduction. For example, functional A-V block in mammals may result from increased vagal action or tone. In such cases it may be abolished by administration of atropine, a cholinergic blocker. In potassium-deficient chicks, whose ECG's exhibited A-V block and premature systoles, atropine and also diethylaminoethanol were effective in reverting the ECG's to nor-

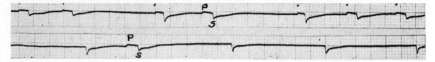

Figure 16. Partial (upper tracing) and complete sinoatrial (S-A) block (lower) with slow heart rate (100 per minute) and mild sinus arrhythmia.

Upper tracing shows examples of normal beats (P's and S's) followed by long pauses, with almost doubled P-P interval, indicating dropped atrial and ventricular beats. Lower tracing shows one normal P and S, followed by no P's and three ectopic beats (complete S-A block). The bird died shortly thereafter. (From Sturkie, *Poultry Sci.,* 1952.)

mal. That the ions of potassium and calcium are concerned in the irritability and activity of cardiac muscle is well known. The requirement of potassium for the bird heart may be higher than for mammals, since, according to Clark (1927), the blood of birds contains more potassium than that of mammals.

Acute thiamine deficiency in pigeons results in sinus arrhythmia, bradycardia, and A-V block (Carter and Drury, 1929), but chronic deficiency of the vitamin rarely produces heart abnormalities (Swank and Bessey, 1941). Sectioning of the vagi or administration of atropine abolishes the disorders, according to Carter and Drury. These and other abnormalities have been observed in thiamine-deficient mammals, (Hundley, Ashburn, and Sebrell, 1945; and others). Deficiencies of niacin, riboflavin, and vitamins A and D have no effect on the ECG of the chicken (Sturkie, unpublished).

Further studies by Sturkie *et al.* (1945) show that deficiencies in the diet of vitamin E alone, of E and B complex vitamins, or of B complex vitamins (mainly thiamine produce abnormal ECG's. (See Figure 18). The principal abnormalities of the vitamin

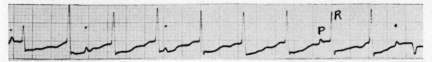

Figure 17. Nodal rhythm and A-V dissociation in the chicken, produced by potassium deficiency in the diet.

The atrial rate (P waves) is very slow (75) and fairly regular, and the nodal rate (R waves) is faster (120). Thus, the S-A node is discharging so slowly that the A-V node initiates its own rhythm, and the two rhythms are independent. Some of the P waves precede, some follow, and the fourth P (not seen) merges with the nodal beats. The sinus impulses reach the A-V junction when the latter is in a refractory state and are not conducted to the ventricles. The last sinus impulse (P) is conducted to the ventricles. (From Sturkie, *Poultry Sci.*, 1952.)

E–deficient birds included right axis deviation, premature ventricular systoles, sinus arrhythmia, and elevated S-T segments. Right axis deviation was rare in thiamine-deficient birds, and the most prominent abnormalities observed were premature ventricular systoles and sinus arrhythmia.

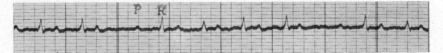

Figure 18. An example of partial atrioventricular (AV) block and prolonged A-V conduction in the electrocardiogram of a chicken. Every fifth ventricular beat (R wave) is blocked. The P-R interval following the dropped beat is shortened, and the interval increases on most successive beats (Wenckebach's phenomenon). The prolonged P-R intervals range from 0.095 immediately following the blocked beat to 0.11 seconds preceding the dropped beat. The heart rate is approximately 370 per minute. Lead 1 chart speed is 75 mm. per second. (From Sturkie *et al.*, Am. J. Vet. Rec. 56:457 [1954].)

REFERENCES

Bonsdorff, R. Von 1950 The electrogram of embryonic heart muscle cultivated *in vitro* and its relation to the electrocardiogram of the embryonic heart. Acta Physiol. Scand. 22 (Suppl. 75).

Carter, C. W., and A. N. Drury 1929 Heart blocks in rice-fed pigeons. J. Physiol. 68:1 (Proc.).

Clark, F. J. 1927 Comparative Physiology of the Heart. The Macmillan Co., New York.

Douglas, S. D. 1960 Correlation between the surface electrocardiogram and air sac morphology in the White Leghorn rooster. Am. J. Physiol. 199:355.

Hundley, J. H., L. L. Ashburn, and W. H. Sebrell 1945 The electrocardiogram in chronic thiamine deficiency in rats. Am. J. Physiol. 144:404.

Kisch, B. 1949 Electrocardiographic studies in sea-gulls. Exp. Med. & Surg. 7:345.

Kisch, B. 1951 The electrocardiogram of birds (chicken, duck, pigeon). Exp. Med. & Surg. 9:103.

Lamb, L. E. 1957 Fundamentals of Electrocardiography and Vectorcardiography. Charles C. Thomas, Springfield, Ill.

Lepeschkin, E. 1951 Modern Electrocardiography, Vol. I. Williams & Wilkins Co., Baltimore.

Lewis, T. 1915 The spread of the excitatory process in the vertebrate heart. V: The bird's heart. Phil. Trans. Royal Soc. London 207:298.

Mangold, E. 1919 Electrographische Untersuchungen des Erregungsverlaufes im Vogelherzen. Arch. ges. Physiol (Pflügers) 175:327.

Sturkie, P. D. 1948 Effects of changes in position of the heart of the chicken on the electrocardiogram. Am. J. Physiol. 154:251.

Sturkie, P. D. 1949 The electrocardiogram of the chicken. Am. J. Vet. Res. 10:168.

Sturkie, P. D. 1950 Abnormal electrocardiograms of chickens produced by potassium deficiency and effects of certain drugs on the abnormalities. Am. J. Physiol. 162:538.

Sturkie, P. D. 1952 Further studies of potassium deficiency in the chicken. Poultry Sci. 31:648.

Sturkie, P. D., and W. G. Hunsaker 1957 Role of estrogen in sex difference of the electrocardiogram of the chicken. Proc. Soc. Exp. Biol. & Med. 94:731.

Sturkie, P. D., E. P. Singsen, L. D. Matterson, A. Kozeff, and E. L. Jungherr 1954 The effects of dietary deficiencies of vitamin E and the B complex vitamins on the electrocardiogram of chickens. J. Vet. Res. 15:457.

Swank, R. L., and O. A. Bessey 1941 Avian thiamine deficiency: Characteristic symptoms and their pathogenesis. J. Nutr. 22:77.

Szepsenwol, J. 1946 A comparison of growth, differentiation, activity, and action currents of heart and skeletal muscle in tissue culture. Anat. Rec. 95:125.

CHAPTER 6

Respiration

ANATOMY OF THE RESPIRATORY APPARATUS

THE respiratory apparatus of birds consists of the lungs and the air passages leading to and from them. The air passages comprise the nasal cavities, pharynx, trachea, and syrinx, the bronchi and their ramifications, and likewise the air sacs and certain of the bones of the body which are pneumatic.

The lungs are small and are attached to the ribs of the thorax; some workers consider them purely passive in action, capable of dilating and contracting only when the ribs and pulmonary diaphragm do so. Others consider them capable of active movements. It is sufficient here to state that the lungs of birds are not capable of the elastic recoil characteristic of the lungs of mammals.

Structure of Lung and Air-Sac System

A great number of workers have reported on the structure of the lungs and air-sac system. For a review of the early work see the monograph of Soum (1896), and for later reviews and contributions consult reports by Locy and Larsell (1916), Dotterweich (1930 and 1936), McLeod and Wagers (1939), Hazelhoff (1951), and Akester (1960).

The trachea bifurcates to form the mesobronchi, or primary bronchi, each of which runs through each lung. From these arise secondary bronchi (ecto- and entobronchi, known by some workers as dorso- and ventrobronchi or as lateral bronchi), and from these in turn arise tertiary bronchi (parabronchi), which branch and anastomose freely (Figures 19 and 21). Thus, the parabronchi

152

are continuous, forming a network of air capillaries, the bronchial circuit, through which course the blood capillaries. Such an arrangement (Figure 22) forms a hexagonal column of almost perfect geometrical design.

The air sacs are connected to the lungs by way of the mesobron-

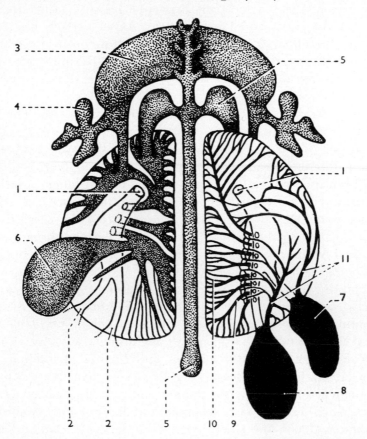

Figure 19. Diagram of lungs, bronchi, and air-sac system of the bird. Left side, ventral view; right side, dorsal view. Black represents the system involved in inspiration, and stippling, that in expiration. 1, mesobronchi; 2, opening of mesobronchi into air sacs; 3, interclavicular sac; 4, diverticula of interclavicular sac; 5, cervical sac; 6, anterior thoracic sac; 7, posterior thoracic sac; 8, abdominal sac; 9, dorsobronchi; 10, parabronchi; 11, recurrent bronchi. (From Portmann, in *Traité de Zoologie,* edited by P. P. Grassé, Tome XV, Figure 200, Masson & Co., Paris, 1950, after Brandes and Hirsch.)

chi and secondary bronchi. Other connections to the lungs are provided by the recurrent bronchi, which bud off from the proximal ends of all of the sacs (except the cervicals) in variable numbers, and extend back to the lungs, where they anastomose with the parabronchi. Thus the sacs are to be thought of as expanded reservoirs on the course of the bronchial circuits, rather than as terminal sacs (Locy and Larsell, 1916). Akester (1960) has stated that the "so-called recurrent bronchi" in adult birds are indistinguishable from ordinary tertiary bronchi. The lungs of flying birds (pigeons, ducks) have considerably more tertiary bronchi than the lungs of chickens.

It is generally agreed that there are 9 air sacs in the chicken, plus their diverticula, which communicate with the lung. They are known by various names. McLeod and Wagers (1939) have listed 4 different terminologies, including one of their own, that have been used in the literature. There are still other variations. The paired sacs are the thoracic sacs and abdominals, or extrathoracic sacs. Most workers have reported that the cervical sacs also are paired in the chicken. There are 2 pairs of thoracic sacs, described by some as the anterior and posterior thoracics. In other terminologies they are known as anterior and posterior intermediates and diaphragmatics. McLeod and Wagers (1939) refer to the posterior intermediate sacs as the lesser abdominals, and to the true abdominal sacs as the greater abdominals. Rigdon *et al.* (1958) reported that the turkey has 7 air sacs, including a single cervical or clavicular sac, 2 paired thoracic sacs, and 2 paired abdominal sacs. Cover (1953), however, describes 9 air sacs in the turkey, designating them as a single anterior thoracic sac, paired posterior thoracic sacs, paired cervical sacs, and paired abdominal sacs. According to Akester (1960), the chicken has 8 air sacs, including a single cervical and interclavicular sac, whereas the pigeon has 9 (including paired cervical sacs), as does the duck. All workers are agreed that the interclavicular sac is single in all species.

Numerous diverticula arise from the interclavicular sac, including in certain species the axillary, suprahumeral, sternal, and subcapsulars. The suprahumeral is the most prominent of these and is responsible for the marked pneumaticity of the humerus of some species of birds (Figure 19).

Pneumatic Bones of the Body

Hunter, who in 1774 described the air sacs and their communications with the bones of the body, stated that for the most part, all except nonflying birds had the following pneumatic bones: femur, humerus, sternum, and vertebral column. He even thought air penetrated the bones of the shank and feet of some birds. A number of workers before and since have held the same views. Baer (1897) stated that the bones of the cranium were not pneumatic and were no different from those of the mammal except that they were more developed.

Kaupp (1918) stated that the abdominal air sacs communicated with the sacrum, the coccygeal vertebrae, the iliac bones, and the femurs.

Groebbels (1932), who reviewed this subject thoroughly, reported considerable variation between species of birds in the number of bones that are pneumatic. He stated that, in general, most small flying birds have few or no pneumatic bones, whereas large flying birds have many pneumatic bones. Thus it would appear that whether or not the bones are pneumatic has little to do with flying ability.

The humerus is pneumatic in most species, and markedly so in the chicken, according to Groebbels (1932). The femur is pneumatic in some species, but not in the chicken (McLeod and Wagers, 1939). More recently, King (1957) has reported that the following bones in the chicken are pneumatic or aerated: most of the cervical vertebrae, all of the throacic vertebrae except the 5th, the pelvic girdle, and the first 2 vertebra ribs; the plate and cranial processes of the sternum; the humerus and distal half of the coracoids.

All of the so-called pneumatic or aerated bones are not connected with the air sacs, but the humerus is, and some birds are able to breathe through the humerus under certain conditions, if the latter is broken and the opening exposed, even though the trachea is occluded.

MECHANICS OF RESPIRATION

A number of workers have described the movements undergone by the thorax and abdomen during respiration. A diagram of the movements of the sternum and ribs on inspiration and expiration is shown in Figure 20. On inspiration (dotted lines) the sternum, coracoid, furcula, and sternal ribs move forward and down. The vertebral ribs are pulled forward and inward. Thus, on inspiration the vertical diameter of the thorax increases greatly and the transverse diameter increases slightly. The lungs are thus expanded on inspiration by the pull of the ribs and sternum, mainly the latter, according to Soum (1896).

Respiratory muscles. The anatomy of these muscles has been described by Soum (1896), Zimmer (1935), and Salt and Zeuthen

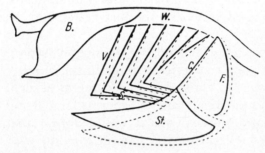

Figure 20. Lateral view of movements of ribs, sternum, coracoids, and furcula in respiration of bird.

Solid lines represent expiration; dotted lines, inspiration. (From Zimmer, *Zoologica,* 1935.)

(1960). Most of these muscles are not necessary for respiration, according to Soum, who studied the effects of sectioning certain of the inspiratory and expiratory muscles. However, his studies were inconclusive and should be repeated. The pectoral muscles do not appear to be necessary for respiration, since transection of these muscles surgically does not inhibit respiration. Likewise, sectioning of the abdominal muscles does not prevent breathing. Curare, however, completely paralyzes all respiratory muscles and causes death, unless artificial respiration is supplied (Sturkie, Joiner, and Freedman, 1962).

Diaphragm. In birds there are two diaphragms, the pulmonary and the abdominal. The pulmonary diaphragm stretches from the dorsal midline and from the ventral surface of the vertebral column to the lateral walls of the thorax. It fuses with the abdominal diaphragm posteriorly. The abdominal diaphragm extends also from the ventral surface of the vertebral column, ventral to the pulmonary diaphragm, to the lateral margins of the sternum in the anterior part of the body, where it is fused to the pericardial sac and reaches posteriorly to the synsacrum (Salt and Zeuthen, 1960).

Little is known about the function of the avian diaphragms. According to Soum (1896), the principal function of the pulmonary diaphragm is to remain tense and stretched over the surface of the lung. This is accomplished by the thin strips of muscle bordering the periphery of the membrane, which are attached to the ribs. In inspiration, when the lung dilates the diaphragm expands; in expiration it contracts whenever the lungs do. However, if this diaphragm is paralyzed by sectioning the spinal cord, breathing still continues (Soum).

The abdominal diaphragm would appear to have no function, since it has been sectioned or destroyed without affecting respiration (see Soum, 1896; and Winterstein, 1921).

Duration of the Phases and Respiratory Rate

The following terms are used to designate the types and rates of breathing: (1) eupnea, the state of ordinary quiet breathing; (2) dyspnea, labored breathing of different degrees; (3) hyperpnea, a moderate increase in rate and/or amplitude of breathing; and (4) polypnea, characterized by rapid, shallow breathing, or panting. In apnea (5) there is a transient cessation of breathing.

The respiratory frequency varies within and between species, depending upon body size, excitement, and other factors. Bert (1870) and Groebbels (1932) presented tables upon the respiratory frequencies of many birds. A compilation of data from their tables and other sources is shown in Table 30 (see also Table 31). In general, the larger the bird the fewer the respirations per minute. The condor and the canary, for example, have respiratory frequencies of 6 and 100 respectively. The frequency is higher for females than males.

Exposure to high ambient temperature, and the resulting hyperthermia, produce panting. With increasing body temperature in the chicken, respiration rate increases and reaches a peak of 140–170 at body temperatures of 43.5 to 44.5°C. (Frankel, Hollands, and Weiss, 1962). The rate was lower in heat-adapted

Table 30. Respiratory rates of birds (per minute)

Species	Male	Sex not stated	Female	Author
Canary		96–120		Groebbels (1932)
Pigeon		25–30		Zander (Groebbels)
Domestic duck		60–70		"
"		32		Hepke (Groebbels)
"	42		110	Kaupp (1923)
Domestic goose		13		Loer (Groebbels)
"	20		40	Kaupp
Domestic turkey		13.4		Loer (Groebbels)
"	28		49	Kaupp
Chicken	20.7		36.7	"
"	12		20	Bert & Heubel (Groebbels)
"	18		31	Stubel (Groebbels)

birds, however, than in nonadapted ones (Weiss, Frankel, and Hollands, 1962). Similar results were obtained in the pigeon by Von Saalfeld (1936), except that respiratory rates were much higher, reaching 510 per minute at a body temperature of 43.6°C.

Duration of inspiration and expiration has been studied by a number of investigators with varying results. Bert (1870) maintained that in the duck there were no true inspiratory or expiratory pauses; he found that the movements followed each other rapidly, but that expiration was slightly longer than inspiration. Huxley also found expiration to be longer in the duck (Winterstein, 1921). Baer (1896) on the pigeon, Soum (1896) on the pigeon and duck, and Kaupp (1923) on the duck, observed inspiration to be of longer duration than expiration. Soum supposed that these differences were due to a partial closure of the glottis, since after tracheotomy, duration of the phases was the same. Kaupp found that in the female chicken the phases were of about equal duration, but that expiration was longer than inspiration in the cock. Expiration is longer than inspiration in both sexes of chickens, according to Graham (1940). In turkeys, inspiration is longer in both males and females (Kaupp). Inspiration in the goose is three times as long as expiration, but in the gander the phases are of the same duration.

CIRCULATION OF AIR IN LUNGS AND AIR SACS

A number of viewpoints have been expressed in the literature as to the manner in which air circulates through the lungs and air sacs, and as to the influence of the latter on pulmonary ventilation. Shortly after Harvey described the air sacs in 1651, Perrault elaborated the antagonism theory, which holds that the thoracic sacs expand on inspiration, while the interclavicular, cervical, and abdominal sacs contract during inspiration. A tenet of this theory is that the lungs are ventilated with fresh air in both inspiration and expiration, thus providing for a more efficient exchange of gases. Mery in 1869 and others since claimed to have demonstrated this so-called antagonism (see Soum, 1896). By placing a bird on its back and arranging recording tambours on the thorax and the abdomen, tracings of these movements were observed to run in opposite directions. Since these movements supposedly represented pressure changes within, it was concluded that the air sacs in these areas also behaved antagonistically. Soum demonstrated conclusively that the movements of the sternum and abdomen are not normally antagonistic. The apparent antagonism reported by earlier workers was based upon records taken on birds lying always on their backs, Soum reported. He showed that when the records were taken on birds in the normal position, standing or prone, the so-called antagonism disappeared. In accordance with the antagonism theory, if the abdominal sacs are destroyed or their action suppressed, this should not affect the volume of air traversing the trachea and the lungs on inspiration, since such sacs are considered expiratory. However, destruction of these sacs in the duck and pigeon as described by Soum (1896) actually decreased the volume of inspired air by approximately 20 percent. Further evidence against the antagonism theory is the fact that pressure changes in the lungs and air sacs are synchronous.

Direction of Air Movement

The direction of air movement in the lungs, in the air sacs and in the primary, secondary, and tertiary bronchi (parabronchi) on inspiration and expiration has been studied in a number of ways. Some investigators have studied the O_2 and CO_2 content of the various sacs, and have inferred from these studies how the air moves in the system on inspiration and expiration. Others have used colored material, which upon inhalation was carried through the system, and the paths traversed by it could be determined upon autopsy. Others have used radiopaque material as the inhalant, and have studied its movement with radiophotographs, and some have made glass models of the lung and air-sac system and have attempted to simulate normal respiration. Some have introduced foreign gases such as hydrogen (Zeuthen, 1942) and nitrogen (Shepard *et al.*, 1959) into the inspired air and determined their contents in the various sacs.

Unfortunately, more heat than light has been generated upon this subject, and more recent speculations (Salt and Zeuthen, 1960; Shepard *et al.*, 1959; and Cohn *et al.*, 1963) have not helped.

Much of the older work was reviewed by Sturkie in 1954 and more recently by Salt and Zeuthen (1960). Only the more recent and pertinent work will be discussed here. Dotterweich (1936), using a glass model of the lungs and air sacs, concluded that the parabronchi received air on inspiration but not on expiration. Inspired air was distributed to the dorsobronchi, ventrobronchi, and laterobronchi, and to the abdominal sacs directly from the mesobronchi. The posterior and anterior thoracic sacs were likewise filled on inspiration, but part of the air in the anterior sacs was vitiated and part was fresh. On expiration all of the air sacs contracted and emptied air into the mesobronchi.

Hazelhoff (1951) studied air movement in the bird lung (crow, chicken, pigeon, heron) by injecting charcoal into the air sacs and tracing the substance later. In other experiments, he injected a liquid containing starch granules into the trachea, lungs, and air sacs of a dead bird. The skin was removed at the point where the large dorsobronchi run beneath the surface of the intercostal muscles. A pump was then attached to the trachea, and inspiration and expiration were induced. By suitable magnification of the dorsobronchi, he was able to observe the movements of the starch granules in inspiration and expiration. In inspiration and expiration the starch granules moved in the same direction, toward the parabronchi (*d-p-v* system, Figure 21). The bird was intact, so Hazelhoff assumed that the volume changes in the various air sacs were approximately the same as in the live animal.

On the basis of these experiments, and of others with a glass model of the lung, Hazelhoff concluded that during expiration,

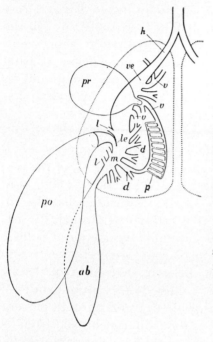

Figure 21. Diagram of the right lung of a bird (ventral aspect).

The outline of the lung is indicated by a dotted line. Of the anterior air sacs, only the anterior thoracic sac is shown. The recurrent bronchi are not reproduced. Only the parabronchi arising from one ventrobronchus and one dorsobronchus are shown as a series of connected, parallel tubes. h, primary bronchus; ve, vestibulum; m, mesobronchus; v, ventrobronchi; p, parabronchi; d, dorsobronchi; l, laterobronchi; pr, prethoracic or anterior sac; po, postthoracic sac; ab, abdominal sac; le, "guiding dam." (From Hazelhoff, *Poultry Sci.*, 30:3, 1951.)

air was forced out of the posterior sacs (which have recurrent bronchi) into the dorsobronchi, and from there to the parabronchi, ventrobronchi, vestibulum, primary bronchi, and trachea. He explained that it was possible for the air to pass in the same direction in both phases of respiration, without the operation of valves (which have not been demonstrated) because of the peculiar structure and arrangement of the bronchi of the lungs. The guiding dam (see *le* in Figure 21) during expiration directs the air from the posterior thoracic sacs (and presumably from the abdominal sacs, although they are not mentioned) toward the dorsobronchi.

During inspiration, the other side of the dam also directs the air toward the dorsobronchi.

According to Salt and Zeuthen (1960), the theories of Hazelhoff, Dotterweich, and others apparently sprang from the conviction that since the primary and secondary bronchi are larger than the parabronchi, all the air will flow through them and none through the parabronchi unless some special directing mechanism is operative. These assumptions are incorrect, according to Salt and Zeuthen, who favor the view that the air flow is partially through the parabronchi during both inspiration and expiration, and that its direction of air flow reverses with each phase. The degree of parabronchial flow is controlled both by aerodynamic forces and by the variation in passage diameter brought about by contraction and relaxation of parabronchial muscle.

Most determinations on the O_2 and CO_2 content of the air sacs (see later section) indicate that CO_2 content of the anterior sacs is greater than that of the posterior sacs, and that the O_2 of the posterior sacs, particularly the abdominal sacs, is almost as high as in atmospheric air. This suggests to many investigators that the anterior air sacs receive vitiated air that had passed through the *d-p-v* system, but that the abdominal sacs must receive most of their air directly through the mesobronchi (pure air). However, Zeuthen (see Salt and Zeuthen, 1960) believes that much of the air reaching the air sacs on inspiration must do so via the parabronchi. He estimated that during inspiration, from 29 to 48 percent of air going to the air sacs traverses the parabronchi, and from 38 to 67 percent of the expired air passes through the parabronchi. Thus, the higher expiratory flow of air through the lungs can be explained by an aerodynamic principle. Dissections of vinyl casts of chicken lungs indicated that the secondary bronchi, including those at the posterior thoracic sacs, leave the primary bronchus at an anteriorly directed angle, so that the openings of these secondary bronchi are directed posteriorly (as Hazelhoff also indicated). Zeuthen speculates that on expiration, air-sac air that is blown posteriorly from the openings of the secondary bronchi increases pressure in the posterior end of the mesobronchus. This increased pressure might divert a larger percentage of air from the posterior thoracic and abdominal air sacs to the saccobronchi and parabronchi.

Shepard *et al.* (1959) determined the partial pressures of O_2 and CO_2 in anterior and posterior thoracic, cervical, abdominal and interclavicular sacs, and reported no differences among them. The same workers found that pCO_2 and pO_2 were approximately 40 and 100 mm. Hg respectively, varied little during the respiratory cycle, and differed little from expired air. Based upon their results, which are contrary to all other data on gas analyses of air sacs, these authors conclude that their results suggest that the air on inspiration goes to main bronchus, to parabronchi and air capillaries, to air sacs, and thence back to main bronchus, via secondary bronchi which have no gas-exchanging surface, and that valving is virtually complete. These results add confusion to an already confused picture.

DIFFUSION OF AIR IN PARABRONCHIAL CAPILLARIES

Zeuthen (1942) and Hazelhoff (1951) calculated that the diffusion of gases in the air capillaries was sufficient to satisfy the birds' requirements at rest and in flight. Hazelhoff's calculations were based on certain assumptions and measurements of crow's lung.

If we look at a 1 mm. segment of a parabronchus 0.5 mm. wide, and its air capillaries [Figure 22], it is clear that the average diffusion distance amounts to 0.3 to 0.4 mm. The total surface of the air capillaries growing out of the segment of the parabronchus is approximately equal to the inner surface of cylinder *a* [see Figure 22]. If the radius of *a* is 0.25 mm. and that of *b* (which for the sake of simplicity, we can think of as a cylinder) is 0.5 mm., then for each mm. length of parabronchus, that is of each 0.25 mm.^{3} of lung volume, there is a system of air capillaries with a total surface of 0.5 mm.^{2} and a diffusion area of 2 mm.^{2} per mm.^{3} of lung volume.

If we estimate the volume of a crow's lungs at 10 cc. and the average diffusion area at 2 mm.^{2} per mm.^{3} of lung volume, the total diffusion area is then 200 cm.^{2} We further assume that the diffusion distance is 0.25 mm. According to Krogh's diffusion coefficient (1941), at a pressure difference of 1 atm. per cm., 11 cc. of O_2 per minute diffuses through a surface of 200 cm.[2]

This is about the pressure difference prevailing in the parabronchi, according to Hazelhoff.

Although diffusion alone could provide sufficient gas exchange, it is likely that other factors are also involved, such as pulsations

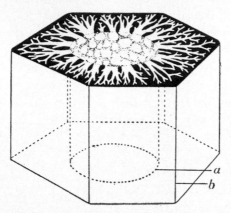

Figure 22. Diagram of a segment of a parabronchus with the air capillaries growing out of it.

The parabronchus (a) and surrounding area are always in the shape of an irregular, five- or six-sided prism (b). The stippled network in the section of the parabronchus represents the ingression of the air capillaries. (From Hazelhoff, *Poultry Sci.,* 30:3 1951.)

of the parabronchi which may extend or shorten the proximal portion of the air capillaries (Salt and Zeuthen).

RESPIRATION DURING FLIGHT

Hazelhoff (1951) concluded that the supply and rate of diffusion of oxygen in the lungs are ample for the requirements of the bird in sustained flight. Krogh (1941), in discussing the heat production of birds in flight, stated that a higher rate of ventilation appears to be necessary to eliminate the extra heat generated than to obtain necessary oxygen. This statement is based upon a consideration of the data and calculations of Zeuthen (1942), who calculated that the heat production of a pigeon flying at the rate of 43.5 miles per hour would be approximately 27 times as great as the heat production at rest, and that 17.8 kcalories per hour would be expended in overcoming the resistance of the air. These calculations have not been verified by actual experiment.

Some investigators have assumed that ventilation of the lungs was synchronized with wing movements in flight, and that downstroke of the wings occurred in expiration, but Zimmer (1935) reported that downstroke was associated with inspiration.

PRESSURE CHANGES IN THE RESPIRATORY APPARATUS

In the thoracic and abdominal cavities of the mammal, which are distinctly separated, the pressures are different. The pressure in the thoracic cavity is ordinarily negative, owing to the elastic recoil of the lungs. In the bird the lungs are fixed and there is no analogous thoracic cavity, since the thoracic and abdominal cavities are not distinctly separated but are continuous. Thus the pressure changes in them should be and are the same. In the respiratory apparatus, the lungs, bronchi, air sacs, and pneumatic bones are intercommunicable; hence we speak not of intrathoracic pressure in the bird, but only of pressure in the lungs and air passages, or intrapulmonic pressure.

Evidence from Baer (1896), Soum (1896), François-Franck (1906), and Victorow (1909) demonstrates conclusively that pressure changes in the air passages are synchronous in the duck, pigeon, and crow, as well as in the chicken (Sturkie, unpublished). In inspiration, pressures in the trachea, the air sacs, and even the humerus become slightly negative and on expiration slightly positive. The negative pressure on inspiration ranges from -4 to -6.5 millimeters of water for the trachea and the thoracic and abdominal sacs of the pigeon, and positive pressure on expiration was of about the same magnitude (Victorow). The pressures in the air passages of the crow were considerably higher.

Tidal and Minute Volume

Tidal air, or the amount of air inspired or expired in a normal respiration, has been determined in a number of birds (Table 31).

Tidal volume varies with respiratory rate. In a panting bird with increased respiratory rate, tidal volume is decreased but minute volume is increased. It can also be observed from the table that minute volume in the chicken may increase threefold in hyperthermia, but that the increase in the heat-adapted bird made hyperthermic is considerably less.

Table 31. Tidal air and minute volume of respiration of birds

Species	Experimental conditions	Respiratory rate per minute	Tidal volume	Minute volume ml.	Reference
Duck	Standing (normal)		38	—	Soum (1896)
"	"		35	—	Scharnke (1938)
"	"		38	—	Vos (1934)
Pigeon	"		5.2	—	Soum (1896)
"	"		4.5	—	Scharnke (1938)
"	Body temp. 41.7°C.	46	4.0	185	Saalfeld (1936)
"	" 42.0	140	2.5	350	"
"	" 42.6	380	1.6	610	"
Chicken, normal	" 41.5	37	15.4	554	Weiss et al. (1962)
Chicken, heat-adapted	" 41.4	28	14.8	397	"
Chicken, hyperthermic[1]	" 42–43.0	68.4	14.0	962	"
"	" 44–45.5	138.0	11.3	1565	"
Chicken, Hyperthermic[2]	"	101.0	11.8	1191	"

[1] Not adapted.
[2] Heat-adapted.

The proportion of inspired air that passes on to the air sacs was estimated by Zeuthen (1942), who introduced H_2 in the inspired air and determined the content of the gas in the air sacs. Approximately 80 percent of the total inspired air goes to the abdominal air sacs, 8 to 15 percent to the anterior thoracic sacs, and 3 to 13 percent to the posterior thoracic sacs.

The volume of inspired air is some where between 8 and 15 percent of the total volume of the air sacs (see Table 32).

Volume of Air in Lungs and Air Sacs

The total respiratory volume of the live bird can be measured by the method of gas dilution, although it is impossible to determine directly the volume of air in the individual air sacs or lungs in the live bird during a given inspiration or expiration; but such volumes may be estimated in the dead bird by filling the lungs and air sacs with molten pariffin (Vos, 1934), with metal (Scharnke, 1938), with cocoa butter (Victorow, 1909), or with other substances (Zeuthen, 1942; King and Payne, 1962). Vos claimed to have inflated the lungs and air sacs of the dead bird to the extent that they were expanded in a normal inspiration. For example, he inflated the lungs and then closed the trachea, following which he froze the bird. He believed that the sacs and lungs were frozen in the normal inspiratory position. He then open the air sacs and filled them with melted paraffin. It is doubtful whether normal conditions were thus simulated; his volumes, particularly for the abdominal air sacs, appear high, and this is true also for the figures of King and Payne (see Table 32). Victorow (1909) states that the lungs and air sacs of the pigeon probably were expanded more than normally, since in a normal inspiration the volume of the abdominal sacs would have been about half the figure shown in the table. One may observe in the opened live bird that the abdominal sacs are never inflated maximally in a normal inspiration, and that the pressure in them is usually low. The remaining sacs are probably expanded relatively more on normal inspiration than are the abdominal sacs. The volume of the anterior thoracic sacs is greater than the posterior thoracic sacs in the pigeon and chicken, but less in the duck.

Table 32. Volume of air (in cc.) in lungs and air sacs

	Lungs	Dead space	Inter-clavicular	Cervical	Thoracic		Abdominal	Reference
					Anterior	Posterior		
Pigeon	8	—	8	2	10	4	20	Victorow (1909)
"		—	—		5.9	3.6	19.9	Scharnke (1938)
Duck		—	53	—	24	57	145	Vos (1934)
Chicken	3	1.6	9	—	17	7.5	62	Zeuthen (1942)
" Male	68	—	79	26	88	29	181	King & Payne (1962*)
" Female	33	—	42	18	48	22	112	King & Payne (1962*)

* Maximum capacities.

Vital capacity. Bert (1870) determined what he regarded as vital capacity of the air sacs and lungs in the chicken and the duck by blowing as much air into the lung through the trachea as possible and measuring the amount expired. The volume expired was 820 cc. for the chicken and 843 cc. for the duck.

ROLE OF THE AIR SACS IN RESPIRATION

That the air sacs increase pulmonary ventilation and the exchange of gases in the lungs has been discussed previously. The sacs, however, are evidently not indispensable structures because respiration continues after destruction of all of them, although tidal air and pulmonary ventilation are decreased. Various other functions have been ascribed to the air sacs.

Many of the earlier workers believed that the air sacs decreased the specific gravity of the body and thus facilitated flying (see Winterstein, 1921). This view has been discredited by Baer (1897) and Victorow (1909).

A belief held by a number of workers, particularly teleologists, is that the air sacs help regulate body temperature by cooling or warming inspired air. Cowles and Nordstrom (1946) believed that the abdominal air sacs, which are in contact with the testes, might lower the temperature in the testes, and thus facilitate spermatogenesis; however, this view has not been confirmed by more recent experiments (Williams, 1958; Hering, Booth, and Johnson, 1960).

That the air sacs do humidify inspired air was demonstrated by Soum (1896), who measured the water vapor in the expired air of pigeons and other birds before and after destruction of the air sacs. From 15 to 30 percent less water vapor was exhaled after the sacs were destroyed, but much of this decrease was due to the decreased intake of air (tidal air) following the operation, and only a small part actually represented decreased humidification of the air sacs, according to Soum.

Soum did not record body temperature after destruction of the air sacs, but Victorow (1909) did. After puncturing and plugging several of the air sacs of the pigeon, and after stressing the bird by stimulation of the brachial nerves, he observed a rise in body temperature of 2.6° to 3.2°C., as compared to 0.7° to 0.9° in the control birds. In view of the small number of birds (2 treated and 2 control) and other conditions of the experiment, these results do not appear to be conclusive.

In preliminary, unpublished experiments on adult chickens not subjected to stress, with the air sacs destroyed, Sturkie found no change in body temperature that could be attributed to the operation. Further studies are needed on the effects of air sac destruction upon body temperature of birds, particularly those in flight.

CONTROL OF RESPIRATION

Relation of vagus nerves to respiration. Most workers agree that unilateral vagotomy results momentarily in moderate slowing of breathing, usually followed by normal breathing. Bilateral vagotomy usually slows respiration in the duck, pigeon, and chicken (Bert, 1870; Orr and Watson, 1913; Grunwald, 1904; Grober, 1899; Graham, 1940; Hiestand and Randall, 1942; and others). The rate may drop as low as 4 to 7 per minute in the chicken, pigeon, and duck, but usually increases and may return to normal within 7 to 30 minutes, or within 2 to 3 days (Hiestand and Randall, 1942; Couvreur, 1891). This suggests that the respiratory center is stimulated by other receptors as well as those related to the vagi. In some cases, the rate may remain slow and the bird (pigeon) may die in 2 to 3 days following the operation (Knoll; see Winterstein). Recent work by Sina (1958) in the pigeon indicates that after bilateral vagotomy there is a transient respiratory standstill, occurring in either the expiratory or the mid position. Cutting the first vagus usually slowed the rate to one-half to one-third of normal; shortly thereafter the rate increased somewhat, but never fully recovered. After transection of the second vagus there was a further reduction in rate and prolongation of the expiratory position, and amplitude was markedly reduced. Cooling the vagus slowed rate and amplitude.

Stimulation of the central end of the vagus with a weak to moderate stimulus usually increases respiration in most species (chicken, pigeon, and duck), but strong stimulation usually inhibits respiration in the inspiratory position, momentarily although some have reported inhibition in the expiratory position (see Winterstein).

Orr and Watson (1913) were able to produce inhibition in only one bird (duck) by strong central stimulation of the vagus. Strong central stimulation of both vagi may cause death in the duck and hen (Bert, 1870).

The report of Sina (1958) indicates that the results obtained after central vagal stimulation depend in part on the type and frequency of stimuli. The response to low frequency stimulation was usually an increased rate with a shift of the expiratory position towards the inspiratory side. Higher frequency stimulation resulted in slowing of rate with a tendency for inhibition in the expiratory position.

Panting in the chicken is abolished by sectioning of the vagi (Hiestand and Randall, 1942), but not in the pigeon (Von Saalfeld, 1936); however, the respiratory rate may be somewhat diminished.

Seifert (see Winterstein, 1921) demonstrated that artificial inflation of the lungs inhibits inspiration and stimulates expiration, and that withdrawal of air from the lungs inhibits expiration and stimulates inspiration; but this does not occur after bilateral vagotomy. Graham (1940) stated that deflation of the lung of the bird had no effect on respiration. Distention of the lungs abolished panting in rabbits, but not in the duck (Hiestand and Randall, 1941 and 1942) except when the latter was anesthetized with sodium amytal. Thus, it appears that birds show the Hering-Breuer reflex (see also Sina). There are two kinds of afferent fibers in the vagi with their receptors in the lungs, which are stimulated by alternate contraction and expansion of the lungs and thorax. Expansion stimulates expiratory fibers and contraction stimulates inspiratory fibers.

Fedde, Burger, and Kitchell (1961) concluded that the Hering-Breuer reflex was not important in maintaining the normal respiratory rhythm in the chicken. They reported that sudden expansion of the lung parenchyma by unidirectional air flow did not cause reflex expiration. We have made similar observations (unpublished); with adequate ventilation rate (unidirectionally) no reflex respiratory movements were noted, but if ventilation rate was decreased to 200 cc. or less per minute, reflex respiratory movements were induced (see also Chapter 3). Whether the neural pathways are via the vagus or intercostal nerves has not been determined.

Respiratory Center

There is some evidence that the respiratory center is located in the medulla of birds (pigeon) as it is in mammals (Figure 23). Saalfeld (1936) reported that transection of the medulla in the pigeon inhibited respiration. Others (see Winterstein, 1921) believed also that the respiratory centers of the duck and chicken were located in the medulla, but their experiments were far from conclusive.

Saalfeld also located a specific panting center in the anterior-

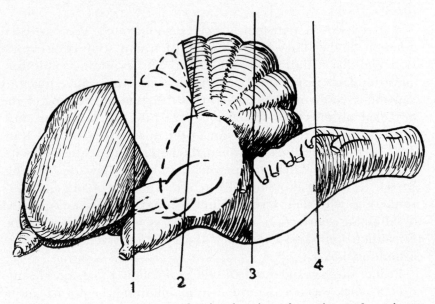

Figure 23. Brain of pigeon showing location of panting and respiratory centers.

The panting center (area between 1 and 2) is in the interbrain, and the respiratory center (area between 3 and 4) is in the medulla. (Modified from Saalfeld, Z. *vergl. Physiol.,* 1936.)

dorsal region of the midbrain (interbrain) of the pigeon (Figure 23). Transection of this region abolished panting. Respiration rate (about 500 per minute) dropped to 60 per minute after transection. After panting was abolished by transection of the panting center, it could be induced again by injections of lobeline (a stimulant of the central nervous system), suggesting that the center in the medulla must respond to the stimulant but not the center in the midbrain. Thus he concluded that although panting is ordinarily controlled by the panting center, this function could be taken over by the true respiratory center. Destruction of the cerebrum of the pigeon does not affect respiration, according to Saalfeld and also Rogers (1928).

The respiratory center of mammals is sensitive to changes in temperature, pH of blood, and other stimuli. The same sensitivity has been demonstrated in the bird, but it is not always clear whether it is the center in the medulla, the panting center, or both that responds to these stimuli. Further research is needed on this point. In mammals, increased CO_2 tension in the blood stimulates the respiratory center, but Orr and Watson (1913) showed that when the duck (*Anas boscas*) breathed CO_2, respiration was inhibited. Dooley and Koppanyi (1929) stated that this occurred because the concentration of CO_2 inspired was so high that it irritated the nasal pathways and therefore probably stimulated inhibitory receptors reflexly. When CO_2 was introduced through the opened humerus, or when the nasal pathways were anesthetized, respiration was stimulated. Hiestand and Randall (1941), who studied the effect of CO_2 inhalation in 11 species of birds, found considerable variation in the responses. In some species CO_2 caused inhibition, in others stimulation; in many cases the results depended upon whether an anesthetic had been used. When the chicken breathes 10 percent CO_2, respiration is stimulated, but amplitude is increased rather than rate. When the chicken is anesthetized with sodium pentobarbital, CO_2 has no effect, but with other anesthesia, CO_2 inhibits or slows respiration. Thus, the respiratory center of birds, like that of mammals, is sensitive to changes in pH of the blood, and the variable responses observed with and without anesthetics indicate that the center is also stimulated or inhibited by anesthetics. Intravenous injections of CO_2 in the duck also increase respiration.

That the respiratory center is also sensitive to postural changes is suggested by the fact that stretching the neck of the duck, experimentally or naturally, as in diving, produces apnea (see also Chapter 3).

The temperature of the blood flowing to the head and to the respiratory and panting centers affects respiration (see Chapter 7).

Emotional disturbances, the result of sudden noises, produce inspiratory gasps and increase respiration reflexively.

REFERENCES

Akester, A. R. 1960 The comparative anatomy of the respiratory pathways in the domestic fowl, pigeon, and domestic duck. J. Anat. 94:488.

Baer, M. 1896 Über die Atmung der Vögel. Jhft. Ver. Vaterl. Naturk. Württemb. 52:123.

Baer, M. 1897 Zur physiologischen Bedeutung des Luftsackes bei Vögeln. Biol. Zbl. 17:282.

Bert, P. 1870 Leçons sur la physiologie comparée de la respiration. Paris.

Cohn, J. D., L. Burke, and H. Markesbery 1963 Respiration in unanesthetized geese. Fed. Proc. 22 (2), part I:1412.

Couvreur, E. 1891 Influence du pneumogastrique sur les phénomènes mécaniques et chimiques de la respiration chez les oiseaux. Ann. Soc. Linn. Lyon 38:33.

Cover, M. S. 1953 Gross and microscopic anatomy of the respiratory system of the turkey. III: The air sacs. Am. J. Vet. Res. 14:239.

Cowles, R. B., and A. Nordstrom 1946 A possible avian analogue of the scrotum. Science 104:586.

Dooley, M. S., and J. Koppanyi 1929 The control of respiration in the domestic duck (Anas boscas). J. Pharma. and Exp. Thera. 36:507.

Dotterweich, H. 1930 Versuch über den Weg der Atemluft in der Vogellunge. Z. vergl. Physiol. 11:271.

Dotterweich, H. 1936 Die Atmung der Vögel. Z. vergl. Physiol. 23:744.

Fedde, M. R., R. E. Burger, and R. Kitchell 1961 The influence of the vagus nerve on respiration. Poultry Sci. Abstracts, p. 34.

François-Franck, M. 1906 Études graphiques et photographiques de mécanique respiratoire comparée. Comp. Rend. Soc. Biol. 2:174.

Frankel, H., K. G. Hollands, and H. S. Weiss 1962 Respiratory and circulatory responses of hyperthermic chickens. Arch. Int. Physiol. Biochem. 70:555.

Graham, J. D. 1940 Respiratory reflexes in the fowl. J. Physiol. 97:525.

Grober, J. A. 1899 Über die Atmungsinnervation der Vögel. Pflüg. Arch. 76:427.

Groebbels, F. 1932 Der Vogel, Erster Band, Atmungswelt und Nahrungswelt. Verlag von Gebrüder Borntraeger, Berlin.

Grunwald, J. 1904 Plethysmographische Untersuchungen über die Atmung der Vögel. Arch. Physiol. Suppl. B., p. 182.

Hazelhoff, E. H. 1951 Structure and function of the lung of birds. Poultry Sci. 30:3. This is a reprint of an article originally published in Verslag van de gewone vergaderingen der Afdeling Natuurkunde van de Nederlanse Akademie van Wetenschappen 52:391 (1943).

Hering, R. A., N. H. Booth, and R. M. Johnson 1960 Thermoregulatory effects of abdominal air sacs on spermatogenesis in domestic fowl. Amer. J. Physiol. 198:1343.

Hiestand, W. A., and W. C. Randall 1941 Species differentiation in the respiration of birds following carbon dioxide administration and the location of inhibitory receptors in the upper respiratory tract. J. Cell. Comp. Physiol. 17:333.

Hiestand, W. A., and W. C. Randall 1942 Influence of proprioceptive vagal afferents on panting and accessor panting movements in mammals and birds. Am. J. Physiol. 138:12.

Kaupp, B. F. 1918 Anatomy of the Fowl. W. B. Saunders, Philadelphia.

Kaupp, B. F. 1923 The respiration of fowls. Vet. Med. 18:36.

King, A. S. 1957 The aerated bones of Gallus domesticus. Acta Anat. 31:220.

King, A. S., and D. C. Payne 1962 The maximum capacities of the lungs and air sacs of Gallus domesticus. J. Anat. 96:495.

Krogh, A. 1941 The Comparative Physiology of Respiratory Mechanisms. University of Pennsylvania Press, Philadelphia.

Locy, W. A., and O. Larsell 1916 The embryology of the bird's lung. II: The air sacs and recurrent bronchi. Am. J. Anat. 20:1.

McLeod, W. M., and R. P. Wagers 1939 The respiratory system of the chicken. J. Am. Vet. Med. Assoc. 95:59.

Orr, J. B., and A. Watson 1913 Study of the respiratory mechanism in the duck. J. Physiol. 46:337.

Rigdon, R. H., T. M. Ferguson, G. L. Feldman, and J. R. Couch 1958 Air sacs in the turkey. Poultry Sci. 37:53.

Rogers, F. R. 1928 Studies on the brain stem. XI: The effects of artificial stimulation and of traumatism of the avian thalamus. Am. J. Physiol. 86:639.

Saalfeld, F. E. von 1936 Untersuchungen über das Hacheln bei Tauben. Z. vergl. Physiol. 23:727.

Salt, G. W. and Erik Zeuthen 1960 The respiratory system, Chapter X in A. J. Marshall, Biology and Comparative Physiology of Birds. Academic Press, New York.

Scharnke, H. 1938 Experimentelle Beiträge zur Kenntnis der Vogelatmung. Z. vergl. Physiol. 25:548.

Shepard, R. H., B. K. Sladen, N. Peterson, and T. Enns 1959 Path taken by gases through the respiratory system of the chicken. J. Applied Physiol. 14:733.

Sina, M. P. 1958 Vagal control of respiration as studied in the pigeon. Helvitica Physiol. et Pharm. Acta 16:58.

Soum, M. 1896 Recherches physiologiques sur l'appareil respiratoire des oiseaux. Ann. Univ. Lyon 28:1.

Sturkie, P. D., P. Joiner, and S. L. Freedman 1962 Role of the "bearing down" reflex on oviposition in the chicken. Endocrinol. 70:221.

Victorow, C. 1909 Die kühlende Wirkung der Luftsäcke bei Vögeln. Pflügers Arch. 126:300.

Vos, H. F. 1934 Über den Web der Atemluft in der Entenlunge. Z. vergl. Physiol. 21:552.

Weiss, H. S., H. Frankel, and K. G. Hollands 1962 The effect of extended exposure to a hot environment on the response of the chicken to hyperthermia. Canad. J. Biochem. Physiol. 41:805.

Williams, D. D. 1958 A histological study of the effects of subnormal temperature on the testis of the fowl. Anat. Rec. 130:225.

Winterstein, H. 1921 Handbuch der Vergleichenden Physiologie, Volume 1, Part II. Verlag von Gustav Fischer, Jena.

Zeuthen, E. 1942 The ventilation of the respiratory tract in birds. Kgl. Danske Videnskab. Selskab. Biol. Medd. 17:1.

Zimmer, K. 1935 Beiträge zur Mechanik der Atmung bei den Vögeln in Stand und Flug. Zoologica 3:1.

CHAPTER 7

Transport of the Blood Gases

A VERY small quantity of oxygen in the blood is in physical solution. The remainder combines with hemoglobin to form oxyhemoglobin:

$$Hb + O_2 \leftrightarrows HbO_2$$

The tissues get oxygen by a drop in partial pressure or tension in the blood, which releases some of the gas in combination with hemoglobin. This will be shown later when oxygen dissociation curves are considered. Very little carbon dioxide is carried by the blood as free CO_2. It exists mainly as carbonic acid and sodium bicarbonate. Much depends upon the correct balance between carbonic acid and sodium bicarbonate, if the pH of the blood is to be maintained within physiological limits.

Our present knowledge concerning the exchange of gases between the lungs and blood, and between the blood and tissues, is based upon determinations of oxygen, carbon dioxide, and nitrogen in the air of the lungs, and in the blood and tissues. These include analysis of the oxygen and carbon dioxide content, capacity, tension and percent saturation in arterial and venous blood, and some of these on the gases in alveolar air and the tissues.

Capacity of blood for a gas represents the maximum amount of the gas (ml./100 ml.) that the blood can hold or combine with under given conditions of pressure, temperature, and pH. Under such conditions the blood is saturated and no more gas can either be bound or transported. The capacity is influenced by the total amount of hemoglobin present in the blood, and also by the affinity of the particular type of hemoglobin for O_2. For example, at the same partial pressure and conditions of temperature and pH, the capacity varies considerably between and within species. Species requiring a higher partial pressure of O_2 to saturate their blood have a lesser affinity for oxygen; the degree of affinity may be expressed as the degree of saturation at a given partial pressure of oxygen (pO_2), or the partial pressure (mm. Hg) required to give 50 percent saturation, thus p_{50} or $t\frac{1}{2}$.

The atmosphere at sea level exerts a pressure of 760 mm. Hg. It is composed of approximately 20 percent oxygen, 79 percent nitrogen, and less than 1 percent carbon dioxide.

According to Dalton's law, the pressure of a mixture of gases is equal to the sum of the pressures of the individual gases. Thus, the partial pressure of oxygen in the atmosphere is equal to 760—31.5 mm. (pressure of water vapor at saturation and 30°C.) multiplied by 20 percent, or 146 mm. Hg. When several gases are in contact with a liquid, each is absorbed independently of the others and in relation to its pressure or tension.

The tension of the gases in arterial blood is dependent upon the partial pressures of the various gases in the alveolar air of the lungs. In man, the O_2 content of the expired air is about 14 volumes percent, and that of CO_2 is 5.3 percent, or about the same as in birds.

If the exchange of gases in the lungs is due to diffusion and is governed by physical laws, then it is to be expected that the tension of O_2 in venous blood coming to the lungs would be less than that of arterial blood, and that the tension of CO_2 in venous blood would be higher than that in arterial blood. Determinations have shown this to be true.

Since O_2 is consumed and CO_2 is produced in the tissues, it is to be expected that O_2 tension in the tissues would be low and CO_2 tension high, and this has been demonstrated.

Oxygen and Carbon Dioxide Content of the Air of the Lungs and Air Sacs

The O_2 and CO_2 contents of expired air and of that in the air sacs are determined by appropriate methods for measuring absorption. Samples of inspired air in the air sacs are obtained by inserting a small cannula into the sacs and withdrawing air at the end of inspiration. The O_2 and CO_2 contents of expired air and of that in the air sacs of the pigeon, duck, and chickens are shown in Table 33.

These figures show that the air in the abdominal sacs at the end of inspiration contains more oxygen than that in the other sacs, and indicate (as discussed previously) that on inspiration almost pure air goes to the abdominal sacs. The oxygen content of the air in these sacs, 18 to 19 percent, is only slightly lower than that of atmospheric air. The O_2 content is lowest in the air of the interclavicular sac and is of the same magnitude, or lower, than that in expired air.

Table 33. O_2 and CO_2 content (percent) of air of air sacs (mostly at end of inspiration) and expired air

Air Sacs	Pigeon			Duck			Chicken		
	O_2	CO_2	Ref.	O_2	CO_2	Ref.	O_2	CO_2	Ref.
Interclavicular	15.5	4.5	A	14.2	5.6	E	14.6	5.0	D
	12.8	6.4	B	12.1	6.4	G	15.5	4.5	F
Anterior thoracic	15.0	4.8	A	14.9	5.1	E	15.4	4.8	C
	—	—					16.3	3.2	D
							16.6	3.8	F
Posterior thoracic	15.8	4.6	A	17.7	2.5	E	14.9	5.3	C
	—	—		—	—		17.4	3.4	D
							17.0	3.0	F
Abdominal	—	—		18.5	2.2	G	18.0	2.0	C
				17.2	2.7	B	19.0	2.0	D
				18.1	2.5	E	18.8	2.3	F
Cervical	—	—		—	—		15.6	3.2	D
Expired air	14.5	3.9	B	15.8	3.0	B	13.5	6.5	F
				14.3	5.1	E			
				13.7	4.8	G			

References: A, Scharnke (1938); B, Soum (1896); C, Zeuthen (1942); D, Wishart (see Graham, 1939); E, Vos (1934); F, Makowski (1938); G, Dotterweich (1936).

No appreciable exchange of gases occurs within the blood vessels of the air sacs, since these vessels are sparse and small.

Blood Gases of the Bird

Details as to the general methods of determining the content, capacity, tension, and saturation of the gases in the blood may be obtained from textbooks on physiology; for details on avian blood, consult the references cited.

Pertinent data on the blood gases of birds are shown in Table 34. Further details are shown in the O_2 dissociation curves (Figure 24) and in Table 35.

Utilization of oxygen is determined by the percentage of difference in the saturation of arterial and venous blood with oxygen, or the difference in O_2 content of arterial and venous blood. It may be observed from the table, and is also indicated in the dissociation curves, that utilization of O_2 in the bird is high, ranging from 54 percent for the chicken to 60 percent for the duck and pigeon. This is much higher than the average figures for most mammals (20 to 30 percent). The efficiency for goose blood is about 26 percent. Thus, the degree of saturation (88 percent) of chicken arterial blood at a given O_2 tension or pressure and temperature is lower than for mammals (about 95 percent). The O_2 saturation of chicken venous blood (40 percent) is also lower than mammals.

Oxygen Dissociation Curves

These curves have been established for the duck, goose, and pigeon (Wastl and Leiner, 1931a and b), pheasant and chicken (Morgan and Chichester, 1935; Christensen and Dill, 1935). Figure 24 is the curve for the chicken, compared to that of the dog and man (Morgan and Chichester). It is observed that the curve for the chicken is displaced to the right (Bohr effect). The chicken blood was equilibrated at 40°C. (near the normal body temperature) and the dog blood at 37.5°C. (near the dog body temperature). Table 35 shows the p_{50}'s of several species of birds.

Wastl and Leiner (1931a and 1931b) reported similar curves for the duck, goose, and pigeon, except that the curve for the goose showed only very slight displacement to the right as compared to that of man. These authors reported that in shape the curves for

Table 34. Data on blood gases for adult birds at temperature of 42°C.

	Species	Arterial blood	Venous blood
O_2 content	Duck	16.22	6.55
Volumes percent	Pigeon	19.20	7.66
	Goose	19.20	—
	Chicken	12.00	5.50
CO_2 content	Duck	46.00	53.50
Volumes percent	Pigeon	34.00	40.70
	Goose	44–46	48–51
	Chicken	40.00	46.00
O_2 capacity	Duck	16.90	—
Volumes percent	Pigeon	20.00	—
	Goose	19.80	—
	Chicken	13.50	12.00
O_2 saturation	Duck	96.00	38.60
Percent	Pigeon	96.50	38.60
	Goose	96–97	69–73
	Chicken	88.00	40.00
O_2 tension	Duck	96–112	35–40
mm. Hg	Pigeon	98–114	35–40
	Goose	91–95	55–57
	Chicken	90.00	50.00
CO_2 tension	Duck	53–55	60–70
mm. Hg	Pigeon	53–55	60–70
	Goose	46–46	53–55
	Chicken	34.00	45.00

Figures on duck, pigeon, and goose taken directly or calculated from the data of Wastl and Leiner (1931a and 1931b). Data on chicken from Morgan and Chichester (1935).

these species were different from those for mammals, and that when the percentage saturation of hemoglobin with oxygen was plotted as a function of oxygen pressure, the curve consisted of 2 sigmoid portions and possessed 2 points of inflection. Christensen and Dill (1935) and Allen and Wyman (1952) repeated this experiment and found that the shape of such curves in these species was not appreciably different from that in mammals.

Christensen and Dill stated that the results of Wastl and Leiner were complicated by the lack of any control of alkaline reserve in the different specimens and therefore no assurance of constant

Table 35. Oxygen saturation of blood (t ½ sat.) of some avian species (Data from Dittmer *et al.*, *Handbook of Respiration*, 1958)

Species	t ½ sat. (mm. Hg)	pH	Temp. (°C.)	pCO_2 (mm. Hg)
Chicken	51	7.14	40	37
"	62	7.10	37.5	—
"	58	—	38.0	31
Duck	45	7.10	37.5	—
"	42	—	37.5	40
Goose	45	7.10	37.5	—
"	37.5	—	42.0	50
Ostrich	26.0	7.35	40.0	24
Pheasant	50.0	7.10	37.5	—
Pigeon	35.0	—	37.5	40
"	40.0	7.10	37.5	—

pH. The curve for chicken blood presented by Christensen and Dill appears to agree fairly closely with that of Morgan and Chichester. The differences observed were probably due to the fact that Christensen and Dill equilibrated the blood at 37°C. instead of 40°C. It is known that at a given pH and O_2 tension the degree of saturation with O_2 varies inversely with the temperature. This has been demonstrated by Wastl and Leiner, and by others. However, at the same temperature, pH, and O_2 and CO_2 tensions, the curve for chicken blood is displaced to the right of curves of mammalian blood. This means that the affinity of avian blood or hemoglobin for oxygen is less than for mammalian blood, and that it unloads its O_2 to the tissues more readily than the latter. The higher body temperature of the bird also facilitates this unloading.

Morgan and Chichester, and also Wastl and Leiner, have determined the effect of pH upon the affinity of chicken blood for oxygen. Here, as with mammalian blood, the affinity decreases with the increase in acidity or decrease in pH. It has been demonstrated in mammalian and avian blood that CO_2 tension affects the affinity of blood for O_2. Wastl and Leiner (1931b) have shown that in blood with a given pH, temperature, and O_2 tension, the percent of saturation with O_2 varies inversely with the CO_2 tension. For example, the percentage saturations of oxygen at an O_2 tension of 50 mm. Hg, and at CO_2 tensions of 50 and 80 mm. Hg, are 77 and 60 respectively. This displacement of the oxygen dissociation curve to the right is influenced by pH, temperature, CO_2 tension, and the natural affinity of hemoglobin for oxygen. The magnitude of the displacement may be expressed as the change in p_{50} or $t\frac{1}{2}$ per unit of change in pH. This value for the duck is -0.67 as compared to -0.62 for man, -0.65 for the dog, and -0.38 for the elephant (Prosser and Brown, 1961).

Effects of age on oxygen dissociation curves. Rostorfer and Rigdon (1946) found a difference in O_2 dissociation curves of young and mature ducks. The O_2 capacities were 16.1 and 13.9 volumes percent respectively for mature and young ducks. Thus, the affinity of blood of young ducks for O_2 is less than that of mature ducks.

It is known that hemoglobin in birds increases with age up to sexual maturity; the authors demonstrated, however, that this does not account for all of the increased O_2-combining ability of adult duck blood. Thus, there is also an increase with age in the efficiency of duck hemoglobin as an oxygen carrier. This, however, is not true for chicken blood. Hall (1934) has shown that O_2 dissociation curves for young and mature chickens are also different, and that the affinity of hemoglobin of young chicks for oxygen is greater than that of adult birds.

Dissociation Curves for Carbon Dioxide

Carbon dioxide dissociation curves for duck and goose blood

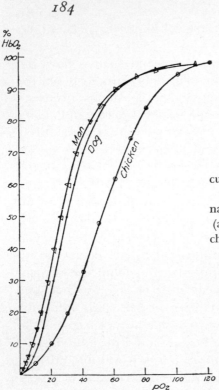

Figure 24. Oxygen dissociation curves of man, dog, and chicken.

O_2 saturation is in percent (ordinates), and O_2 tension (pO_2) mm. Hg (abscissae). (From Morgan and Chichester, *J. Biol. Chem.*, 1935.)

have been determined by Wastl and Leiner. At a given CO_2 tension the curves for the goose and duck are quite similar to those of man and some other mammals. At the same CO_2 tension, goose blood contains from 5 to 10 volumes percent more CO_2 than duck blood.

The difference in CO_2 tension of arterial and venous bloods of birds is greater than that of mammals (10 to 11 mm. Hg in chicken), and this facilitates the removal of CO_2.

The buffering capacity of chicken blood is about the same as that of man (Morgan and Chichester).

In diving birds and mammals, where there is hypoxia, the dive is followed by an increase of lactic acid in the blood, which decreases the buffering capacity for CO_2 and causes an increase in CO_2 (Andersen, 1959).

REFERENCES

Allen, D. W., and J. Wyman, Jr. 1952 The oxygen equilibrium of duck hemoglobin. J. Cell. Comp. Physiol. 39:391.

Andersen, H. T. 1959 A note on the composition of alveolar air in the diving duck. Acta Physiol. Scand. 46:240.

Christensen, E., and D. B. Dill 1935 Oxygen dissociation curves of bird blood. J. Biol. Chem. 109:443.

Dittmer, D. S., and R. M. Grebe, P. L. Altman, J. F. Gibson, and C. C. Wong 1958 Handbook of Respiration. Wright Patterson Air Force Base, Ohio.

Dotterweich, H. 1936 Die Atmung der Vögel. Z. vergl. Physiol. 23:743.

Graham, J. D. 1939 The air stream in the lungs of the fowl. J. Physiol. 97:133.

Hall, F. G. 1934 Hemoglobin function in the developing chick. J. Physiol. 83:222.

Makowski, J. 1938 Beitrag zur Klärung des Atmungsmechanismus der Vögel. Arch. für ges. Physiol. 240:407.

Morgan, V. E., and D. F. Chichester 1935 Properties of blood of the domestic fowl. J. Biol. Chem. 110:285.

Prosser, C. L., and F. A. Brown, Jr. 1961 Comparative Animal Physiology. W. B. Saunders Co., Philadelphia.

Rostorfer, H. A., and R. H. Rigdon 1946 A study of oxygen transport in the blood of young and adult domestic ducks. Am. J. Physiol. 146:222.

Scharnke, H. 1938 Experimentelle Beiträge zur Kenntnis der Vögelatmung. Z. vergl. Physiol. 25:548.

Soum, M. 1896 Recherches physiologiques sur l'appareil respiratoire des oiseaux. Ann. Univ. Lyon 28:1.

Vos, H. F. 1934 Über den Weg der Atemluft in der Entenlunge. Z. vergl. Physiol. 21:552.

Wastl, H., and G. Leiner 1931a Beobachtungen über die Blutgase bei Vögeln, I. Arch. für ges. Physiol. (Pflügers) 227:368 (duck and pigeon).

Wastl, H., and G. Leiner 1931b Beobachtungen über die Blutgase bei Vögeln, II. Arch. für gesamte Physiol. (Pflügers) 227:421 (goose).

Zeuthen, E. 1942 The ventilation of the respiratory tract of birds. Kgl. Danske Videnskab. Selskab. Biol. Medd. 17:1.

CHAPTER 8

Regulation of Body Temperature

BY G. C. WHITTOW

HEAT EXCHANGE BETWEEN THE BIRD
AND ITS ENVIRONMENT

BIRDS, like mammals, are homeothermic. This means that the temperature of the more deeply seated organs, such as the brain, heart, liver, and intestines, remains constant within very narrow limits. In contrast, reptiles, from which birds have evolved, are poikilothermic. Their deep body temperature varies widely, being influenced by the environmental temperature and other factors. In homeothermic animals the amount of heat produced by muscular exercise and by metabolic activity of the tissues is equal to the amount of heat lost from the animal to its environment. If such a thermal balance were not achieved, the deep body temperature would increase when heat production exceeded heat loss and conversely would decrease when heat loss was greater than heat production. Heat is lost to the environment by the processes of radiation, conduction, convection, and evaporation of moisture.

Radiation. Heat is lost by radiation provided that the temperature of the surface of the animal is greater than the temperature of objects and surfaces in the environment. Heat loss by radiation is defined by the following equation

$$H_r = AK_r(e_b T_b^4 - e_s T_s^4)$$

in which H_r represents the heat loss due to radiation; A is the effective radiating surface of the bird; K_r is the constant in the Stefan-Boltzmann law, which relates the amount of heat lost by radiation to the fourth power of the absolute temperature of the radiating surface; e_b is the emissivity of the bird's surface, i.e. the ability of the surface to absorb or radiate heat relative to the ability of a perfect "black body"; T_b is the mean absolute temperature of the bird's radiating surface; e_s is the emissivity of the surroundings, and T_s is the mean absolute temperature of the surroundings. The value of the Stefan-Boltzmann constant is 1.17×10^{-6} (kcal./sq.m./24 hours); the emissivity of the feathers and skin of chickens is very close to that of a black body (Jordan and Dale, 1961). If the temperature difference between the bird and its environment is small, the radiative heat loss is roughly proportional simply to this temperature difference.

Conduction. Loss of heat by conduction involves the direct transfer of heat from the animal's body surface to the air and to any solid objects with which it is in contact. Because of the low thermal conductivity of air, even of moist air, loss of heat by conduction from the body surface to air is negligible. The thermal conductivity of the skin and subcutaneous tissues is also low, and thermal conduction accounts for only a very small part of the transfer of heat from the tissues, in which it is mainly produced, to the skin surface.

Convection. Heat loss by convection occurs because air in direct contact with the body surface is warmed, with the result that it expands and its density decreases. The warm air rises and is replaced by cooler air. If the animal is exposed to moving air the rate of heat loss by convection is greater than in still air. At low air velocities convective heat loss is roughly proportional to the square root of the air velocity. Convective heat loss is also dependent upon the temperature of the moving air. The greater the temperature difference between the body surface and the air, the greater will be the convective heat loss. Total convective heat loss will also depend upon the area of the body surface in contact with air. Convective heat loss may be expressed empirically as follows:

$$H_c = AK_c\sqrt{V}(T_b - T_a)$$

H_c is the convective heat loss; A is the surface area in contact with air; K_c is an empirical constant; V is the air velocity; T_b

is the mean surface temperature of the bird, and T_a is the air temperature. In the respiratory tract the constant movement of air as a result of the activity of the respiratory muscles amounts to forced convection. Although most of the loss of heat from the respiratory tract occurs by evaporation of moisture, some heat is lost by convection. A type of convective heat transfer occurs within the body and largely accounts for the transport of heat from the tissues where it is produced to the surface of the body, from which it is lost. The vehicle for this transport is the blood, and changes in the rate of its flow through the skin produce important changes in the rate of delivery of heat to the skin. For instance, an increase in the skin blood flow usually leads to an increase in the temperature of the skin, and because heat loss by convection and radiation is roughly proportional to the temperature difference between the animal's surface and the environment, heat loss to the environment is thereby increased.

Evaporation. Birds do not possess sweat glands, but they are able to lose some heat by vaporization of moisture from the skin. However, birds are pre-eminently panting animals, and evaporative cooling occurs mostly from the moist lining membranes of the respiratory tract. The amount of heat lost by evaporation of moisture depends upon the difference between the aqueous vapor pressure at the evaporating surface and that of the air, as well as upon the rate of air movement over the moist surface. The evaporative heat loss from the respiratory tract may be represented by an equation suggested by Burton and Edholm (1955), as follows:

$$H_e = V(Q_{sat}.T_b - Q_A) \times 0.6$$

H_e is the rate of evaporative heat loss; V is the pulmonary ventilation rate; $Q_{sat}.T_b$ is the quantity of moisture in air saturated at the deep body temperature; Q_a is the quantity of moisture in the ambient air, and 0.6 is the latent heat of vaporization of water in kcal./g.

Thermal insulation. The insulation of the air immediately adjacent to the surface of the feathers, and of the feathers, skin, and subcutaneous tissues, may be represented mathematically as follows:

$$I_s + I_F + I_a = S \, \frac{(T_b - T_a)}{H_s}$$

I_s, I_F, and I_a represent the insulation provided by the skin, feathers, and air, respectively; S is surface area; T_b is the deep body temperature; T_a is the air temperature, and H_s is the total non-evaporative heat loss. The advantage of this equation is that it may be broken down into other equations which, separately, relate the insulation of the skin, feathers, and air to the temperature difference between the air and the body on the one hand and the total heat loss on the other. The feathers have the highest insulation. The down feathers trap air in which little convective movement occurs, and the distal parts of the contour feathers provide a windproof covering. The feathers are covered with a thin layer of oil secreted by the preen gland, and the spaces between them are extremely small. Both these factors render the plumage of birds resistant to wetting (Hutchinson, 1954). In chickens and many other species of birds, fat deposition is localized in the abdominal cavity, so that variations in the amount of fat would have only a small effect on the heat loss from the bird. In penguins and ducks, and in some other birds, the fat is deposited in a layer beneath the skin, as in mammals, and provides an effective barrier to heat flow from the deep tissues to the surface of the body. The insulations of some species of birds are given in Table 36. In general, the insulation is greater for big birds than for small ones. The insulation decreases sharply for birds with a body weight lower than 10 g. (Lasiewski, 1963). It is interesting to compare the low insulation values for small birds with their high metabolic intensity (see Chapter 9). Small birds have a relatively large surface area from which they can lose heat, and the weight of insulative plumage and fat which they can support is limited. In order to maintain homeothermy it is therefore necessary for small birds to have a rate of heat production relatively higher than that of large birds. Birds tend to have a more effective insulation than do mammals of the same size (Dawson and Tordoff, 1959).

MEASUREMENT OF HEAT EXCHANGE

The balance which is achieved in homeothermic animals between heat production and heat loss, can be summarized in the form of the following equation:

$$M \pm S = E \pm R \pm C_1 \pm C_2$$

M = the rate of heat production

S = heat storage within the body. When the rate of heat production exceeds the rate of heat loss, heat is stored in the body (S is then positive), and this storage manifests itself as an increase in body temperature. Conversely, heat storage is negative and body temperature decreases when the heat production is less than heat loss.

E = the rate of evaporation of moisture which always results in loss of heat and is therefore always positive.

R = The heat exchange due to radiation, which is positive when the body temperature exceeds the temperature of the surroundings and heat is lost from the body. Under some circumstances, heat is gained by the animal as a result of radiation and R is then negative. For example, in many hot countries the temperature of the ground and of objects in the environment is higher than the body temperature, so that heat is gained from the environment. Direct exposure to the sun always results in a gain of heat by the animal.

C_1 = the rate of heat loss by convection. As with radiative heat loss, convection can add heat to the animal if the temperature of the air exceeds the skin temperature (C_1 is then negative).

C_2 = the rate of conductive heat loss, which may be positive or negative depending upon the temperature of the air and of objects in contact with the animal, in relation to the animal's own temperature.

The amount of heat produced by a bird in a given time can be measured in a number of different ways which are described in Chapter 9.

The usual measure of deep body temperature in birds is the rectal temperature. This can be measured easily and without causing any damage to the tissues. The feces, rectal wall, and surrounding viscera constitute a mass of large thermal capacity, and

Table 36. Values for the total insulation provided by the plumage, skin, and subcutaneous tissues in different birds (modified from Misch, 1960; courtesy University of Chicago Press).

Species	Weight (g.)	Insulation (°C./kcal./m²/hr.)	Authority
Manakin	12	0.39	Scholander, Hock, Walters & Irving, (1950); Scholander, Hock, Walters, Johnson, & Irving (1950)
Ortolan bunting	22	0.20	Wallgren (1954)
Yellow bunting	26	0.36	"
Abert's towhee	36	0.36	Dawson (1954, 1960)
Brown towhee	37	0.39	"
Cardinal	40	0.52	Dawson, (1958)
Snow bunting	40	0.48	Scholander, Walters, Hock, & Irving (1950)
Evening grosbeak	58	0.55	Dawson & Tordoff (1959)
Gray jay	64	0.84	Scholander, Hock, Walters, & Irving (1950); Scholander, Hock, Walters, Johnson, & Irving (1950)
Northern blue jay	81	0.54	Misch (1960)
Ptarmigan	—	0.84	Scholander, Walters, Hock, & Irving (1950)
Northwestern crow	306	0.53	Irving, Krog, & Monson (1955)

the rectal thermometer is therefore sited within the region of the body with the highest heat content. The disadvantage of the rectal temperature is that it responds comparatively slowly to changes of temperature elsewhere in the body. Rectal temperatures are measured most accurately by means of a thermocouple or thermistor mounted near the end of a semirigid rod which is inserted into the rectum. The deep body temperature of birds is sometimes measured by insertion of a thermometer into the proventriculus; but it is likely that this procedure interferes with respiratory heat loss, and that it causes more distress to the bird than does the insertion of a rectal thermometer.

Muscle and subcutaneous temperatures can be measured by thermistors or thermocouples threaded through hypodermic needles. Measurement of the temperature of the surface of the skin requires the use of a flat applicator, to which the thermistor or thermocouple is attached.

Total heat loss from a bird is measured by a calorimeter. In order to understand the physiological control of the different pathways of heat loss it is necessary to partition the total heat loss into evaporative, radiative, and convective components. In the gradient-layer calorimeter (see Chapter 9), evaporative heat loss is obtained by condensation of the evaporated moisture in the air and measurement of the heat of condensation by a special gradient layer. Separation of the moisture evaporated from the respiratory tract from the cutaneous moisture loss can be achieved by the collection of respired air separately from the main stream of air in the calorimeter. At present this has not yet been accomplished in birds. It would involve the collection of the expired air by means of a mask attached to the bird's head. Division of the "sensible" heat loss (i.e. nonevaporative heat loss) into its components of radiation and convection is achieved by measurement of the radiant heat loss directly with an instrument called a 4-pi radiometer, which can be incorporated into the walls of the gradient-layer calorimeter. The convective heat loss is the difference between the total sensible heat loss and the radiant component (in most calorimetric experiments the animal is suspended in the calorimeter so that heat loss by conduction is negligible).

The total heat loss and its partition can be estimated more simply but less accurately in the following manner:

total heat loss is equated with heat production estimated from measurements of the respiratory gaseous exchange (see Chapter 9). The amount of water lost by evaporation is estimated by recording the weight loss of the animal, after making due allowance for the weight of feces, urine, or saliva voided, and for the weight change associated with the respiratory absorption of oxygen and elimination of carbon dioxide. Alternatively, the amount of moisture added by the bird to a stream of dry air may be estimated by absorption of the water onto a suitable absorbent and measurement of the change in weight of the absorbent. Radiative heat loss is measured with a small portable radiometer (Hardy, 1934). This instrument has a cone that concentrates the radiant heat onto a detecting element consisting of a number of thermojunctions connected in series. Radiation measurements have to be taken from several regions on the body surface and the readings averaged. Heat loss by conduction is assumed to be zero, and heat loss by convection is calculated by subtracting radiative plus evaporative heat loss from the total heat loss.

Roller and Dale (1962) partitioned the heat loss from chickens in a gradient-layer calorimeter at environmental temperatures of 22.5°, 27.5°, and 32.5°C. The birds were held at each environmental temperature for 17 hours. It may be seen from Table 37 that at the lowest environmental temperature (22.5°C.) most heat was lost by nonevaporative pathways, and that radiation accounted for approximately one-third of the total heat loss. As the environmental temperature rose the evaporative heat loss increased,

Table 37. Partition of the heat loss from chickens at different environmental temperatures (modified from Roller and Dale, 1962, by courtesy of the American Society of Agricultural Engineers)

No. of birds	Mean body weight (g.)	Environmental temperature (°C.)	Mean heat production kcal./hr.	Mean heat loss (kcal./hr.)		
				Evaporative (latent)	Non-evaporative (sensible)	Radiative
9	1755	32.5	6.3	2.4	3.9	1.5
9	1645	27.5	6.8	1.0	5.8	2.4
9	1748	22.5	8.3	0.6	7.7	3.0

while the nonevaporative component of heat loss decreased. At an environmental temperature of 32.5°C. approximately 38 percent of the total heat loss resulted from evaporation.

BODY TEMPERATURES OF BIRDS

The deep body temperature of birds is higher than that of the other group of homeothermic animals, the mammals (Table 38). Variations of temperature are evident between different species of bird, and different members of the same species may also have

Table 38. Deep body temperatures of some adult birds and mammals

Birds[1]		Mammals[2]	
Species	Temperature (°C.)	Species	Temperature (°C.)
Domestic duck	42.1	Mouse	37.9
Domestic goose	41.3	Rat	36.8
Domestic turkey	41.2	Rabbit	38.9
Chicken	41.9	Pig	38.6
Domestic pigeon	42.2	Cat	36.4
English sparrow	43.5	Dog	38.2
Brown pelican	40.3	Sheep	39.0
Downy woodpecker	41.9	Opossum	34.7
Bank swallow	41.4	Echidna	28.1
American magpie	41.8	Polar bear[3]	37.6
Abert's towhee	42.0	Reindeer[3]	38.8

[1] Authority: King & Farner (1961).
[2] Authority: Robinson & Lee (1946).
[3] Authority: Irving & Krog (1954)

different deep body temperatures under the same conditions. The temperature of an individual bird varies widely under different conditions. These differences of temperature are often difficult to explain; but certain factors are known to influence the body temperatures of birds:

Age. The body temperatures of hatched chicks are lower than those of mature birds, but they increase progressively until the adult levels are reached at an age of approximately 20 days (Figure 25), depending on the breed (Lamoreux and Hutt, 1939; Scholes and Hutt, 1942). The increase in the deep body temperature with age appears to be associated with the growth of the

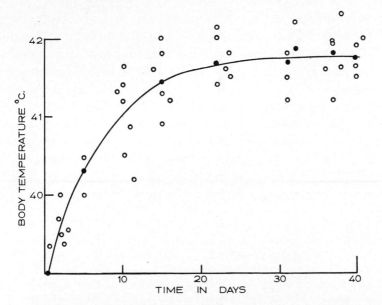

Figure 25. The increase in body temperature of chicks with age, from a few hours after hatching to 40 days. The curve represents average temperature, the open circles the range of variation. The first two averages were obtained from birds in an environmental temperature of 38°–39°C.; for the remainder of the measurements the chicks were in an environment of 20°–26°C. This progressive development in body temperature was studied in 40 birds. (Redrawn from Randall, 1943a; by courtesy of *Am. J. Physiol.*)

plumage and with the increase in the rate of heat production which occurs in the growing bird (Odum, 1942; see also Chapter 9).

Size. There is some evidence that the body temperatures of different species of birds vary inversely with body weights (Rodbard, 1950). This effect of body size may be related to the relatively greater metabolic rate of small birds (see Chapter 9). This relation does not necessarily hold for birds of the same species, however.

Sex. In some species of birds it has been established that there is a difference between the deep body temperatures of male and female birds (Simpson and Galbraith, 1905). For example, the temperature of the female Eastern house wren is approximately 0.4°C. higher than that of the male (Baldwin and Kendeigh, 1932). Sturkie, Whittow, and Stein (unpublished data) found that adult male White Leghorn chickens kept at an environmental temperature of 22°C. had significantly higher rectal temperatures than adult hens maintained under similar conditions. This observation conforms with the higher metabolic rates of male chickens (see Chapter 9). However, the sex difference in the rectal temperatures of chickens varies with the age of the birds (Lamoreux and Hutt, 1939), and with the environmental temperature, as follows (Sturkie, Whittow, and Stein, unpublished observations):

Environmental temp.	*−1°C.*		*22°C.*		*31°C.*	
Sex	*Male*	*Female*	*Male*	*Female*	*Male*	*Female*
No. of birds	5	13	9	12	6	12
Mean (±S.E.)	41.6	41.1	41.3	41.0	41.3	41.3
Rectal temp. (°C.)	±0.10	±0.06	±0.10	±0.07	±0.10	±0.07

Breed. Lamoreux and Hutt (1939) found that White Leghorn chicks had significantly higher rectal temperatures than had Rhode Island Red Chicks at 10 days of age. At an air temperature of 22°–24°C., Heywang (1938) found the mean rectal temperatures of adult White Leghorns and Rhode Island Red hens to be 41.5°C. and 41.3°C. respectively.

Activity. The deep body temperature of wild birds is usually higher when they are captured than after a period of rest (Baldwin and Kendeigh, 1932; Farner, 1958). When chickens are confined in cages and become relatively inactive their body temperatures decrease (Hutchinson, 1954).

Food. The body temperature of birds increases after the ingestion of food and when the plane of nutrition is increased (Robinson and Lee, 1947). Conversely, starvation leads to a decrease in the body temperature (Balwin and Kendeigh, 1932; Hazelwood and Wilson, 1962). In view of the changes in the rate of heat production which result from changes in the food intake (see Chapter 9), the observed variations in body temperature are not surprising.

Diurnal rhythm. The deep body temperature of most birds varies in a predictable manner during the 24-hour period. In birds that are active during the day the highest temperatures occur during the day (see King and Farner, 1961). Nocturnal species, on the other hand, have the highest temperatures during the night (Figure 26). The diurnal variation of body temperature is therefore related to the variation in the activity of the birds, and probably also to periods of food intake. It seems likely that the diurnal rhythm of body temperature is likewise related to the diurnal rhythm of heat production (see Chapter 9). A reduced amplitude of the diurnal rhythm of temperature following the administration of thiouracil to chickens suggests that the thyroid gland is involved in the rhythm of body temperature (Washburn, Siegel, Freund, and Gross, 1962). Because the highest body temperatures of nocturnal birds occur during the night when the environmental temperature is lowest, it might be argued that the rhythm of body temperature is independent of the diurnal rhythm of environmental temperature. However, the degree of change in body temperature can be reduced by exposing the birds to a constant high environmental temperature (Wilson, 1948; Dawson, 1954). Conversely, the diurnal rhythm of body temperature is more pronounced when birds are dehydrated (Dawson, 1954). The reason for this has not been established, but a diminished sensitivity of the thermoregulatory center in the brain, or an impaired circulatory response to thermal stimuli, are possible explanations. In pigeons, cyanosis of the comb develops during dehydration, suggesting that the circulation is inadequate (Wilson and Edwards, 1952). There is evidence that light may also play a part in the diurnal rhythm of body temperature. Thus, Hildén and Stenbäck (1916) and Koskimies (1950) were able to reverse the diurnal rhythm of body temperature by changing the times of illumination for the birds, although the cycle of air temperature was unchanged. Recent work on the emperor penguin has shown that a diurnal cycle of body temperature is absent during the 24-hour Antarctic day, in spite of a diurnal fluctuation of environmental temperature (Goldsmith and Sladen, 1961). However, Eklund

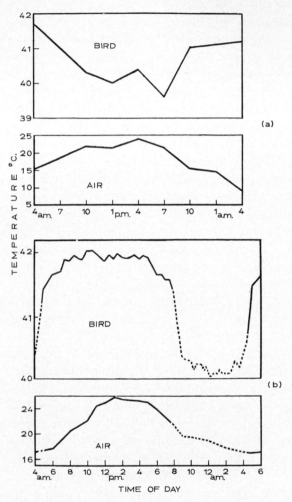

Figure 26. Mean diurnal rhythm in deep body temperature of four owls (a) and twelve passeriform birds (b), together with the temperature of the air. The broken lines indicate the period of inactivity. (Data for the owls from Simpson and Galbraith (1905), courtesy *J. Physiol.;* data for the passeriform species from Baldwin and Kendeigh (1932), courtesy Dr. S. C. Kendeigh.)

(1942) has asserted that a diurnal rhythm of body temperature is evident in the South-Polar skua during a 24-hour day; in some species, therefore, other factors may be more important than light in the genesis of the diurnal rhythm. The amplitude of the diurnal fluctuations of body temperature is greater in small than in large birds (Simpson and Galbraith, 1905), presumably because small birds have a relatively large surface area and therefore lose heat more rapidly than large birds. Removal of the cerebral hemispheres of the pigeon resulted in the abolition of the deep body temperature difference between day and night, but this was thought to be a secondary effect of the elimination of body movements (Kayser, 1929).

Environmental temperature. Young chickens brooded at an environmental temperature of 40.5°C. had higher rectal temperatures than chicks reared at 32.2°C. (King, 1956). The results of Heywang (1938) and Wilson (1949) indicate that the body temperatures of adult chickens also vary with the environmental temperature. A statistically significant correlation between the body temperature of nestling Western gulls and air temperature has been reported by Bartholomew and Dawson (1952).

Season. Small seasonal variations in the body temperature of chickens were reported by Winchester (1940), but it is not clear from his data whether or not these variations were related to a seasonal cycle of environmental temperature.

Molting. In the yellow-eyed penguin the deep body temperature is significantly greater in molting than in nonmolting birds (Farner, 1958). The increased body temperature during molting is presumably the result of an increased rate of heat production because the insulation of the birds decreases during molting (see King and Farner, 1961; also Chapter 9, and below).

Plumage. When the feathers of English sparrows are clipped their body temperatures decrease (Baldwin and Kendeigh, 1932). Frizzle fowls, which have defective plumage, also have subnormal rectal temperatures (Benedict, Landauer, and Fox 1932). This is the result to be expected from a diminution in the insulation of the plumage (see Chapter 9).

Nesting Habits. Species of African birds that build nests have significantly higher body temperatures than those that lay their eggs on the bare ground (Prozesky, 1963).

From all this it is obvious that a single measurement of body temperature has a limited meaning unless it is qualified by information concerning the circumstances under which the measurement was made.

RESPONSES TO CHANGES OF ENVIRONMENTAL TEMPERATURE

For every bird there exists a range within which changes in environmental temperature are associated with little or no change in heat production, and which is known as the thermoneutral range. Within this range, the body temperature is regulated by variations in heat loss. When the environmental temperature rises above or falls below the thermoneutral range the heat production increases. The environmental temperatures at these points are known as the upper and lower critical temperatures, respectively (see Table 39). The range of environmental temperature, above the upper critical temperature, to which birds can adapt is much narrower than the temperature range below the lower critical temperature which is compatible with survival. The thermoneutral range for any given bird may increase in amplitude with age, if the plane of nutrition is increased or if the bird becomes acclimatized to a lower environmental temperature.

The increase in heat production at the lower critical temperature is due mainly to shivering. The rate of increase in heat production at environmental temperatures below the lower critical temperature is known as the temperature coefficient (King and Farner, 1961), and expresses in percentages the increase in the standard rate of heat production per degree C. of reduction in environmental temperature (see Table 39). The value of the temperature coefficient depends to a large extent upon the effectiveness of the bird's insulation; the better the insulation, the lower the temperature coefficient (see also Chapter 9). In some birds the insulation continues to increase even when the environmental temperature has fallen well below the lower critical tem-

Table 39. Thermoneutral range and temperature coefficients of some species of birds (modified from King and Farner, 1961; courtesy Academic Press, Inc.)

Species		Body weight (g.)	Thermo-neutral range (°C.)	Temper-ature coefficient	Authority
Chicken	0–1 weeks	36	34–36		Barott & Pringle (1946)
(Rhode Island	5 weeks	260	32–35		"
Red female)	52 weeks	2430	18–24	1.5	"
Pigeon		260	30.2–35.8		Gelineo (1955)
Cardinal (in winter)		40	18–33	3.7	Dawson (1958)
Cardinal (in summer)		40	24–33		"
Abert's towhee		46.8	25–35	ca. 3.8	Dawson (1954)
Brown towhee		43.7	23–33	ca. 1.8	"
Yellow bunting		26.4	25–33	3.3	Wallgren (1954)
Ortolan bunting		22.0	32–38	4.3	"

perature. This is particularly true of small wild birds. The insulation increases rapidly at first, and then more slowly. In the English sparrow, the insulation was highest at the lowest environmental temperature to which the bird was subjected (West, 1962). The increase in heat production at the upper critical temperature is possibly related to the increased muscular activity associated with panting, but also to the direct accelerator action of the increase in body temperature on the heat-producing chemical reactions in the body (van't Hoff–Arrhenius effect; see Chapter 9).

Behavioral changes. Migratory birds are able to avoid exposure to extremes of heat and cold by moving to cooler or warmer areas. Flying birds may soar in cool air high above the ground to reduce the effects of the heat. Nonflying birds like the chicken, when exposed to heat, reduce their activity and heat production, and hold their wings away from the body to increase heat loss from the poorly insulated undersurfaces (Hutchinson, 1954). Chickens, when hot, will drink more water than usual (Wilson, 1949), and will splash their combs, wattles, and feathers with water, thereby cooling themselves. Birds are also reported to seek a cool place and to reduce their activity during the hot part of the day (Dawson, 1954). The wood stork, when hot, resorts to the bizarre expedient of directing its liquid excrement onto its long legs, which are cooled by evaporation of the water in the excrement (Kahl, 1963). When juvenile Laysan and black-footed albatrosses are exposed to strong solar radiation, they orient themselves so that their backs are to the sun and their large webbed feet are in the shade of their bodies (Howell and Bartholomew, 1961). They also rest on their heels so that a minimal amount of heat is absorbed by their feet from the hot ground.

In a cold environment, a chicken will reduce its surface area, and thereby its heat loss, by hunching up. It will also fluff out its feathers, thereby increasing its insulation (Hutchinson, 1954). Baldwin and Kendeigh (1932) prevented the Eastern house wren from fluffing out its feathers in a cold environment, and they noted that the body temperature decreased more rapidly than did that of control birds. Tucking the head under the wing is an effective way of reducing heat loss, the reduction amounting to about 12 percent in the chicken, according to Deighton and Hutchinson (1940). Huddling is another means of heat conservation in the cold (Kleiber and Winchester, 1933; Bartholomew and Dawson, 1952). A common method of reducing heat loss from the unfeathered parts of the legs is to "sit" on them. The heat loss in the chicken while standing is from 40 to 50 percent greater than while the bird is sitting (Deighton and Hutchinson, 1940). Penguins, in addition to squatting, rest only their tarsometatarsal joints on the ground, thus permitting only minimal conductive cooling between their feet and the ice (Goldsmith and Sladen, 1961). In the Arctic, ptarmigan utilize burrows in the snow to protect themselves from the rigors of the climate (Dawson, 1962). Increased activity in the cold will increase heat production. Food intake is stimulated in a cold environment and depressed under hot conditions (see Chapter 9).

There is evidence that some birds have a well-developed temperature sense. The mallee-fowl, which incubates its eggs in a mound of soil and decaying organic matter, is able to assess the temperature of the mound by thrusting its bill into it (Frith, 1957). Depending on the temperature of the mound, the bird either heaps more material onto the mound or opens it up; in this way a constant incubation temperature is secured for the eggs in the mound. Some wild birds stand over their eggs and shield them from the sun (Huggins, 1941). The different behavioral mechanisms of thermoregulation employed by birds have been summarized by Hafez (1964b).

Physiological Responses to Heat: Hyperthermia

The temperature of the skin underlying the feathered parts of the body is close to the deep body temperature, over a wide range

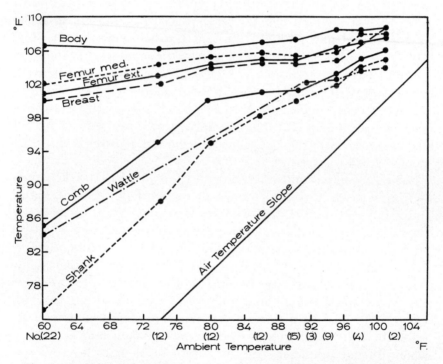

Figure 27. Skin temperatures of hens kept at different ambient temperatures, as measured with a touch thermocouple. Body temperatures (rectal) were measured with a mercury thermometer. The numbers in parentheses indicate the number of observations. (Redrawn from Wilson, Hillerman, and Edwards, 1952; courtesy *Poultry Science*.)

of environmental temperatures (Figure 27). The skin temperatures for the unfeathered extremities, however, are much lower than for the feathered areas of skin. When the environmental temperature increases, the skin temperature of feathered areas does not increase very much, so that little further heat loss from these areas occurs. However, the skin temperatures of the legs, combs, and wattles increase considerably, and heat loss from them must be increased. Large increases in the skin temperatures of the extremities also occur when the environmental temperature is kept constant and when the body of the bird, excluding the extremities, is heated (Figure 28); the increases are largely the result of increases of blood flow to the organs concerned. The temperature of the leg of the California Quail increased more rapidly than that of the air when the latter was rising, suggesting an increased blood flow through the leg (Bartholomew and Dawson, 1958). A similar phenomenon has been observed in the American kestrel (Bartholomew and Cade, 1957). Evidence for an important thermoregulatory function of the long legs of the wood stork has recently been provided by Kahl (1963). The extremities are particularly well adapted for losing heat; they have a large surface area in relation to their volume, and their insulation is absent or poor (Hutchinson 1954).

When the environmental temperature is equal to the body temperature, heat cannot be lost from the bird by nonevaporative means; it can be lost, however, by the evaporation of moisture from the respiratory tract. The deep body temperature at which panting is initiated varies from 41.0° to 43.5°C. in different species of birds (King and Farner, 1961). Panting—or thermal polypnea, as it is sometimes called—consists of an increase in respiratory rate and minute volume and a decrease in tidal volume (see also Chapter 6). The reduction in the tidal volume is thought to restrict the hyperventilation to the surfaces of the respiratory tract, which do not participate in the exchange of gases between the blood and the air in the respiratory tract. In this way, the possibility of the removal of excessive amounts of carbon dioxide from the blood is lessened. The increased respiratory minute volume results in an increased amount of moisture evaporated from the

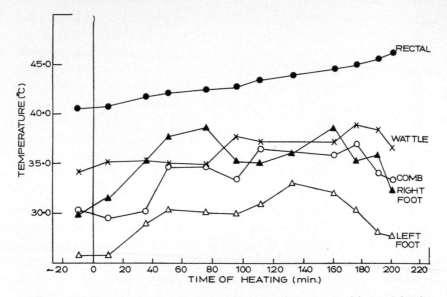

Figure 28. Changes in the skin temperatures of the extremities and in the rectal temperature of an adult White Leghorn hen during hyperthermia, produced by means of a heating pad wrapped around the bird. Heating commenced at time zero; environmental temperature was 23°C. (Whittow, Sturkie, and Stein, 1964; courtesy *Am. J. Physiol.*)

respiratory tract (see above). In pelecaniform birds, panting is supplemented by a fluttering action of the gular pouch (Howell and Bartholomew, 1962), and it has been suggested that evaporative cooling is achieved by this means without a commensurate increase in heat production (Bartholomew and Dawson, 1954). Changes in the respiratory rate and minute volume of chickens during hyperthermia are illustrated in Figure 29. It may be seen that the respiratory rate reaches a maximum at a deep body temperature of approximately 44°C. At higher body temperatures the respiratory rate decreases, but the respiratory minute volume remains constant until just before the bird dies. The decrease in respiratory rate is associated with an increase in tidal volume (see also Chapter 6). Since the minute volume does not increase at body temperatures higher than 44°C., and since the amount of heat lost from the respiratory tract is partly dependent on the minute volume (see above), further cooling from the respiratory tract must be the result of the increase in the temperature of the evaporating surface, which in turn will result in an increase in the aqueous vapor pressure at this surface. Because the tidal volume increases at body temperatures exceeding 44°C., the bird probably incurs the risk of the development of alkalosis (see above). In the chicken the arterial blood pressure and the calculated total peripheral vascular resistance to blood flow are lowered during hyperthermia, presumably in part as a result of the vasodilatation which occurs in the extremities (Figure 28; see also Chapter 3). An increased cardiac output and blood volume ensure that the rate of blood flow through the extremities, and also possibly through the evaporating areas of the respiratory tract and through the respiratory muscles involved in panting, is increased. In the later stages of hyperthermia, when the respiratory rate decreases and the tidal volume increases, the cardiac output and the blood pressure decrease. Circulatory failure is therefore one of the contributory causes to the death of the bird.

In the chicken, the plasma volume increases slightly during hyperthermia in spite of the loss of water by evaporation (see Chapter 3). However, consumption of water by chickens is higher in hot than in cool surroundings; the volume of the feces is also higher (Wilson, McNally, and Ota, 1957). In small birds, the amount of water lost by evaporation from the respiratory tract can be a considerable proportion of the body weight (Bartholomew and Dawson, 1953). The water consumption is also relatively greater in small than in large birds, and it increases with increasing ambient temperature (Bartholomew and Cade, 1956). The availability of water is therefore an important factor in the resistance of small birds to heat exposure (Bartholomew and Dawson, 1953). Kendeigh (1934) enclosed the head of an English sparrow in a ventilated chamber and measured the amount of moisture added to the air at different air temperatures. In this way he was able to separate moisture loss from the respiratory tract (and to a small extent from the skin of the head) from that given off from the remainder of the body. The amount of moisture lost from the head over a 2-hour period, at various air temperatures, was:

Air temp. (°C.)	0.6	5.6	20.0	27.2	31.7	36.1
Weight loss (g.)	0.154	0.141	0.156	0.181	0.581	0.823

Unfortunately, Kendeigh's data do not provide an estimate of the evaporative loss from other parts of the body. In many birds not more than half of the resting heat production can be dissipated by panting (King and Farner, 1961). Exposure to severe conditions in which nonevaporative cooling is prevented must therefore result in an increase in body temperature. The poor-will is exceptional in that it can dissipate 160 percent of its metabolic heat production by panting. This is achieved by a combination of a low heat production and the special form of panting, "gular fluttering," which has a low energy cost, referred to above (Bartholomew, Hudson, and Howell, 1962). In the chicken, under very hot conditions approximately 84 percent of the total heat loss is achieved

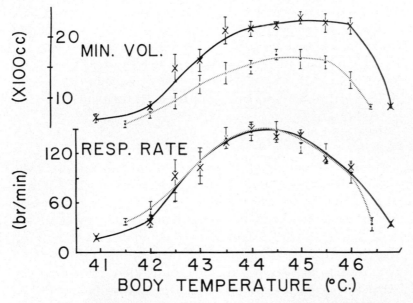

Figure 29. Mean changes in the respiratory rate and minute volume of 5 adult male (continuous lines) and 8 adult female (interrupted lines) White Leghorn chickens, during hyperthermia. (Redrawn from Frankel, Hollands and Weiss, 1962; courtesy *Archives Internationales de Physiologie et de Biochimie.*

by evaporative means (Romijn and Lokhorst, 1961). Hutchinson (1954) has estimated that Brown Leghorn chickens can lose more than 110 g. moisture/sq.m./hr. when they are hyperthermic in a hot dry environment, and the cooling achieved by this means amounted to almost twice the resting heat production. Howell and Bartholomew (1962) taped the bills of nestling red-tailed tropic birds and red-footed boobies during exposure to strong solar radiation. This procedure was followed by a rapid rise in body temperature approaching the lethal level. The contribution of the air sacs to respiratory evaporative cooling is uncertain (see Chapter 6).

When birds become hyperthermic the increase in body temperature leads to an increase in the temperature gradient between the bird and its environment. However, to be of value, the increased heat loss resulting from this increased gradient must exceed the increased heat production consequent upon the hyperthermia and the accelerated contractions of the respiratory muscles (see Chapter 9). The body temperature of the towhee increases to a higher level in a hot environment when the birds are dehydrated than when they are not; the increased body temperature represents storage of heat in the body (Dawson, 1954), and the water that would have had to be vaporized in order to dissipate this heat is a saving to the bird.

Physiological Responses to Cold: Hypothermia

It may be seen from Figure 27 that the skin temperatures of the uninsulated extremities of the chicken decrease as the environmental temperature decreases. The temperature gradient between the skin of these areas and the air is reduced, and the heat loss from the former is also reduced. The maintenance of cold extremities in a cold environment may therefore be regarded as a heat conservation mechanism. In some birds there are special vascular structures (rete) in the legs which permit cooling of the arterial blood going to the feet and lower parts of the legs by cold venous blood returning from the feet. Cooling of the arterial blood going to the distal parts of the legs results in a decrease in the skin temperature of the feet and shanks, and heat loss from these regions to the environment is therefore reduced. The heat lost from the arterial blood warms the venous blood returning to the heart. In this way, heat that would otherwise be dissipated to the environment is returned to the body. These structures are present in the legs of wading birds such as cranes, herons, and flamingos, and also in the flippers of penguins (see King and Farner, 1961, for references). The steepest temperature gradient along the leg of the wood stork occurs in the region of its rete mirabile (Kahl, 1963). The nerves in the metatarsal region of the herring gull's leg are able to conduct impulses at a much lower temperature than are those in the tibial region of the leg (Chatfield, Lyman, and Irving, 1953). Since the temperature of the metatarsal region is normally much lower than that of the tissues overlying the tibia, there is accordingly a functional adaptation of the tissues in the extremities to their habitually low temperature. At environmental temperatures lower than 0°C. the extremities are prevented from freezing by periodic increases in the flow of warm blood through them, which results in periodic increases in their temperature. This phenomenon is known as "cold vasodilatation"; it was first shown to occur in the foot of the chicken during immersion in cold water by Grant and Bland (1931), who believed that cold vasodilatation was associated with the alternate opening and closing of arteriovenous anastomoses in the foot.

The importance of the insulating properties of the plumage of birds during exposure to cold is illustrated in the section on cold tolerance (below) and in Chapter 9.

As the environmental temperature decreases below the lower critical temperature, the rate of heat production increases as a result of increased muscle tone (Steen and Enger, 1957), and of shivering. If the rate of heat loss exceeds the rate of heat production, the body temperature will decrease, i.e. the bird will become hypothermic. Hypothermia may be induced in chickens by immersing them in water at a temperature of approximately 20°C. (Sturkie, 1946). Shivering occurs at first, but the heat produced by this means is inadequate to prevent the body temperature from decreasing. While the bird is shivering the respiratory rate increases slightly, a change that might be associated with a further increase in heat loss. Later the respiratory rate and body temperature decrease (see Chapter 3).

Acclimatization to Heat and to Cold

Acclimatization is the term given to the changes that occur in animals during continuous or repeated exposure to a hot or cold environment that are of benefit to the animal. Daily 4-hour exposures to heat for 24 days are sufficient to induce acclimatization in chickens, as judged by the responses of the rectal temperatures to the hot environment (Hutchinson and Sykes, 1953). It is known that one of the underlying changes during acclimatization to heat in the yellow bunting and the ortolan bunting is a decrease in heat production (Wallgren, 1954; see Chapter 9). The respiratory rate also declines during acclimatization to heat (Hillerman and Wilson, 1955). Presumably part of the decrease in respiratory rate is the result of the diminution in deep body temperature; but in Hillerman and Wilson's experiments the respiratory rate remained elevated after the body temperature had returned to normal. Eventually the respiratory rates and minute volumes of heat-acclimatized chickens decrease below those of control birds (Weiss, Frankel, and Hollands, 1963):

	Control birds	Heat-acclimatized birds
No. of birds	7	14
Respiratory rate (resp./min.)	37	28
Respiratory minute volume (ml.)	554	397

Lamoreux (1943) found that chicks reared at an environmental temperature of 29.4°C. developed larger combs than did birds reared at 2.2°C. In view of the evidence that the combs have a thermoregulatory function, (Figure 28) it seems reasonable to assume that the nonevaporative heat loss would be facilitated from the birds with the larger combs. Lee, Robinson, Yeates, and Scott (1945) have reported, however, that removal of the wattles had little effect on the reaction of chickens to hot environments, and that varnishing the combs and wattles had none. However, it is possible that following removal of the wattles a compensatory increase in heat loss occurred from other areas of the body. There is, in fact, evidence in Wilson's (1949) data that removal of the comb and wattle resulted in an increase in the respiratory rates of chickens under hot conditions. Furthermore, varnishing the combs and wattles would reduce only evaporative cooling of these organs.

A diminution of the hematocrit, the plasma volume, and the specific gravity of the blood appears to be a feature of acclimatization to high environmental temperatures (Wilson, McNally, and Ota, 1957; Huston, 1960; Vogel and Sturkie, 1963). Recent experiments have shown that both the arterial blood pressures (Weiss, 1959; Weiss, Frankel, and Hollands, 1963) and the cardiac outputs (Vogel and Sturkie, 1963) are low in heat-acclimatized chickens (see Chapter 3). The peripheral vascular resistance of heat-acclimatized chickens is higher than that of chickens acclimatized to cold (Vogel and Sturkie, 1963). These results seem to indicate that a high level of peripheral blood flow is not characteristic of heat-acclimatized chickens, in contrast to the immediate effects of heat on chickens.

When birds are kept at low environmental temperatures the rate of heat production increases (see Chapter 9). The lower critical temperature is also less. Attempts by various investigators to show a seasonal variation in heat production have not produced consistent results. A diminution in the lower critical temperature seems to be a more usual finding (Table 39). For instance, Dawson (1958) was unable to demonstrate a significant difference between the oxygen consumption of cardinals in winter and in summer, but the lower critical temperature was lower in winter than in summer. Riddle, Smith, and Benedict (1934) found a higher temperature coefficient in summer-adapted pigeons than in winter-adapted birds. This difference between the effects of artificial and seasonal variations of environmental temperature may be attributed to the variable temperatures encountered under natural conditions. Thus, Wallgren (1954) found that the heat production of the ortolan and yellow bunting was depressed when the birds were exposed continuously to hot conditions, but not when the exposure to heat was alternated with a daily 8-hour exposure to a cool environment. Nevertheless, the lower critical temperatures of many birds inhabiting cold regions are well above the temperatures they regularly encounter in nature during the winter. The birds must therefore augment their rates of heat production, and the consequence of this is that they must increase their food intake when food is likely to be most scarce and the daylight hours for feeding most limited.

Kendeigh (1934) found that the weight of the winter plumage was about 30 percent greater than that of the summer plumage in the English sparrow. For tree sparrows the difference amounted to 25 percent (West, 1962). A greater insulation is therefore a feature of cold-acclimatized birds. According to Scholander and his associates (1950), arctic birds have lower critical temperatures than tropical birds, and the increase in heat production for a given decrease of environmental temperature was also lower in arctic species. These results were attributed to the better insulation of arctic birds.

Tolerance of Heat and Cold

The rectal temperatures of White Leghorn chickens at various air temperatures are given in Figure 30. The highest environmental temperatures that birds can tolerate without a progressive increase in their body temperature depends, among other things, upon the humidity of the air. The effect of an increased humidity is to decrease the aqueous vapor pressure gradient between the evaporating surface of the respiratory tract and the air, so that heat loss is diminished. The humidity of the air has little effect on the body temperature of the chicken at environmental temperatures lower than approximately 32°C. Thermal polypnea is also not very marked below this temperature (Hutchinson, 1954). However, as Romijn and Lokhorst's data (1961) show, an increase in the aqueous vapor pressure of the air, even at an air temperature of 24°C., results in a reduction of evaporative heat loss from Blue North Holland cocks. Since the total heat loss remains constant there is a corresponding increase in nonevaporative heat loss.

Relative humidity (percent)	*Air temperature (°C.)*	*Evaporative heat-loss as a percentage of the total heat loss*
30	24	22.3
90	24	14.2

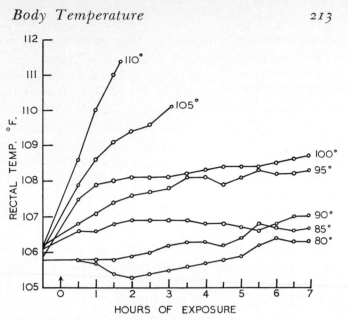

Figure 30. Rectal temperatures of White Leghorn hens during exposure to various environmental temperatures. The figure at the end of each line is the environmental temperature. The relative humidity in each environment was 65 percent. (Redrawn from Yeates, Lee, and Hines, 1941; courtesy *Proc. Roy. Soc. Queensland.*)

The importance of humidity at high environmental temperatures is illustrated by the fact that at an environmental temperature of 43.3°C., the rectal temperature of chickens was 44.4°C. when the relative humidity was 35 percent, and 46.8°C. when the humidity was 55 percent (Yeates, Lee, and Hines, 1941). The rate of air movement has little effect on the amount of heat loss from birds at high environmental temperatures because most of the heat is lost from the respiratory tract, and the rate of air movement over the moist surfaces of the tract, as a result of the contractions of the respiratory muscles, is far in excess of environmental air movement under natural conditions. The survival time of birds at a given environmental air temperature will, however, depend upon the amount of radiant heat to which they are exposed.

The degree of acclimatization also influences heat tolerance. Thus, cardinals tended to become hyperthermic at lower environmental temperatures in winter than in summer (Dawson, 1958).

Chickens acclimatized to summer weather or to a warm artificial environment survived longer, in a hot humid atmosphere, than either chickens tested during the winter or those from a cool artificial environment. The rate of rise of body temperature was less in the heat-acclimatized birds than in the controls (Weiss, 1959; Weiss, Frankel, and Hollands, 1963). Nonlaying hens were more tolerant than layers, but this difference was probably due in part to the lower food intake of the nonlayers and to their smaller size. A lower food intake would result in a lower heat production. Nonlayers were also able to achieve higher respiratory rates during hyperthermia than were layers. They might therefore be able to lose more heat by respiratory evaporative cooling (Weiss, 1959). In the hot environment to which they are acclimatized, layers have higher body temperatures, respiratory rates, and water consumptions than nonlayers, reflecting the inferior heat tolerance of the layers (Hillerman and Wilson, 1955).

In chickens the tolerance of both hot-wet and hot-dry conditions is greater the lower the plane of nutrition (Robinson and Lee, 1947). This effect of diet is related to its total caloric value and not to its protein content, even though protein is known to have a high specific dynamic action (see Chapter 9). When chickens are dehydrated at an environmental temperature of 90°F. their deep body temperatures diminish; but this is probably the consequence of a reduced food intake and therefore of a diminution in heat production (Wilson and Edwards, 1952). Seibert (1949) has suggested that the high water requirements of the white-throated sparrow were correlated with its poor heat tolerance and northward migration in spring.

It is clear that different breeds of chickens have different heat tolerances (Lee, Robinson, Yeates, and Scott, 1945; Wilson, 1949); White Leghorns have proved themselves to be superior in this respect to most other breeds. The greater heat tolerance of the White Leghorns was thought to be due to their greater propensity for splashing water over their bodies (Lee *et al.,* 1945). However, White Leghorns were found to lose more heat by evaporation, per unit of body weight, than either Rhode Island Reds or New Hampshire–Cornish cross birds. It is possible, therefore, that White Leghorns have a better-developed evaporative cooling mechanism than other breeds (Ota and McNally, 1961). There is also evidence that the heat tolerance of different breeds of chickens, especially during exposure to solar radiation, is related to the color of the plumage. Thus, White Leghorns were more heat-tolerant than either Rhode Island Reds or White Leghorns that had had their plumage artificially colored red (Okamoto, Otsubo, Ogawa, and Masumitsu, 1958). Besides differences in heat tolerance between breeds there are also genetically determined differences between members of the same breed (Kheirildin and Shaffner, 1957). A higher tolerance of heat is associated with a greater rate of growth. Romijn and Lokhorst (1961) were able to demonstrate a marked difference in the heat tolerance of male and female Blue North Holland chickens. The cocks had a superior heat tolerance, which was attributed in part to the greater heat loss from their larger combs and wattles, the area of which amounted to 14 percent of the total surface area of the birds. This seems to be a likely explanation because the data both of Hillerman and Wilson (1955) and of Romijn and Lokhorst (1961) reveal that the panting response of the male chicken is inferior to that of the female. As might be expected, removal of the feathers of chickens improved their tolerance of heat (Lee *et al.*, 1945), and chickens with poor feathering were more heat tolerant than birds with a normal plumage (Romijn and Lokhorst, 1961).

It has been demonstrated that the heat tolerance of chickens can also be improved experimentally by the administration of adrenal cortical hormones, tranquilizing drugs, and sympatholytic agents (Burger and Lorenz, 1960). The increased heat tolerance conferred by tranquilizing drugs and sympatholytic agents was thought by Burger and Lorenz to be mediated by a diminished reactivity of the sympathetic nervous system, but Weiss, (1960) concluded that the increased heat tolerance of chickens following administration of reserpine was the result of increased respiratory heat loss. Chicks fed antibiotics in hot summer weather had a lower mortality than the control birds (Osbaldiston and Sainsbury, 1963). The maintenance of a normal body temperature following an increase or a decrease in environmental temperature was facilitated in the chicken by administration of supplementary ascorbic acid (Thornton, 1962). The beneficial effect of ascorbic acid was attributed to an action on the adrenal cortex of the birds. Evidence has been obtained recently that the tolerance of hyperthermia is associated with an increase in cardiac output during hyperthermia (Whittow, Sturkie, and Stein, 1964).

The resistance of birds to cold is also influenced by their state of acclimatization. English sparrows examined during the summer were able to maintain thermal balance only at environmental temperatures above 0°C., in contrast to birds acclimatized to winter weather, which were resistant to environmental temperatures as low as −30°C. (see King and Farner, 1961). The enhanced tolerance to cold in winter was due in part to a greater energy intake and therefore a greater heat production than in summer. Recent work suggests that the ability to tolerate very low temperatures depends upon how long the birds are able to maintain their summit metabolism (see Chapter 9), and that birds acclimatized to winter conditions are superior in this respect to birds examined during the summer (West, 1962). As expected, the tolerance of passerine birds to cold is greater when their food intake is maintained at a high level than when they are starved (Kendeigh, 1934). However, starved English sparrows survived longer at environmental temperatures between −14.9°C. and 35.9°C. in the winter than in the summer (Kendeigh, 1934). The longer survival times of the starved birds in winter were attributed to the greater weight of their plumage. Clipping the feathers of English sparrows resulted in a decrease in their survival times in a cold environment (4.4°C.), according to Baldwin and Kendeigh (1932). Similarly, the survival times of pigeons exposed to air at −40°C. were reduced from more than 48 hours to from 20 to 30 minutes after the feathers had been plucked (Streicher, Hackel, and Fleischmann, 1950). Ortolan and yellow buntings with defective plumage were less resistant to cold but more tolerant of heat than normal birds (Wallgren, 1954). In contrast to the beneficial effects of acclimatization to cold on cold tolerance described above, Ryser and Morrison (1954) found that repeated exposure of 2- to 3-day-old ring-necked pheasants to cool conditions (20°C.) actually impaired their resistance to cold. In older birds, however, this procedure improved the tolerance of the birds to cold.

Birds are better able to tolerate exposure to cold air than exposure to cold water. Thus, chickens survived for 50 to 65 minutes during immersion in water at 6−11°C., but they survived for 3.3 to 29.5 hours at an air temperature of −34°C. to −37°C. (Sturkie, 1946; Horvath, Folk, Craig, and Fleischmann, 1948). Heat loss to water is much greater than that to air at the same temperature because of the greater thermal capacity and conductivity of water, and because the insulation of the feathers breaks down when the feathers are wetted.

Lethal Temperatures

The deep body temperature at which the bird dies during hyperthermia is known as the upper lethal temperature. The upper lethal temperature of the adult chicken is approximately 47°C. (Table 40), and the adult Eastern house wren, the brown towhee, and the Abert's towhee have similar upper lethal temperatures (Baldwin and Kendeigh, 1932; Randall, 1943a; Dawson, 1954). The lower lethal body temperatures of chickens are given in Table 40. The lower lethal temperature of the Eastern house wren during exposure to cold air was found to be 21.7°C. (Baldwin and Kendeigh, 1932). Thus, the lower lethal temperatures of two species of very different body weight, determined by exposure to cold air or by immersion in cold water, were quite similar.

Influence of Different Environmental Temperatures on Reproduction

It has been known for many years that the rate of laying of chickens is decreased by exposure to high temperatures. For example, Wilson (1949) noted a diminution in egg weight, numbers of eggs, and shell thickness in hens kept at 37.8°C. as opposed to birds kept at 21.1°C. The diminished egg production in a hot environment is often related to the lower energy intake. White Leghorns laid more eggs at high environmental temperatures than did either New Hampshires or Plymouth Rocks (Huston, Joiner, and Carmon, 1957). Short daily exposures to heat are sufficient to

Table 40. Upper and lower lethal temperatures of the chicken

Age	Deep body temperature °C.	Authority
	UPPER LETHAL	
Young	46.0–47.8	Randall (1943a)
Adult	47.0	"
1 day	46.7	Moreng & Shaffner (1951)
3 days	47.2	"
Adult	47.2	"
	LOWER LETHAL	
1 day	15.5	Moreng & Shaffner (1951)
2 days	15.5–16.1	"
4 "	16.1–16.6	"
6 "	17.2–18.0	"
8 "	17.2–18.8	"
10 "	18.3–20.5	"
21 "	18.8–20.0	"
16 weeks	19.4–20.5	"
Adult female	23.4	Sturkie (1946)
Adult male	20.7	"

cause a reduction in egg weight (Hutchinson, 1954). Squibb, Wogan, and Reed (1959), however, could not demonstrate an inhibitory effect of high environmental temperature on egg production under natural conditions, provided daily fluctuations of temperature occurred. The inhibitory effect of a hot environment on egg production is intensified if water is withheld from the chickens (Wilson and Edwards, 1952). Birds have the highest productivity at environmental temperatures within the thermoneutral range because their energy requirements for thermoregulatory purposes are then at a minimum (Osbaldiston and Sainsbury, 1963). Variations of environmental temperature from 9.0 to 29.5°C. had no significant effect on egg production, but exposure to air temperatures lower than 9°C. depressed egg production (Wilson, McNally, and Ota, 1957). The fertility and hatchability of hens are reduced by exposure to high temperatures (Wilson, McNally, and Ota, 1957; Huston and Carmon, 1958). If the environmental temperature is variable the fertility and hatchability of the eggs are also less than when the environmental temperature is kept constant. The optimal storage temperature of the egg for the maintenance of blastoderm viability is 10–12°C. The fertility of eggs laid in hot summer weather is low (Heywang, 1944). The frequency of copulation and the quantity and quality of the semen are adversely affected by heat (Heywang, 1944). On the other hand, the initiation of spermatogenesis occurs later when chicks are reared at 0°C. or 10°C. than when they are kept at 30°C. (Hafez, 1964a).

THERMOREGULATION IN THE YOUNG BIRD

The chick embryo cannot regulate its own temperature during the early stages of incubation, but the 19-day-old embryo can respond, although not very effectively, to a lowering of its environmental temperature (Romijn, 1954). The respiratory quotient increases during cooling—an indication of the metabolism of glycogen stores in muscle and liver—and the temperature of the egg remains above that of the environment. The embryos of Western gulls also appear to be able to regulate their body temperatures to some extent (Bartholomew and Dawson, 1952). The embryos of many species possess the ability to withstand temporary periods of hypothermia when the adult is away from the nest (Baldwin and Kendeigh, 1932). Moreng and Bryant (1955) demonstrated that the one-day-old chick embryo can survive an exposure of 76 hours to air at 0°C., although the normal incubation temperature for the chicken is 39–40°C. The tolerance of the chick embryo to cold diminishes with age (Moreng and Bryant, 1956). However, the lower lethal internal temperature of the chicken's egg is from −2.2°C. to −1.1°C. throughout the period of incubation. During the first 5 days of incubation of the chicken's egg, its upper lethal temperature is approximately 42.2°C. (Moreng and Shaffner, 1951). By the 8th day the upper lethal temperature has increased to between 45.6°C. and 47.8°C., and it remains at this level for the remainder of the incubation period. When the eggs of the Eastern house wren are exposed to an air temperature of

45.6°C. for one hour they fail to hatch (Baldwin and Kendeigh, 1932). So it is likely that the lethal temperature of eggs of small wild birds is similar to that of the chicken.

Baldwin and Kendeigh (1932) observed that a bare patch of skin appears on the breast of the adult house wren during incubation of the eggs, which must facilitate heat transfer from the incubating bird to the eggs. A similar patch, which becomes vascularized during incubation, was reported by Farner (1958) in the yellow-eyed penguin. The slow development of the incubation or brood patch in this species was held responsible in part for the slow increase in the incubation temperature (i.e. the temperature at the interphase between the incubation patch and the surface of the egg) to its final level. In passerine birds, estrogen and prolactin are essential for the development of the incubation patch; in those species in which only the males develop the incubation patch, testosterone replaces estrogen (Johns and Pfeiffer, 1963).

During the first 10 days of incubation the evaporative heat loss from the chicken's egg exceeds the heat production, so that the temperature of the egg may be slightly below the ambient dry-bulb temperature. Later, however, the metabolism of the egg exceeds the heat loss, and the temperature of the egg may slightly exceed the air temperature. Toward the end of the incubation period the major channel of heat loss from the egg is the nonevaporative one (Romijn and Lokhorst, 1956, 1960; see Chapter 9).

The thermoregulatory ability of the very young bird depends largely upon its insulation, but also upon the degree of muscular development and on the state of development of its central nervous control. In altricial species the young are unable to regulate their body temperature, and they depend for some time upon the shelter of the nest and upon heat derived from their parents. The altricial Eastern house wren is able to some extent to keep its body temperature above the air temperature when it is 3 to 6 days old (Kendeigh, 1939). This ability is associated with the development of the feathers. The plumage not only protects young Eastern house wrens from cold but also reduces the amount of the heat they gain during exposure to direct sunlight. The metabolic rate also increases from the 3rd through the 6th day, partly as a result of muscle tremors (Odum, 1942; see also Chapter 9). From the 6th to the 9th day the bird is able to increase its metabolic rate in response to cold. On the 15th day thermoregulation is almost at the adult level (see Chapter 9). The Eastern field sparrow and the Eastern chipping sparrow develop rapidly during the nestling period. They are altricial birds which are essentially homeothermic at 7 to 10 days of age. In these birds the appearance of temperature regulation actually precedes the development of an insulating plumage (Dawson and Evans, 1957), being more closely associated with the development of the musculature and the reduction in the surface area/body weight ratio with growth (see below).

The chicken is a precocial bird; the hatched chick is covered with down. An increase in metabolic rate can occur in response to cold, and increased respiratory evaporative heat loss follows exposure to heat in chicks 2 days old (see Chapter 9 and Figure 31). However, the thermoneutral range of chicks is at a higher level of

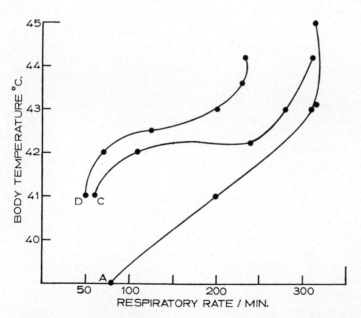

Figure 31. Panting responses in a young chick at different ages. Curve A is that of a 2-day-old chick, C that of the same chick at 15 days, and D that at 28 days. (Redrawn from Randall, 1943a; courtesy *Am. J. Physiol.*)

the temperature scale than that of adults, although it decreases and widens as the feathers develop (see Table 39; also Chapter 9). The temperature coefficient also diminishes with growth. Panting occurs at a lower temperature in the newborn chick than in the adult, reflecting the lower body temperature of the chick (Figure 31). The panting threshold increases as the chick grows and as its body temperature increases. The evaporative water loss from chicks during the first day of life is considerable (Table 41). Medway and Kare (1957) thought this high rate of water loss was due partly to the rapid breathing on the first day and partly to a high cutaneous water loss. The evaporative water loss decreases after the first day but is high again after the second or third week, the increase being associated with the increase in metabolism, in body temperature, and in the insulation provided by the plumage. A similar trend has been observed in the Eastern house wren (Kendeigh, 1939). The rate of evaporative water loss from young Eastern house wrens, unlike that from the adults, increases with environmental temperature within the range of 21.7 to 37.8°C. (Ken-

Table 41. Evaporative water loss, heat loss, and basal metabolic rates of chickens of different ages (modified from Medway and Kare, 1957, courtesy *Am. J. Physiol.*)

Age	Number of birds	Average weight	Evaporative loss (mg. H_2O/ml. O_2 consumed) $\pm$ standard deviation	Heat loss by evaporation of water (percent of total heat loss)	Heat produced (kcal./sq. m./day)
1 day	84	37	15.4 ± 2.8	26.9	611 ± 49
1 week	72	53	9.1 ± 2.1	18.7	939 ± 113
2 weeks	48	98	9.1 ± 1.4	19.0	1081 ± 62
3 weeks	30	140	16.6 ± 0.2	23.2	969 ± 76
4 weeks	54	224	17.0 ± 4.4	24.2	1002 ± 51
8 weeks	17	622	15.9 ± 4.0	21.5	894 ± 117
16 weeks	8	1255	22.8 ± 4.5	23.3	865 ± 82
32 weeks	9	1771	25.9 ± 3.2	26.6	779 ± 155

deigh, 1939). The reason for this difference is that the body temperature of the young birds, although not of the adults, increases with increasing air temperature within this range.

In all birds the increase in body size during growth results in a relative reduction in the surface area, and this in turn must help to reduce the dissipation of heat produced by metabolic activity. Young birds are more dependent upon an increase in metabolism in response to cold than are adults (Kendeigh, 1939; Romijn, 1954). In nestling gulls, temperature regulation amounts to the restriction of body temperature to a range of approximately 8°C., rather than the maintenance of a constant body temperature (Bartholomew and Dawson, 1954), and this may be true of some other birds also. The lower lethal temperature of the young chicken and of the immature Eastern house wren is lower than that of the adult, but it increases as the bird grows (Moreng and Shaffner, 1951; Baldwin and Kendeigh, 1932; see Table 40). Nevertheless, the lower lethal body temperature of the newly hatched chick is higher than that of the embryo (Moreng and Shaffner, 1951). The upper lethal temperature of the day-old chick is very similar to that of the adult (Table 41), but it is slightly higher than that of the embryo. Similarly, the upper lethal temperature of the young Eastern house wren is about the same as that for the adult (Baldwin and Kendeigh, 1932). These differences in upper and lower lethal temperatures between young and adult birds are not to be confused with differences in the upper and lower environmental temperatures which birds can tolerate. Thus, the survival time of young birds during exposure to an environmental temperature of −23.3°C. increases with age (Moreng and Shaffner, 1951). On the other hand, chicks and young Eastern house wrens are able to withstand exposure to higher environmental temperatures than are adults (Barott and Pringle, 1946; Baldwin and Kendeigh, 1932). Survival times at different environmental temperatures are influenced by the rate at which the bird loses or gains heat to or from the environment, whereas the lethal deep-body temperatures are determined by the ability of the tissues to function at different temperatures.

TORPIDITY

Adult birds of some species have the remarkable ability to tolerate periods of quite considerable hypothermia. This phenomenon, which is known as "torpidity," has been observed in the California poor-will, in which the deep body temperature may decrease to 4.8°C. (Bartholomew, Howell, and Cade, 1957; see Chapter 9). According to Jaeger (1949), the poor-will may remain torpid for approximately 3 months. Koskimies (1948, 1950) found that the swift became torpid at night during a period of starvation, and that its deep body temperature decreased to within a few degrees of the environmental temperature. The respiratory rate, respiratory quotient, oxygen consumption, water loss, and rate of weight loss also decreased. However, some thermoregulatory ability evidently remains even during torpor, since a further drop in environmental temperature will elicit shivering (Bartholomew, Hudson, and Howell, 1962). Hummingbirds may also become torpid (Pearson, 1950), especially on cold nights when a considerable expenditure of energy would be necessary to maintain body temperature if the bird did not become torpid. The value of temporary hypothermia to the bird is clearly the conservation of energy at a time when food is not available or when the bird is not feeding, as at night or during very cold weather. Bartholomew *et al.* (1957) were able to induce torpidity in white-throated swifts by subjecting them to conditions which resulted in a depletion of their energy reserves. Birds become torpid so rapidly that the process is thought to be initiated by the central nervous system (Bartholomew *et al.,* 1957).

FLIGHT

Very little is known about the thermoregulation of birds during flight. The deep body temperature of the fairy prion was approximately 1.6°C. higher after flight than during normal activity on the ground (Farner, 1956). The metabolic rate of birds during flight is undoubtedly greater than at rest (see Chapter 9). Convective heat loss is also greater during flight than at rest, because of the high rate of air movement past the bird, a possible decrease in the insulation of the feathers, the flapping movements of the wings, and the greater surface area presented by the outstretched wings. Foot temperatures of the red-tailed tropic bird during flight are lower than deep body temperature but higher than the air temperature, and they are higher than the foot temperatures of resting birds (Howell and Bartholomew, 1962). It is likely therefore that the feet provide an important avenue of heat loss in some flying birds. Most of the heat produced by the flight muscles must, however, be lost by evaporation from the respiratory tract. Red-tailed tropic birds have been observed to have their bills agape during flight, apparently panting in response to heat stress (Howell and Bartholomew, 1962). Recent information obtained by telemetry on the wild duck in flight revealed that the respiratory rate was approximately 7 times greater when the bird was flying at 40 m.p.h. than when it was at rest (Lord, Bellrose, and Cochran, 1962). The increased oxygen requirements of the muscles during flight must result in a greatly increased ventilation, and this in turn must result in increased evaporative cooling. Any additional increase in ventilation necessary for the dissipation of heat would therefore entail the risk of removing too much carbon dioxide from the blood, with a consequent alkalosis.

DISTRIBUTION OF BIRDS IN RELATION TO THEIR THERMOREGULATORY CAPACITIES

Knowledge of the means by which different species of birds regulate their body temperatures under different climatic conditions has provided a rational basis for explaining the distribution and behavior of many species of wild birds.

Thus, Bartholomew and Dawson (1953) concluded that the distribution of desert birds is related to the availability of water or succulent food. Such birds are diurnal, which means that they are exposed to maximal desert temperatures, and they lose a large percentage of their body weight in 24 hours as a result of respiratory evaporation of moisture. Constant replenishment of the water lost from the body is therefore essential for these birds. However, the American kestrel, unlike most birds, does not require water to drink; it is able to derive sufficient water from its fresh carnivorous diet (Bartholomew and Cade, 1957). Some species such as the house finch do not require water; they are able to maintain their body weight if provided with sufficient succulent vegetation (Bartholomew and Cade, 1956). A rather specialized adaptation to a desert climate is evidenced in the poor-will. This bird has, relative to its size, a very low metabolic rate (Hudson, 1962). The amount of heat required to be dissipated is therefore less than in other species. Furthermore, the upper critical temperature for the poor-will is not well defined and appears to be higher than 44°C. This bird utilizes gular fluttering rather than panting in order to increase its evaporative heat loss, and in this way it reduces to a minimum the metabolic cost of panting.

Dawson (1954) made an extensive comparative investigation of two closely related species of birds, one of which, the Abert's towhee, inhabits the Colorado Desert, and the other, the brown towhee, occupies much cooler areas. The results of his investigation showed quite clearly that the desert bird was well adapted to its hot, dry environment. Thus in a hot environment the Abert's towhee as compared with the brown towhee had a lower body temperature, showed a greater resistance to water deprivation, lost less water by evaporation, and drank less water. Furthermore, the thermoneutral range of the Abert's towhee extended to a higher temperature than that of the brown towhee, and the increase in heat production with increasing environmental temperature above the upper critical temperature was less rapid in the Abert's towhee. Conversely, below the lower critical temperature, the rate of increase in heat production was greater in the Abert's towhee. When the environmental temperature was increased, the heat production of the Abert's towhee increased after a longer latent period than did that of the brown towhee.

Bartholomew and Dawson (1954) have cautioned against attempts to explain geographical distributions of birds solely in terms of slight physiological differences. For instance, the brown pelican and the great blue heron are altricial species, inferior in the thermoregulatory capabilities of their young to the precocial Western gull. Yet all three species occupy the same habitat and are exposed to severe direct insolation. Differences in behavior and especially in parental care are often of greater significance than physiological differences (Hafez, 1964b).

NERVOUS CONTROL OF THERMOREGULATION

The maintenance of a body temperature that varies only very slightly in spite of large variations of activity and of environmental temperature requires an exact control system. This system must regulate heat production and heat loss at all times, and there is evidence that in birds this control is performed largely by nerve cells in the hypothalamus.

Heat production. There is evidence that the heat production of birds can be increased by cooling the brain directly or by stimulation of cutaneous cold receptors.

The experiments of Rogers and Lackey (1923) showed that the heat production of pigeons in which the optic thalamus had been destroyed did not increase when they were exposed to cold. Rogers (1928), reported that shivering and an increased body temperature could be produced by the direct application of cold to the pigeon's thalamus. These results pointed to a central nervous control of heat production in the bird. The results of Randall's experiments (1943a), in which he lowered the deep body temperature of 7-day-old chicks by the insertion of a cooling tube into the cloaca, conform with the evidence for a central control of heat production. Shivering occurred although there was little change in skin temperature. The deep body temperature at which shivering is first observed can be altered experimentally. Thus, after chickens have been subjected to hyperthermia, the deep body temperature threshold for shivering is lower than normal (Randall, 1943b).

When chicks are exposed to a cold environment, shivering can be detected before any change occurs in the deep body temperature (Randall, 1943a). It seems likely from this observation that cooling of the skin alone might be sufficient to increase heat production, presumably by means of a nerve reflex. The importance of the vagus nerves in the regulation of heat production seems to be established by the failure of bilaterally vagotomized pigeons to increase their heat production in the face of a decrease in body temperature (see King and Farner, 1961).

Heat loss. Rogers and Lackey (1923) failed to produce thermal polypnea in the pigeon after destruction of the thalamus, and in the same species Sinha (1959) found that destruction of an area of the midbrain between the optic lobes abolished panting. Bilateral lesions in the hypothalamus prevented the usual panting response to heat in chickens (Feldman, Larsson, Dimick, and Lepkovsky, 1957). Behavioral responses to heat were also absent after the lesions. Saalfeld (1936) was able to produce panting by warming the anterior dorsal wall of the midbrain of the pigeon. When this region of the brain is cooled experimentally, panting does not occur even though the deep body temperature elsewhere is well above the panting threshold. Recently, Åkerman, Andersson, Fabricius, and Svensson (1960) succeeded in producing polypnea in the pi-

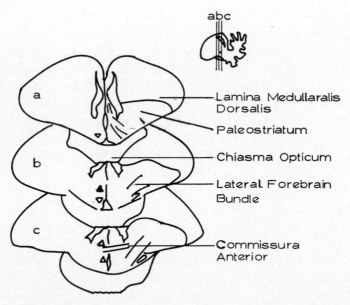

Figure 32. Diagrams (x8) of transverse sections of the pigeon's brain showing the areas from which panting could be elicited in response to electrical stimulation. The levels of the sections are shown in the top right hand part of the figure. ▲ = panting which continued after cessation of stimulation △ = panting during stimulation only ▽ = panting starting immediately after cessation of stimulation (Redrawn from Åkerman *et al.,* 1960; courtesy *Acta Physiol. Scand.*)

geon by electrical stimulation of the anterior hypothalamus and preoptic area (Figure 32). It is clear from these results that thermal polypnea must be brought about at least in part by the activity of a discrete area of the brain. Indeed, it has been asserted that birds, unlike mammals, cannot be made to pant by warming the skin in the absence of an increase in the temperature of the thermoregulatory centers in the brain (Randall, 1943a). This statement is based upon the results of experiments in which cold water was circulated around the neck of a 7-day-old chick while its body surface was heated. Under these conditions thermal polypnea did not occur until the cold collar was removed. Further experiments are needed in order definitely to rule out a peripheral component in the control of panting, and in these experiments the temperature of the thermoregulatory centers in the brain should be measured. Randall (1943b) has reported that the deep body temperature at which panting occurs may be lowered by previous subjection of the bird to hypothermia. However, in Randall's experiments the skin temperature in birds that had been cooled was higher during subsequent heating than it was in birds that had not been cooled. It is possible that the lowered panting threshold was the result of facilitation of the thermoregulatory center in the brain by afferent nerve impulses arising from the increased skin temperature. Evidence that panting can occur before there is any detectable elevation of the deep body temperature has recently been obtained by Howell and Bartholomew (1962) for nestlings of the red-tailed tropic bird and the red-footed booby. Thermal polypnea, once established, can be inhibited by cooling the skin (Randall and Hiestand, 1939; Randall, 1943b). Panting can occur in the vagotomized pigeon (Saalfeld, 1936), although the rate is slightly less than in birds with intact vagi (Sinha, 1959). In the chicken, panting is abolished by bilateral vagotomy (Hiestand and Randall, 1942). The significance of this species difference and of the specific role of the vagi in thermal polypnea has not been established.

Water intake. The control of water intake is involved in the regulation of body temperature, particularly under hot conditions when heat is lost from the bird entirely or largely by evaporation of moisture. The hypothalamus seems to be involved in this control, since Åkerman *et al.* (1960) were able to induce polydipsia by electrical stimulation of the preoptic area and the anterior hypothalamus of pigeons. In one chicken, drinking did not occur after lesions had been placed in its hypothalamus (Feldman *et al.*, 1957).

CONCLUSIONS

The relatively high deep body temperature, the absence of sweat glands, the localized distribution of fat, and the very effective insulation provided by feathers distinguish the thermoregulatory physiology of many birds from that of the other group of homeothermic animals, the mammals. Birds almost without exception are panting animals, and a better understanding of the physiology of panting, with particular regard to the specialized structure and function of the avian respiratory system, is essential to further elucidation of the mechanisms by which birds regulate their body temperature in hot environments. The study of thermoregulation during flight presents a challenge to the avian physiologist. Recent developments in the techniques of telemetry enable the physiologist to meet this challenge. There is already evidence that different species of birds may employ different thermoregulatory mechanisms, which makes the study of individual species a worthy endeavor.

REFERENCES

Åkerman, B., B. Andersson, E. Fabricius, and L. Svensson 1960 Observations on central regulation of body temperature and of food and water intake in the pigeon (Columba livia). Acta Physiol. Scand. 50:328.

Baldwin, S. P., and S. C. Kendeigh 1932 Physiology of the temperature of birds. Sci. Publ. Cleveland Museum Nat. Hist. 3:1.

Barott, H. G., and Emma M. Pringle 1946 Energy and gaseous metabolism of the chicken from hatch to maturity as affected by temperature. J. Nutr. 31:35.

Bartholomew, G. A., and T. J. Cade 1956 Water consumption of house finches. Condor 58:406.

Bartholomew, G. A. and T. J. Cade 1957 The body temperature of the American kestrel, Falco sparverius. Wilson Bull. 69:149.

Bartholomew, G. A. and W. R. Dawson 1952 Body temperatures in nestling Western gulls. Condor 54:58.

Bartholomew, G. A. and W. R. Dawson 1953 Respiratory water loss in some birds of southwestern United States. Physiol. Zoöl. 26:162.

Bartholomew, G. A., and W. R. Dawson 1954 Temperature regulation in young pelicans, herons and gulls. Ecology 35:466.

Bartholomew, G. A., and W. R. Dawson 1958 Body temperatures in California and Gambel's Quail. Auk 75:150.

Bartholomew, G. A., T. R. Howell and T. J. Cade 1957 Torpidity, in the white-throated swift, Anna hummingbird, and poor-will. Condor 59:145.

Bartholomew, G. A., J. W. Hudson, and T. R. Howell 1962 Body temperature, oxygen consumption, evaporative water loss, and heart rate in the poor-will. Condor 64:117.

Benedict, F. G., W. Landauer and E. L. Fox 1932 The physiology of normal and frizzle fowl with special reference to basal metabolism. Univ. Conn. (Storrs) Agr. Expt. Sta. Bull. No. 177:15

Burger, R. E., and F. W. Lorenz 1960 Pharmacologically induced resistance to heat shock. 2: Modifications of activity of the central-nervous and endocrine systems. Poultry Sci. 39:477.

Burton, A. C., and O. G. Edholm 1955 Man in a Cold Environment, p. 30. Edward Arnold (Publishers) Ltd., London.

Chatfield, P. O., C. P. Lyman, and L. Irving 1953 Physiological adaptation to cold of peripheral nerve in the leg of the herring gull (Larus argentatus). Am. J. Physiol. 172:639.

Dawson, W. R. 1954 Temperature regulation and water requirements of the brown and Abert towhees, Pipilo fuscus and Pipilo aberti. Univ. Calif. Publ. Zool. 59:81.

Dawson, W. R. 1958 Relation of oxygen consumption and evaporative water loss to temperature in the cardinal. Physiol. Zool., 31:37.

Dawson, W. R. 1960 Personal communication to M. S. Misch.

Dawson, W. R. 1962 Evolution of temperature regulation in birds, in Comparative Physiology of Temperature Regulation edited by J. P. Hannon and E. Viereck, Part 1, p. 45. Arctic Aeromedical Laboratory, Fort Wainwright, Alaska.

Dawson, W. R., and F. C. Evans 1957 Relation of growth and development to temperature regulation in nestling field and chipping sparrows. Physiol. Zool. 30:315.

Dawson, W. R., and H. B. Tordoff 1959 Relation of oxygen consumption to temperature in the evening grosbeak. Condor 61:388.

Deighton, T., and J. C. D. Hutchinson 1940 Studies on the metabolism of fowls. II: The effect of activity on metabolism. J. Agr. Sci. 30:141.

Eklund, C. R. 1942 Body temperatures of antarctic birds. Auk 59:544.

Farner, D. S. 1956 Body temperature of the fairy prion (Pachyptila turtur) in flight and at rest. J. Appl. Physiol., 8:546.

Farner, D. S. 1958 Incubation and body temperatures in the yellow-eyed penguin. Auk 75:249.

Feldman, S. E., S. Larsson, M. K. Dimick, and S. Lepkovsky 1957 Aphagia in chickens. Am. J. Physiol. 191:259.

Frankel, H., K. G. Hollands, and H. S. Weiss 1962 Respiratory and circulatory responses of hyperthermic chickens. Arch. Int. Physiol. Bioch. 70:555.

Frith, H. J. 1957 Experiments on the control of temperature in the mound of the mallee-fowl, Leipoa ocellata Gould (Megapodiidae). C.S.I.R.O. Wildlife Research 2:101.

Gelineo, S. 1955 Temperature d'adaptation et production de chaleur chez les oiseaux de petite taille. Arch. Sci. Physiol. 9:225.

Goldsmith, R. and W. J. L. Sladen 1961 Temperature regulation of some Antarctic penguins. J. Physiol. 157:251.

Grant, R. T., and E. F. Bland 1931 Observations on arteriovenous anastomoses in human skin and in the bird's foot with special reference to the reaction to cold. Heart 15:385.

Hafez, E. S. E. 1964a Effects of high temperature on reproduction. Int. J. Biomet. 7:223.

Hafez, E. S. E. 1964b Behavioral thermoregulation in mammals and birds. Int. J. Biomet. 7:231.

Hardy, J. D. 1934 The radiation of heat from the human body. I: An instrument for measuring the radiation and surface temperature of the skin. J. Clin. Invest. 13:593.

Hazelwood, R. L., and W. O. Wilson 1962 Comparison of haematological alterations induced in the pigeon and rat by fasting and heat stress. Comp. Biochem. Physiol. 7:211.

Heywang, B. W. 1938 Effect of some factors on the body temperature of hens. Poultry Sci. 17:317.

Heywang, B. W. 1944 Fertility and hatchability when the environmental temperature of chickens is high. Poultry Sci. 23:334.

Hiestand, W. A. and W. C. Randall 1942 Influence of proprioceptive vagal afferents on panting and accessory panting movements in mammals and birds. Am. J. Physiol. 138:12.

Hildén, A., and K. S. Stenbäck 1916 Zur Kenntniss der Tageschwankungen der Körpertemperatur bei den Vögeln. Skand. Arch. Physiol. 34:382.

Hillerman, J. P., and W. O. Wilson 1955 Acclimation of adult chickens to environmental temperature changes. Am. J. Physiol. 180:591.

Horvath, S. M., G. E. Folk, F. N. Craig, and W. Fleischmann 1948 Survival time of various warm-blooded animals in extreme cold. Science 107:171.

Howell, T. R., and G. A. Bartholomew 1961 Temperature regulation in Laysan and Black-footed albatrosses. Condor 63:185.

Howell, T. R. and G. A. Bartholomew 1962 Temperature regulation in the red-tailed tropic bird and the red-footed booby. Condor 64:6.

Hudson, J. W. 1962 Temperature regulation in desert birds and mammals in Comparative Physiology of Temperature Regulation, edited J. P. Hannon and E. Viereck, Part 3, p. 421., Arctic Aeromedical Laboratory, Fort Wainwright, Alaska.

Huggins, R. A. 1941 Egg temperatures of wild birds under natural conditions. Ecology 22:148.

Huston, T. M. 1960 The effects of high environmental temperatures upon blood constituents and thyroid activity of domestic fowl. Poultry Sci. 39:1260.

Huston, T. M., and J. L. Carmon 1958 Influence of high environmental temperature on fertility and hatchability of eggs of domestic fowl. Physiol. Zool. 13:232.

Huston, T. M., W. P. Joiner, and J. L. Carmon 1957 Breed differences in egg production of domestic fowl held at high environmental temperatures. Poultry Sci. 36:1247.

Hutchinson, J. C. D. 1954 Heat regulation in birds. In Vol. 1, Progress in the Physiology of Farm Animals, edited by J. Hammond. Butterworths Scientific Publ., London.

Hutchinson, J. C. D., and A. H. Sykes 1953 Physiological acclimatization of fowls to a hot humid environment. J. Agric Sci. 43:294.

Irving, L. and J. Krog 1954 Body temperatures of arctic and subarctic birds and mammals. J. Appl. Physiol. 6:667.

Irving, L., H. Krog, and M. Monson 1955 The metabolism of some

Alaskan animals in winter and summer. Physiol. Zool., 28:173.

Jaeger, E. C. 1949 Further observations on the hibernation of the poor-will. Condor 51:105.

Johns, J. E., and E. W. Pfeiffer 1963 Testosterone-induced incubation patches of phalarope birds. Science 140:1225.

Jordan, K. A., and A. C. Dale 1961 The measurement of heat transmission components of chickens. Paper No. 61-402, Annual Meeting Am. Soc. Agricultural Engineers, Ames, Iowa.

Kahl, M. P. 1963 Thermoregulation in the wood stork, with special reference to the role of the legs. Physiol. Zool. 36:141.

Kayser, C. 1929 Contribution à l'étude du mécanisme nerveux de la régulation thermique. Ann. Physiol. Physicochim. Biol., 15:131.

Kendeigh, S. C. 1934 The role of environment in the life of birds. Ecol. Monogr. 4:229.

Kendeigh, S. C. 1939 The relation of metabolism to the development of temperature regulation in birds. J. Exp. Zool. 82:419.

Kheirildin, M. A., and C. S. Shaffner 1957 Familial differences in resistance to high environmental temperatures in chicks. Poultry Science 36:1334.

King, J .O. L. 1956 The body temperature of chicks during the first 14 days of life. Brit. Vet. J. 112:155.

King, J. R. and D. S. Farner 1961 Energy metabolism, thermoregulation and body temperature. In Vol. II. Biology and Comparative Physiology of Birds, edited by A. J. Marshall. Academic Press, New York.

Kleiber, M., and C. Winchester 1933 Temperature regulation in baby chicks. Proc. Soc. Exp. Biol. N.Y. 31:158.

Koskimies, J. 1948 On temperature regulation and metabolism in the swift, Micropus a. apus L., during fasting. Experientia 4:274.

Koskimies, J. 1950 The life of the swift, Micropus apus (L) in relation to the weather. Ann. Acad. Sci. Fennicae Ser. A. IV, 15:1.

Lamoreux, W. F. 1943 Effect of differences in light and temperature upon the size of combs on White Leghorns. Endocrinol. 32:497.

Lamoreux, W. F., and F. B. Hutt 1939 Variability of body temperature in the normal chick. Poultry Sci. 18:70.

Lasiewski, R. C. 1963 Oxygen consumption of torpid, resting, active and flying hummingbirds. Physiol. Zool. 36:122.

Lee, D. H. K., K. W. Robinson, N. T. M. Yeates and M. I. R. Scott 1945 Poultry husbandry in hot climates—Experimental inquiries. Poultry Sci. 24:195.

Lord, R. D., F. C. Bellrose, and W. W. Cochran 1962 Radiotelemetry of the respiration of a flying duck. Science 137:39

Medway, W., and M. R. Kare 1957 Water metabolism of the domestic fowl from hatching to maturity. Am. J. Physiol. 190:139.

Misch, M. S. 1960 Heat regulation in the northern blue jay, Cyanocitta cristata bromia Oberholser. Physiol. Zool. 33:252.

Moreng, R. E., and R. L. Bryant 1955 The tolerance of the chicken embryo to periods of low temperature exposure. Poultry Sci. 34:1342.

Moreng, R. E. and R. L. Bryant 1956 The resistance of the chicken embryo to low temperature exposure. Poultry Sci. 35:753.

Moreng, R. E., and C. S. Shaffner 1951 Lethal internal temperatures for the chicken, from fertile egg to mature bird. Poultry Sci. 30:255.

Morrison, P. R., and F. A. Ryser 1952 Weight and body temperature in mammals. Science 116:231.

Odum, E. P. 1942 Muscle tremors and the development of temperature regulation in birds. Am. J. Physiol. 136:618.

Okamoto, S., T. Otsubo, K. Ogawa, and S. Masumitsu 1958 Studies on the heat tolerance in the farm animals. VII: The significance of plumage colour in the heat tolerance of the fowl. World's Poultry Sci. J. 14:57.

Osbaldiston, G. W. and D. W. B. Sainsbury 1963 Control of the environment in a poultry house—the principles and practice, Part I. Vet. Rec. 75:159.

Ota, H., and E. H. McNally 1961 Poultry respiration calorimetric studies of laying hens. U.S. Dept. of Agriculture, A.R.S. 42.

Pearson, O. P. 1950 The metabolism of hummingbirds. Condor 52:145.

Prozesky, O. P. M. 1963 Body temperature of birds in relation to nesting habits. Nature 197:401.

Randall, W. C. 1943a Factors influencing the temperature regulation of birds. Am. J. Physiol. 139:56.

Randall, W. C. 1943b Alterations in response to changing body temperature following artificial fever and chilling. Proc. Soc. Exp. Biol. N.Y. 52:240.

Randall, W. C., and W. A. Hiestand 1939 Panting and temperature regulation in the chicken. Am. J. Physiol. 127:761.

Riddle, O., G. C. Smith and F. G. Benedict 1934 Seasonal and temperature factors and their determination in pigeons of percentage metabolism change per degree of temperature change. Am. J. Physiol. 107:333.

Robinson, K. W. and D. H. K. Lee 1946 Animal behaviour and heat regulation in hot atmospheres. Pap. Dept. Physiol. Univ. Queensland 1: (9),1.

Robinson, K. W., and D. H. K. Lee 1947 The effect of the nutritional plane upon the reactions of animals to heat. J. Anim. Sci., 6:182.

Rodbard, S. 1950 Weight and body temperature. Science 111:465.

Rogers, F. T. 1928 Studies of the brain stem. XI: The effects of artificial stimulation and of traumatization of the avian thalamus. Am. J. Physiol. 86:639.

Rogers, F. T. and R. W. Lackey 1923 Studies of the brain stem. VII: The respiratory exchange and heat production after destruction of the body temperature-regulating centers of the thalamus. Am. J. Physiol. 66:453.

Roller, W. L., and A. C. Dale 1962 Heat losses from Leghorn layers at warm temperatures. Paper No. 62-428, Annual Meeting of the American Society of Agricultural Engineers, Washington, D.C.

Romijn, C. 1954 Development of heat regulation in the chick. X World's Poultry Congress, Section Papers, p. 181.

Romijn, C., and W. Lokhorst 1956 The caloric equilibrium of the chicken embryo. Poultry Sci. 35:829.

Romijn, C., and W. Lokhorst 1960 Foetal heat production in the fowl. J. Physiol. 150:239.

Romijn, C., and W. Lokhorst 1961 Climate and poultry: Heat regulation in the fowl. Tijdschr. Diergeneesk. 86:153.

Ryser, F. A., and P. R. Morrison 1954 Cold resistance in the young ring-necked pheasant. Auk 71:253.

Saalfeld, E. 1936 Untersuchungen über das Hacheln bei Tauben. Z. vergl. Physiol. 23:727.

Scholander, P. F., R. Hock, V. Walters, and L. Irving 1950 Adaptation to cold in arctic and tropical mammals and birds in relation to body temperature, insulation and basal metabolic rate. Biol. Bull. 99:259.

Scholander, P. F., R. Hock, V. Walters, F. Johnson, and L. Irving 1950 Heat regulation in some arctic and tropical mammals and birds. Biol. Bull. 99:237.

Scholander, P. F., V. Walters, R. Hock, and L. Irving 1950 Body insulation of some arctic and tropical mammals and birds. Biol. Bull. 99:225.

Scholes, J. C., and F. B. Hutt 1942 The relationship between body temperature and genetic resistance to Salmonella pullorum in the fowl. Cornell Univ. Agric. Exp. Sta. Memoir 244.

Seibert, H. C. 1949 Differences between migrant and non-migrant birds in food and water intake at various temperatures and photoperiods. Auk 66:128.

Simpson, S. and J. J. Galbraith 1905 An investigation into the diurnal variation of the body temperature of nocturnal and other birds, and a few mammals. J. Physiol. 33:225.

Sinha, M. P. 1959 Observations on the organization of the panting center in avian brain. 21st Int. Congress Physiol. Sci. Buenos Aires.

Squibb, R. L., G. N. Wogan, and C. H. Reed 1959 Production of White Leghorn hens subjected to high environmental temperatures with wide diurnal fluctuations. Poultry Sci. 38:1182.

Steen, J., and P. S. Enger 1957 Muscular heat production in pigeons during exposure to cold. Am. J. Physiol. 191:157.

Streicher, E., D. B. Hackel and W. Fleischmann 1950 Effects of extreme cold on the fasting pigeon with a note on the survival of fasting ducks at −40°C. Am. J. Physiol. 161:300.

Sturkie, P. D. 1946 Tolerance of adult chickens to hypothermia. Am. J. Physiol. 147:531.

Thornton, P. A. 1962 The effect of environmental temperature on body temperature and oxygen uptake by the chicken. Poultry Sci. 41:1053.

Vogel, J. A., and P. D. Sturkie 1963 Cardiovascular responses of the chicken to seasonal and induced temperature changes. Science 140:1404.

Wallgren, H. 1954 Energy metabolism of two species of the genus Emberiza as correlated with distribution and migration. Acta Zool. Fennica 84:1.

Washburn, K. W., P. B. Siegel, R. J. Freund, and W. B. Gross 1962 Effect of thiouracil on the body temperatures of White Rock females. Poultry Sci. 41:1354.

Weiss, H. S. 1959 The interrelationship of reproductive state and seasonal acclimatization on the hen's resistance to lethal high temperature. Poultry Sci. 38:430.

Weiss, H. S. 1960 The effect of continuous treatment with reserpine on body temperature, respiratory-cardiovascular functions and heat tolerance of the hen. Poultry Sci. 39:366.

Weiss, H. S., H. Frankel, and K. G. Hollands 1963 The effect of extended exposure to a hot environment on the response of the chicken to hyperthermia. Canad. J. Biochem. Physiol. 41:805.

West, G. C. 1962 Responses and adaptation of wild birds to environmental temperature, in Comparative Physiology of Temperature Regulation, edited by J. P. Hannon and E. Viereck, Part 3, p. 291. Arctic Aeromedical Laboratory, Fort Wainwright, Alaska.

Whittow, G. C., P. D. Sturkie, and G. Stein, Jr. 1964 Cardiovascular changes associated with thermal polypnea in the chicken. Am. J. Physiol. 207:1349.

Wilson, W. O. 1948 Some effects of increasing environmental temperatures on pullets. Poultry Sci. 27:813.

Wilson, W. O. 1949 High environmental temperatures as affecting the reaction of laying hens to iodized casein. Poultry Sci. 28:581.

Wilson, W. O. and W. H. Edwards 1952 Response of hens under thermal stress to dehydration and chilled drinking water. Am. J. Physiol. 169:102.

Wilson, W. O., J. P. Hillerman, and W. H. Edwards 1952 The relation of high environmental temperature to feather and skin temperatures of laying pullets. Poultry Sci. 31:843.

Wilson, W. O., E. H. McNally, H. Ota 1957 Temperature and calorimeter study on hens in individual cages. Poultry Sci. 36:1254.

Winchester, C. F. 1940 Seasonal metabolic rhythms in the domestic fowl. Poultry Sci. 19:239.

Yeates, N. T. M., D. H. K. Lee, and H. J. G. Hines 1941 Reactions of domestic fowls to hot atmospheres. Proc. Roy. Soc. Queensland. 53:105.

CHAPTER 9

Energy Metabolism

BY G. C. WHITTOW

ENERGY BALANCE

APART from the radiant energy gained from the sun, or from very hot surfaces in the environment, the energy requirements of birds are met entirely by the chemical energy contained in their food. The fate of the gross energy of the food has been depicted by King and Farner (1961) as follows:

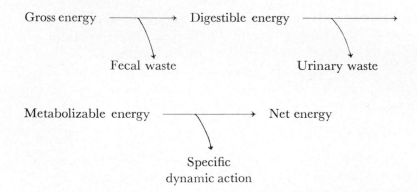

A portion of the energy contained in the substances absorbed from the gut (the digestible energy) is excreted by the kidney, largely as uric acid. The energy retained in the body is the metabolizable energy, amounting to between 70 and 90 percent of the gross energy, depending on the diet, the environmental temperature, the species of bird, and other factors. Not all of the metabolizable energy is available for growth, maintenance, the performance of work, or storage, or for other special functions such as the production of eggs. The absorption of energy from the gastrointestinal tract is followed, soon after its absorption, by an increase in heat production. This heat is referred to variously as the heat increment, the calorigenic effect, or the specific dynamic action (S.D.A.) of the diet. The heat is thought to be derived from the exothermic reactions associated with the metabolism of the absorbed food molecules. The magnitude of the specific dynamic action depends upon the plane of nutrition and upon the composition of the diet. Protein has a greater calorigenic effect than has fat or carbohydrate. In the chicken, the calorigenic effect of protein results in a rate of heat production 15 to 18 percent above the expenditure of basal energy (Barott, Fritz, Pringle, and Titus, 1938). Different proteins, however, have different calorigenic effects; for example, in chickens the calorigenic effect of casein is significantly greater than that of gelatin (Barott, Fritz, Pringle, and Titus, 1938).

The net energy represents the metabolizable energy less the specific dynamic action. If the bird performs work, some of the net energy is transformed into work; but the inefficiency of this transformation is such that some of the energy appears as heat. If no work is performed and if the body weight, composition, and temperature do not change, then all the metabolizable energy appears as heat. It is only under these conditions that the measurement of heat production by a bird is a valid measure of the rate of its metabolism.

THE MEASUREMENT OF ENERGY EXCHANGE

The amount of heat produced by a bird in a given time can be measured by so-called "direct" or "indirect" means. The direct method involves the enclosure of the animal in some form of calorimeter and the measurement of the temperature change of the air circulating through the calorimeter, in addition to the rate of heat loss through the walls of the calorimeter. Calorimeters really measure the total amount of heat lost from the animal; but if the body temperature does not change during the course of the measurements, the heat loss will be the same as the heat production (see Chapter 8). In this sense "direct" is a misnomer. The most recent development in calorimetric technique has been the "gradient layer" calorimeter, which was first developed by Benzinger and Kitzinger (1949) to measure energy exchanges in man. In the gradient layer calorimeter the nonevaporative heat lost from the bird gives rise to a temperature difference across a special layer, the gradient layer, incorporated in the walls of the calorimeter. The gradient layer consists of a large number of copper-constantan thermojunctions interlaced through a very thin layer of sheet plastic. From the temperature difference across this layer the heat flow can be obtained. The heat added to the air flowing through the calorimeter by evaporative loss from the bird is measured by another gradient layer, over which the air passes after it leaves the calorimeter. The temperature of the air is reduced as it passes through this gradient layer, so that the water vapor in the air condenses and the heat of condensation is measured by the gradient layer. The advantages of the gradient layer calorimeter over other types of calorimeters are its fast response, which permits continuous records of heat loss, and the precision with which the climatic conditions inside the calorimeter can be maintained.

Calorimeters are complex instruments, and they are expensive to construct and to operate. Heat production can be measured more simply by indirect calorimetry. The amount of oxygen consumed by the bird in a given time is measured, and the heat production is calculated from the oxygen consumption. The amount of heat produced per liter of oxygen consumed is different for the three main constituents of the diet, namely, fat, carbohydrate, and protein (Table 42). Since the diet normally contains a mixture of fat, carbohydrate, and protein the ratios of these three constituents in the diet have to be known before the heat production can be calculated from the oxygen consumption. This is done by calculation of the respiratory quotient (R.Q.), which is the ratio of the volume of carbon dioxide produced to the volume of oxygen consumed in a given time. If the diet consists entirely of carbohydrate the R.Q. is 1.00, whereas a diet of pure fat gives an R.Q. of 0.71 and a protein diet an R.Q. of 0.73. There are slight differences in the values of R.Q. given by different types of carbohydrates, fats,

Table 42. Summary of factors for use in indirect calorimetry in birds (after King and Farner, 1961; courtesy Academic Press, Inc.)

Substance	Metabolizable energy (kcal./gm.)	Thermal quotient (kcal./1.O_2)	Respiratory quotient
Carbohydrate	4.2	5.047	1.00
Protein*	4.2	4.75	0.73
Fat	9.5	4.686	0.71

* According to King (1957).

and proteins. The values given above represent mean values for mixed carbohydrates, mixed fats, and mixed proteins. The R.Q. values for fat and protein are low because their molecules contain relatively less oxygen and therefore require more oxygen for combustion than do carbohydrate molecules. Furthermore the oxidation of protein is incomplete, so that some of the carbon atoms in the protein molecules are excreted not as carbon dioxide but as uric acid. Different proportions of fat, carbohydrate, and protein in the diet will give rise to R.Q.'s intermediate between 0.71 and 1.00. However, before the proportion of fat, carbohydrate, and protein in the diet can be estimated it is necessary to calculate the "nonprotein R.Q." This is because more than one combination of fat, protein, and carbohydrate can give the same R.Q.

The nonprotein R.Q. is derived as follows: The amount of nitrogen excreted in the urine is measured over the experimental period, and the volumes of oxygen used and of carbon dioxide produced in the metabolism of the protein that gave rise to the urinary nitrogen are calculated. One gram of urinary nitrogen is equivalent to 26.6 kcal. of metabolizable energy, 5.59 liters of oxygen and 4.11 liters of carbon dioxide (King and Farner, 1961). These volumes are subtracted from the total measured volumes of oxygen consumed and of carbon dioxide produced. The remaining volumes of oxygen and carbon dioxide provide the nonprotein R.Q. In birds, the collection of urine is difficult technically, and in practice the heat production is calculated from the total R.Q. without too much loss of accuracy (King and Farner, 1961). Romijn and Lokhorst (1961a) have proposed the following formula for the calculation of heat in chickens:

$$T = 3.871\ O_2 + 1.194\ CO_2$$

T is the heat production in kcal., O_2 is the oxygen consumption in liters, and CO_2 is the carbon dioxide production in liters. The error involved in using this formula is less than 1.5 percent in young and old birds, whether they are fasted or have been fed normally. Problems arise when the R.Q. falls below 0.71 in fasting birds; values as low as 0.63 having been recorded (Romijn and Lokhorst, 1961a). It is not known why such low R.Q.'s occur, nor is it known what thermal equivalent of oxygen should be used under these conditions (King and Farner, 1961; Romijn and Lokhorst, 1961a). Values of R.Q. in excess of 1.00 have been recorded during force-feeding and during lipogenesis and other metabolic interconversions (Benedict and Lee, 1937; Cathcart and Markovitz, 1927; Richardson, 1929). Fortunately, the thermal equivalent of the oxygen consumed at R.Q. values greater than unity has been found to be the same as that for an R.Q. of unity (Benedict and Lee, 1937).

Measurement of the oxygen consumption of birds is usually made by enclosing the bird in a chamber through which air flows at a constant rate. The air leaving the chamber is passed through an automatic carbon dioxide and oxygen gas analyzer; from the rate of flow and the difference in oxygen and carbon dioxide contents of the air entering and leaving the chamber, the rate of oxygen consumption and carbon dioxide production can be calculated. This technique is commonly used for the measurement of heat production in small birds (see, for example, Kendeigh, 1939; Dawson and Evans 1957), for which direct calorimetric measurements on a single bird are not very practicable; it has also been used for chickens (Beattie and Freeman, 1962). Alternatively, the oxygen consumption can be measured gravimetrically by weighing the bird and its container on a sensitive balance. This technique was originally devised by Haldane, and a recent adaptation of the technique for chickens has been described by Zausch (1964).

If one measures the amount of food consumed and feces produced, and the energy content of the food and feces, the amount of energy absorbed from the gastrointestinal tract can be measured. If from this quantity the energy content of the urinary excretory material is subtracted, the amount of metabolizable energy is obtained. When such energy balance studies are made over a long period of time, care has to be taken in equating the metabolizable energy with the metabolic rate, because apart from the energy released as the specific dynamic action, some energy is stored in the form of fat and other substances (see below). The energy retention of a group of animals over a period of time can be measured simply by killing half of them at the start of the experiment and the other half at the end of the experiment. The calorific values of the carcasses of both groups are then determined. This technique is known as the comparative slaughter method, and is particularly suitable for small animals. A simple but crude method of estimating heat production is to measure the weight loss of the bird resulting from evaporation of moisture over a given time. Weight loss is proportional to heat production, provided the bird is not panting (see Chapter 8; also Mitchell, 1962).

STANDARD METABOLIC RATE

In order to make comparative studies the metabolic rate must be measured under carefully standardized conditions; it is then referred to as the "standard" or "basal" metabolic rate. For proper measurement the bird should be in the postabsorptive state, in a thermoneutral environment, not excited or very active, and all factors which are known to have an effect on the metabolic rate (see below) must be either excluded or stated. These conditions have not always been attained. Table 43 gives the standard metabolic rates of several species of wild and domestic birds.

It is clear that the metabolic rate expressed in terms of kcal./24 hr. is greater in big birds than in small ones, but it is also evident that the metabolic rate per unit of body weight (i.e. kcal./kg./24 hr.) decreases with increasing body weight in adult birds (Table 43). In consequence, if a bird's body weight is twice as great as that of another bird, its metabolic rate (kcal./24 hr.) will be less than double that of the smaller bird. Valid comparisons of metabolic rate between birds of different body weight may

Table 43. Standard metabolic rates of some species of birds (after King and Farner, 1961: courtesy Academic Press, Inc.)

Species	Body weight (g.)	Metabolic rate (kcal./24 hr.)	Metabolic rate (kcal./kg. body wt./hr.)	Authority
Domestic goose	5000.0	280.0	56	Benedict & Lee (1937)
Domestic fowl (male)	2000.0	94.0	47	Benedict (1938)
Domestic fowl (female)	2000.0	101.0	50	"
Domestic turkey	3700.0	184.0	50	Giaja (1931)
Domestic pigeon	266.0	33.7	126	Gelineo (1955)
English sparrow	27.3	8.51	312	Steen (1958)
Northwestern crow				
Summer	282.0	73.2	260	Irving, Krog, & Monson (1955)
Winter	306.0	96.7	316	"
Abert's towhee	46.8	15.04	321	Dawson (1954)
Yellow bunting	26.4	9.35	354	Wallgren (1954)
American bittern	600.0	56.0	93	Benedict & Fox (1927)
Mourning dove	126.0	14.9	118	Riddle, Smith, & Benedict (1932)

not, therefore, be made simply on the basis of their metabolic rates per unit of body weight.

In the past, metabolic rate has been related to surface area. The rationale for this procedure was that heat loss occurred from the surface of the animal, and that since heat loss, under conditions of a steady state, must equal heat production, then heat production must be a function of the surface area. Unfortunately, surface area is a very difficult thing to measure; furthermore, the effective surface area from which the animal is losing heat may vary with posture (see Chapter 8); and in addition, the heat loss will depend upon the properties of the body surface other than its area. Attempts to relate the metabolic rate to the mass of "metabolically active tissue" in the body have not produced anything more satisfactory than a correlation between surface area and metabolic rate (Mitchell, 1962). Measurement of the metabolically active tissue mass is not any easier than the estimation of surface area. King and Farner (1961) have recently examined the relation between the metabolic rates of different species of birds and their body weights. They concluded that the relation is best expressed by the following equation:

$$\log M = \log 74.3 + 0.744 \log W \pm 0.074$$

M is the metabolic rate in kcal./24 hr., and W is the body weight in kilograms. The equation is empirically derived and appears to be satisfactory for hummingbirds weighing 2–5 grams (Lasiewski, 1963), as well as for a large number of birds whose body weights varied from 0.125 to approximately 10 kilograms. The only notable exceptions to conformity with this equation are some passerine species. Lasiewski (1963) has suggested that the relation between the metabolic rate and body weight of the passerines in question may be represented by a straight line with a slope similar to that given by the King and Farner equation, but with a different intercept on the metabolic rate axis. A warning against the routine use of any fixed relation between metabolic rate and a power of the body weight has recently been given by Mellen (1963), who has drawn attention to Winchester's observation (1940a) that the heat production of hens varied with the body weight raised to different powers during different months of the year. Mellen (1963) has made the important suggestion that in all experiments in which metabolic rate and body weight vary, the contribution of the change in body weight to the change in metabolic rate has to eliminated before the effect of any other factor on metabolic rate can be evaluated. Statistically this can be accomplished by covariance analysis, by which the variation due to differences in body weight is eliminated or minimized (Mellen, 1963). Poczopko and Kowalczyk (1964) have recently examined the relation between the metabolic rate and the body weight in the young growing chicken. In all measurements of body weight for the purpose of relating metabolic rate to body weight, account must be taken of the weight of the contents of the alimentary tract.

FACTORS AFFECTING THE METABOLIC RATE

Age. The metabolic rate of the hatched chick (a precocial bird) is lower than that of the adult. The metabolism increases during the first 4 weeks after hatching, to reach a level considerably higher than the adult level. It then decreases until the adult level is reached. Variation in the metabolic rate of the young bird with growth should not be confused with the change in the metabolic rate of adult birds with body size. A similar variation of metabolism with age is evident in the pigeon, an altricial species (see Chapter 8). In another altricial species, the Eastern house wren, Kendeigh (1939) found that the increase in heat production with age was greater at lower air temperatures than at higher temperatures, within the range 21.7°–40.6°C. In some rapidly growing passerine species, however, an increase in heat production above the adult level is not evident (Dawson and Evans, 1957). The increase in heat production during growth, when it occurs, is associated with an increase in the body temperature (see Chapter 8), and is probably related to the growth of muscle and other metabolically active tissue (see below). Beattie and Freeman (1962) have postulated that a metabolic accelerator is responsible for the initial rapid increase in heat production in the chick. The diminution in metabolic rate following the peak metabolic rate is possibly related to the development of a more effective insulation, so that the need for an increased heat production in order to maintain body temperature is lessened.

Sex. Adult male chickens have a standard metabolic rate, expressed in relation to surface area, which is from 5.7 to 13.0 percent higher than that of females, depending on the breed (Mitchell and Haines, 1927; Kibler and Brody, 1944; Table 44). The sex difference in heat production also depends upon the age of the birds, and it is not always evident when heat production is related to body weight (Table 43).

The difference in heat production between male and female chickens is apparent when the birds are fed ad libitum, as well as when they are starved before heat production is measured. In birds that were fed the difference in heat production amounted to 39 percent when the body weight of the birds was 1,000 grams (Freeman, 1963):

Body weight (g.)	O_2 consumption (ml./hr.)	
	Males	*Females*
40	106	106
60	184	177
100	265	255
300	670	594
500	1097	847
1000	1431	1028

There was also a difference between the two sexes in the patterns of increase in metabolic rate during growth, even though all the birds were fed the same diet (Freeman, 1963). Castration of cocks led to a reduction in their metabolic rate (Mitchell, Card, and Haines, 1927). The metabolic rate of male mourning doves is also

Table 44. Basal metabolic rate of Rhode Island Red chickens; variations between sexes and individuals and within individuals (from Mitchell, 1962; courtesy Academic Press, Inc.)

Sex	Number of birds	Number of observations	Mean basal metabolic rate (kcal./sq. m./day)	Variation in metabolic rate expressed as coefficients of variation	
				Interindividual (%)	*Intraindividual* (%)
Hens	14	44	676	17.3	8.8
Cocks	7	14	772	11.6	5.4

higher than that of female doves (Riddle, Smith, and Benedict, 1932).

Breed. Different breeds of chickens have different rates of heat production, even when variations in their surface area and body weight are taken into account. Thus, White Leghorns had a higher heat production than Rhode Island Reds, which in turn produced more heat than did New Hampshire-Cornish cross birds (Ota and McNally, 1961):

	White Leghorns	Rhode Island Reds	New Hampshire– Cornish crosses
Heat production (kcal./sq.m./hr.)	62.4	51.5	47.7

Diurnal rhythm. There is a diurnal rhythm of metabolism in fasting birds which is independent of the effects of food intake. The metabolic rate of the chicken is highest in the forenoon and lowest at about 8:00 P.M. When chickens are allowed to feed ad libitum, however, there is a diurnal rhythm of food consumption which precedes, in time, the rhythm of heat production (Eriksson and Kivimäe, 1954). Greater diurnal variations of metabolism are evident in young birds than in adults. The reduction in the heat production at night amounts to from 18 to 30 percent in the chicken, but to as much as 49 percent in the English sparrow. Small birds tend to show greater diurnal variations than do large birds (see King and Farner, 1961). In migratory birds the magnitude and the time sequence of the diurnal variation in heat production varies with the season. In the whitethroat, the greatest variation occurs in winter and summer and the least in spring and autumn (Merkel, 1958). In the brambling, the minimal metabolic rate occurs between 0300 and 0400 hours in February and between 0100 and 0200 hours in April (Rautenberg, 1957). These seasonal differences may, however, be explained by the migratory activity of the birds in spring and autumn. There is evidence that the diurnal rhythm of metabolic rate is associated with variations in muscle tone contingent upon changes of posture, and that they can be abolished by transection of the lumbar and brachial plexi (Hiebel and Reys, 1951). The changes in muscle tone and posture are evidently the result of visual and auditory information, for surgical blinding and isolation of the bird from all auditory stimuli abolished the diurnal rhythm of metabolism (Burckard, Dontcheff, and Kayser, 1933). In addition, reversal of the daily photoperiod results in an inversion of the time relations of the diurnal rhythm in heat production (Fill, 1942). It might be expected from these results that removal of the cerebral hemispheres of the pigeon would abolish the diurnal rhythm of metabolic rate, since the visual and auditory sensory nerve pathways terminate in the cerebral hemispheres. Although ablation of the cerebral hemispheres reduced the amplitude of the diurnal rhythm of metabolism the rhythm was not abolished, which suggests that lower levels of the brain are also concerned in the genesis of the rhythm. Deighton and Hutchinson (1940) attempted to eliminate the effects of activity on the diurnal rhythm of heat production in fasting Light Sussex fowls. They concluded that the diurnal rhythm was not entirely the result of diurnal variations of activity (see below).

Activity. Activity undoubtedly brings about an increase in the metabolic rate. Standing alone can increase the heat production of Light Sussex cocks by from 40 to 50 percent (Deighton and Hutchinson, 1940). The heat production of birds during flight has been measured only in the hummingbird. In this species the effect of flight was to increase the heat production to a value 6 or 7 times greater than that at rest (Pearson, 1950; Lasiewski, 1963). In birds that glide or soar the increase in metabolic rate during flight is probably less than that for the hummingbird. However, birds that flap their wings have been estimated to increase their heat production by 27 times during vigorous flight (Zeuthen, 1942).

Starvation and feeding. When birds are deprived of food their heat production diminishes. The R.Q. decreases also because fat is preferentially metabolized during starvation (Koskimies, 1950). Minimal R.Q. values are attained in the chicken after a 48-hour period of starvation (Mitchell and Haines, 1927; Barott and Pringle, 1946). In smaller birds the fasting R.Q. is attained after a shorter fast. Thus, the pigeon requires 28 hours and the ortolan and yellow bunting only 3 hours (Benedict and Riddle, 1929; Wallgren, 1954). The glycogen reserves of pigeons are depleted within 24 hours of the start of a fast (see Wallgren, 1954). Young swifts lost 60 percent of their body weight during a fast, whereas adults lost 38 percent before death (Koskimies, 1950). Young birds were heavier and had greater fat deposits than adults. Next to adipose tissue, liver and muscle incurred the greatest losses of weight during the fast. In the pigeon, adipose tissue lost 93 percent, spleen 71 percent, pancreas 64 percent, liver 52 percent, heart 45 percent, and muscle 42 percent of their respective initial weights during a fast (see Kleiber, 1961).

When chickens are fed a sufficient amount of food to maintain constant body weights on a so-called "maintenance diet," their heat production is approximately 50 percent greater than their standard metabolic rates (Mitchell, 1962). Some of the increased heat production on a maintenance diet, over and above that of fasting birds, is the result of greater activity. After a single meal the heat production of chickens remained elevated for between 24 and 48 hours (Mitchell and Haines, 1927). According to Mellen, Hill, and Dukes (1954), male chickens on a high energy diet have a higher standard metabolic rate than those on a low energy diet. This effect of the energy content of the previous diet was apparent when the oxygen consumptions were measured even in fasting birds. The difference in a standard metabolic rate between birds on high and low energy diets was attributed to differences in body composition as a result of feeding. Variations in the energy content of the diet did not appear to influence the fasting oxygen consumption of female chicks; there is no explanation for this sex difference. Freeman (1963) found that the effect of feeding a high-energy, high-protein diet to chicks persisted for some time after the diet of the birds had been changed. Not only the energy content, but also the ratio of protein to metabolizable energy in the diet has an influence on the heat production of chickens. A reduction of the dietary protein/energy ratio results in an increase in heat production (Davidson, 1964).

Baldini (1961) made the interesting observation that a diet deficient in methionine results in an increase in the oxygen consumption of chickens. This finding was explained partly by the fact that the productive energy of a methionine-deficient diet is less than that of a normal diet, the energy diverted from productive uses being given off as heat. Furthermore, this dietary deficiency appeared to increase the metabolizable energy content of the diet. An increase in the oxygen consumption of hens was noted by Thornton and Moreng (1959), when the diet of the hens contained added vitamin C. The effects of the vitamin were more marked in a hot environment than in a cool one, and they were thought to be associated with an increased thyroid activity.

Body temperature (van't Hoff–Arrhenius effect). The rate of heat production increases exponentially with increases of body temperature according to the equation

$$Hp = Hs \cdot e^{k\Delta T_b}$$

Hp is heat production; Hs is the heat production within the thermoneutral range; e is the base of natural logarithms; k is the van't Hoff coefficient and ΔT_b is the increase in deep body temperature. The importance of this equation is that it demonstrates a logarithmic, not a rectilinear, relation between heat production and body temperature. Other physiological properties such as heart rate are often related logarithmically to body temperature (Whittow, Sturkie, and Stein, 1964). The relation is often expressed numerically as a factor called the Q10, which expresses the heat production (or other quantity) at any given deep body temperature divided into the heat production at a temperature 10°C. higher. Some birds become torpid under natural conditions, their body temperature decreasing almost to the temperature of the en-

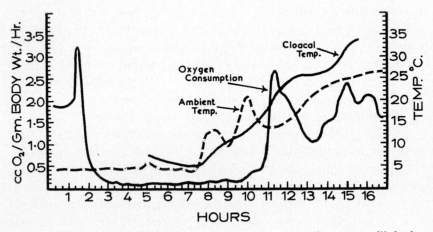

Figure 33. Body temperature and oxygen consumption in a poor-will during a period of torpidity (Redrawn from Bartholomew, Howell and Cade, 1957; courtesy *The Condor*)

vironment (see Chapter 8). The diminution in body temperature is associated with a decrease in heat production (Figure 33), which in hummingbirds is probably the result of diminished thyroid activity (Shellabarger, Lasiewski, and Hyncik, 1961).

Environmental temperature. When birds are exposed to environmental temperatures below their critical temperature, their heat production increases to a maximal value ("summit metabolism") that may be 3 or 4 times greater than normal. This is illustrated in Figure 34. The increase in heat production is brought about largely by shivering. The intensity of the shivering increases as the environmental temperature decreases (West, 1962). Birds, unlike mammals, do not appear to display nonshivering thermogenesis, i.e. an increased heat production believed to be brought about by noradrenaline in the absence of shivering (West, 1962). If birds are kept in a cold environment for a prolonged period, their production of heat increases as they become acclimatized to cold, to a level from 20 to 40 percent higher than that before exposure to the cold (Riddle, Smith, and Benedict, 1934; Gelineo, 1955). The changes in the heat production of a pigeon when it is transferred from an environment of 15.0°–20.5°C. to one of 1°–3°C. are illustrated by Gelineo's data:

Heat production after 18 days at 15.0°–20.5°C. (kcal./sq.m./24 hr.)	*Heat production after 1 day at 1°–3°C. (kcal./sq.m./24 hr.)*	*Heat production after 17 days at 1°–3°C. (kcal./sq.m./24 hr.)*
2637	2842	3043

However, birds acclimatized either to summer weather or to hot-room conditions had a higher heat production during subsequent exposure to a very cold environment (–11°C.) than had birds tested in winter (Wallgren, 1954). This suggests that in long-term acclimatization to cold other factors are involved which reduce the need for a high level of heat production (see Chapter 8).

Acclimatization to heat results in a diminution of heat production. In the chicken (Hoffman and Shaffner, 1950; Huston, Edwards, and Williams, 1962; Heninger, Newcomer, and Thayer, 1960) this has been attributed to a decrease in the rate of secretion of thyroxine, a hormone known to stimulate metabolic activity (see also Chapter 19). The reduction in oxygen consumption which occurs in hens when they are exposed to heat is less when vitamin C is added to their diet (Thornton and Moreng, 1959). This effect was also thought to involve the thyroid gland.

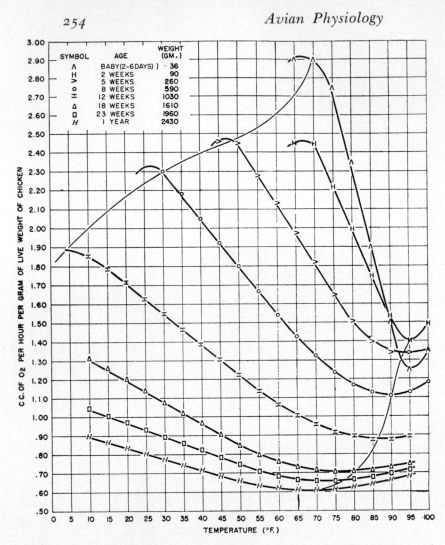

Figure 34. Oxygen consumption by Rhode Island Red female chickens of various ages at different environmental temperatures. Each point represents the mean oxygen consumption measured between 8 A.M. and 8 P.M. (From Barott and Pringle, 1946; courtesy *J. Nutrition.*)

Recent experiments by West (1962) have thrown some doubt on the results of experiments in which heat production has been measured for only a few hours at any given environmental temperature. When the heat production, measured over a 24-hour period, is plotted against environmental temperature, no clearly defined thermoneutral zone or critical temperature is evident. These experiments suggest the interesting possibility that marked differences in diurnal and nocturnal heat production and levels of activity occur at different ambient temperatures, at least in some birds (West, 1962).

Humidity. Wallgren (1954) asserted that the minimal metabolism of the ortolan and yellow bunting was less in moist than in dry air. The lower critical temperature of the ortolan bunting was also depressed in moist air. Wallgren explained his results by the decrease in the amount of heat lost by evaporation in moist air, which meant that less heat was required to maintain the body temperature. This effect of humidity on heat production was not found in the chicken (Romijn and Lokhorst, 1961b). At high environmental temperatures, increasing the humidity of the air causes an increase in heat production in chickens. This increase arises from the curtailment of heat loss under hot humid conditions, so that the body temperature increases, thereby increasing heat production (Romijn and Lokhorst, 1961b).

Season. Reports of seasonal variation in heat production have not been consistent (see Chapter 8). King and Farner (1961) have marshaled some impressive theoretical considerations to show that an increase in heat production during the cold season would have little effect on the thermal economy of the bird and might even be wasteful of energy. When seasonal variations of heat production have been demonstrated, they are usually related to concomitant changes in egg production, thyroid activity, or other unidentified factors (see Winchester, 1940a, 1940b). Winchester's data (1940a) for the heat production of full-fed New Hampshire hens throughout the year are as follows:

	Feb.	*Apr.*	*June*	*Sept.*	*Nov.*	*Jan.*
No. of hens	11	11	15	15	13	12
Heat production kcal./hr./kg.0.73	4.16	3.92	3.44	2.94	3.06	2.98

Migratory behavior. Riddle, Smith, and Benedict (1932) reported that the migratory mourning dove had a higher metabolic rate than the related nonmigratory pigeon and domestic dove. They thought the high energy cost of maintaining this high metabolic rate might be associated with the migratory behavior of the mourning dove. Mourning doves also showed a higher rate of increase in heat production during exposure to cold than did their nonmigratory congeners.

Molting and plumage. The standard metabolic rate increases during molting. In the chaffinch, the maximal increase amounted to 25 percent (Koch and de Bont, 1944); in the ortolan bunting the increase was 26 percent (Wallgren, 1954); and Perek and Sulman (1945) observed an increase of 45 percent during the molt in the chicken. The greatest increase in metabolic rate coincides with the regeneration of the flight feathers (Koch and de Bont, 1944). The increase in metabolic rate during the molt is less in young birds than in adults (Wallgren, 1954). There is good evidence that molting is associated with an increase in thyroid activity, which is probably one of the causes of the increase in meta-

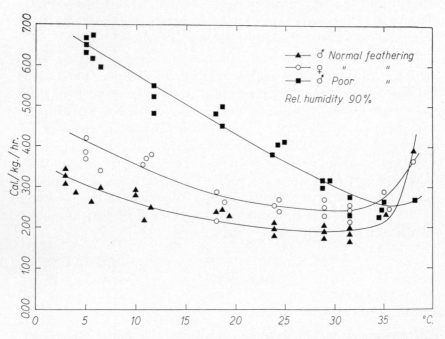

Figure 35. Metabolic rate of Blue North Holland fowls with normal and poor plumage, at different environmental temperatures (from Romijn and Lokhorst, 1961b; courtesy Dr. C. Romijn).

bolic rate (see also Chapter 19). Loss of feathers and an increased blood flow to the growing feather papillae may reduce the insulation provided by the feathers and skin; part of the increase in heat production during molting may therefore be to compensate for the reduced insulation. An increase in heat production can be induced in normal chickens by removal of the plumage (Hoffman and Shaffner, 1950). The differences in heat production between chickens with normal plumage and those with poor feathering is clearly illustrated in Figure 35. Not only is the heat production of poorly feathered birds greater than that of birds with normal plumage, within the thermoneutral zone of environmental temperature, but the rate of increase in heat production at lower environmental temperatures is also greater. On the other hand, the increase in heat production at environmental temperatures above the thermoneutral zone is greater in birds with a normal plumage (Romijn and Lokhorst, 1961b). The frizzle fowl has a scant plumage and its heat production is greater than that of normal fowls (Benedict, Landauer, and Fox, 1932). There is also evidence that frizzle fowls have a relatively high rate of thyroid activity.

Endocrine activity. Variations of thyroid activity have an important effect on the rate of heat production. Removal of the thyroid results in a depression of heat production in pigeons (Marvin and Smith, 1943), in geese (Lee and Lee, 1937), and in chickens (Winchester, 1939). The diminution in heat production in chickens ranged from 5.9 to 14.1 percent. Reduction of thyroid activity by the administration of thiouracil also causes a depression of heat production in chickens (McCartney and Shaffner, 1950; Mellen, 1958). Feeding iodinated casein or thyroprotein resulted in a hyperthyroid condition and an increased heat production (McCartney and Shaffner, 1950; Singh and Shaffner, 1950). The effect of the added thyroprotein was related to the energy level of the diet; the higher the energy content, the greater was the increase in oxygen consumption in response to dietary thyroprotein. The stimulating effect of thyroprotein and the depressing effect of thiouracil on heat production disappear rapidly when those drugs are removed from the diet (Mellen, 1958). If the birds are starved for longer than 18 hours (when thiouracil is given), or a few hours (when thyroprotein is given), little effect on heat production is observed.

A synthetic estrogen added to the diet tended to increase the metabolic rate of male chicks (Mellen and Hill, 1953). This observation is difficult to reconcile with the known differences between the metabolic rates of male and female chickens.

When all or most of the factors known to influence heat production have been kept constant, there remains some variation of heat production in the same birds tested on different days (Table 44). The variation in heat production between different individuals is approximately twice as great as that between different tests made on the same individual.

ENERGY INTAKE

The food intake of birds on a low energy diet is greater than that of birds on a high energy diet (Mellen, Hill, and Dukes, 1954). The feed intake of chickens is also determined by the protein/energy ratio of the diet; the lower this ratio, the greater the energy intake (Davidson, 1964). The feed consumption of chickens was found to be higher when the diet contained added vitamin C (Thornton and Moreng, 1959). Amino acid imbalance in the diet has an adverse effect on the energy intake of chicks (Combs, 1964). Lysine deficiency, for instance, results in the restriction of food intake (Hill, 1964). Restricting the food intake of chickens to two 1-hour periods per day resulted in less efficient utilization of ingested energy than in birds permitted access to food for 24 hours each day (Fisher, 1964). There are breed differences in energy intake in chickens (Davidson, 1964).

Energy intake, like heat production, is affected by the environmental temperature (Table 45). Thus, the gross energy intake of English sparrows increased linearly with decreasing environmental temperature (Davis, 1955). However, the energy intake of the birds did not vary with environmental temperature, within the range 10°–29°C., when the environmental temperature was allowed to fluctuate. This observation conforms with other evidence (see Chapter 8) that birds react differently to constant temperatures and to fluctuating temperatures such as occur naturally.

Table 45. The energy intake of English sparrows at various environmental temperatures (from Kendeigh, 1949)

Environmental temperature (°C.)	Number of birds	Mean weight of birds (g.)	Food intake (kcal./bird/day)
−31	3	24.3	39.60
−25	3	24.2	35.20
−13	6	24.7	31.24
− 4	6	23.1	26.40
+10	12	24.3	25.96
+24	12	23.1	18.04
+34	12	22.9	16.28

Davis' explanation (1955) for this phenomenon was that under conditions of fluctuating temperature there is insufficient time for adjustments of energy intake to occur. The net energy intake by chicks was found by Kleiber and Dougherty (1934) to be maximal at an environmental temperature of 32°C. At environmental temperatures above and below this level the net energy intake diminished. The net energy amounted to 34 percent of the gross energy intake at an environmental temperature of 32°C., to 16 percent at a temperature of 21°C., and to 29 percent at a temperature of 40°C. The heat increment of the feed was least at an environmental temperature of 38°C., and it increased at both lower and higher environmental temperatures. Steen (1957) asserted that the lower critical temperature for increased food intake in the pigeon was identical with that for increased heat production, but his data do not show a clearly defined critical temperature.

The part played by light in the diurnal rhythm of metabolic rate has already been mentioned. Davis (1955) noted that English sparrows ate less food per hour when they were exposed to a 15-hour daily photoperiod than when they were on a 10-hour period, although the total daily food consumption on the two photoperiods was the same.

A significantly decreased feed consumption of chickens resulted from a lowering of the ventilation rate from 2 to ¾ cu. ft./min.

(Prince, Potter, and Irish, 1961) within the range of 7°–24°C. in the enviromental temperature. This effect was presumably the result of a diminished heat loss at the lower wind speed.

The migratory behavior of birds seems to affect their energy intake. Thus Seibert (1949), who studied two migratory species, the slate-colored junco and the white-throated sparrow, and two non-migratory species, the English sparrow and the blue jay, found that the migratory species were not able to increase their metabolizable energy intake during exposure to cold as rapidly as were the nonmigratory species. This may explain why the junco and white-throated sparrow are not able to remain in high latitudes during the cold season; their energy intake would inadequate. The high energy requirements of the field sparrow might be correlated with its limited northward migration.

There is general agreement that the energy value of the diet is best expressed in terms of the metabolizable energy to which it gives rise (Titus, 1956; Hill, 1964). The metabolizable energy per unit weight of diet is unaffected by the level of food intake, rate of growth, egg production, breed, sex, or wide differences in the nutrient balance of the diet.

ENERGY STORAGE AND GROWTH

Energy is stored partly as glycogen in liver and muscle but mainly as fat. When geese were forcibly fed, they were able to deposit fat at the rate of 3 grams per hour (Benedict and Lee, 1937). Chickens fed a high energy diet deposit more fat than those on a low energy diet (Mellen, Hill, and Dukes, 1954). An increase in the body weight of hens when the diet of the hens contained added vitamin C was noted by Thornton and Moreng (1959). An increase in body weight has been observed in a number of species of birds prior to migration (Wallgren, 1954). The increase in the body weight of the ortolan bunting before migration was associated with only a very slight increase in the metabolic rate. The metabolic rate per unit of lean body weight was unchanged during the fattening period, indicating that the deposition of fat had no accelerator effect on the metabolic processes. One of the functions of the accumulated fat is presumably to provide a reserve of energy for the migratory flight.

Although there is a general parallelism between growth and metabolic rate, the time of the highest growth rate may not coincide with the time of the greatest metabolic rate. Thus, Riddle, Nussman, and Benedict (1932) have pointed out that the stage of most rapid growth in the pigeon is at 3 days after hatching, whereas the highest rate of metabolism occurs at 11 days. In chickens, the patterns of change in growth, expressed in grams of body weight per square meter per day, and of metabolism in kcal. per square meter per day are similar (Kibler and Brody, 1944).

The rate of growth of male chickens is greater than that of females, but the energy equivalent of the growth increments is greater in pullets than in cockerels (see Mitchell, 1962; Freeman, 1963). This may be due to the greater ability of the hen to fatten during growth, because the energy equivalent of the gained body weight varies directly with the fat content of the increased body weight. The difference between the male and the female chicken in this respect is largely abolished if the males are caponized (Mitchell, 1962). If testosterone propionate is administered to pullets their rate of growth increases to equal that of cockerels. Male turkeys also grow at a greater rate than do females (Asmundson and Pun, 1954).

The increase in body weight during growth mainly involves the synthesis of protein. According to Kielanowski (1964), the energy cost of protein deposition in chickens is 7.74 kcal. of metabolizable energy per gram protein. The deposition of 1 gram of fat required 15.64 kcal. of metabolizable energy. The main factor determining the amount of fat deposited is the protein content of the diet in relation to the total energy. The greater the protein/energy ratio, the lower the fat content of the bird (see Mitchell, 1962). Methionine-deficient chicks gained more fat but less protein than did chicks that received supplementary methionine (Hill, 1964). Lysine deficiency also leads to the development of fat chicks. The percentage utilization of the metabolizable energy of the diet for gains in tissue energy is significantly increased in chickens by the addition of supplementary methionine to the diet (Davidson, 1964). Chickens utilize metabolizable energy derived from animal fat as efficiently as that from starch (Davidson, 1964).

The growth of young chicks is adversely affected by exposure to hot weather, light breeds being more affected than heavy breeds. The impaired growth is partly due to diminished food intake but also to less efficient food conversion (Kleiber and Dougherty, 1934; see also Osbaldiston and Sainsbury, 1963b). The optimal environmental temperature for growth in chicks seems to be approximately 35°C. Osbaldiston and Sainsbury (1963b) found that for a given food consumption, growth was greater at an environmental temperature of 21.1°C. than at 18.3°C. or 15.6°C. They attributed this difference to a greater efficiency in the conversion of food into tissue at 21.1°C., which in turn was the result of a lower heat production at the higher temperature. Prince, Potter, and Irish (1961) demonstrated a linear relation between feed efficiency in chickens and environmental temperature within the range 7°–24°C.

The composition of the gained body substance during growth is also influenced by the environmental temperature. Thus, the amount of fat stored per gram of increase in body weight was maximal at an environmental temperature of 32°C., and was less at temperatures of 21° or 40°C. (Kleiber and Dougherty, 1934). The maximal energy content of a unit increase in body weight occurred at a temperature of 38°C., and was least at an environmental temperature of 21°C.

Growth rates of chicks are adversely affected by cold winds (Wilson, Kelly, Lourenzen, and Woodward, 1957), probably because heat loss is accelerated under these conditions, and energy that would otherwise be available for growth is used to maintain the body temperature. The most rapid rate of growth occurs when the light is continuous, at least in the early stages of growth (Osbaldiston and Sainsbury, 1963a). A reduction in thyroid activity as a result of the administration of thiouracil is associated with a reduced rate of growth (Mellen and Hill, 1953). The reduced rate of growth is probably related to the reduced metabolic rate. The inclusion of antibiotics in the diet of chicks produces an increase in their rate of growth (Branion, Anderson, and Hill, 1953).

ENERGETICS OF EGG PRODUCTION

Dukes (1937) found that the metabolic rate of hens laying a large number of eggs was slightly greater than that of hens laying fewer eggs. However, Mitchell (1962) has assembled evidence that the process of egg formation has little or no effect on the standard metabolic rate of chickens. The energetic efficiency of egg production in chickens was investigated by Brody, Funk, and Kempster (1938), and discussed by Mitchell (1962). Maximal production of eggs occurred at a body weight of 4 pounds in White Leghorns and of 5¾ pounds in Rhode Island Reds. At body weights below these levels the efficiency of conversion of digestible energy into eggs was independent of body weight, but at higher body weights the efficiency declined. The explanation for this relation between body weight and the energetic efficiency of egg production seems to be that the variation of the energy cost of maintenance with body weight differs from the variation of egg production with body weight. The gross energetic efficiency of egg production was comparable to that of growth on an ordinary diet.

ENERGY METABOLISM OF THE EMBRYO

The heat production of the chicken's egg increases continuously throughout the incubation period (Table 46). The increase in heat production is associated with a progressive decrease in the R.Q., suggesting that protein and fat play an increasingly important role in the production of heat as the embryo grows. The oxygen consumption increases further at the time of hatching, and it has been postulated by Freeman (1962) that this increase is the result of a hormonal stimulus. The humidity of the air surrounding the egg appears to have an important effect on the energy metabolism of the embryo (Romijn and Lokhorst, 1962). After the 15th day of incubation an increase in the atmospheric humidity results in a diminution in the rate of diffusion of oxygen into the egg and part of the heat production of the embryo is then derived from anaerobic sources. A reduction of the barometric pressure below approximately 600 mm. results in a decrease in metabolic rate (Romijn and Lokhorst, 1964).

CONCLUSIONS

The very small size of some birds, their relatively high metabolic rates, and the metabolic demands of flight make the study of the quantitative aspects of energy metabolism in birds of unusual interest. The proximity of small birds to the extreme limits of meta-

Table 46. Heat production, evaporative heat loss, and R.Q. of a chicken's egg during incubation at a temperature of 37.7°C. (After Romijn and Lokhorst, 1960; courtesy *J. Physiol.*)

Day of incubation	Heat production (cal./24 hrs.)	Evaporative heat loss (cal./24 hrs.)	R.Q.
1	—	403	1.63
2	27.0	362	0.84
3	37.8	362	1.00
4	89.0	362	1.00
5	89.0	362	0.94
6	139	357	0.86
7	180	362	0.80
8	276	362	0.92
9	376	362	0.88
10	584	357	0.85
11	888	414	0.81
12	1296	397	0.74
13	1726	414	0.69
14	2196	414	0.71
15	2510	426	0.69
16	2683	408	0.69
17	2716	443	0.67
18	2873	426	0.69
19	2698	408	0.73
20	3124	426	—
21	—	—	—

bolic performance has resulted in the adoption by some of them of the facility to become spontaneously torpid and thus to survive in unfavorable circumstances. Birds seem to differ from mammals in that they do not utilize nonshivering thermogenesis as a means of increasing their heat production during exposure to cold. Although a great deal is known about the total heat production of birds in different conditions, practically nothing is known about their regional thermogenesis, i.e. the contribution of different tissues and organs to the total heat production. Information about regional thermogenesis of birds in different climates is of practical as well as theoretical interest. Thus, to give just one illustration, the composition of muscle is likely to be related to the extent to which it is called upon to produce heat. The marked differences that have often been found between birds exposed to natural seasonal variations of climate and those subjected to controlled conditions of temperature, humidity, and light, suggest that the physiological effects of climate on birds are by no means completely understood.

REFERENCES

Asmundson, V. S., and C. F. Pun 1954 Growth of bronze turkeys. Poultry Sci. 33:981.

Baldini, J. T. 1961 The effect of dietary deficiency on the energy metabolism of the chick. Poultry Sci. 40:1177.

Barott, H. G., J. C. Fritz, Emma M. Pringle, and H. W. Titus 1938 Heat production and gaseous metabolism of young male chickens. J. Nutr. 15:145.

Barott, H. G.. and E. M. Pringle 1946 Energy and gaseous metabolism of the chicken from hatch to maturity as affected by temperature. J. Nutr. 31:35.

Bartholomew, G. A., T. R. Howell, and T. J. Cade 1957 Torpidity in the white-throated swift, Anna humming-bird and the poorwill. Condor 59:145.

Beattie, J., and B. M. Freeman 1962 Gaseous metabolism in the domestic chicken. I: Oxygen consumption of broiler chickens from hatching to 100 gm. body weight. Brit. Poultry Sci. 3:51.

Benedict, F. G. 1938 Vital energetics: A study in comparative basal metabolism. Carnegie Inst. Wash. Publ. No. 503.

Benedict, F. G., and E. L. Fox 1927 The gaseous metabolism of large wild birds under aviary life. Proc. Am. Phil. Soc. 66:511.

Benedict, F. G., W. Landauer, and E. L. Fox 1932 The physiology of normal and frizzle fowl with special reference to basal metabolism. Univ. Conn. (Storrs) Agr. Expt. Sta. Bull. 177:15.

Benedict, F. G., and R. C. Lee 1937 Lipogenesis in the animal body, with special reference to the physiology of the goose. Carnegie Inst. Wash. Publ. No. 489.

Benedict, F. G., and O. Riddle 1929 The measurement of the basal heat production of pigeons. II: Physiological technique. J. Nutr. 1:497.

Benzinger, T. H., and C. Kitzinger 1949 Direct calorimetry by means of the gradient principle. Rev. Sci. Instr. 20:849.

Branion, H. D., G. W. Anderson, and D. C. Hill 1953 Antibiotics and the growth of ducks. Poultry Sci. 32:335.

Brody, S., E. M. Funk, and H. L. Kempster 1938 Growth and development with special reference to domestic animals. XXIV: Energetic efficiency of egg production with the influence of live weight thereon. Mo. Agric. Exp. Sta. Res. Bull. 278.

Burckard, E., L. Dontcheff, and C. Kayser 1933 Le rythme nycthéméral chez le pigeon. Ann. Physiol. Physicochim. Biol. 9:303.

Cathcart, E. P., and J. Markovitz 1927 The influence of various sugars on the respiratory quotient. A contribution to the significance of the R.Q. J. Physiol. 63:309.

Combs, G. F. 1964 Predicting amino acid requirements of chicks based on growth rate, body size, and body composition. Fed. Proc. 23:46.

Davidson, J. 1964 The efficiency of conversion of dietary metabolizable energy to tissue energy in young chickens as measured by body analyses. European Association for Animal Production; 3rd Symposium on Energy Metabolism, Troon.

Davis, E. A., Jr. 1955 Seasonal changes in the energy balance of the English sparrow. Auk 72:385.

Dawson, W. R. 1954 Temperature regulation and water requirements of the brown and Abert towhees, Pipilo fuscus and Pipilo aberti. Univ. Calif. (Berkeley) Publ. Zool. 59:81.

Dawson, W. R., and F. C. Evans 1957 Relation of growth and development to temperature regulation in nestling field and chipping sparrows. Physiol. Zool. 30:315.

Deighton, T., and J. C. D. Hutchinson 1940 Studies on the metabolism of fowls. II. The effect of activity on metabolism. J. Agr. Sci. 30:141.

Dukes, H. H. 1937 Studies on the energy metabolism of the hen. J. Nutr. 14:341.

Eriksson, S., and A. Kivimäe 1954 Diurnal variation of food consumption and carbon dioxide production in laying hens. Acta. Agric. Scand. 4:71.

Fill, W. 1942 Der Einfluss des Lichtes auf Stoffwechsel und Geschlechtsreife bei Warmblütern. Z. Wiss. Zool. 155:343.

Fisher, H. 1964 Feeding patterns in chickens and their effect on body composition. Fed. Proc. 23:88.

Freeman, B. M. 1962 Gaseous metabolism in the domestic chicken.

II: Oxygen consumption in the full-term and hatching embryo, with a note on a possible cause for "death in shell." Brit. Poultry Sci. 3:63.

Freeman, B. M. 1963 The gaseous metabolism of the domestic chicken. III: The oxygen requirements of the chicken during the period of rapid growth. Brit. Poultry Sci. 4:169.

Gelineo, S. 1955 Température d'adaptation et production de chaleur chez les oiseaux de petite taille. Arch. Sci. Physiol. 9:225.

Giaja, A. 1931 Contribution à la thermorégulation des oiseaux. Ann. Physiol. Physicochim. Biol. 7:12.

Heninger, R. W., W. S. Newcomer, and R. H. Thayer 1960 The effect of elevated ambient temperatures on the thyroxine secretion rate in chickens. Poultry Sci. 39:1332.

Hiebel, G., and P. Reys 1951 Le rythme nycthéméral de la calorification et de l'activité. Étude faite sur le pigeon et le rat blanc. Compt. Rend. Soc. Biol. 145:1224.

Hill, F. W. 1964 Utilization of energy for growth by chicks. European Association for Animal Production, 3rd Symposium on Energy Metabolism, Troon.

Hoffman, E., and C. S. Shaffner 1950 Thyroid weight and function as influenced by environmental temperatures. Poultry Sci. 29:365.

Huston, T. M., H. M. Edwards, Jr., and J. J. Williams 1962 The effects of high environmental temperature on thyroid secretion rate of domestic fowl. Poult. Sci. 41:640.

Irving, L., H. Krog, and M. Monson 1955 The metabolism of some Alaskan animals in winter and summer. Physiol. Zool. 28:173.

Kendeigh, S. C. 1939 The relation of metabolism to the development of temperature regulations in birds. J. Exp. Zool. 82:419.

Kendeigh, S. C. 1949 Effect of temperature and season on energy resources of the English sparrow. Auk 66:113.

Kibler, H. H., and S. Brody 1944 Metabolic changes in growing chickens. J. Nutr. 28:27.

Kielanowski, J. 1964 Estimates of the energy cost of protein deposition in growing animals. European Association for Animal Production, 3rd Symposium on Energy Metabolism, Troon.

King, J. R. 1957 Comments on the theory of indirect calorimetry as applied to birds. Northwest Sci. 31:155.

King, J. R., and D. S. Farner 1961 Energy metabolism, thermoregulation and body temperature, in vol. 2, Biology and Comparative Physiology of Birds, ed. A. J. Marshall. Academic Press, New York.

Kleiber, M. 1961 The Fire of Life: An Introduction to Animal Energetics. John Wiley & Sons, New York.

Kleiber, M., and J. E. Dougherty 1934 The influence of environmental temperature on the utilization of food energy in baby chicks. J. Gen. Physiol. 17:701.

Koch, H. J., and A. F. de Bont 1944 Influence de la mue sur l'intensité de métabolisme chez le pinson, Fringilla coelebs coelebs L. Ann. Soc. Zool. Belg. 75:81.

Koskimies, J. 1950 The life of the swift, Micropus apus (L) in relation to the weather. Ann. Acad. Sci. Fennicae, Ser. A, IV, 15:1.

Lasiewski, R. C. 1963 Oxygen consumption of torpid, resting, active and flying hummingbirds. Physiol. Zool. 36:122.

Lee, M., and R. C. Lee 1937 Effect of thyroidectomy and thyroid feeding in geese on the basal metabolism at different temperatures. Endocrinol. 21:790.

McCartney, M. G., and C. S. Shaffner 1950 The influence of altered metabolism upon fertility and hatchability in the female fowl. Poultry Sci. 29:67.

Marvin, H. N., and G. C. Smith 1943 Technique for thyroidectomy in the pigeon and the early effect of thyroid removal on heat production. Endocrinol. 32:87.

Mellen, W. J. 1958 Duration of effect of thyroxine and thiouracil in young chickens. Poultry Sci. 37:672.

Mellen, W. J. 1963 Body size and metabolic rate in the domestic fowl. Agric. Sci. Rev. 1:20.

Mellen, W. J., and F. W. Hill 1953 Effects of thiouracil, thyroprotein, and estrogen upon the basal metabolism and thyroid size of growing chickens. Poultry Sci. 32:994.

Mellen, W. J., F. W. Hill, and H. H. Dukes 1954 Studies of the energy requirements of chickens. 2: Effect of dietary energy level on the basal metabolism of growing chickens. Poultry Sci. 33:791.

Merkel, F. W. 1958 Untersuchungen über tages- und jahresperiodische Änderungen im Energiehaushalt gekäfigter Zugvögel. Z. vergl. Physiol. 41:154.

Mitchell, H. H. 1962 Comparative Nutrition of Man and Domestic Animals, Vol. 1. Academic Press, New York.

Mitchell, H. H., L. E. Card, and W. T. Haines 1927 The effect of age, sex, and castration on the basal heat production of chickens. J. Agr. Res. 34:945.

Mitchell, H. H., and W. T. Haines 1927 The basal metabolism of mature chickens and the net-energy value of corn. J. Agr. Res. 34:927.

Osbaldiston, G. W., and D. W. B. Sainsbury 1963a Control of the environment in a poultry house. Part I: The principles and practice. Vet. Rec. 75:159.

Osbaldiston, G. W., and D. W. B. Sainsbury 1963b Control of the environment in a poultry house. Part II: Broiler house experiments. Vet. Rec. 75:193.

Ota, H., and E. H. McNally 1961 Poultry respiration calorimetric studies of laying hens. U.S. Dept. of Agr. A. R. S. 42.

Pearson, O. P. 1950 The metabolism of hummingbirds. Condor 52:145.

Perek, M., and F. Sulman 1945 The basal metabolic rate in molting and laying hens. Endocrinol. 36:240.

Poczopko, P., and J. Kowalczyk 1964 Oxygen consumption in growing chickens as related to their body composition. European Association for Animal Production, 3rd Symposium on Energy Metabolism, Troon.

Prince, R. P., L. M. Potter, and W. W. Irish 1961 Response of chickens to temperature and ventilation environments. Poultry Sci. 40:102.

Rautenberg, W. 1957 Vergleichende Untersuchungen über den Energiehaushalt des Bergfinken (Fringilla montifringilla L.) und des Haussperlings (Passer domesticus L.). J. Ornithol. 98:36.

Richardson, H. B. 1929 The respiratory quotient. Physiol. Rev. 9:61.

Riddle, O., T. C. Nussman, and F. G. Benedict 1932 Metabolism during growth in a common pigeon. Am. J. Physiol. 101:251.

Riddle, O., G. C. Smith, and F. G. Benedict 1932 The basal metabolism of the mourning dove and some of its hybrids. Am. J. Physiol. 101:260.

Riddle, O., G. C. Smith, and F. G. Benedict 1934 Seasonal and temperature factors and their determinations in pigeons of percentage metabolism change per degree of temperature change. Am. J. Physiol. 107:333.

Romijn, C., and W. Lokhorst 1960 Foetal heat production in the fowl. J. Physiol. 150:239.

Romijn, C., and W. Lokhorst 1961a Some aspects of energy metabolism in birds. Proceedings, 2nd Symposium on Energy Metabolism, Wageningen, 1961, p. 49.

Romijn, C., and W. Lokhorst 1961b Climate and poultry: Heat regulation in the fowl. Tijdschr. Diergeneesk. 86:153.

Romijn, C., and W. Lokhorst 1962 Humidity and incubation. XII World Poultry Congress, Section Papers, p. 136.

Romijn, C., and W. Lokhorst 1964 Barometric pressure and incubation. European Association for Animal Production, 3rd Symposium on Energy Metabolism, Troon.

Seibert, H. C. 1949 Differences between migrant and non-migrant birds in food and water intake at various temperatures and photoperiods. Auk 66:128.

Shellabarger, C. J., R. C. Lasiewski, and G. E. Hyncik 1961 Thyroid function in active, sleeping and torpid hummingbirds. Nature 191:1318.

Singh, H., and C. S. Shaffner 1950 Effect of thyroprotein and caloric level of diet on metabolic rate of chickens. Poultry Sci. 29:575.

Steen, J. 1957 Food intake and oxygen consumption in pigeons at low temperatures. Acta Physiol. Scand. 39:22.

Steen, J. 1958 Climatic adaptation in some small northern birds. Ecology 39:625.

Thornton, P. A., and R. E. Moreng 1959 Further evidence on the value of ascorbic acid, for maintenance of shell quality in warm environmental temperature. Poultry Sci. 38:594.

Titus, H. W. 1956 Energy values of feedstuffs for poultry. Proceedings, Semi-Annual Meeting, Nutrition Council of the American Feed Manufacturers Association.

Wallgren, H. 1954 Energy metabolism of two species of the genus Emberiza as correlated with distribution and migration. Acta. Zool. Fennica, 84:1.

West, G. C. 1962 Responses and adaptation of wild birds to environmental temperature, in Comparative Physiology of Temperature Regulation, edited by J. P. Hannon and E. Viereck, Part 3, p. 291. Arctic Aeromedical Laboratory, Fort Wainwright, Alaska.

Whittow, G. C., P. D. Sturkie, and G. Stein, Jr. 1964 Cardiovascular changes associated with thermal polypnea in the chicken. Am. J. Physiol. 207:1349.

Wilson, W. O., C. F. Kelly, R. F. Lourenzen, and A. E. Woodward 1957 Effect of wind on growth of fryers after two weeks of age. Poultry Sci. 36:978.

Winchester, C. F. 1939 Influence of thyroid on egg production. Endocrinol. 24:697.

Winchester, C. F. 1940a Growth and development with special reference to domestic animals. II: Seasonal metabolic and endocrine rhythms in the domestic fowl. Mo. Agric. Exp. Sta. Res. Bull. 315.

Winchester, C. F. 1940b Seasonal metabolic rhythms in the domestic fowl. Poultry Sci. 19:239.

Zausch, M. 1964 Modifications in techniques and apparatus to installations for the study of respiration in small animals. European Association for Animal Production, 3rd Symposium on Energy Metabolism, Troon.

Zeuthen, E. 1942 The ventilation of the respiratory tract in birds. Kgl. Danske Videnskab. Selskab. Biol. Medd. 17:1.

CHAPTER 10

Alimentary Canal: Anatomy, Prehension, Deglutition, Appetite, Passage of Ingesta, Motility

ANATOMY OF THE ALIMENTARY CANAL

THE organs of the digestive tract of the bird include the beak, mouth, salivary glands, tongue (but no teeth), pharynx, esophagus, crop, proventriculus, gizzard, intestines, ceca, rectum, and cloaca (see Figure 36). The length of various parts of the tract vary with size of bird, type of food eaten, and other factors. Birds eating coarse, fibrous food tend to have especially large digestive tracts, and grain-eating birds have larger tracts than carnivores. The length of various parts of the tract of the chicken are shown in Table 47. For details concerning the anatomy and histology of the tract of several species, see Calhoun, 1933; Farner, 1960; Malewitz and Calhoun, 1958.

Mouth and pharynx. There is no sharp line of demarcation between the mouth and pharynx, and there is no soft palate in most birds. The hard palate is pierced by a median slit which communicates with the nasal cavities. The cavity of the mouth is lined with stratified squamous epithelium. Branched tubular salivary glands are present (Calhoun, 1933; Halnan, 1949).

Esophagus and crop. The esophagus of the mature fowl is 6 to 8

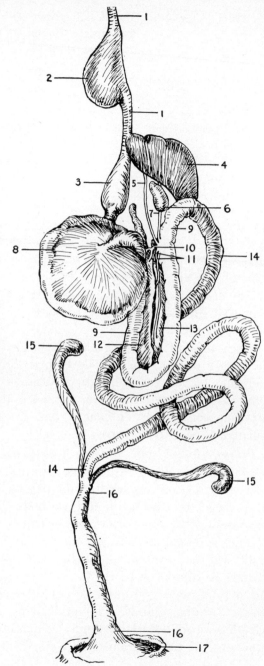

Figure 36. Digestive tract of the chicken.

1 and 2, esophagus and crop; 3, proventriculus; 4, liver; 5, hepatic duct; 6, gall bladder; 7, cystic duct or duct from gall bladder; 8, gizzard; 9, duodenum; 10, pancreatic ducts from dorsal lobe; 11, pancreatic ducts from ventral lobe; 12, dorsal lobe of pancreas; 13, ventral lobe of pancreas; 14, upper and lower segments of small intestines; 15, ceca; 16, large intestine or rectum; 17, cloaca.

Table 47. Length of the digestive tract of chickens (averaged from five birds; Calhoun, 1933)

Part measured	Age	
	20 days	1½ year
Entire digestive tract	85 cm.	210 cm.
Angle of beak to crop	7.5 cm.	20 cm.
Angle of beak to proventriculus	11.5 cm.	35 cm.
Duodenum (complete loop)	12 cm.	20 cm.
Ileum and jejunum	49 cm.	120 cm.
Cecum	5 cm.	17.5 cm.
Rectum and cloaca	4 cm.	11.25 cm.

inches long and is lined with stratified squamous epithelium. Mucous glands are present.

The crop has essentially the same structure as the esophagus except that mucous glands are present only at the juncture of the esophagus (Calhoun).

The crops of certain grain-eating birds, such as the chicken, duck, and pigeon, are well developed; but in some other species they may be very large, in others rudimentary, and in some insect-eating birds, absent (Browne, 1922; see also Farner). In males of certain species the esophagus has diverticula which become inflated during the courting season.

Proventriculus and gizzard. The proventriculus or glandular stomach is usually a fusiform organ, and varies in size with the species. It is relatively small in the pigeon and chicken but may be quite large and distensible in certain species such as the storks, albatrosses, gulls, and cormorants (Farner).

The crop of doves and pigeons is especially adapted to produce milk, and the proliferation of the crop epithelium and production of milk is influenced by the hormone prolactin. The proventriculus is lined with columnar or cuboidal epithelium, formed into simple tubular glands. The underlying mucous layer contains well-developed lobular glands, which communicate with the lumen of the proventriculus by a duct. The outer muscular coats are similar to those of the esophagus. The gastric glands of birds (chickens) contain only one type of cell, which produces both acid and pepsinogen granules; in this they are unlike the gastric glands of mammals, where cells of different types produce the two secretions (Bowie, 1936).

In a number of birds there is a separate or partially separated chamber between the gizzard and intestine (Farner).

Small intestine. The small intestine consists of the duodenum (loop) and a jejunum and ileum, according to the terminology of some authors; beyond the duodenum there are no delimited areas in the small intestine. Some authors refer to the upper and lower ileum as corresponding to the jejunum and ileum in mammals. The remnant of the attachment of the yolk stalk may be found about midway along the small intestine. In relation to body length, the intestines of birds are shorter than those of mammals (Browne, 1922); however, there is considerable variation in the length, which is influenced by food habitat. It is longer in herbivores and grain-eaters, and shorter in carnivores.

The mucosa of the small intestine is characterized by crypts of Lieberkühn of varying degrees of development. In some species of birds (carnivores) there are well developed and figurelike villi, and in others (herbivores) the villi are flattened and leaflike (Farner). The epithelium usually consists of simple columnar cells with many goblet cells. The layers or coats from the epithelial surface outward comprise a muscularis mucosae, a thin submucosa containing a few blood vessels and nerves, and an outer muscular layer made up of an inner circular and an outer longitudinal layer, rich in blood vessels and nerves. Brunner's glands are absent in the chicken (Calhoun), but in some species tubular glands may be present which are similar to or homologous with Brunner's glands of mammals (Farner).

Ceca, large intestine, and cloaca. The ceca are situated at the juncture of the small and large intestines. In some species they are large and prominent (about 6 inches long in the chicken) and are paired, whereas in some species they may be single, rudimentary, or absent (Browne, 1922). Guarding the entrance of the ceca into the intestine are the muscular ileo-cecal valves. The histology of the ceca is similar to the rest of the tract, except that the villi are not as tall.

The large intestine in birds is relatively short, and there is no line of demarcation between the rectum and colon, as in mammals. The large intestine or rectum empties into the cloaca.

The liver and pancreas, although not part of the alimentary canal, are organs concerned in digestion. The liver is relatively large, and is bilobed. Some species of birds (chicken, duck, and goose) have gall bladders; others, such as the pigeon, do not. The gall bladder is located on the dorsal surface of the liver, and gives rise to the bile ducts, which open into the duodenum, near the distal loop (see Figure 36). The pancreas is discussed in Chapter 20.

Circulation in the Digestive Tract

The esophagus and crop receive arterial blood from branches of the external carotid arteries, and are drained by branches of the jugular veins. The coeliac artery and its branches supply the liver, proventriculus, gizzard, pancreas, duodenum, and small intestine. The caudal mesenteric artery supplies the cloaca and rectum. Blood is drained from the stomach, gizzard, and intestines by the gastroduodenal, cranial, and caudal mesenteric veins. The latter empty into the portal vein, which carries the blood to the liver (Bradley and Grahame, 1960).

The nerves of the alimentary canal are discussed under motility of the tract.

PREHENSION, DEGLUTITION, AND APPETITE

The bird picks up feed with the beak, and the food is mixed with saliva in the mouth and swallowed. The act of swallowing (deglutition) differs in certain species. The food mass (bolus) and water, are forced downward in the goose, chicken, and duck by gravity and by the negative pressure in the esophagus as the bird raises its head and extends the neck. These birds do not possess a soft palate, which in certain mammals and birds (e.g. the pigeon) aids in forcing the bolus downward (Cannon and Moser, 1898; Halnan, 1949). The pigeon, like the horse, can drink with its head down.

The mechanisms involved in hunger and appetite and the satisfaction of hunger (satiety) in mammals have received considerable attention in recent years (see Brobeck, 1957). It was believed for many years that the level of blood sugar played a key role in regulating appetite and satiety (the glucostatic theory). Since 1940, however, evidence has been accumulating that appetite and satiety are regulated by centers in the hypothalamus. Stimulation of the lateral hypothalamus produces voracious eating, and lesions in the same area cause loss of appetite. Conversely, stimulation of the ventromedial nuclei produces satiety, and lesions stimulate appetite. Thus various stimuli reaching the central nervous system may influence food intake. Some of the factors that facilitate feeding or appetite include contraction of empty stomach, cold environment, and visual stimuli (sight of food). Factors that tend to inhibit feeding are dehydration, distention of stomach and intestines or injury to the intestines and rectum, warm environment, and exercise.

Little is known about the neural control of food intake in birds, and studied have been undertaken only recently. Lesions produced in the lateral hypothalamus of chickens cause loss of appetite or aphagia (Feldman *et al.*, 1957). Preliminary work from the same laboratory (Lepkovsky and Feldman, 1962) indicates that lesions in the medial hypothalamus produce hyperphagia. Stimulation of the lateral hypothalamus in pigeons also causes hyperphagia (Åkerman *et al.* 1960).

Sturkie and Joiner (1959) demonstrated that lesions or small foreign bodies placed in the rectum of chickens decreased food intake markedly, and that food consumption returned to normal after removal of the foreign bodies. It is presumed that the effect was produced via the hypothalamic centers, as has been reported in mammals.

PASSAGE OF INGESTA THROUGH THE TRACT

The time required for feed to pass through the alimentary canal can be studied in several ways: (1) Birds fed at the same time may be killed at different intervals to observe the location of feed in tract. (2) The food may be stained with certain dyes so that it may be identified in the feces. (3) Certain types of feed, such as oats, may be recognized in the feces without marking (Browne, 1922). (4) The passage of the food may also be observed with X-rays, or (5) the food may be collected by placing cannulas into the different portions of the tract, a method employed by a number of German workers (see Groebbels, 1932, for a review).

Passage of food down the alimentary canal of birds has been studied by a number of workers, with considerable variation in the results (see Keith, Card, and Mitchell, 1927; Groebbels, 1932; and Heuser, 1945). Some of these results, based on the chicken, are shown as follows:

Type of feed	Amount of feed in crop Grams	Time required for feed to disappear from crop Hours	Amount	Author
Wheat, oats or corn	5	$1\frac{1}{2}$–2	all	Ihnen (1928)
"	30	7–$9\frac{1}{2}$	"	"
"	60	10–18	"	"
Oats	full crop	18–20	"	Browne (1922)
Corn	30	12	"	Schwarz & Teller (1924)
"	35–65	70	"	Hubeck (1930)
Wheat	"	102	"	"
Barley	"	119	"	"
Grain	40–60	4	20–30%	Heuser (1945)
"	"	24	90%	"

The data of Ihnen show that the amount of feed consumed greatly influences its passage from the crop. This has also been reported by Steinmetzer (1924) and by Henry, MacDonald, and Magee (1933). Halnan (1949) showed that when the crop of the chicken is full, the first half of its contents passes to the gizzard much faster than the second half.

The rate of passage of ingesta is also influenced by the consistency, hardness, and water content of the feed. Dry oats remain in the crop longer than corn or wheat, and longer than boiled oats (Heuser, 1945). The same author revealed, also, that equal quantities of wet mash pass from the crop faster than dry mash. Whether or not dry oats are whole, ground, or crushed does not materially affect their sojourn in the crop, according to Henry *et al.* (1933).

Soft potatoes leave the crop of the goose more rapidly than grain, but chopped meat remains in it longer than grain (Groebbels, 1932).

Most of the studies reported above were based upon the disappearance of feed from the crop. A better idea of the speed of passage of ingesta through the tract may be gained by the use of X-rays, and by the first appearance, after feeding, of the feed in the feces.

Henry *et al.* (1933), who fed 2 ounces of oats mixed with barium sulfate to hens, reported the complete disappearance of feed from the tract (on the basis of X-ray shadows) within 16 to 25 hours.

Most investigators who have used markers have shown that some of the feed first given appears in the feces within anywhere from $2\frac{1}{2}$ to 12 hours, depending on the type and amount fed and the physiological state of the bird. Kaupp and Ivey (1923), who fed corn meal and wheat middlings mixed with various dyes, reported the appearance of the dye in the feces within approximately 4 hours for growing and laying chickens, 8 hours for nonlaying hens, and approximately 12 hours for broody hens.

The results obtained with the use of dyes are subject to error, according to Browne (1922). He showed that soluble dyes tend to pass through the tract faster than hard particles, particularly when large amounts are ingested. If the food to be tested is impregnated with an insoluble dye, this objection is overcome. Such a dye is chromic oxide. Experiments indicate that it can be detected in the feces within $2\frac{1}{2}$ hours after feeding, and that most of it is recovered in the feces 24 hours afterward (Dansky and Hill, 1952). Imabayashi, Kametaka, and Hatano (1956), who administered radioactive barium to chickens, reported that approximately half of the feed ingested was excreted within 4 or 5 hours. The passage of feed through young chicks is faster (Thornton *et al.*, 1956). The time of passage of food through the adult turkey is similar to that for the chicken, but time for passage was longer in old turkey hens than in younger ones (Hillerman *et al.*, 1953).

Crop Motility

The crop undergoes contractions which vary considerably in rhythm and amplitude. The irregularity of movements is influenced by the nervous state of the animal, by hunger, and by other factors. Extreme excitement, fear, or struggling may inhibit or retard crop contractions in the chicken and pigeon (Rogers, 1915; Henry, MacDonald, and Magee, 1933). In order to study crop movements supposedly not influenced by nervous impulses reaching the central nervous system, the cerebral hemispheres have been removed (decerebration) from pigeons and chickens (Ashcraft, 1930; Rogers, 1915 and 1916; and Paterson, 1927). Rogers, and also Ashcraft, concluded that hunger produced restlessness and irregular crop activity in normal and decerebrate pigeons and chickens, but that fear had no effect upon crop activity of the decerebrate pigeon (Rogers). Paterson (1927), however, reported that crop motility in hungry decerebrate pigeons was fairly regular.

Peristaltic contraction begins in the esophagus and spreads down the crop to the gizzard (Halnan, 1949). It usually occurs in groups of varying number and speed, depending upon state of hunger, amount of feed in the crop, and other factors. The waves usually appear in groups of from 2 to 15, at intervals of from 1 to 40 minutes, according to Ashcraft (1930), and at intervals of 1 per minute according to Groebbels (1932). That the speed of contraction is greater when the crop is empty, is illustrated in the chicken from data of Lieberbarb (see Groebbels, 1932):

Hours of starvation	$1\frac{1}{2}$	6	10	27
No. of contractions per hour	13	36	55	75
Duration of contractions in seconds	42	45	30	26.5

When the gizzard and crop are full, crop contractions may cease (Halnan), and may be absent in the pigeon for 30 to 40 minutes (Paterson, 1927, and Rogers, 1916).

Within one to two hours after feeding the pigeon, peristaltic waves appear in groups of 3 or 4 and at intervals of 15 to 20 minutes. After five to twelve hours they appear in groups of 6 to 20, at intervals of 10 to 30 minutes. In the hungry bird, with an empty crop, the contractions occur in groups of 8 to 16 and at intervals of 10 to 60 minutes.

The pressure in the crop of the hen ranges from 7 to 18 cm. of water (Groebbels).

Nervous control. The motility of the esophagus and crop is under nervous control. These organs receive parasympathetic excitatory fibers from the vagus, according to Ihnen (1928), and also both excitatory and inhibitory fibers from the sympathetic system, according to Nolf (see Babkin, 1950). Stimulation of the peripheral end of the left vagus causes contraction in the left side of the crop (cephalic and dorsal region), and stimulation of the right vagus causes contraction of the right side (Ihnen). Transection of the right vagus alone has little effect upon crop motility, but ligation of the left vagus inhibits motility and particularly the ability of the crop to empty itself (Mangold, 1929). According to Ihnen, the left vagus nerve apparently controls the peristaltic movements of the esophagus, since after ligation of this nerve these movements were abolished. According to Hanzlik and Butt (1928), stimulation of the vagus produces contraction in the circular muscles of the crop; stimulation of the sympathetics causes contraction of the longitudinal muscles. These authors believe that the latter have little influence on normal crop motility.

The parasympathomimetic drugs acetylcholine and pilocarpine produce strong contraction in the crop (see Groebbels, 1932).

Motility of Proventriculus

Apparently few observations have been made on the motility of the glandular stomach. Ashcraft (1930) reported that the wave of contraction in the proventriculus of the chicken was fairly regular, rhythmical, and of high amplitude. Rate of contraction was approximately one per minute in the hungry chicken. Amplitude and frequency of contractions are greater in the male, and this is due to the hormone androgen, according to Ikegami (1938). He castrated male chickens and reported a decrease in frequency and amplitude of contractions, which could be restored to normal after injections of androgen. The vagus sends fibers to the proventriculus, and presumably motility is influenced by the nerve. Certainly the vagus influences gastric secretion.

Motility of Gizzard

The gizzard exhibits regular and rhythmic contractions. Motility has been studied by observing the organ in the opened bird, by fluoroscopic examination, and by placing balloons, attached to a suitable manometer and recording device, in the gizzard (for details see Groebbels, 1932; Mangold, 1929; Ashcraft, 1930; and Henry, MacDonald, and Magee, 1933). The type of wave produced varies somewhat with the location of the balloon in the gizzard.

The contractions or grinding sounds of the gizzard can be heard in the bird with a stethoscope, particularly when coarse or hard food and grit are present (Groebbels, 1932). The movements appear to be rotary in nature, judging from the circumferential arrangement of fibrous food in the gizzard (Browne, 1922).

The frequency of contractions appears to vary little in the hen, and ranges from 2 to 3 per minute, according to most investigators (Ashcraft, Mangold, Henry, *et al.,* and others). To what extent state of hunger influences the frequency is not clear. Henry *et al.* (1933), and also Mangold (1929), reported a slightly higher frequency in fed birds as compared with those that had been starved, but Rossi's results (see Groebbels, 1932) showed the opposite effect. Gizzard contractions in hens starved for one to two days ranged from 2.5 to 3 per minute, and in those fed, from 1.5 to 2 per minute.

The duration of contractions ranges, in most cases, from 20 to 30 seconds, and is influenced by hunger, as well as by the type of feed (Mangold, 1929). Starvation of birds that had previously been fed wheat increased the amplitude and duration of individual contractions from a range of 15 to 25 seconds to one of 30 to 50 seconds. Ingestion of hard or fibrous food shortens contraction time. For example, when wheat and barley are fed the durations range from 15 to 22 seconds, and after feeding potatoes and corn meal the range is from 22 to 30 seconds.

The amplitude of the gizzard movements is greater when grit is present (Groebbels). Apparently grit remains in the gizzard for a considerable time, and is not ordinarily passed out with the feed, particularly when only small amounts are present. Browne (1922) fed, four small pebbles, to a bird that had been denied access to grit, and three of these were found in the gizzard three weeks later. Groebbels (1932), after employing the duodenal cannula, reported that very little grit was collected in the cannula; yet the gizzard of the domestic goose may contain as much as 30 grams, and the duck 10 grams.

The pressure exerted by the gizzard has been measured by Mangold and co-workers, by Kato, and by others (see Mangold, 1929), in a number of birds, as follows (in mm Hg) :

| Buzzard | 8–26 | Duck | 180 |
| Hen | 100–150 | Goose | 265–280 |

The pressure is much lower in carnivores such as the buzzard, where the gizzard is poorly developed. Hard, fibrous feeds, such as barley, produce higher gizzard pressure than wheat. The amplitude of contractions is greater in males than females.

In a more recent publication Mangold (1950) provides more details on the muscles involved in gizzard contraction. Apparently the lateral muscles contract first, and then the intermediate muscles.

Nerves. The gizzard receives extrinsic fibers from the vagus and the sympathetic system. Nolf, and also Doyon (see Groebbels, 1932) reported the presence of excitatory and inhibitory fibers in the vagus. Nolf reported both types of fibers in the sympathetic nerves to the gizzard also, but Doyon reported only inhibitory fibers. Ligation of the vagus causes slowing of the gizzard movements, which, however, soon return to normal (Mangold, Nolf, and others). Cutting both nerves produces permanent slowing in the movements of the organ, and thinning of the walls of the gizzard (Nolf, 1927).

The gizzard is capable of automatic movements, which are governed by its intrinsic nerve supply. When the gizzard is deprived of its extrinsic nerve supply, by ligation of such nerves or removal of the organ from the body, it continues to undergo movements (see Babkin, 1950; Groebbels, 1932; and also Nolf, 1927).

The excitatory and inhibitory effects of parasympathomimetic and sympathomimetic drugs on the gizzard have been reported

(Henry *et al.*, 1933). Pilocarpine increases the rate of contraction; adrenaline, and likewise atropine, decreases it.

Motility of Small Intestines

The intestines of birds undergo peristaltic and segmenting movements (Vonk and Postma, 1949; Mangold, 1929; Groebbels). This has been demonstrated by *in vitro* studies. The peristaltic wave proceeds aborally.

Nolf (1929) reported that sectioning of the vagi did not affect the rhythmic movements of the small intestine, although the progress of the waves aborally was slower. His evidence indicated that in the chicken as in man, the lower part of intestine is not well supplied with vagal fibers.

Stimulation of the vagus increases the motility of the intestine, but its coeliac and mesenteric nerves may also increase intestinal movements (Nolf, 1934). The role of Remak's nerve on intestinal motility is not clear.

Where regurgitation of the contents from the duodenum into the gizzard, the proventriculus, and even the crop have been reported, there would appear to be reverse peristalsis.

Motility of Ceca and Large Intestines

According to Browne (1922), the ceca undergo peristalsis, the wave passing from the intestinal junction to the blind end of the organ, which he observed in the open bird. He suggested that the ceca are filled in this manner. Other workers have suggested that they are filled by antiperistaltic movements of the intestines or by pressure in the latter. In order for the ceca to fill and empty, the valves guarding their entrance into the intestines must open and close; but the physiology of these in filling and emptying of the structures is not understood.

The contents of the ceca are homogeneous and pultaceous in consistency, and are usually chocolate-colored. Cecal contents or droppings can be readily distinguished from rectal feces. Such knowledge has been used in determining when the bodies are evacuated. The ratio of cecal to rectal evacuations for the hen ranges from 1 to 7.3, after the feeding of barley, to 1 to 11.5, after the ingestion of corn (Röseler, 1929).

The mechanism for the evacuation of the ceca is unknown. It is believed by some (see Mangold, 1929) that as the ceca are filled, the pressure builds up to a point that the ileo-cecal valves are opened, or that the pressure in the cecal walls mechanically stimulates and causes contraction of the organs.

It is presumed that the ceca, like the rest of the digestive tract, receive sympathetic and parasympathetic fibers, which are concerned in their motility. It is known that the automatic movements of the organs *in vitro* are inhibited by epinephrine and stimulated by acetylcholine. In fact, the chicken cecum is a very sensitive indicator of epinephrine and related substances, and is used for assaying the potency of such substances in the blood and other solutions (Ostlund, 1954).

Yasukawa (1958), employing balloons, reported peristaltic and antiperistaltic waves in the large intestine, the latter occuring at intervals of from 5.6 to 6.3 seconds.

REFERENCES

Åkerman, B., B. Anderson, E. Fabricius, and L. Svensson   1960   Observations on central regulation of body temperature and of food and water intake in the pigeon (Columba livia). Acta Physiol. Scand. 50:328.

Ashcraft, D. W.   1930   Correlative activities of the alimentary canal of fowl. Am. J. Physiol. 93:105.

Babkin, B. P.   1950   Secretory Mechanism of the Digestive Glands. 2nd ed. Paul B. Hoeber, Inc., New York.

Bowie, D. J.   1936   A method of staining the pepsinogen granules in gastric glands. Anat. Rec. 64:357.

Bradley, O. C., and T. Grahame   1960   The Structure of the Fowl, 4th ed. Oliver and Boyd, Edinburgh and London.

Brobeck, J. R.   1957   Neural control of hunger, appetite, and satiety. Yale J. Biol. & Med. 29:565.

Browne, T. G.   1922   Some observations on the digestive system of the fowl. J. Comp. Path. & Thera. 35:12.

Calhoun, M. L.   1933   The microscopic anatomy of the digestive tract of Gallus domesticus. Iowa State Coll. J. Sci. 7:261.

Cannon, W. B., and A. Moser   1898   The movements of the food in the esophagus. Am. J. Physiol. 1:435.

Dansky, L. M., and F. W. Hill   1952   Application of the chromic oxide indicator method to balance studies with growing chickens. J. Nutr. 47:449.

Farner, D. S. 1960 Digestion and digestive system, Chapter XI in Biology and Comparative Physiology of Birds, Vol. I, edited by A. J. Marshall. Academic Press, New York.

Feldman, S. E., S. Larsson, M. K. Dimick, and S. Lepkovsky 1957 Aphagia in chickens. Am. J. Physiol. 191:259.

Groebbels, F. 1932 Der Vogel. Erster Band: Atmungswelt und Nahrungswelt. Verlag von Gebrüder Borntraeger, Berlin.

Halnan, E. T. 1949 The architecture of the avian gut and tolerance of crude fiber. Brit. J. Nutr. 3:245.

Hanzlik, P. J., and E. M. Butt 1928 Reactions of the crop muscles under tension, with a consideration of the anatomical arrangement, innervation and other factors. Am. J. Physiol. 85:271.

Henry, K. M., A. J. MacDonald, and H. E. Magee 1933 Observations on the functions of the alimentary canal in fowls. J. Exp. Biol. 10:153.

Heuser, G. F. 1945 The rate of passage of feed from the crop to the hen. Poultry Sci. 24:20.

Hillerman, J. P., F. H. Kratzer, and W. O. Wilson 1953 Food passage through chickens and turkeys and some regulating factors. Poultry Sci. 32:332.

Hubeck, R. 1930 Wiss. Arch. Landwirtschaft 2:626. Cited by Groebbels, 1932.

Ihnen, K. 1928 Beiträge zur Physiologie des Kropfes bei Huhn and Taube. I: Bewegung und Innervation des Kropfes. Arch. ges. Physiol. (Pflügers) 218:767.

Ikegami, Y. 1938 The function of the testes and the stomach movement. Jap. J. Gastroenterol. 10:103 (Biol. Abs. 14547, 1940).

Imabayashi, K., M. Kametaka, and T. Hatano 1956 Studies on digestion in the domestic fowl. Tokyo J. Agr. Res. 2:99.

Kaupp, B. F., and J. E. Ivey 1923 Time required for food to pass through the intestinal tract of fowls. J. Agric. Res. 23:721.

Keith, M. H., L. E. Card, and H. H. Mitchell 1927 The rate of passage of food through the digestive tract of the hen. J. Agric. Res. 24:759.

Lepkovsky, S., and S. E. Feldman 1962 (unpublished).

Malewitz, T. D., and M. L. Calhoun 1958 The gross and microscopic anatomy of the digestive tract, spleen, kidney, lungs and heart of the turkey. Poultry Sci. 37:388.

Mangold, E. 1929 Handbuch der Ernährung und des Stoffwechsels der landswirtschaftlichen Nutztiere. Zweiter Band. Verlag von Julius Springer, Berlin.

Mangold, E. 1950 Die Verdauung bei den Nutztieren. Akademie, Berlin.

Nolf, P. 1927 Du rôle des nerfs vague et sympathique dans l'innervation motrice de l'estomac de l'oiseaux. Arch. Int. Physiol. 28: 309.

Nolf, P. 1929 Le système nerveux entérique: essai d'analyse par la méthode à la nicotine de Langley. Arch. Int. Physiol. 30:317.

Nolf, P. 1934 Les nerfs extrinsèques de l'intestin chez l'oiseaux. II: Les nerfs coeliaques et mésentériques. Arch. Int. Physiol. 39:165.

Ostlund, E. 1954 The distribution of catecholamines in lower animals and their effect on the heart. Acta Physiol. Scand. 31:Suppl. 112.

Paterson, T. L. 1927 Crop movements in the pigeon. J. Lab. & Clin. Med. 12:1003.

Röseler, M. 1929 Die Bedeutung der Blinddärme des Haushuhnes für die Resorption der Nahrung und Verdauung der Rohfaser. Z. f. Tierz. u. Zücht. 13:281.

Rogers, F. T. 1915 The hunger mechanism in birds (prelim. report). Proc. Soc. Exp. Biol. & Med. 13:119.

Rogers, F. T. 1916 Contribution to the physiology of the stomach: The hunger mechanism of the pigeon and its relation to the central nervous system. Am. J. Physiol. 41:555.

Schwarz, C., and H. Teller 1924 Beiträge zur Physiologie der Verdauung. VIII: Mitteilung über die Kropfverdauung des Haushuhnes. Fermentforschung 7:269.

Steinmetzer, K. 1924 Die zeitlichen Verhaeltnisse beim Durchwandern von Futter durch den Magendarmkanal des Huhnes. Arch. ges. Physiol. (Pflügers) 206:500.

Sturkie, P. D., and W. P. Joiner 1959 Effects of foreign bodies in cloaca and rectum of the chicken on feed consumption. Am. J. Physiol. 197:1337.

Thornton, P. A., P. J. Schaible, and L. F. Wolterink 1956 Intestinal transit and skeletal retention of radioactive strontium in the chick. Poultry Sci. 35:1055.

Vonk, H. J., and N. Postma 1949 X-ray studies on the movements of the hen's intestine. Physiol. Comp. & Oecol. 1:15.

Yasukawa, M. 1959 Studies on movements of the large intestine. VII: Movements of the large intestine of fowls. Jap. J. Vet. Sci. 21:1 (English summary).

CHAPTER 11

Digestion, Absorption, Secretion of Gastric Juices, pH, Liver

RELATIVELY little is known about digestion in birds, and practically no work has been conducted upon it in recent years. For reviews see Groebbels (1932), Mangold (1929 and 1934), Halnan (1949), and Farner (1960).

Digestion involves all of the physical and chemical changes which ingested food must undergo before it can be absorbed in the intestines. These processes include swallowing, maceration, and grinding of food in the gizzard, and the action of digestive enzymes from the saliva, stomach, intestines, and pancreas, of bile from the liver, of hydrochloric acid from the stomach, and also of bacteria.

Ingested carbohydrates must be converted into the simple sugars, the monosaccharides, before they can be absorbed. Some of the enzymes concerned in the breakdown of the complex carbohydrates are ptyalin and amylopsin (amylases), lactase, maltase, and invertases.

The fats are hydrolyzed to fatty acids and glycerol before absorption into the small intestines. This is accomplished by the action of bile, which emulsifies the fats, and of the lipase, fat-splitting enzyme.

Ingested proteins are hydrolyzed to amino acids, in which form they are absorbed in the intestines. In this process the primary protein derivatives, which are insoluble, are broken down to the secondary proteins, mainly proteoses, peptones, and peptides. Although these are soluble, normally they are not absorbed, but are converted finally into amino acids. The enzymes concerned in the cleavage of proteins in the bird are pepsin from the stomach, and trypsin and possibly others from the pancreatic and intestinal juices respectively.

In the digestion of fats, carbohydrates, and proteins, a number of intermediary products are formed. For details, consult textbooks on biochemistry and nutrition.

The principal enzymes present in the digestive tract of the chicken, and their effects, are shown in Table 48. Further details concerning these are discussed in the text.

Table 48. Enzymes of the digestive tract of the chicken

Organ and secretion	Enzyme	Substance acted upon	Intermediate or end product
Saliva	Amylase (ptyalin)	Starch	Maltose
Proventriculus (gastric juice)	Pepsin	Protein	Proteoses and peptones
Gizzard and extracts	{ pepsin (from proventriculus)		
Pure intestinal juice or tissue	{ Amylase* Invertase* Trypsin*	Proteoses, peptones, and peptides	Amino acids
Pancreas; pancreatic juice	{ Amylase Invertase Trypsin Lipase	— Sucrose Intermediate N products Fat	Simple sugars Amino acids Fatty acids and glycerol
Bile	Amylase	—	—

* See text.

DIGESTION IN THE MOUTH, ESOPHAGUS, AND CROP

The amylase, ptyalin, is present in saliva and scrapings from the mouth and esophagus of the fowl (Shaw, 1913; Leasure and Link, 1940), and although its content is not as high as in human saliva (Leasure and Link), enough of it is present to hydrolize starch to sugar within one hour (Shaw). However, Jung and Pierre (1933), who fed chickens carbohydrates, found little or no conversion of starch into sugar in the crop, and concluded that saliva plays a very minor role in enzymatic digestion.

The presence of enzymes in the crop and their role in digestion have been a subject of controversy. A number of workers have reported the presence of proteolytic and amylolytic enzymes in the crop or its contents, whereas others have not (see Groebbels, 1932). Klug (1891) and Shaw (1913) found no enzymes present in extracts of crop tissue or crop mucosa, but Plimmer and Rosedale (1922) did find proteolytic and amylolytic enzymes (amylase and lactase) in crop tissue; Hamilton and Mitchell (1924) also found lactase in crop tissue. The presence of such enzymes in crop tissue, however, does not mean that they play a significant role in digestion, nor does their presence in the contents of the crop prove that they are normally produced there. In fact, diastase found in the crop is usually from an exogenous source, namely the feed itself. Since regurgitation into the crop of contents from the proventriculus, gizzard, and duodenum, including bile, has been demonstrated (Klug, 1891, and others), it is likely that most of the enzymes found in the crop come from the duodenum and proventriculus. Thus, the crop appears to play a minor role in enzymatic digestion and also absorption. Introduction of botulinus toxin into the crop, which was separated from the proventriculus by a ligature, had no ill effect upon the bird, indicating that the toxin was not absorbed (Leasure and Foltz, 1940). Surgical removal of crop does not affect feed consumption or growth of the chicken (Fisher and Weiss, 1956).

DIGESTION IN THE PROVENTRICULUS

The proteolytic enzyme, pepsin, is preformed in the cells of the proventriculus as pepsinogen, and its presence has been reported by many workers (Groebbels, 1932). In the mammal, pepsinogen granules are secreted by the chief cells and hydrochloric acid by the parietal cells of the gastric glands, but in birds both are apparently secreted by the chief cells. The bird has no cells comparable to parietal cells of mammals. Bowie (1936) and others, using a method specific for pepsinogen granules, found them in all cells of the body of the gastric glands. Before feeding, the pepsinogen granules are abundant, but shortly after feeding they virtually disappear, indicating that they are concerned in digestion (see Groebbels, 1932).

Shaw (1913), and Plimmer and Rosedale (1922), found only pepsin in the tissues of the proventriculus, and this appears to be the only enzyme formed by it; although few comparative studies have been made, the meager evidence suggests that avian and mammalian pepsin are similar (Herriott, 1941). Farner (1960) believed that appreciable digestion took place in the stomach of carnivorous birds but not of grain eaters. Actually the pH of the proventriculus of the latter birds (3 to 4.5) is higher than the optimum pH required for peptic digestion, and the food spends little time in the proventriculus.

DIGESTION IN THE GIZZARD

Pepsin is always present in the contents of the gizzard, and the pH of the latter is 2 to 3.5. This pH is more nearly optimum for peptic digestion than other parts of the tract, and might suggest that most of peptic digestion occurs in the gizzard. However, removal of the gizzard, whose chief function is grinding food, has little effect upon digestion if the food is soft (Fritz, Burrows, and Titus, 1936). This suggests that peptic digestion may take place in the intestine, where the pH is much higher (6 to 7), or that most of the protein digestion is accomplished by other enzymes (trypsin or others), which are more active at this pH than pepsin. The optimum activity of these enzymes in the mammal, however, is at pH 7.5 to 8.5.

The pepsin in the gizzard comes from the stomach, but one investigator (Paira-Mall, according to Mangold, 1929) claims to have extracted minute amounts from the epithelial lining of the gizzard. Carbohydrate-splitting enzymes have also been reported in the gizzard contents. Bernardi and Schwarz (1932) extracted invertase from the epithelium of the gland. Groebbels (1932) reportedly demonstrated the digestion of carbohydrates in the gizzard, but Mangold (1929 and 1934) believed that the gizzard's role in carbohydrate digestion is of no importance.

Grit and digestion. Grit is essential for optimum digestion because it increases the motility and grinding action of the gizzard and the digestibility of coarse feed (Fritz, 1937). The digestibility of whole grains and seeds may be increased about 10 percent, and of all-mash by about 3 percent, with the addition of grit (Titus, 1955). Grit is evidently not indispensable, since chicks can be raised to maturity (8 months of age) without it, and growth and egg production are not affected (Bethke and Kennard, 1926; Buckner, Martin, and Peter, 1926).

Gizzard erosion. Lesions of the epithelial lining of the gizzard (gizzard erosion), comparable to peptic ulcers in mammals, have been reported in chickens under a variety of conditions. Some workers believe there is one anti-gizzard erosion factor or nutrient, whereas others think a number of factors may be concerned in the prevention of the lesions. Evidence from Almquist and Mecchi (1941), Manwaring (1942), and others, suggests that cholic acid or oxycholic acid (constituents of bile) are the principal factors, since the lesions occurring normally or produced by cinchophen can be prevented, improved, or cured by these bile acids. However, a number of feedstuffs, such as alfalfa meal, oats, wheat by-products, milk, pork liver, and kidney, will reduce the incidence and severity of gizzard erosin (Titus, 1955), and this suggests that several factors may be involved.

Chickens afflicted with gizzard erosion secrete hyperacid gastric juice (Cheney, 1938). The hyperacidity appears not to be the cause of the lesions, but to develop as a result of them.

DIGESTION IN THE INTESTINES

Enzymes in the Small Intestine and Pancreas

Extracts of ground whole intestine of chickens contain protease, amylase, and invertase (Plimmer and Rosedale, 1922), but lipase is absent in the goose (Klug, 1891), and so is lactase in the hen

(Hamilton and Mitchell, 1924; Plimmer and Rosedale, 1922). More recent evidence indicates that lactose is poorly absorbed and is not hydrolyzed in the intestinal tract (Rutter, Krichevsky, Scott, and Hansen, 1953).

Pancreatic juice and bile are emptied into the distal end of the loop of the duodenum. Pure pancreatic juice is obtained by cannulating the pancreatic ducts. Langendorff (1879), who obtained pancreatic juice from the pigeon in this manner, found that it was slightly alkaline, and that it contained preteolytic enzymes, amylase, and lipase. He further demonstrated that pancreatic juice is essential for life, for when the pancreatic ducts were ligated, the bird, deprived of pancreatic enzymes, died within 6 to 12 days.

The presence of amylase in the pancreatic tissues of birds was demonstrated as early as 1846 by Bonchardat and Sondras, and by Claude Bernard in 1856 (see Groebbels, 1932; also Mangold, 1929). Later work by Shaw (1913) and by Plimmer and Rosedale (1922) also shows that the pancreas of the adult chicken contains proteolytic, amylolytic, and lipolytic enzymes, but that in the very young chick, before 7 days of age, not all enzymes are present.

The proteolytic enzymes present in intestinal tissue exhibit maximum activity in an acid medium, and only slight activity in an alkaline one, suggesting that the enzyme in greatest concentration is pepsin, or pepsin-like in activity.

The enzymes contained in pure intestinal juice apparently have not been determined, but mixed intestinal juice contains pancreatic juice, which contributes proteases acting principally in an alkaline medium, and presumably trypsin, or others. There has been no isolation and identification of these in the intestinal tract of birds. From the meager data available it appears that digestion by pepsin, trypsin, and possibly other proteolytic enzymes takes place in the bird intestine; but which of these enzymes plays the dominant role is unknown. The hydrogen ion concentration of the intestine (see later section) is slightly acid (pH about 6); at this pH, digestion by pepsin or trypsin probably would not be appreciable, judging from the pH requirements for activity of these in the mammal. The higher body temperature of the bird, however, could increase the activity even though pH is not optimum.

Secretin

One of the factors influencing the secretion of pancreatic juice in mammals is secretin, a hormone that is formed in the walls of the intestine. This hormone, which has been crystallized, when injected causes a copious secretion of pancreatic juice. Its distribution in the intestines varies, but it is present in the duodenum in all species of mammals, and in some it is found in other parts of the intestine also. In the chicken and pigeon it has been isolated from the walls of the duodenum and other segments of the small intestine, but not from the large intestine, rectum, cloaca, esophagus, or crop (Koschtojanz, Mirjeeff, Korjuieff, and Otschakowskaja, 1933).

Absorption in the Small Intestine

Few studies have been made on absorption in the bird, but it is presumed that the rate of absorption is rapid because of the higher metabolic rate, body temperature, and circulation time than in many mammals. Golden and Long (1942) reported that glucose absorption in the chicken was indeed rapid. Aramaki and Weiss (1962), who determined the concentrations of glucose and amino nitrogen in portal venous blood and wing vein blood, showed that within 15 minutes after eating there was a significantly higher concentration of these substances in portal blood, indicating a high rate of digestion and absorption. (See also Chapter 12).

Similar experiments were performed on the fatty acid content of portal and nonportal blood of chickens following a test meal (Conrad and Scott, 1942). These authors concluded that most of the fatty acids were absorbed via the portal vein, and that the rate of absorption ranged from 1.1 to 2.0 millimoles per hour.

Intestinal absorption of methionine and histidine has been studied in chickens having permanent Thiery-Vella fistules (method of Newman and Taylor, 1958). The L-forms of both methionine and histidine were absorbed more rapidly than the D isomers, but methionine was absorbed faster than histidine (Paine, Newman, and Taylor, 1959). The stereospecific absorption of these amino acids in the chicken has also been observed in the rat.

DIGESTION IN THE CECA AND
LARGE INTESTINE

Presumably, little or no digestion takes place in the large intestines of birds other than in the ceca, but there is evidence of water resorption in the large intestine and rectum.

Digestion in the ceca has been reviewed by Mangold (1929 and 1934), Groebbels (1932), Halnan (1949), and Farner (1960).

For many years it was thought that little or no crude fiber was digested by birds. Although it is now recognized that birds can digest appreciable quantities of crude fiber of certain types, they do indeed digest considerably less than mammals. Cellulose, lignin, and pentosans from corn fodder are almost completely indigestible, but lignin and pentosans from grains are digestible to the extent of 10 to 40 percent (Tscherniak, 1936).

The coefficients (percents) of digestibility of crude fiber for poultry are quite variable, even within the same species and with different varieties of the same grains (Mangold, 1934). The coefficients for crude fiber digestion for different grains, as reported by a number of workers for the hen, are shown below. Most of these figures are taken from Groebbels (1932).

Corn, 0.12 to 28.2, 17.2, 19.2, up to 43.5
Wheat, 0.0 to 3.5, 5.1, 4.6 to 5.7, 9.8, 0.0 to 16.9, 17.7, 29.8
Barley, 0.0 to 0.24, 0.0 to 13.3, 8.9 to 13.4
Oats, 0.0 to 6.6, 9.25
Cellulose, 0.0

Mangold believed that much of the variation in digestibility was due to the varietal differences in the chemical and structural makeup of the cell membranes of the feedstuffs.

The site of digestion of most of the crude fiber in the fowl is the ceca (Mangold, 1934). Radeff (1928) and Henning (1929) determined the coefficients of digestibility of crude corn fiber before and after surgical removal of the ceca of hens. The coefficients for corn before cecectomy were 17.1 (Radeff, 1928) and 19.7 (Henning, 1929), and 0.0 after the operation. The figures for oats and wheat with ceca intact were 9.25 and 5.7, and after the operation they were 1.31 and 1.4 respectively.

The digestibility of crude fiber in the pigeon, a species with rudimentary ceca, is less efficient than in the chicken (Radeff; also Mangold and Hock, 1938). Beattie and Shrimpton (1958) have shown that the microbial decomposition of cellulose in the cecum is primarily fermentative. The ceca are not essential structures, however, for they can be removed surgically without ill effects on the bird.

Synthesis of Vitamins by the Ceca

Digestion of crude fiber is facilitated by enzymes in the cecal juice (Maumus and Launoy, 1901), and by the presence of bacteria.

The cecal contents contain considerably higher concentrations of the B vitamins than do those of other parts of the digestive tract (Sunde *et al.*, 1950; Couch *et al.*, 1950), suggesting that these vitamins may be synthesized in the ceca, and that the required level of these in the feed might be less for birds with ceca. Removal of the ceca, however, did not increase the required vitamin level in the feed or affect the concentration of these vitamins in the feces. This indicates that the B vitamins are not synthesized in the ceca. In fact, the requirement for biotin is slightly less after cecectomy than before, suggesting that some of the biotin present in the ceca is normally used by bacteria (Sunde *et al.*).

Absorption of Water in the Ceca

Evidence that the ceca absorb some water is based upon the findings of Röseler (1929), who demonstrated that the amount of water in cecal contents is lower than in feces and rectal contents. He further revealed that after cecectomy, the water content of the feces is higher than in unoperated birds.

DIGESTIBILITY OF FEEDSTUFFS

In order to find the digestibility coefficient of each nutrient in the feed, it is necessary to determine the composition of the feed and, after feeding, to collect the feces unmixed with urine, and to determine quantities of nutrients present or undigested. Separation of the feces and urine in birds presents difficulties because the two are voided together in the cloaca. Thus, the feces must be separated from the urine, a matter that involves surgery, the preparation of an artificial anus, or exteriorizing the ureters (see Chapter 13). If feces and urine are collected together, a correction for the amount of nitrogen contained in the urine must be made. The results thus obtained compare favorably with determinations made on uncontaminated feces.

The coefficients of digestibility of some common feeds in the chicken are as follows (Titus, 1955):

Feed	Organic matter	Crude protein	Crude fiber	Nitrogen free extract	Fat	Total digestible nutrients
Barley	76	74	9	82	69	67
Corn, whole	87	76	12	90	86	80
Oats	65	73	13	72	82	61
Wheat	84	79	9	88	50	73
Wheat bran	45	61	8	46	58	41

Except for crude fiber, the coefficients of digestibility of these feeds for chickens compare favorably with those for mammals.

GASTRIC JUICE

Collection of Gastric Juice

Gastric juice of the fed bird may contain feed and also contents from the gizzard and duodenum as a result of regurgitation. Gastric juice, free from food, may be obtained by starving the bird, but little is secreted under such conditions, unless some other stimulus is employed. Even under these conditions the juice, although free from food, may contain intestinal juice unless the proventriculus or the gizzard is cannulated. In order to study the stimulating effects of food ingestion upon rate of secretion and the composition of pure gastric juice, one of two methods may be used: (1) preparation of a fistula or opening of the esophagus, so that when food is ingested it does not pass to the stomach, but drops out of the opening (sham feeding); (2) preparation of a pouch of the stomach with an intact nerve and blood supply which opens to the outside through the body wall (Pavlov or

Heidenhain pouch). Food entering the main stomach, but not the pouch, stimulates both stomachs, and pure juice is collected from the pouch.

Most of the studies on the gastric juice of birds are based upon samples collected by cannulation of the proventriculus (Friedman, 1939) in starved birds (relatively pure juice), by aspiration of stomach contents through catheters inserted by way of the mouth and crop of the starved bird (Cheney, 1938), or by insertion of needles into the gizzard of the fed bird (Farner, 1943a; Collip, 1922).

Composition of Gastric Juice

Gastric juice of the bird is composed principally of water, with smaller amounts of hydrochloric acid, pepsin, mucin, and certain salts (see Table 49). The composition varies with rate of secretion and with other factors.

The pH of mixed gastric juice collected by aspiration from the gizzard of the live bird averages 2.05 (Farner, 1943c). The pH of the tissues or of the contents of the proventriculus of dead birds is considerably higher (see Tables 49 and 50). The total acidity and free HCl in the gastric juice of fed chickens average 59.2 and 25.0 milliequivalents (m.eq.) per liter respectively (Farner, 1943c); for chickens starved for 12 to 24 hours it ranges from 40 to 75 for total acidity and 30 to 55 m.eq. for free HCl (Cheney, 1938). In the starved pigeon, total acidity ranges from 60 to 148, and free HCl from 60 to 148 m.eq. (Friedman, 1939).

The pepsin content of avian gastric juice has received little study. According to Friedman (1939), the concentration of pepsin in relatively pure gastric juice from starved pigeons ranges from 0 to 38, and from 700 to 1000 Mett units in the chicken. Thus, the pepsin concentration of the pigeon stomach is much lower than that in certain mammals, particularly the dog. This is true also for the goose stomach, in which the pepsin concentration is about one-tenth that in the dog (Karpov, 1919). The Mett unit refers to the ability of the pepsin to digest egg albumin when placed with it in small glass tubes.

Table 49. Gastric secretion of birds under different conditions

Species	No. of birds	Treatment	Rate of secretion* cc.	Acidity in m.eq. per liter		Pepsin activity Mett units	Author
				Free	Total		
Pigeon	13	Normal, starved 24 hours	*per hour* 0.2–4.2	40–136	60–148	0–36	Friedman
"	1	Histamine	1.3	70–160	120–195	0	"
"	1	pilocarpine "	*per 15 min.* 0.9	—	—	16	"
"	1	Acetylcholine "	0.9	Not given, but high		64	"
"	1	Acetylcholine & histamine	1.6	—	150	52	"
Chicken	—	Normal, starved 24 hours	—	—	—	700–1,000	"
"	—	Normal, starved 12–24 hours	*per hour* 7.0	30–55	40–75	—	Cheney
"	22	Normal, fed	—	25	59.2	—	Farner
"	—	Histamine, starved	—	80–150	120–180	125	Friedman
"	—	"	15.0	110	125–160	—	Cheney

* The data of Friedman (1939) and of Cheney (1938) are based on starved birds, in which the rate of secretion is low and highly variable (see text). Cheney's figures on secretion are based upon contents withdrawn from the stomach (mixed juice) with catheter, and are only rough estimates of amount secreted.

Factors Affecting Secretion of Gastric Juice

Food. Braitmaier, according to Friedman (1939), reported that the secretion of gastric juice in the chicken was regular and continuous; but Friedman's experiments, and those of Cheney (1938), show that it is not continuous but intermittent. This was demonstrated in starved chickens and pigeons before and after injection of certain drugs. In the studies of Friedman (1939) and Cheney (1938), food was withheld for 12 to 24 hours, and the tract was presumably free from food. This is particularly true of the stomach, where food remains for a very short time. Starvation decreases or inhibits flow of gastric juice in the pigeon (Friedman), the chicken (Collip, 1922) and the duck (Keeton, Koch, and Luckhardt, 1920). Friedman showed that in 87 percent of the pigeons starved for at least 24 hours, gastric secretion was practically inhibited. At autopsy starved birds had no feed in the gizzard or proventriculus. In the remaining starved pigeons some juice was collected, but the rate of secretion and amount collected varied considerably, ranging from 0.2 to 4.2 cc. per hour (see Table 49). Cheney (1938), who withheld feed 12 to 24 hours from chickens, reported a volume of about 7 cc. per hour, in a few individuals, but the figure is only a rough approximation (see Table 49).

Fedorovskij and Konopleva (1959) studied gastric secretion in geese with stomach pouches (Pavlov), before and after starvation and on different diets. The volume of juice secreted in 30 minutes ranged from 18.2 to 30.5 cc., depending on the diet and time of starvation, and the pH varied from 2.16 to 3.2. Among the diets fed, green clover stimulated the greatest secretion, meat and bone meal less, and oats the least secretion of gastric juice. The pH of the gastric juice was lowest (1.71) when oats were fed; it was 3.71 after the feeding of clover, 4.2 after feeding meat and bone meal, and 4.7 after feeding mixed concentrates. Thus, the stimulating effect of food as it enters the stomach (gastric phase) is like that in mammals.

The stimulating effect of food ingestion on rate of gastric secretion was also studied in the chicken by Collip (1922), and in the goose by Karpov (1919), who employed the esophageal fistula. Sham feeding, where food does not reach the stomach, stimulates

Table 50. The pH of the contents of the digestive tract of different species of dead adult birds (Farner, 1942) and of live chickens (Winget et al., 1962). All birds had food in the digestive tract.

Species	Crop	Proventriculus	Gizzard	Duodenum	Jejunum	Ileum	Rectum or colon	Ceca	Bile
Chicken	4.51	4.40	2.60	5.76–6.01	5.78–5.90	6.27–6.42	6.26	5.71	5.88
Pigeon	4.28	4.80	2.00	5.23–5.39	5.32–5.89	5.59	5.43	—	—
Pheasant	5.78	4.74	2.06	5.62–6.01	6.18–6.81	6.77	6.61	5.39	6.18
Duck	4.92	3.41	2.33	6.01–6.19	6.11–6.69	6.87	6.73	5.88	6.14
Turkey	6.07	4.72	2.19	5.82–6.52	6.71–6.95	6.85	6.46	5.86	6.01
	Mouth			*Small Intestine*		*Large Intestine*			
Chicken	6.75	3.17		6.67		7.09			

the proventriculus and increases the rate of gastric secretion. This is known as the cephalic phase of stimulation; the sensations of eating evoke the discharge of impulses from the gastric secretory center in the brain, probably by way of nerve fibers in the vagi, to the gastric glands.

Farner (1960) reported that sham feeding with esophageal fistulas above the crop in chickens gave equivocal results, but was markedly stimulatory on gastric secretion when the fistula was below the crop. He reported that the sight of food, even after prolonged periods of hunger, failed to increase gastric secretion, and concluded that a true cephalic phase of secretion is lacking in chickens. Psychic stimulation of gastric secretion in ducks by auditory stimuli has been reported by Walter (1939).

Effects of drugs. Histamine, injected into the pigeon (0.05 mg.), the chicken (0.25), or the duck, increases the rate of gastric secretion within 7 to 15 minutes (Friedman, 1939; Cheney, 1938; Keeton, Koch, and Luckhardt, 1920). It increases the acidity of the secretion and diminishes the pepsin concentration considerably (Table 49). Continued injections of histamine decrease the volume of flow, and increase the pepsin concentration of the secretion (Friedman). The volume dropped from about 1.3 cc. to 0.2 cc. per hour after histamine, and the pepsin increased from a low of 10 to 130 Mett units. There was also a slight increase in acidity. These changes are due to dehydration and a loss in blood volume. When saline or glucose solutions were injected, the birds responded to histamine, as before, with an increased rate of flow.

Ethanol (0.5 percent) administered into the duodenum (30 cc.) or intravenously (5 cc.) to the pigeon, increases the volume of secretion after a latent period of 35 minutes, and otherwise has an effect similar to that produced by histamine, except that it is usually not as pronounced (Friedman).

Pilocarpine (0.5 mg. per kg.) produces a secretion of moderate volume, along with peptic activity, in the pigeon (Friedman, 1939). Acetylcholine (0.1 mg. per kg.) induces the secretion of only small amounts of gastric juice in the pigeon, which is very rich in pepsin and mucin and high in acidity, according to Friedman; but his data on volume are inconclusive, and he shows none on acidity. When pilocarpine or acetylcholine is injected one or two hours after the histamine, the volume of secretion increases and there is a decrease in pepsin content, but apparently no change in the acidity of the secretion. Pilocarpine is not as effective as acetylcholine in increasing pepsin content.

According to Friedman, adrenaline alone (1 cc. of 1/10,000) has no effect on gastric secretion in the pigeon; but when injected after the bird has received histamine there is a dimunition in rate of secretion, although with no marked effect on the concentration of pepsin (no data).

In mammals, histamine stimulates the parietal cells of the gastric glands to produce acid, and parasympathomimetic drugs stimulate the production of pepsin from the chief cells. The effects of these agents in birds are the same except that one type of cell produces both products. The volume and rate of gastric secretion is influenced by the volume of fluid in the blood and tissues.

Nervous Control of Gastric Secretion

The results obtained with acetylcholine and pilocarpine (parasympathomimetic agents) suggest that the secretion of pepsin and possibly of acid (although data on the latter are inconclusive) are controlled by parasympathetic nerves. The negative results obtained with adrenaline suggest that sympathetic nerves are not concerned in gastric secretion.

It is known that the proventriculus is innervated by both sympathetic and parasympathetic fibers, but apparently no studies have been made on the effects of the stimulation of these nerves on gastric secretion.

HYDROGEN ION CONCENTRATION OF THE DIGESTIVE TRACT

The hydrogen ion concentration, or pH, of the different regions of the digestive tract is dependent mainly upon the amount of HCl secreted in the proventriculus, and upon the action of bile and pancreatic juice, which in the mammal tend to neutralize the acid in the tract.

The pH of the alimentary canal of birds and particularly that of the chicken, has been determined by a number of workers. The results obtained by some of these are presented in Table 50. Most of the determinations have been made from the contents of different parts of the tracts of dead birds not previously starved. When food is in the tract, the secretion of gastric and intestinal juices is at a maximum. Steinmetzer (1924) believed that if the crop and gizzard were empty, then the secretion of gastric juice would be low in relation to the amount of intestinal juice formed, which would tend to make the lower tract more alkaline. However, if the upper tract is empty, then the lower tract, except for a short time, would be empty or contain little food, and the secretion of intestinal juice might also be low. The pH under these conditions has not been determined. Some of the investigators used pH meters, and others used a colorimetric method to determine pH. Farner (1942) believed that some of the variation in the reported results was due to differences in the methods employed.

According to Farner (1942), all parts of the alimentary canal of chickens, pigeons, ducks, turkeys, and pheasants are acid, with the lowest pH recorded in the gizzard (2.0 to 2.6) and the highest in the lower half of the small intestine (5.59 to 6.87). The pH of the chicken gizzard is significantly higher than that of the other species, whereas the pH of the pigeon duodenum is lower than that of the other species. The upper portions of the small intestine of the pigeon and chicken are more acid than in the other species. In the ileum, or lower part of the small intestine, the pH increases in the following order: pigeon, chicken, pheasant, turkey, and duck. There are no significant differences in the pH of the bile, ceca, or large intestines of these species (Farner).

Farner's results for the chicken are compared with those of other investigators who recorded pH after death of the bird. The reports of Mussehl, Blish, and Ackerson (1933), and of Buckner, Insko, and Henry (1944) agree with Farner that all parts of the digestive tract are acid, and all investigators show that the duodenum and upper tract are acid, except Olson and Mann (1935), whose average figure for the duodenum approaches neutrality (pH, 7.04). The figures of Olso and Mann for all parts of the intestinal tract are higher (pH, above 7) than all others reported.

Whether or not the determinations were made from the contents of the organs concerned, or from scrapings from the mucosa of the organs, does not affect the results, according to Buckner, Insko, and Henry (1944). Recent work by Wiseman, Bushnell, and Rosenberg (1956) indicates that all parts of the tract of the chicken are acid except the lower part of small intestine, which was found to be slightly alkaline.

Farner (1943a) showed that contents of the gizzard of the chicken became less acid after death of the bird, presumably because some of the gastric juice had drained from the gizzard into the lower tract, and that this might conceivably account in part for the higher acidity of the intestine as compared to that of mammals. However, more recent data by Winget *et al.* (1962) who inserted pH electrodes in the alimentary tract of live birds, show the pH of the small intestines to be acid, and their figures compare favorably with those reported by others on the dead bird. This work shows that the large intestine is slightly alkaline when food is in the tract, and that the pH of the large intestine particularly, and to a lesser extent the small intestine, tended to become lower as the length of feed removal or starvation increased. The pH of the mouth and proventriculus tended to become less acid after food was withheld.

The work of Winget *et al.* shows clearly that the pH of the alimentary tract of birds is not static but ever-changing. For example, the pH in the intestines exhibited a curvilinear response with time of starvation, and a similar response was observed in the proventriculus. The changes in pH in the mouth, however, were linear with time. Thus, according to most authors, most of the digestive tract of birds is acid. The bile of birds is acid (pH 5.0 to 6.8), unlike that of mammals, in which it is alkaline (pH about 7.5 to 8.5). This difference may account, in part, for the higher pH in the intestinal tract of mammals as compared to birds.

Age appears to have little effect on pH in birds over 13 weeks of age. In younger birds, from 10 to 11 weeks old, the pH of the lower intestinal tract is higher, according to Mayhew (1935), although his data on this point are inconclusive. According to Vonk, Brink, and Postma (1946), the pH of the gizzard of young chickens (23 days of age) is lower (2.7) than that of adults (3.06).

Buckner, Insko, and Henry (1944) found no difference in the pH of the digestive tract of male and female chickens one and two years of age. Moreover, the pH was not influenced by molting or state of reproduction.

The effect of different feeding regimes on pH of the digestive tract has been studied by a number of researchers (Beach, 1925; Ashcraft, 1933; Mussehl *et al.,* 1933; Heller and Penquite, 1936; Farner, 1943b; Wiseman *et al.,* 1956). The effects of pH of the gizzard have been discussed previously, and the effects on the remainder of the tract are similar. The ingestion of very large quantities of basic salts tends to lower the acidity of all parts of the tract (Heller and Penquite, 1936; Farner, 1943b). Diets high in milk products tend to increase the pH of certain parts of the tract (Ashcraft; Farner); according to Farner, diets high in protein increase the pH of gastric juice, but according to Vonk, Brink, and Postma (1946) they decrease it. The fiber of the diet, in amounts ranging from 13.6 to 14.9 percent, has no effect upon pH of the tract (Heller and Penquite).

LIVER AND BILE

The avian liver is large and bilobed. A hepatic duct from each lobe leads to the duodenum. The left hepatic duct communicates directly with the duodenum, but the right one may have a branch going to the gall bladder, or may be enlarged locally as a gall bladder; hence, in its terminal part it serves as a cystic duct (Farner, 1960). The gall bladder, which is not present in all species, serves as a storage and concentrating organ (Schmidt and Ivy, 1937).

The pH of avian bile is acid (Table 50); but otherwise, its composition is similar to that of mammals, according to Mangold (1929). Amylase is found in chicken bile, and its activity in bile from the gall bladder is greater than in bile from the liver. It is present in all chickens above 8 weeks of age, but is absent in some at 4 weeks (Farner, 1943c). Little is known about the function of bile in birds, but presumably it aids in the absorption of fats, by its emulsifying action and activating effects on pancreatic lipase, and in the digestion of carbohydrates by virtue of the amylase present.

Few studies have been conducted on the secretion of bile; however, it has been reported in the chicken by Clarkson, King, and Warnock (1957). White Leghorn cockerels (14 weeks of age) secrete approximately 1 ml. of bile per hour. The administration of gallogen and of sulfarlem, both substances reported to increase bile secretion in mammals, was followed by a slight increase in secretion (after feeding gallogen) and by a highly significant increase, viz. 200 or 300 percent (after feeding sulfarlem).

Liver function. Apart from its digestive function in the production of bile, the liver has many other functions. It is involved in protein, fat, and carbohydrate metabolism and in the detoxication of metabolites. Some of its metabolic functions have been discussed in Chapter 2, 12, and 18. The liver is the site of the formation of plasma proteins and phospholipids (Ranney and Chaikoff, 1951).

The female sex hormone, estrogen, has a pronounced effect on the liver of birds, particularly on the formation of plasma proteins and lipids, and has a significant influence on the clearance of certain substances by the liver. One method of determining the functional state of the liver is its rate of clearance of, or its ability to extract, sodium bromsulphthalein (BSP) from the blood and to excrete it in the bile. Campbell (1957a) showed that laying hens or estrogenized males or capons clear BSP at different rates from those shown by normal males or capons. The clearance curve (concentration of BSP in blood with time) of males had a steep gradient, which levels off fairly abruptly at about 10 minutes. The female curve, however, is characterized by a less steep gradient, which levels off more slowly. The reason for these differences is not clear, but the author suggests that the ability of the liver cells of estrogenized birds to clear the dye is impaired, and that this may be associated with the increased fat content of the liver resulting from estrogen. Campbell (1957b) has reported that estrogen tends to protect the liver from damage produced by a sublethal dose of hepatotoxic alkaloid, seneciphylline. The degree of liver damage was reflected by clearance of BSP. In the chronically damaged liver (Campbell, 1957c) estrogen tends to speed up its regeneration.

REFERENCES

Almquist, H. J., and E. Mecchi 1941 Influence of bile acids, vitamin K, and cinchophen on erosions of the chick gizzard lining. Proc. Soc. Exp. Biol. & Med. 46:168.

Aramaki, T., and H. S. Weiss 1962 Patterns of carbohydrate and protein digestion in the chicken as derived from sampling the hepatic portal system. Arch. Internat. Physiol. Bioch. 70:1.

Ashcraft, D. W. 1933 Effect of milk products on pH of intestinal contents of domestic fowl. Poultry Sci. 12:292.

Beach, J. R. 1925 The effect of feeding various milk products on the hydrogen ion concentration of the contents of the ceca of chickens. Hilgardia (Calif. Sta.) 1:145.

Beattie, J., and D. H. Shrimpton 1958 Surgical and clinical techniques for in vitro studies of intestinal microflora of domestic fowls. Quart. J. Exp. Physiol. 43:399.

Bernardi, A., and M. A. Schwarz 1932 Über das Verkommen einer Invertase im Kaumagen der Hühner. Biochem. 256:406.

Bethke, R. M., and D. C. Kennard 1926 Does the growing chick require grit? Poultry Sci. 5:285.

Bowie, D. J. 1936 A method of staining the pepsinogen granules in gastric glands. Anat. Rec. 64:357.

Buckner, G. D., W. M. Insko, and A. H. Henry 1944 Does breed, age, sex, or laying conditions affect the pH of the digestive tract system of chickens? Poultry Sci. 33:457.

Buckner, G. D., J. H. Martin, and A. M. Peter 1926 Concerning the growth of chickens raised without grit. Poultry Sci. 5:203.

Campbell, J. G. 1957a Studies on the influence of sex hormones on the avian liver. I: Sexual differences in avian liver clearance curves. J. Endocrinol. 15:339.

Campbell, J. G. 1957b II: Acute liver damage in the male fowl and the protective effect of estrogen, as determined by a liver function rest. J. Endocrinol. 15:346.

Campbell, J. G. 1957c III: Estrogen induced regeneration of the chronically damaged liver. J. Endocrinol. 15:351.

Cheney, G. 1938 Gastric acidity in chicks with experimental gastric ulcers. Am. J. Digest Dis. 5:104.

Clarkson, T. B., J. S. King, and N. H. Warnock 1957 A comparison of the effect of gallogen and sulfarlem on the normal bile flow of the cockerel. Am. J. Vet. Res. 18:187.

Collip, J. B. 1922 The activation of the glandular stomach of the fowl. Am. J. Physiol. 59;435.

Conrad, R. M., and H. M. Scott 1942 Fat absorption in the laying hen. Poultry Sci. 21:407.

Couch, J. R., H. L. German, D. R. Knight, P. S. Parks, and P. B. Pearson 1950 Importance of the cecum in intestinal synthesis in the mature domestic fowl. Poultry Sci. 29:52.

Farner, D. S. 1942 The hydrogen ion concentration in avian digestive tracts. Poultry Sci. 21:445.

Farner, D. S. 1943a Gastric hydrogen ion concentration and acidity in the domestic fowl. Poultry Sci. 22:79.

Farner, D. S. 1943b The effect of certain dietary factors on gastric hydrogen ion concentration and acidity in the domestic fowl. Poultry Sci. 22:295.

Farner, D. S. 1943c Biliary amylase in the domestic fowl. Biol. Bull. 84:240.

Farner, D. S. 1960 Digestion and digestive system, Chapter XI in Biology and Comparative Physiology of Birds, edited by A. J. Marshall. Academic Press, New York.

Fedorovskij, N. P., and V. I. Konopleva 1959 Physiology of gastric digestion in the goose. Pticevodstuo 10:39 (Abs. in Worlds Poultry Sci. 17:61, 1961).

Fisher, H., and W. S. Weiss 1956 Feed consumption in relation to dietary bulk and energy level: The effect of surgical removal of crop. Poultry Sci. 35:418.

Friedman, M. H. F. 1939 Gastric secretion in birds. J. Cell. & Comp. Physiol. 13:219.

Fritz, J. C. 1937 The effect of feeding grit on digestibility in the domestic fowl. Poultry Sci. 16:75.

Fritz, J. C., W. H. Burrows, and H. W. Titus 1936 Comparison of digestibility in gizzardectomized and normal fowls. Poultry Sci. 15:239.

Golden, W. R. C., and C. N. H. Long 1942 Absorption and deposition of glucose in the chick. Am. J. Physiol. 136:244.

Groebbels, F. 1932 Der Vogel. Erster Band: Atmungswelt und Nahrungswelt. Verlag von Gebrüder Borntraeger, Berlin.

Halnan, E. T. 1949 The architecture of the avian gut and tolerance of crude fiber. Brit. J. Nutr. 3:245.

Hamilton, T. S., and H. H. Mitchell 1924 The occurrence of lactase in the alimentary tract of the chicken. J. Agric. Res. 27:605.

Heller, V. G., and R. Penquite 1936 Effect of minerals and fibers on avian intestinal pH. Poultry Sci. 15:397.

Henning, H. J. 1929 Landw. Versuchsstat. 108:253. Cited by Groebbels, 1932.

Herriott, R. M. 1941 Transformation of swine pepsinogen into swine pepsin by chicken pepsin. J. Gen. Physiol. 21:575.

Jung, L., and M. Pierre 1933 Sur le rôle de la salive chez les oiseaux granivores. Comp. Rend. Soc. Biol. 113:115.

Karpov, L. V. 1919 Russ. Physiol. J. 2:185 (abstracted in Physiol. Abs. 5:469, 1920).

Keeton, R. W., F. C. Koch, and A. B. Luckhardt 1920 Gastrin studies. III: The response of the stomach mucosa of various animals to gastrin bodies. Am. J. Physiol. 51:454.

Klug, F. 1891 Beiträge zur Kenntnis der Verdauung der Vögel. Ztbl. Physiol. 5:131.

Koschtojanz, I. I., M. Mirjeeff, P. Korjuieff, and S. Otschakowskaja 1933 Zur Frage der Spezifitat des Sekretins: Vergleichende physiologische Untersuchung. Z. für vergl. Physiol. 18:112.

Langendorff, O. 1879 Versuche über die Pankreasverdauung der Vögel. Arch. f. Anat. u. Physiol. 18:1.

Leasure, E. E., and V. D. Foltz 1940 Experiments on absorption in the crop of the chicken. J. Am. Vet. Med. Assoc. 96:236.

Leasure, E. E., and R. P. Link 1940 Studies on the saliva of the hen. Poultry Sci. 19:131.

Mangold, E. 1929 Handbuch der Ernährung und des Stoffwechsels der landwirtschaftlichen Nutztiere: Zweiter Band. Verlag von Julius Springer, Berlin.

Mangold, E. 1934 The digestion and utilization of crude fiber. Nutrition Abs. & Rev. 3:647.

Mangold, E., and A. Hock 1938 Die Verdaulichkeit der Futtermittel bei der Taube. Arch. f. Geflügelkunde 12:334.

Manwaring, W. H. 1942 Bile deficiency and gizzard erosion. Calif. & West. Med. 56:61. (abstracted in Biol. Abs. 16531, 1942).

Maumus, J., and L. Launoy 1901 La digestion caecale chez les oiseaux. Bull. Mus. d'Hist. Nat. Paris 7:361.

Mayhew, R. L. 1935 The hydrogen ion concentration of the digestive tract of the fowl. J. Am. Vet. Med. Assoc. 86:148.

Mussehl, F. E., M. J. Blish, and C. W. Ackerson 1933 Effect of dietary and environmental factors on the pH of the intestinal tract. Poultry Sci. 12:120.

Newman, H. J., and M. W. Taylor 1958 A cannulated Thiry-Vella fistula in the chicken. Am. J. Vet. Res. 19:473.

Olson, C., and F. C. Mann 1935 The physiology of the cecum of the domestic fowl. J. Am. Vet. Med. Assoc. 87:151.

Paine, C. M., H. J. Newman, and M. W. Taylor 1959 Intestinal absorption of methionine and histidine by the chicken. Am. J. Physiol. 197:9.

Plimmer, R. H. A., and J. L. Rosedale 1922 Distribution of enzymes in the alimentary canal of the chicken. Biochem. J. 16:23.

Radeff, T. 1928 Die Verdaulichkeit der Rohfaser und die Funktion der Blinddärme beim Haushuhn. Arch. f. Geflügelkunde 2:312.

Ranney, R. E., and I. L. Chaikoff 1951 Effect of functional hepatectomy upon estrogen induced lipemia in the fowl. Am. J. Physiol. 165:600.

Röseler, M. 1929 Die Bedeutung der Blinddärme des Haushuhnes für die Resorption der Nahrung und Verdauung der Rohfaser. Z. f. Tierz. u. Zücht. 13:281.

Rutter, W. J., P. Krichevsky, H. M. Scott, and R. H. Hansen 1953 The metabolism of lactose and galactose in the chick. Poultry Sci. 32:706.

Schmidt, C. R., and A. C. Ivy 1937 The general function of the gall bladder: The bile and pigment output of various species of animals. J. Cell. Comp. Physiol. 10:365.

Shaw, T. P. 1913 Digestion in the chick. Am. J. Physiol. 31:439.

Steinmetzer, K. 1924 Die zeitlichen Verhaeltnisse beim Durchwandern von Futter durch den Magendarmkanal des Huhnes. Arch. ges. Physiol. (Pflügers) 206:500.

Sunde, M. L., W. W. Cravens, C. A. Elvehjem, and J. H. Halpin 1950 The effect of diet and cecectomy on the intestinal synthesis of biotin in mature fowl. Poultry Sci. 29:10.

Titus, H. W. 1955 The Scientific Feeding of Chickens. 3rd ed. The Interstate Press, Danville, Ill.

Tscherniak, A. 1936 Über die Verdauung der Zellwandbestandteile des Futters (Lignin, Pentosone, Cellulose, und Rohfaser) durch das Haushuhn. Biedermans Ztbl. d. Tierernährung 8:408 (abstracted in Nutri. Abst. & Rev. 6:1127, 1937).

Vonk, H. G., G. Brink, and N. Postma 1946 Digestion in the stomach of birds. I: The acidity in the stomach of young chickens.

Proc. K. Nederland Akad. Wetenschap. Amsterdam 49:972 (abstracted in Biol. Abst. 20863, 1949).

Walter, W. G.   1939   Bedingte Magensaftsekretion bei der Ente. Acta Brevia Neerl. 9:56.

Winget, C. M., G. C. Ashton, and A. J. Cawley   1962   Changes in gastrointestinal pH associated with fasting in the laying hen. Poultry Sci. 41:1115.

Wiseman, R. W., O. A. Bushnell, and M. M. Rosenberg   1956   Effects of rations on the pH and microflora in selected regions of the intestinal tract of chickens. Poultry Sci. 35:126.

CHAPTER 12

Carbohydrate Metabolism

BY R. L. HAZELWOOD

Biochemical Pathways of Carbohydrate Metabolism

THE major function of all ingested carbohydrate is to provide a source of immediate energy to the host organism. Through the action of the enzymes amylase and maltase, starch of plant food and glycogen of meat are split into their constituent parts, the monosaccharides. Starch and glycogen are broken down (hydrolyzed) to glucose by maltase and amylase, the disaccharide lactose to glucose and galactose by lactase, and the disaccharide sucrose to glucose and fructose by sucrase. These products of enzymatic digestion appear in the small intestine and are transported across the intestinal wall to the blood stream, whence they are carried to the liver for subsequent metabolic reactions. A fourth monosaccharide, mannose, may appear in the intestinal lumen and be carried to the liver along with glucose, fructose, and galactose.

The monosaccharides are presented to the intestinal mucosa as free sugars, and cross the intestinal barrier either by diffusion or by an active transport process, the details of which are largely unknown. Mannose apparently crosses into the portal vein circulation at a rate consistent with diffusion laws. Fructose may diffuse, also, and some of the molecules may be converted to glucose while crossing the intestinal barrier. There is ample evidence that both glucose and galactose are transported against a concentration gradient in the blood stream by an active process requiring energy. Whether any of these sugars have inorganic phosphorus added to their structure (phosphorylation) as a prerequisite for their transportation is yet to be determined. A certain amount of carbohydrate utilization by the intestinal cells, however, may occur during the transport process. Once across the gut wall all the monosaccharides appear in the portal circulation as free, nonphosphorylated sugars, and are carried immediately to the liver.

Within the liver cell biochemical transformations occur which may vary from hour to hour, from day to day, and from species to species, depending upon the physiological status of the animal. Glucose, in the presence of adenosine-triphosphate (ATP) and the enzyme glucokinase (hexokinase), becomes phosphorylated at the carbon-6 position and as such enters the general metabolic scheme (see below). Fructose and galactose each proceed through a series of complex reactions to form glucose phosphates, and then enter the general metabolic scheme. After being phosphorylated at the carbon-1 position (ATP + galactokinase required) galactose is reacted with uridine diphosphoglucose (UDPG enzyme: galactose-1-P-transferase) to produce glucose-1-phosphate and UDP-galactose. Fructose may be phosphorylated at either the carbon-1 or the carbon-6 position (fructokinase + ATP), the former entering the metabolic path after being split into 3-carbon fragments (glyceraldehyde or dihydroxyacetone phosphate) fructose-6-phosphate and entering the glycolytic path directly. The hexose-phosphates formed are therefore: glucose-1-phosphate (from galactose), glucose-6-phosphate (from glucose), and fructose-6-phosphate, (from fructose). From Figure 37 it can be seen that the products of both galactose and fructose phosphorylation can be converted into the same intermediate as that resulting from glucose phosphorylation (glucose-6-phosphate) by proceeding, respectively, either down or up the glycolytic scheme. Thus, glucose-6-phosphate is a key substrate for liver cells since it may follow one of four different pathways, namely 1) be degradated to CO_2, H_2O, and energy; 2) enter the oxidative pentose cycle with the result that reduced triphosphopyridine nucleotide (TPN) is formed; 3) be polymerized to form glycogen; or 4) to be dephosphorylated (enzyme: glucose-6-phosphatase) to free glucose. This phosphatase is absent in muscle; thus, only three potential routes are available to muscle glucose-6-phosphate.

Glycogen is the chief storage form of carbohydrate in animal tissues, and is analogous to depots of plant starch. The tissues involved in glycogen synthesis (glycogenesis) appear to be mainly the liver and skeletal muscle (fed glycogen levels: 3–6% and 0.4–0.6%, respectively). When blood glucose is plentiful the sugar which is not degradated to release energy is converted to

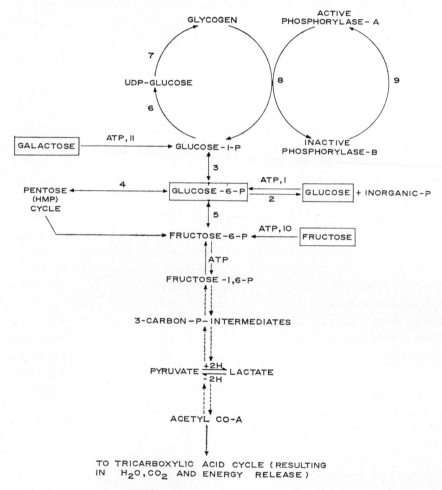

Figure 37. Interrelations of carbohydrate metabolism.

Enzymatic Reactions: 1. Glucokinase 2. Glucose-6-phosphatase 3. Phosphoglucomutase 4. Glucose-6-dehydrogenase 5. Phosphohexosisomerase 6. UDPG-pyrophosphorylase 7. Branching enzyme + transglycosidase 8. Phosphorylase + debranching enzyme 9. ATP, cyclic 3',5'-AMP 10. Fructokinase or glucokinase (F-1-P). 11. Galactokinase + UDPG

glycogen via the UDPG pathways (Figure 37). Thus glucose-1-phosphate is converted to UDP-glucose, which in turn reacts with transglucosidase and a branching enzyme to form glycogen. There is ample evidence that glycogenesis occurring from UDPG pathways may be regulated in part by hormonal influences. Thus, some hormones may affect either the amount of active enzyme or the concentration of important activating substances (i.e., glucose-6-phosphate).

In time of need such as during fasting (overnight) and exercise (increased peripheral oxidation), depot glycogen can be broken down (glycogenolysis) to its constituent glucose residues, glucose-1-phosphate being the first phosphorylated entrant into the glycolytic scheme. Normal blood sugar levels can thus be maintained. Glycogenolysis occurs as a result of the formation of cyclic 3′,5′-adenosinemonophosphate (3′,5′-AMP), which in turn "activates" the inactive enzyme phosphorylase. Some glycogenolytic hormones (see below) are believed to act by making available more cyclic 3′,5′-AMP. Phosphorylase then cleaves the 1–4 linkages of glycogen in successive steps. The result of liver glycogenolysis is hyperglycemia, due to increased free glucose, and increased degradation (glycolysis) to 3-carbon fragments such as pyruvate and lactate. The result of muscle glycogenolysis is only the ultimate formation of 3-carbon fragments via glycolysis, since this tissue does not contain hexose-6-phosphatase essential to split glucose-6-phosphate to free glucose. Thus, muscle glycogen does not contribute directly to circulating blood glucose levels. Rather, it can do so only by releasing lactate which is taken up by the liver and converted to glycogen. Glycogenolysis in liver tissue leads to free glucose, which is released to the blood stream as follows:

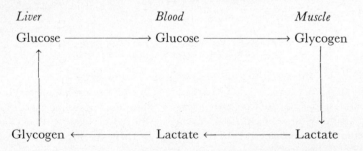

Liver	*Blood*	*Muscle*
Glucose ⟶	Glucose ⟶	Glycogen
↑		⎮
⎮		↓
Glycogen ←	Lactate ←	Lactate

Interrelations of Fat and Protein Metabolism

Whereas glycolysis is the principal source of the stepwise release of energy to all animal cells, fat and protein can enter the intermediate metabolic scheme at several specific biochemical steps. These substances do not enter as fat and protein, but rather are degradated in separate schema to yield respectively, fatty acids and amino acids (alanine, aspartic, and glutamic acids), which do enter the oxidative glycolytic cycle (Figure 38). These end-products of fat and protein catabolism can either be broken down further to CO_2, H_2O, and energy, or they can be used as substrates to resynthesize free glucose and/or glycogen. Such formation of carbohydrates from noncarbohydrate precursors (gluconeogenesis) occurs mainly in the liver, and to a much smaller extent in the kidney.

Mammalian vs. Avian Pathways

There are no major differences in the various ways which glucose-6-phosphate can be utilized by birds and mammals, and both phylogenetic classes have virtually identical "machinery" to metabolize carbohydrate in liver, kidney, and cardiac and skeletal

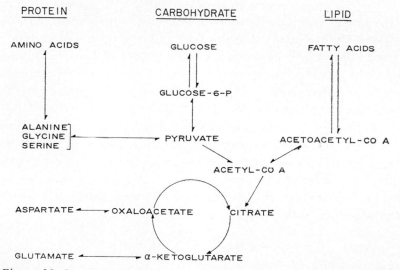

Figure 38. Summary of interrelations of protein, carbohydrate, and lipid metabolism.

muscle. What differences do exist are those concerned with *how much* each reaction contributes to overall carbohydrate metabolism and *when* the enzymatic systems appear in pre- and post-birth life, not *what* substrates are the predominant precursors of synthetic or degradative sequences.

Generally, in both birds and mammals, the synthesis of glycogen from pyruvate in the liver leads to a complete randomization of the original carbon atoms. Therefore, 3-carbon fragments do not give rise to glucose molecules simply by a reversal of glycolysis. Rather, a thorough rearrangement of carbon atoms is effected in the liver through both carboxylation and tricarboxylic cycle reactions. Fetal mammalian liver (guinea pig, mouse, etc.) differs from the embryonic chick liver in the potential for glucuronide synthesis. The chick embryo resembles adult mammals rather than the fetus in this respect, since unlike the latter, the 8-day chick embryo can synthesize glucuronides. Evidently, early in its development the avian embryo possesses hepatic UDP-glucuronyl transferase, an enzyme absent from mammalian fetuses (Dutton, 1963). Thus, glucuronic acid and glycogen synthesis may occur in the absence of insulin in the early chick embryo. Unlike that in the liver, glycogenesis in muscle tissue in birds and mammals occurs by the simple reversal of glycolytic reactions. The pentose pathway apparently is not involved in this synthesis of glycogen in muscle.

Other differences exist between the tissues of birds and mammals. The metabolism of organic acids by the nucleated avian red corpuscles differs greatly from that observed in the non-nucleated mammalian erythrocytes (see also Chapter 2). Mammalian RBC's do not metabolize acetate or other organic intermediates; glucose is metabolized by the phosphopentose cycle. Nucleated avian red cells, however, possess enzymes essential to the metabolizing of organic acids through the tricarboxylic cycle. The metabolism of such organic acids by the fowl may be related to porphyrin synthesis preparatory to the formation of hemoglobin.

THE EMBRYO

Albumen and Yolk Carbohydrates

The yolk and albumen compartments of the avian egg form the only source of nutrition for the zygote and developing embryo for a period of 21 to 22 days. From this static form of diet the organism must derive, independent of maternal influences, such complex tissues and organ systems as muscle, viscera, and feathers. The average egg is approximately 1 percent carbohydrate, waterfowl eggs containing slightly more, land fowl slightly less than this figure (see also Chapter 15). Of this total amount of carbohydrate the albumen contains about 75 percent, most of which is in combination with proteins. Mannose and galactose are the only two monosaccharides found in combination with albumen proteins, and both are found in highest concentrations in the ovomucin moiety (15 percent). Lesser amounts are located in ovomucoid and ovoglobulin. Although there appear to be traces of fructose in the avian egg, most free carbohydrate appears to be glucose (Romanoff and Romanoff, 1949).

Seventy percent of the yolk carbohydrates are uncombined. Protein-bound sugars in egg yolk appear to be predominantly of the mannose-glucosamine type (ovovitellin and ovolivetin), while lipid-carbohydrate combinations are represented by galactose (ovolecithin and various cerebrosides). It is interesting to note that glycogen exists in both egg yolk and egg white in the freshly laid, unincubated egg (total about 10 mg.). Little information exists as to the influence of maternal diet on the carbohydrate content of hen eggs, or even on the content of enzymes associated with carbohydrate metabolism. Yet a wide variety of enzymes, including amylase, peptidase, phosphatase (mainly yolk), and ovomucoidases (Lineweaver), Morris, and Kline, 1948) are available on the utilization of carbohydrates in such unincubated eggs.

The respiratory quotient for the early developing chick embryo approximates a value of 1.0, suggesting that in early development, at least, carbohydrate serves as a major source of fuel for growth and differentiation. Homogenates of early whole embryos have been shown to contain substantial amounts of all the intermediate degradative products of the classical Embden-Meyerhoff glycolytic scheme (Stumpf, 1947). Thus, as early as the 6th day of incubation there exist, in the chick embryo, phosphorylation mechanisms which are probably identical with those found in bacteria, plants, and animal tissues. Other workers have found indications in homogenates of embryos from days 3 to 10 that phosphorylating mechanisms are complete and active in hydrolyzing glucose and phosphorylated carbohydrate intermediates. The concentrations of such glycolytic intermediates as glucose-1-phosphate, glucose-6-phosphate, fructose-6-phosphate, fructose-diphosphate, and triosephosphates are equal to those found in adult avian tissues (Novikoff, Potter, and LePage, 1948). Working on excised chorioallantoic membranes, Kun (1953) found that these tissues oxidize glucose-6-phosphate and fructose-6-phosphate aerobically if provided with a source of triphosphopyridine nucleotide (TPN). This implies pentose cycle activity at an early age, and thus the Embden-Meyerhoff pathway may not be the only route of energy release available to the embryo. It should be emphasized, however, that the amounts of embryonic tissue available for enzymic assay are usually limited. The failure to identify a particular enzyme may more accurately reflect the limited quantity of tissue available than it does the absence of the organic catalyst *per se.*

Van Deth (1963) has demonstrated that although differences in avian species exist, trends are similar in the changing levels of total carbohydrate in different parts of the avian egg during incubation. Thus, glucose concentrations in blood and in the amnionic and allantoic fluids are high during the first week of embryonic life, whereupon they decrease and remain at a much lower level for the next 7 days, only to rise again during the last week of incubation. Such fluctuations in total carbohydrate are complemented by evidence that the lactic acid of yolk and albumen undergoes a threefold increase by day 7, decreasing sharply from days 8 to 15, and that it subsequently increases to the pre-8th-day level at hatching. Thus, the possibility that carbohydrate is not the only energy source during early development is indicated. Furthermore, in a series of carefully planned experiments Spratt (1949, 1950a, 1950b) clearly demonstrated that the explanted developing embryo requires different nutritive substrates for differentiation, morphogenesis, and growth. By explanting blastoderms to synthetic media lacking in one or more essential nutrients, Spratt observed that glucose alone could support differentiation and morphogenesis characteristic of the first two days of incubation (1949). Only the naturally occurring hexoses can be utilized by the early embryo, and as such they are identical to those sugars most commonly fermented by yeast cells. Such sugars are of the dextro-configuration and include glucose, mannose, fructose, galactose, and maltose. Subsequent investigation has shown that both qualitative and quantitative differences exist so far as carbohydrate requirements for organogenesis are concerned. Thus, glucose substrate levels sufficient to support development and autorhythmicity of the embryonic heart are insufficient for normal differentiation of the neural tube and brain. As a group, morphogenetic processes require fewer carbohydrate nutrients than the processes of differentiation during early embryonic growth (Spratt, 1950a). Studies employing inhibitors of anaerobic or aerobic glycolysis (fluoride, iodoacetate, malonate, citrate, etc.) confirm the premise that there are different levels in the energy requirements (especially for carbohydrate substrates) for patterns of morphogenesis and differentiation, and that the inhibition of development observed with fluoride or iodoacetate is readily reversed by the addition of pyruvate or lactate to the *in vitro* media (Spratt, 1950b). Respiratory quotient data obtained throughout the entire period of incubation indicate that the energy sources utilized by the chick embryo vary over the 20 days from carbohydrate to protein to lipid. Thus, during the first week carbohydrate is employed mainly as an energy source (morphogenesis and differentiation); during the second week protein serves as a major source of energy (rapid growth); and during the last 7 days lipid metabolism takes precedence (embryonic growth termination). The rapid increase in lipolytic activity in the embryonic liver, together with the observation that up to 90 percent of the total caloric requirement of the embryo is derived from egg fatty acids, complements the earlier observations of Needham that the RQ approaches 0.70 during the last week of embryonic development (George and Iype, 1962). It is interesting to note that in the early development of such diverse animal classes as the minnow, grasshopper, crab, nematode, and earthworm, the same sequence of nutrient utilization (carbohydrate-protein-lipid) prevails with respect to energy substrates.

Generally, only mannose can substitute for glucose in supporting morphogenesis and differentiation in early embryo development. The fact that galactose cannot substitute for glucose as an energy source for chick embryos may indicate the lack of specific enzymes either to cleave the carbohydrate moiety from that of the protein, or to facilitate galactose conversion to glucose-1-phosphate. Apparently, glycogen is also utilized by the early embryo, its distribution and localization being related primarily to areas of morphogenetic activity (McCallion and Wong, 1956).

In conclusion, then, the generalization can apparently be made that morphogenesis requires less exogenous energy than differentiation, and also that the nutritional requirement for chick embryo growth (a source of nitrogen for protein synthesis) is quite different from and independent of the two former processes. Such differences are more clearly observable in the first week of incubation with respect to carbohydrate requirements and utilization, since during this time (especially the first 3 or 4 days) the avian embryo may be considered an "eviscerated" preparation, devoid of endocrine and/or hepatic influences over its carbohydrate metabolism.

Blood and Extraembryonic Fluid Carbohydrates

The estimation of circulating blood glucose in the developing chick embryo is necessarily limited by the development and enlargement of the vascular system to the point where adequate aliquots of blood are available for analysis. Significant differences exist in blood glucose levels of various breeds of chicks even when the embryos are at identical stages of development (Witmer and Lane, 1960). Between days 8 and 18 circulating blood glucose levels rise from 150 mg percent to over 200 mg. percent, which is well within the range found at hatching or in the postabsorptive state (Table 52). Circulating glucose levels obviously serve as an energy source to all metabolic and tissue-organizational processes in the developing embryo, including dividing erythrocytes.

Extraembryonic sources of carbohydrate in the avian egg are restricted to the amnionic and allantoic compartments. In contrast to fetal ruminants and some fetal mammals, fructose does not appear to be present in any detectable amounts in the avian embryo, the blood or the amnionic or allantoic fluids. Amnionic glucose, however, doubles in concentration from day 12 to day 17 of incu-

Table 51. Blood glucose and tissue glycogen levels of chick embryos*

Day of incubation	Blood glucose mg./100 ml.	Liver	Muscle	Heart	Glycogen body total, mg.
		—mg./100 gm. tissue—⌐			
8	154	554	65	1192	0.004
10	154	757	78	1623	0.007
12	161	1156	98	1277	0.055
14	171	625	94	688	0.110
16	202	1648	217	1278	0.57
18	228	2890	359	541	1.42
20	—	1236	334	986	2.22
21	—	1772	333	546	3.35

* Data compiled from Lee, 1951; Watterson *et al.*, 1958; Thommes and Tambornino, 1962; and Thommes and Firling, 1964.

bation (0.055 percent to 0.115 percent), and in allantoic compartments meager data indicate almost identical levels of glucose on day 11 (Festenstein, 1957). No fructose appears in the latter fluid on day 11 of incubation.

Little is known about the blood glucose response of chick embryos to the onset of secretory activity of endocrine tissues while in ovo. However, the administration of exogenous (bovine) insulin to the chorio-allantoic membrane of embryos ranging from day 12 through day 16 induces a prolonged hypoglycemia. The length of this hypoglycemic period varies according to the day of insulin administration, recovery being most rapid if the hormone is injected between day 14 and day 16 (Thommes and Tambornino, 1962). Embryos 15 and 16 days of age appear twice as resistant to insulin injections in comparison with younger embryos, an observation which simulates adult avian insulin resistance (see below). This response indicates either sudden organogenic development or marked alterations in peripheral tissue characteristics at or about the 14th day of incubation. Glucagon, the glycogenolytic hormone secreted by the pancreas, (Chapter 20), when applied to the chorio-allantoic membrane of embryos 8 to 16 days old, induces a precipitous increase in embryonic blood glucose. The degree to which this hormone increases blood glucose is augmented with embryon-

ic age except for day 12 (Thommes and Firling, 1964). The cause
of such an exception may be that glucagon's elevating effect on
blood glucose is dependent upon hepatic glycogenolysis, and that
on day 12 the liver glycogen depots are at a low level. Demonstration of a glucagon-effect as early as 8 days is in agreement with the
observation that hepatic glycogen granules are present histochemically from day 6 onward. Rapid recovery of the 8-day embryos
after exogenous glucagon administration is due to normal hepatic
glycogenesis at this time, concomitant with the onset of insulin secretion by the pancreas. Injection of the adrenocortical steroid,
cortisone, into developing embryos leads to increased allantoic
glucose and chloride levels, effects which closely resemble the
renal effects of cortisone in man.

Endocrine Control of Carbohydrate Metabolism

Consideration of those tissues which control carbohydrate metabolism in adult Aves and Mammalia of necessity include the pancreas, adrenal cortex, adrenal medulla, thyroid, and hypophysial
secretions, particularly adrenocorticotrophin (ACTH), prolactin
(LTH), and growth hormone (GH). The anatomy and histology of
these avian organs are described in Chapters 17, 19, 20, 21, and 22.

Employing special staining techniques, Heckerman (1955)
found primary islet cells (precursors to adult islets) in the pancreas
of 3-day embryos; these cells persist through day 17 of incubation.
Pancreatic dark (red) cells, which later develop into glucagon-se-
creting alpha cells (day 10), are first seen on day 6. Secondary islets, containing both alpha and beta cells identical with those observed in adult birds, are present by day 12. Alpha and beta cells
can be demonstrated several days earlier (i.e., on days 7 and 8 respectively) than can their respective secretory granules or even
islet formation. Histochemically demonstrable insulin and histological beta granulations (insulin) appear first near day 7 of incubation (Thommes, 1960), whereas alpha granules do not appear
until day 14 or 15 (Liévre, 1957). The concentration of beta granules in the beta cells is sparse at first but increases rapidly from
day 8 to day 13 of incubation. Concomitant with such alterations
in insulin-secreting capacity are the hepatic glycogen changes de-

scribed above. Generally, the appearance and accumulation of zymogen granules (in acinar tissue) follows the ontogeny of insulin and glucagon secretion, occurring between day 12 and day 16 of incubation. Grillo (1961a) has described the presence of protein-bound sulfhydryl groups in pancreatic beta cells, indicative of the presence of insulin, from day 14 of incubation onward. Bioassay of both pancreatic tissue extracts and plasma obtained from embryos during the first 14 days of incubation indicates that insulin is present in the pancreas as early as day 12 and can be detected in the blood by day 13 (Grillo, 1961a; Leibson, Zheludkova, and Chilingaryan, 1961). There are no indications of the presence of insulin in extraembryonic tissues and/or fluids, however. Neither is there any apparent influence of the beta-cytotoxic agent, alloxan, on the morphogenesis or differentiation of the insulin-secreting cells. In summary, therefore, it would seem that at some time between the appearance of the secreting cells and the appearance of granules in these cells (between days 7 and 14 for alpha, 8 and 12 for beta), elaboration of both glucagon and insulin occurs in the developing embryo. The detection of circulating insulin as late as day 13 does not preclude earlier insulinogenesis and release in amounts too small to detect (with present techniques), but still "physiological" to the rapidly growing embryo.

Information regarding the control of carbohydrate metabolism by organs other than the pancreas is sparse indeed. Evidence exists that the embryonic avian adrenal medulla forms and releases catecholaminelike materials, which are powerful glycogenolytic substance in both Aves and Mammalia, as early as day 4 of incubation. The presence of these substances in allantoic fluid indicates previous formation and secretion by the adrenal medulla. The catecholamine concentration in allantoic fluid increases rapidly from day 5 through day 11, and actually increases fourfold from day 1 to day 12. Boucek and Bourne (1962) describe a daily increment of 0.3 μ g. of catecholamine between day 12 and 15. No attempts have been made to differentiate between norepinephrine and epinephrine as a predominant component of the total catecholamine elaboration in early embryos. It thus appears that to a certain extent early embryo carbohydrate metabolism, is under the glycogenolytic influence of the catecholamines, possibly as early as day 3 of incubation. Exogenous epinephrine when injected into air cells of 8-day embryos has no effect on liver, muscle, and blood carbohydrate moieties. However, when it is injected into air cells of 11- to 18-day embryos, liver glycogenolysis occurs within an hour. Muscle glycogen is depleted only in 18-day or older embryos possibly indicating that phosphorylase is not present in muscle until this late day.

The physiological impact of the embryonic adrenal cortex and thyroid gland in the carbohydrate metabolism of the embryo has not been elucidated. Mitotic activity in the adrenal cortex increases rapidly on day 8 (concomitant with initial hypophysial elaboration of ACTH) and after from 36 to 48 hours returns to near normal. Hypophysectomy prevents such adrenal histological differentiation, and merely indicates that the pituitary-adrenal axis is developed in the avian embryo prior to day 8 (Toth, Simon, and Szekely, 1957). What control such adrenocortical activity may exert over the metabolic demands of the embryo remains obscure.

Selective hypophysectomy in the early embryo is not possible, for obvious reasons, but by employing a decapitate-hypophysectomy technique Konigsberg (1954) has studied carbohydrate metabolism in chick embryos from day 8 through day 16 of incubation. The "decapitated" embryo exhibits a progressive hyperglycemia from day 8 to day 12, at which time the blood glucose levels are 55 percent greater than on the previous day. Concomitant with the developing hyperglycemia is a marked hepatic glycogenesis. From day 10 to day 12, liver glycogen increases 40 percent in these 'hypophysectomized" embryos; normal intact embryos lose about the same amount of glycogen during this same 48-hour period (Konigsberg, 1954). Which of the hypophysial secretions are specifically responsible for controlling these carbohydrate mechanisms in the normal embryo is not known, but from studies on mammals the most likely candidates are ACTH and/or GH. Both of these hormones influence blood glucose and liver glycogen under a wide variety of physiological conditions. After the 12th day of development, the blood sugar levels of the hypophysectomized embryos decrease, returning to normal by day 16; they probably reflect the onset of insulin release by the embryonic pancreas. Although the suggestion has been made that the carbohydrate alterations observed in the decapitate embryos are a result of decreased metabolic rate in the absence of a pituitary-thyroid axis, it should be noted that hypophysectomy in adult mammals and birds leads to hypoglycemia, and possibly to increased insulin sensitivity. Also, hyperthyroidism is commonly associated with a mild hyperglycemia. Interestingly, mucoprotein granules believed to consist of stored thyroid-stimulating hormone (TSH) are present in the adenohypophysis of chick embryos at the 5th day, and increase in size and number until day 12 (see Chapter 19). The release of TSH at 12 to 14 days is coincident with the marked liver and blood carbohydrate alterations described previously. Small quantities of thyroxine injected into allantoic compartments of 5-day embryos cause hydrolysis of hepatic glycogen prior to day 8 of incubation. Such delayed action by the thyroid hormone is typical of many of its manifestations in mammals also.

The injection of growth hormone (bovine) during the last half of embryogenesis leads to a wide variety of tissue effects, most of which are related to protein synthesis and bone growth. Also, however, exogenous GH elevates the blood glucose if injected chorioallantoically on day 13, a response which is still apparent at the time of hatching and apparently is related to the hormone dosage (Hsieh, Wang, and Blumenthal, 1952; Wang, Wang, and Blumenthal, 1952). Female embryos are more sensitive to the hyperglycemic effect and in body weight increase in response to administered GH, observations that are in accord with those in adult females in response to other hyperglycemic agents. The response of the chick embryo to the carbohydrate effects of GH is in direct contrast to that seen in adult Aves over a wide range of doses (Hazelwood and Lorenz, 1959). The specific time period in which adenohypophysial GH is manufactured and released to the embryonic circulation has not been established with certainty.

Nonendocrine Glycogenic Tissues

Liver. Whole chick embryo extracts, as well as embryo liver tissue, contain enzymes for glycolytic and phosphorylative oxidation pathways of glucose from the time reliable estimates of enzyme presence can be made (about day 4). The concentration of enzymes, as well as the enzymic reaction rates, varies with the age of the chick. This is particularly apparent in comparing embryonic liver with adult liver (Rinaudo, 1961). Utilization of ribose-5-phosphate in the early embryonic liver occurs at a rate three times faster than that of the adult chicken liver (Cazorla and Barron, 1958). Pentose cycle (HMP) activity is apparent and quite noticeable as early as the 40th hour of incubation in chick embryos, reaching a maximum at 72 hours. Concentrations of glucose-6-phosphate dehydrogenase fluctuate accordingly, and possibly indicate that the alternating maxima and minima of this dehydrogenase concentration reflect alternating periods of cell proliferation and differentiation (Burt and Wenger, 1962; Newburgh, Buckingham, and Herrmann, 1962).

Although hepatic glycogen is histochemically demonstrable in embryos 4 to 7 days of age, the polysaccharide is difficult to determine biochemically prior to day 7 or 8 of incubation. As was mentioned previously, hepatic glycogen increases with embryonic age, even though several depressions occur from day 7 to day 20, and notably between days 13 and 14 (Lee, 1951). It is possible that the first appearance of glycogen in hepatic cells is due to innate liver cell activity and not dependent upon hematologic components. Thus, O'Connor (1953) has demonstrated that the appearance of hepatic glycogen on day 7 coincides with altered liver cell metabolism. The R.Q. of liver slices from embryos varying in age indicates an abrupt change away from carbohydrate metabolism and toward protein utilization. Thus, liver tissue excised from embryos prior to day 7 definitely relies on glucose in incubation media for continued cellular activity; omitting glucose from such media decreases the respiratory rate of liver slices. However, if the donor tissue is obtained from embryos older than 8 days, no change in respiratory rate or R.Q. is apparent in the absence of a glucose source (O'Connor, 1953). Such data lend support to the belief that the appearance of glycogen in hepatic cells may well be due to a decrement in activity, or to either a loss of or a switch from the enzymatic machinery essential for glucose catabolism.

Additional enzymes associated with carbohydrate metabolism are also found in the avian liver during the first week of development. Almost as soon as glycogen can be detected in the liver, glucose-6-phosphatase and beta-glucuronidase activity can be detected. The activity of both these enzymes increase in direct proportion to liver weight; their properties are similar to those found in adult liver of chickens as well as of other species, and thus indicate that the avian embryo liver is capable of glucose formation as well as glycogenolysis (Kilsheimer, Weber, and Ashmore, 1960). Grillo (1961b) and Guha and Wegmann (1961) have demonstrated phosphorylase in various avian embryonic tissues. Chick liver contains reasonable amounts of phosphorylase, especially from day 7 on, and up until day 12 the enzyme appears to be in the active form only (phosphorylase-a). After day 12, both inactive (phosphorylase-b) and active phosphorylase are present in substantial amounts in hepatic tissue, and together with the UDPG-glycogen pathway the phosphroylases probably form the major avenues by which hepatic glycogen is synthesized and hydrolyzed, respectively. Actually, it would appear that the UDPG-pathway is quite active and well developed in the early embryo, since glycogen droplets can be detected in liver cells prior to the finding of phosphorylase. This mechanism may be even more important in skeletal muscle, where glycogen can be determined on day 3 of incubation but where phosphorylase is not present until 10 days later (Grillo, 1961b). Grillo and Ozone (1962) have found that the UDPG-pathway is operating in the early embryo; in liver, heart, skeletal muscle, and brain, UDPG-synthetase activity is found prior to the appearance of phosphorylase enzymes. Also, this enzymic activity parallels the appearance of glycogen in the embryo. Since the appearance of UDPG-enzyme activity antedates the appearance (but not necessarily the genesis) of insulin by 9 days, it appears likely that early glycogen metabolism of the avian embryo occurs in the absence of the pancreatic hormone.

The injection of cortisol or of cortisone into chick embryos between days 4 and 10 of incubation depletes liver glycogen, a finding which is at variance with the effects of these hormones in adult birds and mammals (Clawson and Domm, 1961). Glucagon, when injected via chorio-allantoic vessels of 8-16-day-old embryos, hydrolyzes hepatic glycogen rapidly (Thommes and Firling, 1964). Since even 8-day embryos are capable of restoring hepatic glycogen to normal after hormonal depletion, the existence of the UDPG-synthetic pathway may again be emphasized. The possibility does exist, however, that the embryonic chick pancreas produces and releases insulin earlier than bioassay techniques indicate.

Heart. Cardiac tissue from chick embryos has been studied by many workers, and there is general agreement that at day 3 the glycogen concentration is approximately 20 times higher than in any other embryonic tissue; that total myocardial glycogen increases rapidly up to day 13; and that it then decreases during the last 7 days prior to hatching (Lee, 1951). Phosphorylase can be detected in cardiac tissue on day 3, that is, about one day after glycogen can be found in this tissue (Grillo, 1961b). The actual presence of myocardial glycogen precedes the appearance of the first contractile units (myofibrils). Freshly explanted embryonic chick hearts cultivated on synthetic media can substitute mannose, fructose, and galactose for glucose as sources of energy. However, such explanted avian hearts are progressively less efficient in utilizing components of the glycolytic (Embden-Meyerhoff) pathway in replacement of glucose as one proceeds down this pathway (Morgan and Morton, 1960). Although insulin increases carbohydrate utilization by 13-day-old explanted chick embryo hearts concomitant with increases in lipid-phosphates, RNA, DNA, and total protein nitrogen (Leslie and Paul, 1954), the hormone is totally without effect on embryonic hearts less than 6 days of age (Guidotti, Kanameishi, and Foa, 1961). It would appear that 5-day-old embryonic hearts are freely permeable to both glucose and to sorbitol ,and that the rate of uptake by the myocardial cells is regulated by the rate of intracellular phosphorylation. Between days 7 and 8, a physiological barrier develops in the embryonic heart whereby glucose transport, distinct from the intracellular events, becomes rate-limiting (Guidotti and Foa, 1961). Whereas anoxia encourages glucose uptake at all incubation ages, insulin was effective in doing so only after day 7. Such a reversal of cardiac response to hormonal influence has also been observed with catecholamines. Four-day-old chick hearts are quite sensitive to both the inotropic and the chronotropic influence of epinephrine, responses which persist for a long time. However, the 6-day-old chick does not show so persistent a response to epinephrine, a finding probably explained by the sudden development of a catecholamine degradating enzyme system (McCarty and Shideman, 1960).

Cardiac lipase is available by the 40th hour of incubation, and quantitative changes in its activity in embryonic hearts parallel the increase in heart rate (George and Iype, 1962). It should be recalled that at this time cardiac glycogen is approximately 20 times the level found in other embryonic tissues, and may therefore indicate an early utilization of cardiac fatty acids with resultant sparing of glycogen depots. Such a mechanism of energy release and utilization would be somewhat contrary to that observed in other embryonic tissues and in the embryo as a whole. The differentiation of cardiac lipase may therefore be directly related to functional differentiation (George and Iype, 1962). Certainly the embryonic heart and liver have different morphogenetic enzyme patterns.

Muscle. In skeletal muscle, the concentration of glycogen increases slowly but steadily for the first 14 days of incubation. Presumably most of this glycogen depot is the result of the UDPG-synthetic pathways; phosphorlyase does not appear in striated muscle in any great amounts until days 12 and 13 (Grillo, 1961b). An abrupt increase in skeletal muscle glycogen occurs between days 15 and 18 (Lee, 1951), and is paralleled by a concurrent sharp increase in gluokinase (hexokinase) levels. Hexokinase activity in skeletal muscle declines gradually after day 18, and continues to do so after hatching until, within two weeks, it reaches adult fowl levels. Contributions of the pentose pathway to the energetics of muscle growth in appendages appear to be minimal in the first two weeks of incubation, a period in which growth differences of legs and wings are the greatest. Glucose-6-phosphate dehydrogenase activity is at a maximum on day 16, after which it decreases to one-third of this value by the time of hatching (Mahaffey, 1961).

Intestine. Normally, glycogen does not accumulate to any great degree in the intestinal epithelium; however, this polysaccharide is deposited in the avian embryo intestine over a brief period of time during incubation. Duodenal glycogen increases from six- to eightfold between days 14 and 18 of incubation, only to decrease rapidly immediately thereafter (Moog and Thomas, 1957). It appears that intestinal glycogen accumulation may serve as an energy source for the rapid cellular differentiation which this tissue undergoes between days 18 and 21. The intestinal epithelium differentiation which normally occurs apparently is under the control of endogenous adrenocortical secretions (glucocorticoids), as is the accumulation of epithelial glycogen. Intestinal glycogen accumulation is accompanied by increasing alkaline phosphatase levels (Moog and Richardson, 1955; Moog and Thomas, 1957). Although intestinal glycogen depots probably are not a major source of carbohydrate for the entire organism even after hatching, alterations in the ability with which certain sugars can pass the intestinal barrier are of interest. Bogner (1957) measured sugar absorption coefficients (mg./100 gm. body wt./min.) in 18-day embryos and found that d-xylose, d-glucose, and d-mannose were absorbed with decreasing ease, respectively. Yet three days later d-mannose, d-xylose, and d-glucose are absorbed with decreasing ease, respectively, by the newly hatched chick.

Teratogenic Effects of Hormones Associated with Carbohydrate Metabolism

Before leaving the subject of the avian embryo and the carbohydrate environment in which it resides, some mention should be made of the many hormonally induced developmental defects that can be observed in embryos. Injections into the yolk sac of such substances as insulin, eserine, sulfonamides, and sodium cacodylate induce teratogenic defects in chick embryos. One of the best-known teratogenic agents is insulin, which has been employed extensively in both duck and chick embryos. With proper dosage and timing of insulin injections, different phenotypic responses can be produced, the body regions most affected being the tail (rumplessness), the legs (micromelia), the maxillae (beak defects), and the skull (Landauer, 1951; Landauer and Rhodes, 1952; Landauer, 1954; Barron and McKenzie, 1962). Thus, by the administration of insulin at 24 hours of incubation deformations resembling certain mutant conditions (rumplessness) can be produced which are distinct from the abnormalities observed if the hormone is applied at 5 or 6 days of incubation (micromelia and maxillary defects). All defects appear to be restricted to the skeletal and central nervous systems, and selected abnormalities can be prevented by the simultaneous administration of certain substances such as pyruvate, glucose-1-phosphate, DPN (but not DPNH), nicotinamide, and oxalacetic acid (Landauer and Rhodes, 1952; Barron and McKenzie, 1962). Biochemically, there appears to be no common denominator among the wide variety of substances that produce developmental abnormalities and phenocopies in avian embryos. However, the diversified substances that prevent such abnormalities if injected simultaneously with the chemical teratogens have at least one thing in common: all are involved in normal carbohydrate metabolism in some way. Thus, the observed malformations may well be a reflection of altered carbohydrate metabolism. Zwilling (1951a, 1951b, 1952) has studied the effect of insulin on carbohydrate metabolism of the embryo and extraembryonic compartments in an attempt to localize the effect of this hormone in producing rumplessness in the early embryo. He concluded that there was a causal relation between the degree of induced hypoglycemia and the loss of sacral vertebral elements. The protracted hypoglycemia induced by insulin is accompanied by a shift from embryonic blood and tissues to the yolk-sac membranes of carbohydrate which is then deposited as glycogen. In addition, however, yolk-sac glycogenolysis is inhibited in these insulin-injected embryos. Nevertheless, hypoglycemia *per se* is evidently not a prerequisite for the observed teratogenic effects, since aberrations in morphogenetic patterns can exist in complete absence of glycemic alterations. Sulfanilamide is such a teratogenic agent. It appears that the effect of these teratogenic substances is to deny the availability of certain enzymes to the embryo, thus leading to secondary differential effects upon it (Landauer, 1954). Insulin damage may be prevented during early developmental stages (anaerobic) with substances that aid reoxidation of pyridine nucleotides. Thus, the complete protection afforded by DPN—but not DPNH—may possibly indicate that insulin damage is associated with a dysfunctioning hydrogen transport system (Barron and McKenzie, 1962).

Hyperglycemic agents have been injected either into the yolk sac or into the chorio-allantoic vessels of chick embryos and their effects studied in relation to the production of developmental abnormalities. Purified glucagon injected over a wide dosage range is without effect in producing total embryo weight changes or malformations (Elrick, Konigsberg, and Arai, 1958). Sympathomimetic agents, known to elevate blood glucose levels (catecholamines) when injected via chorio-allantoic vessels into embryos 10 to 12 days old, produce not only vasoconstriction of peripheral embryonic vessles but also cephalic hematomas. No evidence of skeletal malformations is seen after injection with these agents (Gatling, 1962). Another hyperglycemic substance, thyroxine, when injected in low doses of less than 5 µg., reduces embryonic thyroid weights and yolk sacs, and produces longer third toes and increased body weights (Adams, 1958).

Next to insulin, adrenocorticoids (Chapter 21) are the most commonly employed carbohydrate-regulating hormones in studying developmental malformations in avian embryos. DeFranciscis and Landauer (1959) found that whereas cortisone (17-hydroxy-11-dehydrocorticosterone) alone caused dwarfed embryos if injected into the yolk sac on day 4 to 8, there was no skeletal malformation. The combined injection of adrenal cortical extract (a mixture of adrenal steroids) along with insulin during these four days potentiates the teratogenic action of insulin (DeFranciscis and Landauer, 1959). Combining cortisone with insulin does not increase the frequency of the occurrence of abnormalities regardless of whether the injection day was before or after day 8. It appears that specific biochemical changes occur in the chick embryo between days 4 and 8 viz. changes in reactions which render the organism insensitive to combined adrenal cortical extract and insulin treatment after day 8 of incubation. A wide variety of corticosteroids produce varying degrees of edema, decreased hepatic mitotic activity, liver damage, and feather growth abnormalities, in addition to the retardation of body weight (Weston and Morimoto, 1961; Karnofsky, Ridgway, and Patterson, 1951; Burnet and Warner, 1960). Such effects are not restricted to the glucocorticoids; desoxycortisterone acetate also decreases embryo weights at dose levels 50 percent lower than is seen with cortisone (Sames and Leathem, 1951). The specific step at which the adrenocorticosteroids exert their effect in producing teratogenic abnormalities is not known. However, the observation that steroids (other than cortisone) can potentiate the teratogenic effect of insulin as well as the localization of glucocorticoid mechanism of carbohydrate action—possibly to a step involving transfer of hydrogen to a suitable acceptor—indicates that both of these carbohydrate regulators may produce abnormalities in the developing embryo by interference with the organism's reoxidation of pyridine nucleotides.

THE CHICK AND ADULT BIRD

The observation that birds differ from mammals in the metabolism of carbohydrates was indicated as early as 1893 by the classic work of Minkowski on diabetes in many animal species. Since that time much work on birds has been devoted to the study of normal and fasting blood glucose levels, to the avian liver and its control of carbohydrate metabolism, and to avian carbohydrate responses to pancreatectomy and to the administration of alloxan. From such studies it is generally accepted that after hatching the fed bird, in comparison with most mammals, has twice as high a blood glucose level, about the same level of skeletal muscle and hepatic glycogen, and cardiac glycogen levels about one-fourth as high. Although some workers have reported that carnivorous birds (horned owl, falcon, etc.) have normal glycemias in excess of 250 mg. percent, other studies have demonstrated that these species have blood glucose levels that fall in the upper part of the range considered normal for fed birds, i.e. 175–250 mg. percent. For reviews of blood glucose levels and avian carbohydrate metabolism the reader is referred to the first edition of this book and to Opdyke (1942), Golden and Long (1942a), Riddle and Dotti (1947), and Snedecor, Mathews, and MacGrath (1956); also to Chapter 2.

Blood Glucose in the Fed and Fasted Chick

It has been known since the turn of the last century that avian blood glucose is in the d-glucose form, as it is in mammals. However, the use of widely diverse methodology in determining avian blood sugar levels, as well as the employment of birds in various nutritional and reproductive states, has led to reports of blood glucose values as low as 110 mg. percent as well as to levels as high as 350 mg. percent for the fed bird. (see also Chapter 2). Although slight variations in normal blood glucose levels may exist among various breeds and species (carnivorous vs. granivorous), most if not all fall between 175 and 225 mg. percent. Sugars other than glucose appear to be minimal contributing factors to the overall hexose content of avian blood, fructose and galactose both being present in less than 4 mg. percent and 1 mg. percent respectively. Mannose has not been found in avian blood.

Glucose and other avian blood components have been described in detail in Chapter 2. Over 95 percent of the total blood glucose is transported by the plasma of birds in the form of d-glucose. Actually, the amount of glucose found in the erythrocytic compartments of newly hatched and young chicks is less than those levels reported in the neonatal and young animals of other species (Tapper and Kare, 1960). Because of this distribution, avian plasma should be employed for accurate glucose determinations, since alteration of red blood cell concentration may lead to erroneous estimates if whole blood samples are employed. Most of the data, however, are on whole blood glucose.

The effects of fasting in newly hatched chicks as well as in adults have led to interesting observations (see also Chapter 2). Employing fatal starvation periods, Houpt (1958) reported that baby chicks immediately after hatching, and at 2, 6, 10, and 14 days of age are resistant to acute hypoglycemia (unlike fasted newborn pigs), and that the blood glucose levels were correlated with alterations in body temperature (Table 52). Golden and Long (1942a) studied older chicks and found that a 24-hour fast decreased blood glucose approximately 10 mg. percent. During the same fasting period liver glycogen levels fell from 3.0 percent to less than 0.5 percent, and pectoral (skeletal) muscle, which contains 3 to 4 times more glycogen than other avian skeletal muscle, decreased from over 1000 mg. percent to about 750 mg. percent. Diurnal variations, which occur in avian tissue glycogen concen-

Table 52. Blood glucose alterations of baby chicks in response to
prolonged fasting (mg./100 ml.)*

Age of chicks, days	Days fasted						
	0	1	2	3	4	5	6
0	203	193	195	201	208	190	153
2	208	170	166	171	161	148	—
6	204	158	177	176	182	166	152
10	217	180	174	181	192	176	164
14	194	160	158	166	158	140	162

Blood glucose levels for fed controls of all age groups averaged 194–214
mg./100 ml.

* Data assembled from Houpt, 1958.

trations apparently at a rate much faster than that observed in
mammals, to a certain degree are a reflection of alternate periods
of feeding and abstinence in birds. Other factors which may be of
equal importance are to be discussed later. Hazelwood and Lorenz
(1959) studied the effects of prolonged fasting in adult chickens,
and after observing the usual decrease in blood glucose 24 to 36
hours after the starvation period commenced, found that a progressive rise in blood glucose occurred, reaching a maximum (22
mg. percent above fed levels) some 6 days later. Concurrently,
liver glycogen, depleted early during fasting, was partially replaced by prolongation of the starvation period. Simultaneous
studies of nitrogen metabolism indicate that increased gluconeogenesis appears likely not only to be responsible for the blood glucose increase but also to play a role in the restoration of liver glycogen after the initial glycogenolysis induced by fasting. Similar
observations have been made in mammals. Cardiac glycogen levels
of fed birds are approximately 110 mg. percent; they increase to
more than twice the prefasting levels with but 12 hours of fasting,
continue to increase to a peak of over three times control levels
after 48 hours of fasting, and then decline rapidly as starvation
continues. Rat heart-muscle glycogen responds in a similar man-

Table 53. Effects of prolonged fasting on blood components and tissue glycogen levels in 8–10-week-old chickens*

Days of fasting	Blood, mg./100 ml.		Tissue glycogen in mg./100 gm. wet wt.		
	Glucose	NPN	Liver	Muscle†	Heart
(Fed)	202	35.1	1850	1168	103
$\frac{1}{4}$	199	—	574	—	178
$\frac{1}{2}$	195	—	225	—	254
1	180	45.3	254	773	210
2	179	41.1	431	889	323
3	182	38.3	466	—	157
4	207	59.8	628	—	—
5	—	—	—	—	—
6	224	49.7	795	—	—
7	191	56.9	423	—	—
8	177	72.9	185	—	—

* Data compiled from Hazelwood and Lorenz (1959) with those on pectoral muscle from 6-week-old bird groups of Golden and Long (1942a).
† Pectoral muscle.

ner to prolonged fasting, although it both starts at and reaches higher concentrations than those observed in birds. During fasting the heart deposits glycogen concomitant with the loss of hepatic glycogen; the heart loses the glycogen with continued fasting concurrent with hepatic redeposition of glycogen (Table 53).

Absorption and Metabolism of Carbohydrates in Birds

Starch is most rapidly degradated in the crop and proventriculus, and passes through the entire gastrointestinal tract of the adult chicken in a little less than 4 hours (see Chapter 10). Bogner (1957) found that the absorption coefficient of various sugars by the 14-day-old chick was greatest for galactose and least for fructose (d-galactose > d-glucose > d-xylose > d-fructose). While the numerical coefficients are higher than those observed in mammals, the decreasing order in which these sugars are absorbed by the avian gut is identical with the sequence observed in mammals. However, in this respect the 14-day chick differs from both embryos and newly hatched chicks. That absorption of both glucose and galactose occurs via an active transport process has been demonstrated in 18-day embryos and in newly hatched, 2-, 4-, and 8-day-old chicks. Utilization of glucose by intestinal segments is highest at 2 days of age, leveling off thereafter. Galactose utilization does not increase with age but rather remains constant at approximately one-fifth of the glucose utilization observed in the intestinal tissue of the 8-day-old chick (Bogner and Haines, 1960; Bogner and Haines, 1961). Galactose is actively transported by the upper and lower third of the avian intestine in newly hatched chicks. These intestinal segments (but not the middle third) are capable of metabolizing galactose, a utilization which does not lead to the production of either glucose or lactate (Bogner, Bogner, and McLain, 1964). Employing older chicks (150–250 grams), Golden and Long (1942b) studied the absorption of glucose loads from the intestinal tract and the disposition of it in liver and skeletal muscle. These workers found that their chicks transported and/or utilized 400 mg. glucose per hour per 100 grams of body weight. Such an absorption rate remains constant for at least 4 hours, after which liver glycogen rises to almost 6 percent, and that of skeletal muscle to 1.3 percent. Glycogenesis over a 4-hour period accounts for only 20 percent of the total glucose administered, and thus suggests that rapid oxidative mechanics and/or lipogenesis account for the remaining 80 percent of the glucose load. Absorption of both glucose and amino acids leads to a near-maximum concentration of these substances in portal vein blood within 15 to 30 minutes after chickens are fed a test meal (Table 54). However, glucose may be absorbed at a slower rate, continuing for as long as 6 hours after eating (Aramaki and Weiss, 1962). The absorption coefficients obtained in many *in vivo* experiments on chick intestines are considerably higher quantitatively than those from *in vitro* studies (Sato, Homma, and Gotoh, 1960). Normally the chick has an *in vivo* glucose absorption rate 3 to 4 times greater than rats, and the coefficient for glucose increases with growth until about the 25th day after hatching. Furthermore, if birds are trained to eat their entire daily ration in a restricted time period, very little metabolic adaptation occurs; the adapta-

Table 54. Plasma glucose and amino nitrogen levels of 1–2-year-old chickens fasted 16–18 hours prior to presentation of a test meal*

	Minutes after presentation of feed											
	0	15	30	45	60	75	90	105	120	180	240	360
No. of observations	22	22	20	22	21	11	20	11	21	9	9	8
Plasma glucose, mg.%	203	236	255	259	252	251	243	259	237	221	213	216
Plasma amino nitrogen, mg.%	7.9	8.9	8.7	8.1	7.9	7.6	7.8	7.8	7.6	7.6	7.3	7.0

* Taken from Aramaki and Weiss, 1962.

tion occurs primarily at the crop, enabling them to accommodate larger quantities of food. However, such "training" delays digestion of carbohydrates, and less hepatic glycogenesis is observed during the peak of digestion (Lepkovsky, Chari-Bitron, Lemmon, Ostwald, and Dimick, 1960).

Fructose and galactose metabolism in birds have interested many workers because of the former's relative absence in avian tissues and the latter's high absorption coefficient. Fructose oxidation by avian liver slices occurs rapidly and is not influenced by the simultaneous presence of glucose, regardless of the concentration of the latter. This is in contrast to the mammalian liver, where fructose metabolism is not attended by an increased oxygen uptake. Respiratory quotients from avian liver slices actively metabolizing fructose indicate a value greater than 1.0. Thus, the liver of the domestic fowl appears to differ from mammalian liver, at least in a quantitative sense, in its ability to handle fructose. In mammals, the liver phosphorylates fructose to fructose-1-phosphate, which is subsequently split to form glyceraldehyde and dihydroxyacetone phosphate. The high R.Q. observed by hepatic tissue may indicate the ease with which birds can convert such intermediates to glycerophosphates (Heald, 1962, 1963).

Dietary galactose at the levels of 10 percent or less are readily tolerated by chicks without any deleterious physiological effect. Above 10 percent, however, a characteristic nervous syndrome occurs, attended by epileptiform convulsions. The inclusion of galactose (55 percent) in the diet of young chicks leads to diminished liver glycogen depots, normal muscle glycogen levels, high blood galactose levels, normal calcium levels, normal blood glucose levels, severe kidney damage, convulsions, and death (Sondergaard, Prange, Dam, and Christensen, 1957; Rigdon, Couch, Creger, and Ferguson, 1963). High lactose diets do not lead to any CNS disorders, and examination of blood carbohydrates reveals (in addition to normal glucose levels) the presence of small amounts of lactose but no evidence of galactose (Rutter, Krichevsky, Scott, and Hansen, 1953). Presumably, chicks cannot hydrolyze lactose to its normal component sugars, galactose and glucose. Female chickens appear to be more sensitive to the toxic effect of galactose than male chickens, and part of this difference is probably due to basic metabolic differences. Female erythrocytes have little ability to oxidize galactose, and in comparison with male chicks given a galactose load, the female chick requires a much longer time to return blood levels to normal (Nordin, Wilken, Bretthauer, Hansen, and Scott, 1960). Galactose readily penetrates into the intracellular water of tissues, and its toxic effect is therefore probably related, to its depressant effect on glucose utilization. Although the avian liver content of uridine diphosphate nucleotides is reduced in galactose poisoning, the injection of UDPG (which is known to be a coenzyme in the transformation of galactose to glucose) does not eliminate the toxicity symptoms. Administration of uridine, uracil, or thiamine does not alter the toxic state, either; this, together with the observations that blood galactose levels in birds are reduced with intravenous administration of UDPG, indicates that galactose poisoning is not merely the result of the absence of a single enzyme or co-factor in the galactose to glucose transformation (Rutter *et al.*, 1953; Sondergaard *et al.*, 1957; Nordin *et al.*, 1960). The same conclusion is further indicated by the early presence of the UDPG-glycogen pathway in chick embryos and the persistence of this pathway in adult tissues, as discussed above.

The chick's tolerance of dietary fat is virtually unlimited, growth occurring normally even when fat is supplying over 95 percent of the nonprotein calories of the diet. As has been indicated, such tolerance is not true for all carbohydrates. Growth inhibition by various carbohydrates is widely recognized, and the nutritional efficiency of many carbohydrates has been studied extensively (Monson, Dietrich, and Elvehjem, 1950). Growth inhibition is observed when cornstarch replaces dietary glucose; raw soy-bean meal depresses liver and muscle glycogen depots. However, quantitative studies on both the metabolizable energy and the productive energy of glucose indicate that the former is approximately 3.64 Cal./gram dry matter (97 percent of the heat of glucose combustion), and that the latter is about 2.90 Cal./gram carcass in growing chicks (Anderson, Hill, and Renner, 1958).

Once absorbed by the intestinal tract, carbohydrates are carried to the liver via the portal vein, where they are either stored as glycogen, transformed into fat (lipogenesis), or degradated to CO_2, H_2O, and energy. Hepatic glycogen levels are subject to diurnal variations, which are considered normal for birds but which must be taken into account whenever quantitative avian carbohydrate studies are carried out. Whereas the chick embryo displays a rhythm of three cycles a day, chicks that have been newly hatched and older chickens apparently undergo one complete diurnal cycle (Elfvin, Petren, and Sollberger, 1955). Fisher and Bartlett (1957) describe overnight decreases in the liver fat and glycogen of blackbirds and starlings; the decrease in liver weight is directly related to loss of hepatic fat. Blackbirds and starlings have peaks of hepatic fat and glycogen level in the early evening, and the greatest depressions occur in early morning. Some of the observations concerning them are presented in Table 55. Reversal of the night-day light pattern by 12 hours likewise reverses hepatic glycogen patterns by 12 hours. The intermediary level of the descent of liver glycogen occurs at night, and its length is directly related to the length of darkness (Elfvin et al., 1955). Seasonal changes in tolerance to glucose and glycogenesis in poikilotherms is well established (DiMaggio and Dessauer, 1963), and thus the ecological and environmental implications of changing light periodicity on avian hepatic glycogen depots are obvious.

Other factors which alter tissue carbohydrate metabolism in birds are the ambient temperature and possibly certain neurogen-

Table 55. Diurnal variations in body and liver components of female blackbirds*

Time	Body weight gm.	Total liver weight gm.	Liver glycogen mg./gm., fresh wt.	Liver fat mg./gm., fresh wt.
9 P.M.	48.5	1.82	4.98	228
9 A.M.	43.3	1.42	2.34	99
Noon	42.1	1.56	2.65	—
3 P.M.	42.6	1.16	1.17	174
6 P.M.	41.6	1.13	2.18	258

* Data collected during March 1956, Jackson County, Ill.

ic controls. Induction of hypothermia (25°C.) in the chick depresses existing blood glucose levels to 41 percent below control values (170 vs. 100 mg. percent); re-warming birds to normal body temperature after the siege of hypothermia returns the blood sugar levels to normal. Induction of a febrile state elevates the blood glucose to levels about 18 percent above normal control levels (Rodbard and Goldstein, 1950). In all cases there is a time lag of about 3 minutes from induction of body temperature change to the time a blood glucose response can be noted. If the vagi are doubly sectioned this thermoglycemic relation is abolished; atropine modifies but does not completely abolish the phenomenon. If there is a neurogenic control over avian glycemia in response to changes in body temperature, it is evidently not mediated by the pancreas, since pancreatectomy does not inhibit the thermoglycemic response. As compared to mammals (rabbits) glycogenolysis is increased markedly (200 percent) in avian (pigeon) liver if these two species are exposed to 48° C. for 2½ hours (Sandhu and Chaudhuri, 1961). Apparently the increase in body temperature increases hepatic carbohydrate reaction rates, leading to a hydrolysis of glycogen. Hyperglycemia then ensues. The complete significance of vagal nuclei activity, and of the associated body temperature and blood glucose alterations, is not evident at this time, but awaits further investigation.

Endocrine Control of Avian Carbohydrate Metabolism

Although both the metabolic activity of the liver, and the rate and efficiency of sugar absorption by the intestinal tract, markedly influence carbohydrate metabolism in animals, the circulating blood glucose level reflects interrelated hormonal secretion patterns as well. Endocrine control over carbohydrate metabolism is well established in mammals, and there is little evidence to indicate that the same influences are not exerted in control of avian carbohydrate metabolism also. Nonetheless, there exist in birds certain striking differences in endocrine control over glucose metabolism when compared with mammals, such as warrant special consideration at this point. Endocrine tissues most commonly identified with carbohydrate metabolism are the pancreatic islets (alpha and beta cells), adrenal gland (medulla and cortex), pituitary gland (growth hormone, adrenocorticotrophic hormone, and prolactin), thyroid, and to a much lesser extent the gonads.

Pancreas. The histological appearance of the bird pancreas is described in Chapter 20, where it is indicated that in the adult bird alpha cells are much less numerous than beta cells; that the distribution of the alpha cells throughout the pancreas is unequal, being restricted largely to the third and splenic lobes; and that alpha cells are thought to be the origin of the hormone glucagon. It is possible that there may be two types of alpha cells in the duck pancreas, but as is suggested by Hellman (1961), these cells may actually reflect different functional states of the same alpha cell. The duck pancreas contains more zinc than is found in the mammalian pancreas, and the alpha tissue has about 10 times the concentration of this element found in the rest of the pancreatic tissue. Vuylsteke and DeDuve (1953) have demonstrated that the pancreas of ducks and chickens contains about 10 times more glucagon than is found in equivalent amounts of mammalian pancreatic tissue. This appears to be true regardless of whether or not the species is carnivorous (as in the barn owl and kestrel). Injection of pancreatic extracts from ducks and chickens into fed rabbits results in a rapid and marked hyperglycemia followed by a slow subsequent period of hypoglycemia. In mammals, glucagon is considered a natural secretion of the pancreatic alpha tissue, which upon reaching liver cells activates hepatic phosphorylase, which in turn leads to glycogenolysis and attendant hyperglycemia. There is no evidence that birds differ from mammals in this respect; the glycogenolytic response to exogenous glucagon of the former is the same or even greater than that observed in the latter (Table 56). The hyperglycemia seen in chickens injected with glucagon is rapid and transitory, and is apparently due to glycogenolytic and not to gluconeogenic mechanisms (Hazelwood and Lorenz, 1957). The lizard also is very sensitive to the hyperglycemic effects of exogenous glucagon, and in contrast to birds, alligators injected with glucagon may demonstrate elevated blood glucose levels up to 70 hours after injection. The time after injection at which glucagon induces the maximal hyperglycemia varies directly with the dosage; the sensitivity of the chick to this hormone is the basis for a fairly sensitive bioassay for glucagon (Beekman, 1958).

Certain biguanides are cytotoxic agents which specifically damage and/or destroy pancreatic alpha cells. Synthalin A (decamethylene diguanide) is such an alpha-cytotoxic substance; in the fowl it produces cytological alterations and necrosis of alpha cells identical with those observed in mammals. The administration of synthalin A produces a diphasic change in blood glucose concentration, in birds characterized by a transitory hyperglycemia followed by a severe and prolonged hypoglycemia which leads to convulsions and death (Beekman, 1956). The hyperglycemia is probably due to the release of preformed glucagon from the alpha cell; it appears earlier and is much less extreme than that observed in mammals. The subsequent hypoglycemia may be due to the loss of alpha cell secretion concomitant with continued secretion of insulin from the pancreatic beta cells. In lizards, synthalin A evokes a severe hypoglycemia associated with alpha cell degranulation; removal of the entire pancreas also induces a severe hypoglycemia, unlike that occurring in mammals. Such observations may indicate that lizards are very dependent upon the alpha cell for maintenance of normoglycemias (Miller and Wurster, 1958). Mikami and Ono (1962) have tested the functional significance of the avian

Table 56. Effects of various hormones on carbohydrate levels of avian tissues*

Dose of hormone; fed or fasted	Age of bird	Hours since last injection	Blood glucose (mg./100 ml.)	Tissue glycogen (mg./100 gm. wet wt.)		
				Liver	Muscle	Heart
			Insulin			
Control; fast 24 hr.	6 weeks	0	182	364	773	—
1 u./kg.; "	"	2	87	154	763	—
5 u./kg.; "	"	2	49	192	844	—
60 u./kg.; fed	"	24	226	4950	—	—
120 u./kg.; fast 24 hr.	"	24	182	434	—	—
			Epinephrine			
Control; fast 24 hr.	5 weeks	0	162	449	910	—
0.2 mg./kg.; "	"	1	188	—	869	—
0.5 mg./kg.; "	"	1	224	363	687	—
			Glucagon			
Control; fed	10 weeks	0	202	1836	—	108
0.15 mg./kg.; fed	"	1	251	2481	—	214
Control; fed	6 weeks	5	222	674	—	—
0.15 mg./kg.; fed	"	5	340	2182	—	—
			Growth hormone			
Control; fed	8–10 weeks	0	212	1850	—	103
0.5 mg./kg.; fed	"	1	185	1380	—	104
1.0 mg./kg.; fed	"	1	191	1763	—	208

* Compiled from Golden and Long (1942a); Opdyke (1942); Hazelwood and Lorenz (1957, 1959).

alpha cells by extirpating alpha cell lobes in White Leghorn chickens and following the acute effects on the blood sugar pattern. "Selective removal" of the alpha islets leads to a severe hypoglycemia, convulsions, and death 12 to 36 hours after the operation. Convulsions commence when the blood glucose declines to levels below 50 mg. percent; the hypoglycemia induced by excision of alpha cells can be repaired by the administration of glucagon, only to reappear after expiration of the effective period of this hormone. It appears possible, therefore, that alpha cell secretion plays a homeostatic role in avian carbohydrate metabolism, a point which has not been clearly established in mammals. Furthermore, the presence of glucagon in the fowl pancreas in amounts 10 times greater than those found in the mammalian pancreas may partially explain the higher avian glycemic levels. Whether avian glucagon stimulates release of adrenal catecholamines coincident with its rapid hepatic glycogenolytic effect as has been shown in mammals (Sarcione, Back, Sokal, Mehlman, and Knoblock, 1963) is not known at this time.

The avian pancreatic beta cells are regarded as the primary and probably sole source of insulin production. However, insulin can be extracted from liver and kidney of normal intact fowl, in addition to the pancreas, although not from the depancreatized fowl. The insulin concentration of the pancreas in late embryos, as well as in that of the adult chicken, approximates that found in mammals on a tissue weight basis. The alpha/beta cell ratio in mammals (rats and bats) decreases with maturity, owing primarily to increased multiplication of beta cells. Although estimates of the rate of insulinogenesis and release, as well as estimates of normal circulating levels of insulin, are not available, the avian pancreas does respond to dietary and hormonal manipulations, which have been shown to alter insulin content in mammals. Thus starvation, high-fat diets, and the administration of exogenous insulin (carried out for a long enough time) all decrease insulin content of the avian pancreas. One of the classic ways in which to assess the pancreatic content of insulin is to perform a glucose tolerance test in which a glucose load (1.75 gm/kg. body weight) is given to an animal, and serial blood glucose determinations are made for several hours thereafter. The shape and duration of the hyperglycemic response, as well as the time taken for the reattainment of normal blood glucose levels, are indicative of glucose oxidation via insulin release. Such studies in birds describe tolerance curves similar to if not identical with those observed in mammals, the younger fowl having less tolerance than the older bird. Subjecting chickens to a fast prior to administering a glucose load results in a tolerance curve that is remarkably similar to the one observed in diabetic mammals, and which is presumably due, to a reduction in circulating insulin levels. No information is available regarding the biochemistry and/or physiological properties of avian insulin at this time.

Administration of alloxan, a substance related to uracil (pyrimidine base) selectively destroys mammalian pancreatic beta cells within minutes after injection. Scott, Harris, and Chen (1945) studied the effect of intravenous administration of alloxan to barn owl, horned owls, pigeons, ducks, and chickens; except in pigeons, they found no changes in the blood glucose levels of these species. The pigeons died one or two days after alloxan injection. In all species examination showed all tissues to be negative except for a few necrotic beta cells and uric acid deposition on some serosal surfaces. These observations contrast sharply with the profound beta cell destruction and associated diabetic state that alloxan produces in mammals, as well as contrasting with the fairly typical diabetic picture observed in depancreatized carnivorous owls (Nelson, Elgart, and Mirsky, 1942). Since Minkowski's classic observation in the dog that surgical ablation of at least 85 percent of the total pancreatic tissue leads to a diabetic syndrome, many investigators (see Chapter 20) in addition to Minkowski have reported the effects of similar procedures in birds. It is well established that surgical removal of the pancreas in pigeons, doves, chickens pheasants, some owls and ducks does not lead to permanent hyperglycemia, glycosuria, or even low hepatic glycogen levels. Such depancreatized birds have no impairment of glucose utilization; also, they respond in a normal fashion to administered hypoglycemic agents such as insulin. Depancreatized fowl readily develop fasting ketosis, as do both the normal fowl and mammal. Extirpation of the pancreas in carnivorous birds (falcon, buzzard, kestrel, and raven) apparently results in a transitory hyperglycemia and glycosuria, which may disappear within a week after the operation or remain as a "low-grade" diabetic state. Feeding meat diets to depancreatized chickens and ducks does not induce a diabetic syndrome. Normal owls exhibit glucose tolerance curves similar to those found in mildly diabetic mammals; fasting induces the accumulation of blood acetone bodies. Pancreatectomy in this species results in severe hyperglycemia (up to 1200 mg. percent), an anorexia, increased ketogenesis, and ultimately death, whether or not insulin replacement is employed (Nelson *et al.,* 1942). The only herbivorous bird that demonstrates a syndrome similar to diabetes mellitus after pancreatectomy appears to be the goose. Extirpation of the pancreas in this species leads to a hyperglycemia, glycosuria, and concomitant impaired glucose utilization (Mirsky and Gitelson, 1958). Thus, geese respond to pancreatectomy in a manner similar to most mammals. Such a response casts doubt upon the validity of the hypothesis that a carnivorous diet is a predisposing factor essential for inducing diabetes in fowl. It appears, therefore, that normal glucose metabolism can and does occur in the absence of pancreatic tissue in most birds. Destruction of beta cells by alloxan is without effect on avian carbohydrate metabolism, and extirpation of the pancreas leads to a syndrome indistinguishable from diabetes mellitus only in geese and some carnivorous birds. In contrast to its lack of an effect on carbohydrate metabolism, pancreatectomy in the bird definitely influences lipid metabolism adversely, resulting in ketonemia, lipemia, and spontaneous atherosclerosis (Stamler, Bolene, Katz, Harris, and Pick, 1950).

Response to insulin. Since the discovery of insulin and its subsequent use in birds, whose normoglycemia approximates the hyperglycemia of diabetic mammals, divergent reports as to the "normal" response of birds to exogenous insulin have been abundant. Interpretation of these early studies is clouded by the use of birds in various nutritional and reproductive stages, as well as by the use of different insulin preparations probably containing varying amounts of glucagon as a contaminant. (See Riddle and Opdyke, 1957; Golden and Long, 1942a; and Snedecor *et al.,* 1956). In mammals, insulin produces hypoglycemia, promotes glycogenesis, is antiketogenic, inhibits gluconeogenesis, and depresses blood phosphorus and potassium. The early observations that insulin administered to birds led to a prolonged hyperglycemia are readily explained by the pre-existing glucagon contaminant of these insulin preparations (Snedecor *et al.,* 1956) and/or increased activity of the adrenal gland in releasing epinephrine and glucocorticoids to promote a "rebound" effect (Hazelwood and Lorenz, 1959). In either case, a hyperglycemic effect is observed, especially if large doses of insulin are administered. Employing more "physiological" doses of insulin, Golden and Long (1942a) demonstrated that from 1 to 2 units per kilogram of insulin produce marked hypoglycemia, and that larger doses of insulin, if administered on successive days, produced convulsions and death. Opdyke (1942) found similar results, and observed no convulsions if less than 5 units per kilogram were injected into chickens (Table 56). The blood sugar response of turkey poults to exogenous insulin is the same as that witnessed for chickens if less than 500 units per kilogram are administered (Snedecor *et al.,* 1956). Above this dose, hyperglycemia results. Chen, Anderson, and Maze (1945) compared the blood glucose and convulsive response to graded doses of insulin in several avian species, and found the canary, pigeon, and duck up to 500 times more resistant to insulin than the dog, rat, or rabbit. Roosters demonstrate no convulsions even at 5,000 units of insulin per kilogram of body weight (Table 57). Depancreatized owls (Nelson *et al.,* 1942) and depancreatized chickens (Hazelwood, 1958) respond to insulin injections in a manner similar to that observed in the intact bird. Thus, although birds may respond readily and decisively to doses of insulin normally employed in mammalian studies, they are extremely resistant to pharmacological insulin doses such as are lethal in other animals. Whereas 1.0 u./kg. of insulin lowers blood glucose of chickens 26 percent in $1\frac{1}{2}$ to 2 hours, a dose 50 times greater lowers the glucose level only 16 percent more. Blood nonprotein nitrogen is depressed to the same extent (30 percent) by both dose levels of insulin (Hazelwood and Lorenz, 1959). Part of this resistance undoubtedly, is due to a well-developed insulin-destroying system in the avian liver, since hepatectomized chickens are hypersensitive to low doses of insulin (Hazelwood, 1958). Other contributing factors to this insulin insensitivity may be that the metabolism of the avian nervous system differs from that in mammals; that the avian peripheral tissues have different energy requirements such that these peripheral tissues do not "recognize" insulins prepared from non-avian sources; or that the adrenocortices compensate readily and efficiently by releasing their blood glucose-increasing glucocorticoids.

Other evidence indicates that the adrenal medulla may also be involved in protecting the bird from the severe hypoglycemic effects of insulin. Hyperglycemic rebound following repeated insulin injections occurs in depancreatized pigeons but is prevented by adrenal medullary blocking drugs (Hazelwood and Lorenz, 1959). Repeated administration of insulin (1 to 2 u./kg.) to fasted chicks encourages greater depletion of the already low hepatic glycogen stores; in addition, some workers report skeletal muscle glycogen decreases in response to insulin. These observations are in contrast to those observed in mammals and can be duplicated in the fowl by the injection of epinephrine. Thus, insulin-induced hypoglycemia in the bird may encourage adrenal medullary release of glycogenolytic catecholamines, which in turn favor release of glucose to the blood stream. With the exception of this glycogenolytic response of hepatic and peripheral muscle tissue to insulin, the bird appears to respond to insulin in the same direction but to a lesser degree than does the mammal. Gluconeogenesis is depressed in birds injected with insulin; blood inorganic phosphorus depression occurs also, and follows blood glucose trends.

Antidiabetogenic substances other than insulin. Unlike insulin, certain sulfonylureas, when administered by mouth, are effective in ameliorating the diabetic syndrome in man. The evidence at hand indicates that functional beta cells are a prerequisite for the hypoglycemic effect of these sulfonylureas. This appears to be true at least for man, dog, cat, rabbit, and toad, and implicates these agents in the release of previously formed insulin. The chicken, duck, and turkey respond readily to the administration of tolbutamide, one of the aryl sulfonylureas. Irrespective of the route of administration, the bird is equally sensitive to tolbutamide and will respond to doses as low as 10 mg./kg. body weight with a hypoglycemia more rapid than that observed with exogenous insulin (Hazelwood and Lorenz, 1957). Mirsky and Gitelson (1957) have

Avian Physiology

Table 57. Comparative lethal doses of insulin*

Species	No. of observations	Body weight kg.	Lethal or convulsive dose units/kg. body weight
Chicken	60	3.0	5,000
Canary	24	0.016	2,396
Pigeon	67	0.299	705
Duck	26	2.189	157
Dog	35	7.03	23
Rat	60	0.091	21
Rabbit	49	1.89	5

* Taken from Chen *et al.*, 1945.

demonstrated that whereas alloxanized dogs, rabbits, and rats show no hypoglycemic response to tolbutamide, alloxanized chickens, depancreatectomized ducks, and completely enterectomized (by removal of intestinal tract) ducks develop a pronounced hypoglycemia after tolbutamide injections. These workers conclude that the blood glucose–depressing effect of tolbutamide is not dependent upon the presence of beta cells in the bird. An exception is the goose (but not the duck), which Mirsky and Gitelson (1958) found to react as do mammals to tolbutamide so long as pancreatic tissue was present. Not only does the depancreatized goose exhibit a marked inhibition of glucose utilization, but it also exhibits an impaired response to tolbutamide. Hazelwood (1958) found that there was no difference in response to tolbutamide by the hepatectomized fowl, or the fowl which had been both hepatectomized and depancreatized. It appears unlikely, therefore, in birds other than geese, unless there is an extrapancreatic and extrahepatic source of avian insulin, that the hypoglycemic action of tolbutamide is mediated via insulinogenesis and/or release. Possibly the action of tolbutamide is mediated through the peripheral tissues in these birds.

Adrenal medullary hormones. The injection of epinephrine into the domestic fowl produces in a rapid but transistory hyperglycemia. This is due to this hormone's effect in activating previously inactive tissue of phosphorylase. Thus, glycogenolysis of hepatic and of muscle glycogen stores occurs as a result of the administration of epinephrine, the latter leading to a simultaneous lactic acidemia since muscle does not contain glucose-6-phosphatase. Such hyperglycemic observations have been made in the normal fed, fasted, and depancreatized fowl. Golden and Long (1942a) present evidence that the chick is no more sensitive to epinephrine than are mammals (Table 56). Since epinephrine elevates blood pressure in chicks, and also forces plasma fluid into the extravascular compartments, the blood glucose–increasing effect of this medullary hormone must indeed be a direct effect on tissue carbohydrate metabolism. (It should be recalled that most avian blood glucose resides in the plasma.) In contrast to mammals, in birds neither epinephrine nor norepinephrine increases the release of free fatty acids from adipose depots (Carlson, Liljedahl, Verdy, and Wirsen, 1964). Such a lipid-mobilizing effect of the catecholamines has been observed in most mammals and is considered a compensatory safeguard to maintain energy-forming substrates during deprivation of food.

The fundamental significance of the adrenal medulla in maintaining normal carbohydrate patterns in birds is difficult to assess, not only because adrenalectomy is so difficult in birds but also because such an operation deprives the organism of both medullary and cortical secretions. However, Golden and Long's review states that bilateral adrenalectomy decreases blood glucose in birds more than does unilateral removal of adrenals, and that an adrenal cortical extract (ACE) replacement regimen repairs blood glucose levels to normal in the completely adrenalectomized bird. Factors that increase avian secretion of catecholamines include high environmental temperatures, insulin-induced hypoglycemia, anoxia, restraint, and fright. The pigeon adrenal medulla releases both epinephrine and norepinephrine in response to high ambient temperatures. This observation may be a result of hyperthermic augmentation of hypothalamic centers (Chaudhuri and Sadhu, 1962). One to three hours after subcutaneous injection of insulin (thus, during the blood glucose nadir) there can be observed a decrease in the size and number of the medullary cellular elements associated with avian secretion of catecholamines (Fujita, Kano, Kun-ishima, and Kido, 1959). Such observations are in accord with those of Hazelwood and Lorenz, in which repeated daily insulin injections resulted in a gradual hyperglycemic rebound effect.

Adrenal cortex. In mammals, the adrenocortical hormones concerned with carbohydrate metabolism are mainly the 11-oxygenated corticosteroids possessing oxygen (in either keto or hydroxyl form) at carbon 11 of the parent steroid ring. An hydroxyl group (–OH) at carbon 17 intensifies the carbohydrate effect of these adrenal cortex hormones. The major secretions of the mammalian adrenal cortex associated with carbohydrate metabolism (glucocorticoids) include cortisone (sometimes called compound E), hydrocortisone (compound F, cortisol), corticosterone (compound B) and 11-dehydrocorticosterone (compound A). Corticosterone is the major secretory product of the avian adrenal cortex. Although the electrolyte-controlling hormone, aldosterone, is also found, the only other glucocorticoid identified was that of 11-dehydrocorticosterone, along with traces of hydrocortisone (see Chapter 21).

Early observations on the effects of adrenal cortex extracts (ACE) on the carbohydrate metabolism of hypophysectomized, thyroidectomized, and partially adrenalectomized pigeons and doves indicate a delayed (by 7 hours) hyperglycemia of about 15 percent above pre-injection levels. Studies with similar adrenal cortical extracts in fed and fasted chickens demonstrated a hyperglycemia (32 percent) in both cases, as well as increasing glycogenesis in the liver of fasted chicks by about 144 percent. Muscle glycogen depots are unaffected by ACE regardless of the nutritional state of the chick. However, the precise composition of such cortical extracts, in light of present knowledge of anywhere from 30 to 40 naturally occurring adrenal steroids, remains obscure. Greenman and Zarrow (1961) have shown that corticosterone and cortisol (hydrocortisone) are the most active hyperglycemic agents when injected into adult White Leghorn chickens. Cortisone is virtually inactive as a glucocorticoid in birds, an observation which contrasts markedly with findings in mammals. Hepatic glycogenesis in one-day-old White Rock chicks is augmented most greatly by hydrocortisone, whereas corticosterone has a glycogenic potential one-eighth of the former steroid. Some of Greenman and Zarrow's data are used in Table 58.

Hydrocortisone and slow-absorbing ACTH both induce carbohydrate, lipid, and protein metabolism alterations in young (8-week-old) cockerels. This is true for the intact, alloxanized, and depancreatized bird. Actually, depancreatized cholesterol-fed cockerels injected daily with 1 to 2 mg. of hydrocortisone develop a steroid diabetic syndrome, and compared to normal birds on the same diet exhibit a hyperglycemia (410 vs. 239 mg. percent), lipemia (hypercholesterolemia: 1502 vs. 692 mg. percent), and retarded growth (942 vs. 1824 gm. body weight). Glycosuria persists in some birds (Stamler, Pick, and Katz, 1954). Again, cortisone was without glucocorticoid effect in birds, although it did produce certain cardiovascular and atherogenic effects.

The sources of carbohydrate made available to the bird by exogenous adrenal steroids appear to come from noncarbohydrate precursors. Thus, although there is some evidence that adrenal

Table 58. Blood glucose and liver glycogen responses to various adrenal steroids in the domestic fowl

Group	Daily dose, mg.	Blood glucose* mg./100 ml.		Liver glycogen,† mg./100 gm. liver		
		Initial	Maxi-mum**	Group	Total dose	Ten hours post-injection
Control	—	170	175	Control	—	248
Hydrocortisone	1.0	174	202	Hydrocortisone	25 μg.	356
"	2.5	171	335	"	50 μg.	662
"	5.0	181	546	"	100 μg.	738
Corticosterone	5.0	159	448	Cortisone	4 mg.	280
Cortisone	10.0	190	203	"	8 mg.	325
"	20.0	174	199	"	16 mg.	326
"	40–50	166	221	Corticosterone	200 μg.	348
Desoxycorticosterone	5	150	227	"	400 μg.	466
Stilbesterol	1–2	181	193	"	800 μg.	741

* Adult hens.
** Usually 1–3 days after start of daily injections.
† Chicks, 300–600 gm., fasted 24 hours.

steroids decrease hepatic glycogenolysis (and thus increase glycogen storage) in mammals, there is good reason to believe that in birds both the hyperglycemic and the glycogenic effects of corticosterone and hydrocortisone are due to conversion of protein substrate to carbohydrate (gluconeogenesis) as well as due to augmented hexose phosphatase activity. This was evident with the ACE studies in fasted chicks (Golden and Long, 1942a), as well as in fed birds (Brown, Brown, and Meyer, 1958; Baum and Meyer, 1960; Stamler, 1952).

Pituitary hormones. Failure to induce alterations in blood glucose or tissue glycogen levels of fasted or fed chicks by the injection of crude saline extracts of ox pituitary glands (Golden and Long, 1942a) and rat pituitary glands (Hazelwood, Hazelwood, and McNary, 1962) has been reported. Similar results have been obtained in chicks by employing saline extracts of avian adenohypophyses (Hazelwood *et al.*, 1962). From the standpoint of carbohydrate metabolism, the hormonal substances contained in these crude saline extracts are growth hormone (GH), adrenocorticotrophic hormone (ACTH), and prolactin (LTH). Assay of avian hypophysial extracts in hypophysectomized rats demonstrates little GH content. Injection of purified GH (porcine) preparations into pullets or hens results in little growth augmentation and in marked decrease in egg production, but in no alteration of carbohydrate metabolism (Carter, Risner, and Yacowitz, 1955). Injection of purified bovine GH preparations (1–5 mg.) into 3-to-4-week-old fed chicks does not alter glycemic levels or hepatic glycogen levels (Hazelwood *et al.*, 1962), but when injected at lower dose levels it does increase cardiac glycogen levels (up to 100 percent) of nonfasted adult chickens (Hazelwood and Lorenz, 1959; Table 56).

Mammalian ACTH can and does encourage glucocorticoid release, and in fairly large doses (8 units) will elicit a hyperglycemia (259 vs. 344 mg. percent) 2 to 4 hours after injection into fasted chicks (Hazelwood *et al.*, 1962; Siegel, 1962). No evidence exists to demonstrate that such an ACTH action is mediated by extra-adrenal mechanisms. Apparently, porcine ACTH has no fat-mobilizing potential in chicks as it does in the rat, or as does glucagon in both rats and chicks.

Early reports indicate that a mild hypoglycemia occurs after removal of the avian pituitary gland (see Sturkie, 1954, and Chapter 2). Subsequent fasting is without influence on tissue carbohydrate levels. This is in contrast to the near-fatal effects of short-term fasting in most hypophysectomized mammals. In contrast to that in mammals, hypophysectomy in pigeons triples liver glycogen levels. Early work by Riddle and co-workers indicated that removal of the pituitary led to an insulin hypersensitivity in pigeons similar to that seen in mammals. In chickens, however, such hypersensitivity is observed only if doses exceeding 5 u./kg. body weight are injected into hypophysectomized recipients (Koike *et al.*, 1964). There is no evidence that gonadotrophin or thyrotrophin has any effect on avian carbohydrate metabolism in the hypophysectomized pigeon (Miller, 1942), although the latter hormone may greatly increase glycolysis via the pentose shunt in mammals. Prolactin, however, may be a significant regulator of avian carbohydrate. In dogs, intact and partially depancreatized, prolactin injections are diabetogenic to a lesser degree than GH but to a greater degree than ACTH. This effect can be seen in both the hypophysectomized and the adrenalectomized mammal, and does not involve release of glucagon from the pancreatic alpha cells. Since prolactin plays so dominant a hormonal role in birds (leading to broodiness, crop-secretory activity, etc.), it appears likely that this hormone may be involved in regulating avian carbohydrate metabolism. The precise mechanism by which prolactin acts as an anti-insulin agent, reduces insulin sensitivity associated with hypophysectomy, and induces hyperglycemia in mammals, is not known with certainty. However, recent work with purified preparations indicates that prolactin furthers pyruvate metabolism by forcing it into oxidative or synthetic pathways. In this way lactate formation is reduced (see review by Riddle, 1963).

The role that posterior pituitary hormones may play in avian carbohydrate metabolism has never been clearly elucidated. Early studies by Visscher, Marvin, and Riddle (1947) indicated that administration of alkaline extracts of bovine posterior pituitary glands in pigeons and doves produced a mild hyperglycemia (less than 15 percent) 10, 17 and 24 hours after a single injection. Concurrent observations included muscle glycogenolysis (23 percent) in fasted intact birds, with hepatic glycogenesis (3 times greater) or inhibited hepatic glycogenolysis. These workers did not consider their observations of physiological importance, and subsequent studies with highly purified preparations in birds appear to be lacking.

Thyroid. In mammals hyperthyroidism is associated with mobilization of liver glycogen, leading to a low-grade hyperglycemia. In addition, the hormone facilitates transfer of carbohydrate across the intestinal wall and increases glucose uptake in the peripheral tissues of most animals. Early reports that thyroidectomy in fowl reduced blood sugar have been amply confirmed, and Riddle and Opdyke (1947) have found that in pigeons thyroxine depletes liver glycogen and produces a mild hyperglycemia. In fasted pigeons thyroxine has a hepatic glycogenolytic effect simultaneously with a glycogenic effect in cardiac and skeletal muscle. Placing 8-day-old chicks on low-iodine diets concurrent with the administration of an antithyroid substance (thiouracil) increases liver glycogen 50 times over control levels; liver lipid is markedly increased also (Snedecor and King, 1960).

Gonads. Sturkie (see Chapter 2) found that the level of whole blood sugar in fed female chickens was about 14 percent higher than in males, and slightly but significantly greater than in fed capons. Fasting for 17 to 24 hours reduces the glucose levels in all three groups, with females responding most (20 percent). It is known that most of blood glucose is located in the plasma (Chapter 2); and both Bell (1957) and Tapper and Kare (1956) have found that the depression in blood glucose brought about by injecting females with androgens is effected by changes in erythrocytic volume. Thus it is quite likely that androgens, endogenous and exogenous, alter circulating blood glucose levels by their action in increasing red blood cells rather than by a primary action upon carbohydrate metabolism.

AVIAN GLYCOGEN BODY

Embryogenesis and Carbohydrate Metabolism

Brief mention should be made of an opaque, gelatinous-appearing structure, peculiar to Aves, which lies within the vertebral column dorsal to the spinal cord. This tissue was first described, early in the 19th century, as the "corpora sciatica" because of its location at the level of emergence of the sciatic plexus from the lumbosacral portion of the spinal cord. However, from studies that have been reported concerning its development, histochemical appearance, biochemical content, and possible function, the one consistent feature of this structure is its glycogen concentration. The glycogen in the "glycogen body" represents up to 28 percent of that found in the nonfasted liver; such a depot approximates 5 to 10 percent of the total body glycogen in the chick (Doyle and Watterson, 1949). The total glycogen of this structure ranges from 60 to 80 percent of its lipid-free dry weight and is found occupying the entire cell interior as closely packed granules of low density; the nucleus resides in the periphery, and the organelles are confined to the juxtanuclear cytoplasm (Revel, Napolitano, and Fawcett, 1960). Watterson and his associates have detailed the normal morphogenesis, vasculogenesis, and anatomical relationships of the avian glycogen body (Watterson, 1952).

Studies on the glycogen body of the chick embryo have been few, but those that have been carried out under well-controlled conditions indicate that avian glycogen body morphogenesis is not dependent upon influences from the higher central nervous system (DeGennaro, 1959), although the accumulation of glycogen is very much dependent upon some higher center, presumably the hypophysis. Thus, embryos that are decapitate-hypophysectomized prior to day 2 of incubation have glycogen bodies that accumulate only one-fourth the usual amount of glycogen by hatching time (Watterson, Veneziano, and Brown, 1958). The earliest indication of formation of the glycogen body occurs around day 7 or 8 of incubation (DeGennaro, 1959), when glycogen-storing cells appear in the medial and lateral roof plates of the nerve cord at the lumbosacral level. DeGennaro (1961) has demonstrated that the stored carbohydrate in this avian structure is indeed glucose, and not another carbohydrate form as has been suggested by some workers. Jenkens (1955) studied in detail the relation between glycogen body glycogenesis and hepatic glycogen fluctuations during days 7 to 15 of incubation. His results suggest that embryonic hepatic glycogen decreases rapidly and markedly on day 12 only, and returns to the level of day 11 on day 13 of incubation. Furthermore, removal of the glycogen body prior to day 11 slightly diminishes excursions of liver glycogen between incubation days 11 and 15, though the disappearance of glycogen on day 12 is still very much in evidence. Removal of nerve cord tissue in juxtaposition to, but not containing, the glycogen body is without effect on either the accumulation or the depletion of the hepatic polysaccharide. Since the rate of glycogen synthesis in the body appears to increase sharply between days 11 and 15, the possibility exists that hepatic tissue delivers the substrate for such glycogenesis in the glycogen body during this time.

Post-hatch Content, Activity, and Function

Immediately after hatching the weight of the glycogen body, as well as the total glycogen content, increases gradually until the third week, at which time glycogen concentrations reach a peak level of approximately 32 percent. Subsequently the glycogen levels decline to hatching levels, reaching 25 percent at the fourth week, and continue to decline until the eleventh week, when the adult levels of 21 to 22 percent are reached (Snedecor *et al.,* 1963). The constancy of the polysaccharide moiety of this avian structure is impressive, and has received considerable attention from various investigators. Thus, the level of glycogen in post-hatch chick glycogen bodies is unaltered by fasting, death, or dietary manipulation (Szepsenwol and Michalski, 1951), by propylthiouracil-induced hypothyroidism (Snedecor and King, 1960), or by the wide variety of hormones that normally control or modify carbohydrate metabolism in both Mammalia and Aves (Snedecor *et al.,* 1963; Hazelwood *et al.,* 1962). That some hormonal control over glycogenesis in this tissue exists seems likely from Watterson's observation that decapitate-hypophysectomy during incubation leads to diminished glycogen levels in the glycogen body at hatching (Watterson *et al.,* 1958). Hazelwood *et al.* (1962) were unsuccessful in altering the glycogen levels in 4-week-old chick glycogen bodies with purified beef growth hormone, but were successful in increasing these levels by employing saline extracts of avian anterior pituitary glands. Such extracts have no influence on carbohydrate levels in other tissues, and because of their low content of growth hormone (Hazelwood and Hazelwood, 1961) probably do not implicate somatotrophin as the causative hormonal agent. That pharmacological doses of bovine ACTH have a modest glycogenic effect in the glycogen body possibly indicates that avian ACTH in the crude hypophysial extracts mentioned above normally plays a role in controlling glycogenesis in the glycogen body. Furthermore, the resistance displayed by the glycogen body to hormones from mammalian sources may be due to species (and thus probably molecular) differences in hormone preparations relative to the avian recipient.

The glycogen body is resistant to the glycogenolytic effect of exogenous epinephrine and glucagon (Snedecor *et al.,* 1963; Hazelwood *et al.,* 1962). Hydrolysis of this polysaccharide has not been observed *in vivo* regardless of the dosage or route of administration of these two glycogenolytic hormones; yet interestingly, both phosphorylase and alkaline phosphatase have been described as being present in adequate amounts within the glycogen body (Snedecor, Ghareeb, and King, 1961; Hazelwood *et al.,* 1962). Questioning whether the polysaccharide moiety of this structure was labile or metabolically active, Snedecor, King, and Henrikson (1963) injected radioactive glucose into 7-day embryos and serially sacrificed them at intervals up to 48 hours after injection. Enzymatic digestion of the glycogen-body glycogen demonstrated labeled peripheral maltose tiers as well as labeled inner cores (limit dextrin) of the polysaccharide molecule. The specific activity data indicate that the replacement of glucosyl units was greater in the maltose fraction of glycogen than that in the dextrin fraction, and reached a peak 18 hours after injection only to decrease subsequently. Such observations may indicate that both glycogenesis and glycogenolysis occur in the glycogen body, but at equivalent rates such that the glycogen concentration remains virtually constant. That such reaction rates may not be very rapid is indicated further by DeGennaro's observations that C^{14} glucose injected on day 10 of incubation is incorporated into glycogen-body glycogen and that little disappearance of the label occurs up to 7 days after hatching (1962). Thus, the glycogen body appears to be relatively inactive from a metabolic point of view. Furthermore, fasted chicks that are subsequently tube-fed and injected concurrently with various labeled hexoses fail to incorporate the radioactive label in the glycogen molecules of the glycogen body. Hazelwood, Hazelwood, and Olsson (1963) found in comparing glycogenesis in liver tissue with that in the glycogen body that the former tissue readily incorporated C^{14} labels from glucose, fructose, and galactose into glycogen, preferentially employing glucose over the other two sugars. In contrast there was no evidence of uptake or turnover of any of the labeled hexose substrates in the glycogen body, a further sign of its inactivity.

The data presented thus far fail to elucidate the physiological function and/or importance of the avian glycogen body. The proximity of the glycogen body to the avian central nervous system tempts one to consider the role the former may play in the latter's carbohydrate metabolism. Possibly the decrease in hepatic glycogen, concomitant with glycogen deposition in the glycogen body, on incubation days 12 and 13 reflects a protective mechanism by which the central nervous system is assured of adequate nutrition. Such a protective influence would be presumed to carry over into adulthood, since the bird is remarkably resistant to insulin-induced convulsions and/or comas. Definitive answers to such questions are not yet available but are certainly called for.

REFERENCES

Adams, A. E.   1958   Effects of thyroxine on chick embryos. Anat. Rec. 131:445.

Anderson, D. L., F. W. Hill, and R. Renner   1958   Studies of the metabolizable and productive energy of glucose for the growing chick. J. Nutrition 65:561.

Aramaki, T., and H. S. Weiss   1962   Patterns of carbohydrate and protein digestion in the chicken as derived from sampling the hepatic portal system. Arch. Int. Physiol. Bioch. 70:1.

Barron, P., and J. McKenzie   1962   The inhibitory action of insulin in the early chick embryo. J. Embryol. Exp. Morph. 10:88.

Baum, G. J., and R. K. Meyer   1960   Effect of adrenal steroids and diethylstilbestrol on growth and fat content of cockerels. Am. J. Physiol. 198:1263.

Beekman, B. E. 1956 The effect of synthalin A on blood sugar and pancreatic alpha islet cells of the fowl. Endocrinology 59:708.

Beekman, B. E. 1958 A bioassay for glucagon based on the hyperglycemic response of the fowl. Poultry Sci. 37:595.

Bell, D. J. 1957 The distribution of glucose between the plasma water and the erythrocyte water in hen's blood. Quart. J. Exp. Physiol. 42:410.

Bogner, A. P. H. 1957 The absorption of various reducing sugars from the gastrointestinal tract of embryos and young chickens. Dissert. Abst. 17:2654.

Bogner, A. P. H., R. L. Bogner, and P. L. McLain 1964 Active transport of galactose-1-C^{14} by young chick. Fed. Proc. 23:211.

Bogner, A. P. H., and I. A. Haines 1960 A study of active transport and utilization of sugars by chick intestine before and after hatch. Anat. Rec. 137:342.

Bogner, A. P. H., and I. A. Haines 1961 Development of intestinal selective absorption of glucose in newly-hatched chicks. Proc. Soc. Exp. Biol. & Med. 107:265.

Boucek, R. J., and B. B. Bourne 1962 The catecholamines of the allantoic fluid in the developing chick embryo. Fed. Proc. 21:345.

Brown, K. I., D. J. Brown, and R. K. Meyer 1958 Effect of surgical trauma, ACTH and adrenal cortical hormones on electrolytes, water balance and gluconeogenesis in male chickens. Am. J. Physiol. 192:43.

Burnet, F. M., and N. L. Warner 1960 Assay of corticosteroids in the chick embryo. Nature 187:938.

Burt, A. M., and B. S. Wenger 1962 A quantitative study of glucose-6-phosphate dehydrogenase activity in the spinal cord of the developing chick. Anat. Rec. 142:220.

Carlson, L. A., S. Liljedahl, M. Verdy, and C. Wirsen 1964 Unresponsiveness to the lipid mobilizing action of catecholamines *in vivo* and *in vitro* in the domestic fowl. Metabolism 13:227.

Carter, R. D., R. N. Risner, and H. Yacowitz 1955 Some effects of growth hormone preparations in pullets and mature hens. Poultry Sci. 34:1407.

Cazorla, A., and E. S. G. Barron 1958 The formation of glutathione and the development of some enzymes for carbohydrate metabolism during the development of chicken embryo. Exp. Cell Res. 14:68.

Chaudhuri, S., and D. P. Sadhu 1962 Histochemical demonstration of adrenaline and noradrenaline in the adrenal medulla of pigeons and baby rabbits exposed to higher ambient temperature. J. Histochem. & Cytochem. 10:2.

Chen, K. K., R. C. Anderson, and N. Maze 1945 Susceptibility of birds to insulin as compared with mammals. J. Pharm. & Exp. Therap. 84:74.

Clawson, R. C., and L. V. Domm 1961 The effect of cortisol on growth and liver glycogen in the embryo of the domestic fowl. Anat. Rec. 139:217.

DeFranciscis, P., and W. Landauer 1959 Combined effects of cortisone and insulin on developing chicken embryos. Nature 184:101.

DeGennaro, Louis D. 1959 Differentiation of the glycogen body of the chick embryo under normal and experimental conditions. Growth 23:235.

DeGennaro, Louis D. 1961 The carbohydrate composition of the glycogen body of the chick embryo as revealed by paper chromatography. Biol. Bull. 120:348.

DeGennaro, Louis D. 1962 The incorporation and storage of glucose C-14 by the chick glycogen body. Am. Zool. 2:516.

DiMaggio, A., and H. C. Dessauer 1963 Seasonal changes in glucose tolerance and glycogen disposition in a lizard. Am. J. Physiol. 204:677.

Doyle, W. L., and R. L. Watterson 1949 The accumulation of glycogen in the "glycogen body" of the nerve cord of the developing chick. J. Morphol. 85:391.

Dutton, G. J. 1963 Comparison of glucuronide synthesis in developing mammalian and avian liver. Ann. N.Y. Acad. Sci. 113:259.

Elfvin, L. G., T. Petren, and A. Sollberger 1955 Influence of some endogenous and exogenous factors on diurnal glycogen rhythm in chickens. Acta Anat. 25:286.

Elrick, H., I. R. Konigsberg, and Y. Arai 1958 Effect of glucagon on growth of chick embryo. Proc. Soc. Exp. Biol. & Med. 97:542.

Festenstein, G. N. 1957 Reducing substances in allantoic fluid of the chick embryo. Biochim. Biophys. Acta 26:645.

Fisher, H. I., and L. M. Bartlett 1957 Diurnal cycles in liver weights in birds. Condor 59:364.

Fujita, H., M. Kano, I. Kunishima, and T. Kido 1959 Electron microscope observations on the adrenal medulla of the chick after injection of insulin. Arch. Histol. Japon. 18:411.

Gatling, R. R. 1962 The effect of sympathomimetic agents on the chick embryo. Am. J. Path. 40:113.

George, J. C., and P. T. Iype 1962 Lipase activity in the chick liver during development. Proc. Soc. Exp. Biol. Med. 109:826.

Golden, W. R. C., and C. N. H. Long 1942a The influence of certain hormones on the carbohydrate levels of the chick. Endocrinol. 30:675.

Golden, W. R. C., and C. N. H. Long 1942b Absorption and disposition of glucose in the chick. Am. J. Physiol. 136.244.

Greenman, D. L., and M. X. Zarrow 1961 Steroids and carbohydrate metabolism in the domestic bird. Proc. Soc. Exp. Biol. & Med. 106:459.

Grillo, T. A. I. 1961a The ontogeny of insulin secretion in the chick embryo. J. Endocrinol. 22:285.

Grillo, T. A. I. 1961b A histochemical study of phosphorylase in the tissues of the chick embryo. J. Histochem. & Cytochem. 9:386.

Grillo, T. A. I., and K. Ozone 1962 Uridine diphosphate glucose-glycogen synthetase activity in the chick embryo. Nature 195:902.

Guha, S., and R. Wegmann 1961 Phosphorylase in chick-embryo liver. J. Histochem. & Cytochem. 9:454.

Guidotti, G., and P. P. Foa 1961 Development of an insulin-sensitive glucose transport system in chick embryo hearts. Am. J. Physiol. 201:869.

Guidotti, G., D. Kanameishi, and P. P. Foa 1961 Chick embryo heart as a tool for studying cell permeability and insulin action. Am. J. Physiol. 201:863.

Hazelwood, R. L. 1958 The peripheral action of tolbutamide in domestic fowl. Endocrinol. 63:611.

Hazelwood, R. L., and B. S. Hazelwood 1961 Effects of avian and rat pituitary extracts on tibial growth and blood composition. Proc. Soc. Exp. Biol. & Med. 108:10.

Hazelwood, R. L., B. S. Hazelwood, and W. F. McNary 1962 Possible hypophyseal control over glycogenesis in the avian glycogen body. Endocrinol. 71:334.

Hazelwood, R. L., B. S. Hazelwood, and C. A. Olsson 1963 Comparative glycogenesis in the liver and glycogen body of the chick. Proc. Soc. Exp. Biol. & Med. 113:407.

Hazelwood, R. L., and F. W. Lorenz 1957 Responses of the domestic fowl to hyper- and hypoglycemic agents. Endocrinol. 61:520.

Hazelwood, R. L., and F. W. Lorenz 1959 Effects of fasting and insulin on carbohydrate metabolism of the domestic fowl. Am. J. Physiol. 197:47.

Heald, P. J. 1962 Oxidation of fructose by liver of the domestic fowl. Nature 195:603.

Heald, P. J. 1963 The metabolism of carbohydrate by liver of the domestic fowl. Biochem. J. 86:103.

Heckerman, R. O. 1955 The role of the golgi element in the differentiation of cells within the primary and secondary islets of the embryonic chicken pancreas. Dissert. Abst. 15:667.

Hellman, Bo 1961 Nuclear differences between the argyrophil (= A_1) and non-argyrophil (= A_2) pancreatic A cells in the duck. Acta Endocrinol. 36:603.

Houpt, T. R. 1958 Effects of fasting on blood sugar levels in baby chicks of varying ages. Poultry Sci. 37:1452.

Hsieh, K., T. Wang, and H. T. Blumenthal 1952 The diabetogenic and growth-promoting activities of growth hormone (somatotrophin) in the developing chick embryo. Endocrinol. 51:298.

Jenkens, F. A. 1955 Liver glycogen storage in the chick embryo and its relation to the glycogen body. Wasmann J. Biology 13:9.

Karnofsky, D. A., L. P. Ridgway, and P. A. Patterson 1951 Growth-inhibiting effect of cortisone acetate on the chick embryo. Endocrinol. 48:596.

Kilsheimer, G. S., D. R. Weber, and J. Ashmore 1960 Hepatic glucose production in developing chicken embryo. Proc. Soc. Exp. Biol. & Med. 104:515.

Koike, T., A. Nalbandov, M. Dimick, Y. Matsumura, and S. Lepkovsky 1964 Action of insulin upon blood glucose levels of fasted hypophysectomized, depancreatized, and normal chickens. Endocrinol. 74:944.

Konigsberg, I. R. 1954 The effects of early pituitary removal by "decapitation" on carbohydrate metabolism in the chick embryo. J. Exp. Zool. 125:151.

Kun, E. 1953 Occurrence of hexose-6-phosphate dehydrogenase in chorioallantoic membrane of the chick embryo. Proc. Soc. Exp. Biol. & Med. 83:532.

Landauer, W. 1951 The effect of insulin on development of duck embryos. J. Exp. Zool. 117:559.

Landauer, W. 1954 On the chemical production of developmental abnormalities and of phenocopies in chicken embryos. J. Cell. Comp. Physiol. 43:261.

Landauer, W., and M. B. Rhodes 1952 Further observations on the teratogenic nature of insulin and its modification by supplementary treatment. J. Exp. Zool. 119:221.

Lee, W. H. 1951 The glycogen content of various tissues of the chick embryo. Anat. Rec. 110:465.

Leibson, L. G., Z. P. Zheludkova, and L. I. Chilingaryan 1961 Insulin secretion by the pancreas of the chick embryo. Biull. Eksptl. Biol. i Med. 52:768.

Lepkovsky, S., A. Chari-Bitron, R. M. Lemmon, R. C. Ostwald, and M. K. Dimick 1960 Metabolic and anatomic adaptations in chickens "trained" to eat their daily food in two hours. Poultry Sci. 39:385.

Leslie, I., and J. Paul 1954 The action of insulin on the composition of cells and medium during culture of chick heart explants. J. Endocrinol. 11:110.

Lievre, F. 1957 Contribution à l'histogenise du pancreas endocrine chez l'embryon de poulet. Arch. Anat. Microscop. et Morph. Exp. 46:61.

Lineweaver, H., H. J. Morris, and L. Kline 1948 Enzymes of fresh hen eggs. Arch. Bioch. 16:443.

McCallion, D. J., and W. T. Wong 1956 A study of the localization and distribution of glycogen in early stages of the chick embryo. Canad. J. Zool. 34:63.

McCarty, L. P., and F. E. Shideman 1960 Mechanisms for terminating the action of epinephrine on the embryonic chick heart. Fed. Proc. 19:111.

Mahaffey, W. C. 1961 Glucose-6-phosphate dehydrogenase levels in appendages of the developing chick embryo. Fed. Proc. 20:83.

Mikami, S. I., and K. Ono 1962 Glucagon deficiency induced by extirpation of alpha islets of the fowl pancreas. Endocrinology 71:464.

Miller, M. R., and D. H. Wurster 1958 Further studies on the blood glucose and pancreatic islets of lizards. Endocrinol. 63:191.

Miller, R. A. 1942 Effects of anterior pituitary preparations and insulin on islet cells of the pigeon pancreas. Endocrinol. 31:535.

Mirsky, I. A., and S. Gitelson 1957 Comparison of the hypoglycemic action of tolbutamide in the fowl and other species. Endocrinol. 61:148.

Mirsky, I. A., and S. Gitelson 1958 The diabetic response of geese to pancreatectomy. Endocrinol. 63:345.

Monson, W. J., L. S. Dietrich, and C. A. Elvehjem 1950 Studies on the effect of different carbohydrates on chick growth. Proc. Soc. Exp. Biol. & Med. 75:256.

Moog, F., and D. Richardson 1955 The functional differentiation of the small intestine. IV: The influence of adrenocortical hormones on differentiation and phosphatase synthesis in the duodenum of the chick embryo. J. Expt. Zool. 130:29.

Moog, F., and E. R. Thomas 1957 Functional differentiation of small intestine. VI: Transient accumulation of glycogen in intestinal epithelium of chick embryo under normal conditions and under influence of hydrocortisone. Physiol. Zool. 30:281.

Morgan, J. F., and H. J. Morton 1960 Carbohydrate utilization by chick embryonic heart cultures. Canad. J. Biochem. Physiol. 38:69.

Nelson, N., S. Elgart, and I. A. Mirsky 1942 Pancreatic diabetes in the owl. Endocrinology 31:119.

Newburgh, R. W., G. Buckingham, and H. Herrmann 1962 Levels of reduced TPN generating systems in chick embryos in ovo and in explants. Arch. Biochem. & Biophy. 97:94.

Nordin, J. H., D. R. Wilken, R. K. Bretthauer, R. G. Hansen, and H. M. Scott 1960 A consideration of galactose toxicity in male and female chicks. Poultry Sci. 39:802.

Novikoff, A. B., Van R. Potter, and G. A. LePage 1948 Phosphorylating glycolysis in the early chick embryo. J. Biol. Chem. 173:239.

O'Connor, R. J. 1953 Metabolism and glycogen formation in the liver of the chicken embryo. J. Embryol. Exp. Morph. 1:105.

Opdyke, D. F. 1942 Response of fasted and non-fasted chicks to insulin. Endocrinol. 31:363.

Revel, J. P., L. Napolitano, and D. W. Fawcett 1960 Identification of glycogen in electron micrographs of thin tissue sections. J. Biophys. & Biochem. Cytol. 8:575.

Riddle, O. 1963 Prolactin in vertebrate function and organization. J. Nat. Cancer Inst. 31:1039.

Riddle, O., and L. B. Dotti 1947 Concerning pituitary and other glycemias in pigeons. Carnegie Institute Publ. 569:1.

Riddle, O., and D.F. Opdyke 1947 The action of pituitary and other hormones on the carbohydrate and fat metabolism of young pigeons. Carnegie Institute Publ. 569:49.

Rigdon, R. H., J. R. Couch, C. R. Creger, and T. M. Ferguson 1963 Galactose intoxication pathologic study in the chick. Experientia 19:349.

Rinaudo, M. T. 1961 Glycogenesis in the liver of chicken embryo. Enzymologia 24:230.

Rodbard, S., and M. S. Goldstein 1950 Neurogenic control of the blood sugar elicited by induced variations in the body temperature of the chick. Am. J. Physiol. 162:175.

Romanoff, A. L., and A. J. Romanoff 1949 The Avian Egg. John Wiley & Sons, New York.

Rutter, W. J., P. Krichevsky, H. M. Scott, and R. G. Hansen 1953 The metabolism of lactose and galactose in the chick. Poultry Sci. 32:706.

Sadhu, D. P., and S. Chaudhuri 1961 Tissue respiration and glycogenolysis in birds and young mammals. Comp. Biochem. & Physiol. 4:72.

Sames, G. L., and J. H. Leathem 1951 Influence of desoxycorticosterone acetate and cortisone acetate on body weight of chick embryos. Proc. Soc. Exp. Biol. & Med. 78:231.

Sarcione, E. J., N. Back, J. E. Sokal, B. Mehlman, and E. Knoblock 1963 Elevation of plasma epinephrine levels produced by glucagon *in vivo*. Endocrinol. 72:523.

Sato, K., K. Homma, and J. Gotoh 1960 Studies on the absorption of glucose in chicks. Jap. J. Vet. Sci. 22:155.

Scott, C. C., P. N. Harris, and K. K. Chen 1945 Effects of alloxan in birds. Endocrinol. 37:201.

Siegel, H. S. 1962 Age and sex modification of responses to adrenocorticotrophin in young chickens. 2: Changes in adrenal cholesterol and blood constituent levels. Poultry Sci. 41:321.

Snedecor, J. G., G. E. Ghareeb, and D. B. King 1961 In vitro studies of chick glycogen body. Am. Zool. 1:470.

Snedecor, J. G., and D. B. King 1960 Refractoriness of the chick glycogen body to hypothyroidism. Anat. Rec. 137:393.

Snedecor, J. G., D. B. King, and R. C. Henrikson 1963 Studies on the chick glycogen body: effects of hormones and normal glycogen turnover. Gen. & Comp. Endocrinol. 3:176.

Snedecor, J. G., H. Mathews, and W. B. MacGrath, Jr. 1956 The blood sugar response of turkey poults to insulin. Poultry Sci. 35:355.

Sondergaard, E., I. Prange, H. Dam, and E. Christensen 1957 Uricemia and kidney damage in galactose-poisoned chicks. Acta Path. & Microbiol. Scandin. 40:303.

Spratt, N. T., Jr. 1949 Nutritional requirements of the early chick embryo. I: The utilization of carbohydrate substrates. J. Exp. Zool. 110:273.

Spratt, N. T., Jr. 1950a Nutritional requirements of the early chick embryo. II: Differential nutrient requirements for morphogenesis and differentiation of the heart and brain. J. Exp. Zool. 114:375.

Spratt, N. T., Jr. 1950b Nutritional requirements of the early chick embryo. III: The metabolic basis of morphogenesis and differentiation as revealed by the use of inhibitors. Biol. Bull. 99:120.

Stamler, J. 1952 Effects of adrenal steroid compound F in depancreatized, cholesterol-fed cockerels. Fed. Proc. 11:153.

Stamler, J., C. Bolene, L. N. Katz, R. Harris, and R. Pick 1950 Influence of pancreatectomy on lipid metabolism and atherogenesis in the chick. Fed. Proc. 9:121.

Stamler, J., R. Pick, and L. N. Katz 1954 Effects of cortisone, hydrocortisone and corticotrophin on lipemia, glygemia and atherogenesis in cholesterol-fed chicks. Circulation 10:237.

Stumpf, P. K. 1947 Phosphorylated carbohydrate compounds in developing chick embryo. Fed. Proc. 6:296.

Sturkie, P. D. Avian Physiology (1st ed., 1954) Cornell University Press, Ithaca, N.Y.

Szepsenwol, J. and J. V. Michalski 1951 Glycogenolysis in the liver and glycogen body of the chicken after death. Am. J. Physiol. 165:624.

Tapper, D. N., and M. R. Kare 1956 Distribution of glucose in blood of the chicken. Proc. Soc. Exp. Biol. & Med. 92:120.

Tapper, D. N., and M. R. Kare 1960 Blood glucose distribution in the domestic fowl. Proc. Soc. Exp. Biol. & Med. 103:789.

Thommes, R. C. 1960 A histochemical study of insulin in the chick embryo pancreas. Growth 24:60.

Thommes, R. C., and C. Firling 1964 Blood glucose and liver glycogen levels in glucagon-treated chick embryos. Gen. & Comp. Endocrinol. 4:1.

Thommes, R. C., and A. Tambornino 1962 Effects of insulin administration upon blood-glucose levels of the chick embryo. Physiol. Zool. 35:256.

Toth, N., P. Simon, and Gy. Szekely 1957 Dependence of the early differentiation of the adrenal cortex from the anterior pituitary in the chick embryo. Acta Biol. Acad. Sci. 8:289.

Van Deth, J. H. M. G. 1963 Glucose metabolism of the avian egg. Austral. J. Exp. Biol. 41:129.

Visscher, F., H. Marvin, and O. Riddle 1947 Actions of alkaline extract of posterior pituitary gland and of pituitrin on some aspects of carbohydrate and fat metabolism in pigeons. Carnegie Institute Publ. #569:97.

Vuylsteke, C. A., and C. DeDuve 1953 Le contenu en glucagon du pancreas aviaire. Arch. Internat. Physiol. 61:273.

Wang, T. Y., K. M. Wang, and H. T. Blumenthal 1952 Effect of growth hormone on the development of chick embryo. Fed. Proc. 11:433.

Watterson, R. L. 1952 Development of the glycogen body of the chick spinal cord. III: The paired primordia as revealed by glycogen specific stains. Anat. Rec. 113:29.

Watterson, R. L., P. Veneziano, and D. A. Brown 1958 Development of the glycogen body of the chick spinal cord. V: Effects of hypophysectomy on its glycogen content. Physiol. Zool. 31:49.

Weston, J. C., and G. Morimoto 1961 The effect of cortisone on mitotic activity in embryonic chick liver. Anat. Rec. 139:325.

Witmer, D. G., and H. K. Lane 1960 Blood sugar concentrations in various breeds of chick embryos. Proc. Penn. Acad. Sci. 34:236.

Zwilling, E. 1951a Insulin-induced hypoglycemia and rumplessness in chick embryos. J. Exp. Zool. 117:65.

Zwilling, E. 1951b Carbohydrate metabolism in insulin-treated chick embryos. Arch. Biochem. 33:228.

Zwilling, E. 1952 The effects of some hormones on development. Ann. N.Y. Acad. Sci. 55:196.

CHAPTER 13

Kidneys and Urine

STRUCTURE OF KIDNEY

THE urinary organs of birds consist of the paired symmetrical kidneys and ureters. The ureters transport the urine to the cloaca, where it is voided with the feces. A urinary bladder is absent in most birds.

The kidneys of birds are relatively larger than those of mammals, ranging from 1 to 2.6 percent of the body weight, depending on the species (Benoit, 1950). They comprise three lobes, which are ventrolateral to the vertebral column, occupying the depression formed by the vertebrae and the ilia (see Figure 74, Chapter 16).

There is no sharp line of demarcation between the cortex and medulla of the kidney of birds (or of reptiles) as there is in mammals. Each lobe is divided into lobules, which are bounded by interlobular veins (see Figures 39 and 41). According to Liu (1962), the number of lobules within each lobe varies, and the greatest number is found in the anterior lobe.

Within each lobule are found the nephrons, the functional units of the kidney. The nephrons may be divided into two types: one that is solely confined to the cortical portion of the lobule, and one that contains the loops of Henle which reach into the medullary portion (Sperber, 1960). The nephron includes the glomerulus, which gives way to a thinner straight portion, the descending limb of Henle's loop (which is absent in some birds), and a thicker ascending (distal) limb of the loop, which opens into the collecting tubules, or the periphery of the lobule. These in turn empty into the ureter (Figures 39 and 40).

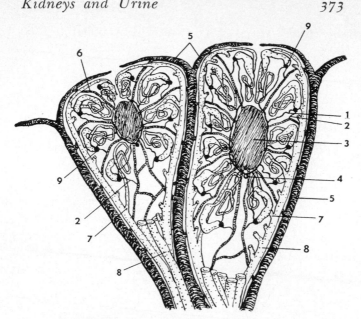

Figure 39. Diagram of the bird kidney showing the arrangement of the glomeruli and tubules in two lobules and blood vessels supplying them.

1, afferent artery of glomerulus; 2, efferent artery of glomerulus; 3, intralobular vein; 4, intralobular artery; 5, interlobular vein; 6, branch of interlobular vein which empties into intralobular vein; 7, end of tubules, emptying into excretory duct; 8, urinary collecting tubules leading to ureters which are not shown; 9, glomerulus. (Modified slightly from Spanner, *Morph. Jahrb.,* 1925.)

There is considerable variation in the detailed structure of the nephron of different species; the general description that follows is based upon the review and work of Sperber (1960). The proximal tubule possesses a distinct brush border. The thin segment of Henle's loop in birds has higher cells than that of mammals. The thick segment of the loop exhibits striations as in that of mammals, but these are not present in the distal tubule.

The collecting tubules are lined with columnar epithelium, and the primary and secondary ureteric tributaries and the main ureteric duct have pseudostratified columnar epithelium (Liu, 1962).

The dimensions of the nephron of the hen kidney, according to

Groebbels (1932), are as follows (see also Marshall, 1934):

	Diameter *(microns)*	*Length* *(mm.)*
Glomerulus	86.00	—
Principal part of proximal tubule and descending limb	62.90	4.5–5.5
Thinner part (descending loop)	18.60	2.1
Thick part (ascending loop)	34.40	2.4
End part	29.00	2.7–3.0

The glomeruli of birds are considerably smaller and more numerous than those of mammals. The number of glomeruli of certain birds, according to Marshall (1934) and others reviewed by him are as follows:

	Body weight (gm.)	*No. of glomeruli in both kidneys (thousands)*	*Author*
Chicken	2,500	840	Marshall
Duck	3,670	1,989	Kunkel
Goose	5,400	1,659	"
Pigeon	232–420	274–535	"

The number of glomeruli range from 30,000 in small passerines to 200,000 in the chicken, according to Benoit (1950). Each glom-

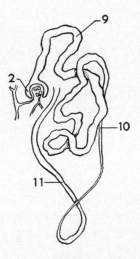

Figure 40. Diagram of glomerulus and tubule of bird kidney. 2, glomerulus with blood vessels; 9, proximal convoluted tubule; 10, descending limb of Henle's loop; 11, ascending limb of Henle's loop.

erulus comprises a few, capillary loops, or sometimes only one
(Sperber, 1960).

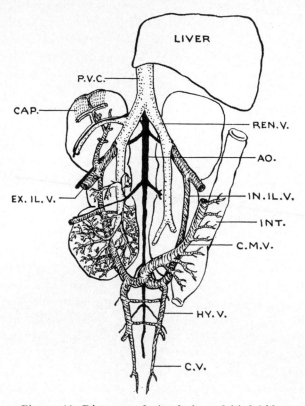

Figure 41. Diagram of circulation of bird kidney.
Black represents arteries; stippling, efferent veins;
and crosshatching, afferent veins. P.V.C., posterior
vena cava; EX.IL.V., external iliac vein; REN.V.,
renal vein; AO., aorta; IN,IL.V., internal iliac vein;
INT., intestine; C.M.V., coccygeo-mesenteric vein;
HY.V., hypogastric vein; C.V., coccygeal vein. (Modified slightly from Spanner, *Morph. Jahrb.,* 1925.)

Circulation in Kidney

The main blood vessels which supply and drain the kidney, and
the arrangement of these vessels within the lobules, are shown in
Figures 39 and 41. There are three pairs of arteries from the aorta.

each of which supplies a lobe of the kidneys (Spanner, 1925; Sperber, 1948). The anterior renal artery supplies the cranial lobes, and the femoral artery sends branches into the middle lobe and the lower part of the cranial lobe. The third artery, the ischiadic or sciatic, courses between the borders of the middle and the posterior lobe and supplies mainly the posterior lobe. The renal arteries send branches—the intralobular arteries—into each of the lobules, and these branches ramify to supply the glomeruli. The afferent and efferent branches of the intralobular arteries carry the blood to and away from the glomeruli, entering and leaving by way of the same opening in the capsule. The efferent arterial blood empties into the branches of the interlobular veins (figures 39 and 41), which in turn drain into the intralobular veins. The arterial blood supply of the bird kidney is sparse in relation to the venous supply (Spanner, 1925; Gordeuk and Grundy, 1950).

The kidney receives venous blood from the renal portal system, which includes blood from the coccygeomesenteric, caudal hypogastric, ischiadic, and iliac veins. This system is afferent, and distributes blood to tubules of each lobule by way of the interlobular veins and their branches. These veins empty into the large intralobular veins, which course through the center of the lobule. The intralobular veins drain the lobules and then empty into the main renal veins.

The endings of the renal portal veins form a capillary network and a peritubular blood supply. They also form a network that is continuous with the efferent venous network of the kidney (Spanner, 1925; Sperber, 1948; Mouchette and Cuypers, 1959). Apparently the tubules do not receive an afferent arterial supply, but the efferent arterioles from the glomeruli anastomose with the capillary network of the afferent veins, and thus the peritubular blood is mixed with arterial and venous (renal portal) blood. Physiological evidence, however, suggests that most of the afferent blood to the tubules comes from the renal portal system. Sperber (1948) showed that if phenol red or other substances secreted by kidney tubules are injected into the femoral vein or external iliac vein (portal system), the substance is excreted in the urine from the ureters on the injected side before being excreted on the contralateral side.

Located at the juncture of the renal vein and the iliac vein is a prominent valve, which apparently governs the flow of blood into the renal vein (Spanner, 1925 and 1939). This valve varies in shape and structure among the different species. Little is known concerning its physiology but pressure conditions in the renal portal vessels and renal veins may influence its opening and closure, and thus the relative amounts of afferent venous blood supplying the kidney by way of the interlobular veins, and of extrarenal blood, which bypasses the kidney. Rennick and Gandia (1954) studied the effects of certain pharmacologic agents on the valve *in vitro,* and reported that histamine and acetylcholine cause it to close and that epinephrine causes it to open. The effects of acetylcholine and epinephrine on the valve suggest that it is under autonomic control. Gilbert (1961) reported that the valve in the chicken has a rich nerve supply, with fibers terminating in the smooth muscle of the valve. However, he was unable to determine whether this nerve supply was sympathetic, parasympathetic, or both.

Sperber (1960) has estimated that much of the blood supply to the kidney comes from the leg vein, and Rennick and Gandia have suggested that opening the valve would facilitate flow of blood directly through the renal portal vein to the heart and thereby reduce the load on the kidney when muscular activity of the leg is high.

Cuypers (1959) attempted to assess the role of renal portal circulation on urine flow in chickens, and also that of the main renal arteries, by ligation of these in a two-stage operation. The surgery was indeed drastic, and the meaning of his results are questionable.

FILTRATION, EXCRETION, AND ABSORPTION

The kidney performs three main functions: filtration, excretion or secretion, and absorption. From the blood it filters water and some substances normally used by the body, along with waste products of metabolism which are voided in the urine. It con-

serves needed body water, glucose, and other substances by reabsorption. By these processes the kidney becomes an important
homeostatic mechanism whereby the body water and solutes are
maintained at fairly constant levels. For details concerning kidney
physiology, see the book by Smith (1951).

Filtration takes place in the glomeruli, where crystalloids, and
substances with molecules of medium to small size pass through
the capillary walls of the glomeruli into the capsule. The plasma
proteins, which are composed of large molecules, do not normally
pass through the capillary walls and are not filterable. Some of the
filterable substances of the blood include sodium, potassium, chloride, inorganic phosphate, glucose, urea, creatinine, and uric acid.
These substances have the same concentration in the capsular
fluid as in the blood plasma and this is evidence of filtration.

The concentration of some of these substances in the urine may
be higher or lower than that in the blood plasma. A lower concentration usually indicates that the substance is being reabsorbed by
the kidney tubules. Glucose normally does not appear in the
urine, but it is completely filterable, and therefore must be reabsorbed. When the kidney tubule suffers impairment, such as follows administration of the glucoside phlorizin, or when the blood
sugar level is inordinately high, not all of the glucose that is
filtered is reabsorbed, and some appears in the urine.

The kidney tubules also reabsorb water, which aids in maintaining normal blood volume.

The concentration of certain substances in the tubules and
urine may be higher than that in the plasma or glomerular filtrate.
When the increased concentration cannot be accounted for by
reabsorption of water from the tubules, it is evidence of tubular
secretion.

In the aglomerular kidney of lower vertebrates, where there is
no filtration, the kidney tubules secrete the urine. Tubules of the
mesonephric kidney of chick embryos, cultured *in vitro* in a medium containing phenol red, are able to pick up the dye, transport
it across the tubular cells without storage, and discharge it in higher
concentration into the tubular urine (Chambers and Kempton,
1933). Certain metabolites are excreted by the tubules, including

uric acid in birds and reptiles, and creatinine in fishes, chick, man, and anthropoid apes (Smith). A number of foreign substances, such as phenol red, diodrast, and hippuran, when administered to mammals and birds, have a higher renal clearance than inulin, indicating tubular secretion.

Energy is expended by the tubular cells in secretion and reabsorption. Reabsorption occurs even when the substance reabsorbed is many more times concentrated in blood than in the urine, and could therefore not be accomplished by simple diffusion.

Changes in arterial pressure do no appreciably affect secretion or reabsorption but do affect rate of filtration.

Filtration and Renal Blood Flow and Pressure

The pressure required to drive the fluid through the glomerular blood vessels must be sufficient to overcome the pressure exerted by the capsular membrane and the osmotic pressure of blood colloids. Thus the effective filtration pressure (Pf) equals the pressure in the glomerular blood vessels (Pb) minus the capsular pressure (Pc) and the osmotic pressure of the blood colloids (Po). Thus $PB(Po + Pc) = Pf$.

Direct measurements of glomerular capillary pressure (Pb) have not been made on the intact avian or mammalian kidney. Pb and Pf can be estimated by determining the pressure required in the kidneys or ureters to stop urine flow. This can be done by cannulating the ureter or pelvis of the kidney, and connecting the cannula to a vertical glass tube until the hydrostatic pressure equals the filtration pressure and urine flow ceases. Such determinations indicate that glomerular capillary pressure in the dog is approximately 60 percent of mean arterial pressure. If mean arterial pressure in the dog equals 150 mm. Hg, then capillary pressure equals 90 mm. Hg. If osmotic blood pressure equals 25 mm. Hg and capsular pressure equals 10 mm. Hg, the effective filtration pressure is 55 mm. Hg. The ureteral or intrapelvic pressure required to stop urine flow would be the capillary pressure minus the osmotic pressure, or 90−25 = 65 mm. Hg.

The pressure required to stop urine flow in the chicken ureter varies considerably, but may be as high as 32 mm. Hg, according to Gibbs (1929a). However, part of the pressure he recorded is due to the milking action of the ureters, which, when they are in active state, force the urine toward the cloaca. Gibbs estimated that the highest pressure at which urine is formed, independent of the ureters' action, ranges from 7.5 to 15 mm. Hg. Thus, this estimate of effective filtration pressure is considerably lower than that for the dog and man.

Gibbs (1929a) and Marshall (1934) believed that filtration must play a less important role in kidney function of birds than mammals, because of the smaller number of capillary loops and the poorer filtering areas in bird glomeruli. The rate of filtration in the bird kidney, as determined by inulin clearance, is as high per unit of body weight as it is in man. Thus filtration plays an equally important role.

The amount of urine formed by filtration varies directly with blood pressure and blood flow. Constriction of the efferent glomerular arteries of mammals and presumably birds by the vasoconstrictor nerves (sympathetic), or by small doses of epinephrine, causes an engorgement of the glomerulus with blood and an enlargement of the kidney. Accompanying these changes there may be dilatation of the afferent arterioles, and thus a greater volume of blood with higher pressure available to the glomerulus, and a higher filtration pressure is the result. Constriction of the efferent arterioles, such as occurs after large doses of epinephrine, decreases the blood flow and filtration pressure.

Renal blood flow. At low plasma concentrations certain substances are almost completely excreted by the tubules. Thus, the volume of the substance cleared per minute (see later section for details) is theoretically equal to the volume of plasma flowing through the kidney during the same time. In the bird, paraminohippuric acid (PAH), diodrast, and uric acid are very efficiently cleared from the plasma, and the clearance of these has been used to estimate renal plasma flow. Figures reported in the literature vary considerably, depending upon the method used and upon other factors. Sykes (1960a) reviewed much of the old data on renal plasma flow, and also presents recent data. He reported mean clearances of uric acid and PAH of 68.5 and 67.6 ml./min. respectively for Light Sussex chickens ranging in weight from 2.3 to 2.9 kg. Others using PAH have reported clearances ranging from 31 to 136 ml./min. According to Sykes, there is less variation in the clearance of uric acid than PAH, hence uric acid may be preferable for estimating plasma flow.

Attempts have been made to measure renal blood flow directly, but the results have been highly variable and may not include renal portal blood. Saperstein and Hartman (1959), using a dilution technique, estimated plasma flow to be 23 ml./kg. per minute, a figure not much lower than estimates obtained by Sykes, who employed PAH and uric acid clearances. Their estimate, however, does not include the contribution of the portal system. The presence of a functional valve in the renal portal system may account for some of the variability between the clearances and direct estimates of flow.

Adrenaline, which increases blood pressure, may cause an increase in urine flow in the chicken (Sharpe, 1912; Mayrs, 1924; Gibbs, 1928; and Korr, 1939), and an increase in renal blood flow (Gibbs, 1928; Mayrs, 1924), but according to Gibbs the effect is inconstant.

Ergotoxin decreases, and acetycholine increases, renal blood flow (Gibbs, 1928). Changes in urine flow do not always parallel the changes in renal blood flow and pressure. Pitts (1938), Shannon (1938a and b), and Sykes (1960b) demonstrated that glomerular filtration in the chicken (inulin clearance) remains fairly constant over a wide range of changes in urine flow, and concluded that the flow is affected mainly by reabsorption and excretion in the tubules.

RENAL CLEARANCE

Renal clearance may be defined as the volume of blood which one minute's excretion of urine suffices to clear of a given substance, or the minimum volume of blood required to furnish the quantity of substances excreted in the urine in one minute's time (Smith, 1951). The volume of blood cleared of a particular substance by the kidney in one minute may be expressed as follows:

$$Ux = \text{concentration of } x \text{ in each cc. of urine}$$
$$V = \text{rate of urine formation in cc. per minute}$$
$$Px = \text{concentration of } x \text{ in each cc. of plasma}$$
$$UxV = \text{rate of excretion of } x \text{ in mg. per minute}$$

Then $\dfrac{UxV}{Px}$ = volume of plasma required to supply the quantity of x excreted in each minute's time. Thus, UV/P equals the clearance of a given substance, x, in the plasma.

The substance to be tested is usually infused at a constant rate, and urine samples are collected at regular and frequent intervals (usually at intervals of 2 to 7 minutes in the chicken). Blood samples are usually taken near the middle of the collection periods. The plasma concentrations are plotted against time, and the exact values at the middle of each urine collection period are determined by interpolation.

Inulin Clearance

A substance suitable for measuring glomerular filtration must be completely filterable and physiologically inert, and must not be reabsorbed, excreted, or synthesized by the kidney tubules (Smith). Such a substance is inulin, a starchlike polymer containing 32 hexose molecules with a molecular weight of 5,200. Inulin is neither reabsorbed nor excreted by by the kidney tubules of mammals, amphibians, reptiles, or birds, and varies directly with the concentration of inulin in the plasma. Since UV/P is constant and independent of plasma concentration, the clearance of inulin is a measure of glomerular filtration (Smith).

The ratio of the inulin clearance to the simultaneous clearance of other substances, such as urea, uric acid, creatinine, and phenol red, indicates whether the substance in question is reabsorbed or secreted by the kidney tubules. Thus, a ratio of less than 1 indicates reabsorption, and a ratio greater than 1 indicates excretion or secretion by the tubules.

Korr's data indicate that the rate of urine flow increases with inulin clearance, and that both are influenced by the degree of hydration of the body, although hydration increases the filtration rate more than it does urine flow (Korr, 1939). However, the data

Table 59. Figures for inulin clearance in the chicken

Mean inulin clearance per kg./min. in ml.	Conditions	Mean urine flow per bird per minute in ml.	Author
1.84	Hydration	0.89	Pitts (1938)
1.87	"	0.90	Shannon (1938a)
1.70	"	1.20	Shannon (1938b)
2.15	"	1.13	Pitts & Korr (1938)
1.71	—	—	Lambert
1.37	No water given	0.33	Korr (1939)
0.60	Dehydrated 48–60 hrs.	0.15	"
2.45	Bird very hydrated	1.4	"
3.00	Laying hen not fasted	—	Sperber (1960)
1.96	Not stated	0.38	Sykes (1960b)
1.81	Fasted 18 hrs., mild hydration	0.92	Berger *et al.* (1960)

of Pitts (1938) and Shannon (1938a), based on birds hydrated to a lesser extent, show only a slight increase in inulin clearance, with urine flows from 0.4 to 1.8 cc. per minute. Most of the clearance figures shown in Table 59 are in fair agreement, except the figure reported by Sperber (1960), which is higher, and which he attributes to the fact that most of the other workers fasted their animals, whereas his were laying birds and not starved at all.

An inulin clearance of 1.8 ml. per kg. of body weight per minute means that for a chicken weighing 2 kilograms, the fluid filtered through the kidneys in 1 minute amounts to 3.6 ml. and that in 1 hour to 216 ml. or 5.18 liters in 24 hours. On a body weight basis, this rate compares favorably with that in man. Since approximately 130 ml. of urine are voided by the chicken in 24 hours (Hester, Essex, and Mann, 1940), most of the water filtered through the kidney (nearly 98 percent) is reabsorbed into the tubules, and this figure is of the same order as that for man.

Phenol Red Clearance

The dye, phenol red, is filtered by the glomeruli and is also secreted or excreted by the tubules of man, dog, and chicken. Some of the dye is bound by the plasma proteins, and only the free dye is filterable. The amounts bound and free depend upon the concentration of the dye in the plasma. At very low concentrations in chicken plasma (1 mg. percent), only 15 to 20 percent of the dye is free or filterable, but at concentrations of 15 mg. percent, 60 percent is filterable, and at higher concentrations more is filterable because more is free (Pitts, 1938).

The ratio of free phenol red in the plasma to that in the urine is not constant, and this ratio decreases after the concentration in the plasma has reached a certain point. At low plasma levels of the dye (1 to 3 mg. percent) the clearance ratio of phenol red to inulin ranges from 10-to-1 to 17-to-1 in the chicken (Pitts), as contrasted with ratios of 3.3-to-1 in man and 1.7-to-1 in the dog (Smith).

Thus, tubular excretion of the dye is much greater in the chicken than in the mammal. This may be related to the fact either that the tubules of birds receive an independent blood supply by way of the renal-portal system, or that the tubules are more efficient in extracting the dye. At high concentrations of the dye, the clearance ratio of phenol red to inulin approaches 1 (Figure 42). This means that as the plasma concentration reaches a certain point, proportionately less of the dye is excreted by the tubules, and that the tubules have a limited capacity to excrete the dye. The absolute clearances of phenol red and inulin in the chicken at low plasma concentrations are 28 and 1.8 cc. per kg. per minute, and at high concentrations (100 mg.) they are 2.59 and 2.57 respectively (Pitts). The differences in the excretion of phenol red in relation to that filtered by the bird and mammal have been calculated by Smith (1951), who showed that the quantities of dye excreted by the tubules per cc. of dye filtered for the dog, man, and chicken are 0.079, 0.21, and 0.62 mg. respectively. Phlorizin, which impairs or inhibits tubular function, depresses the excretion of phenol red in the chicken (Pitts). Different phenol red derivatives have different maximal transport rates (Sperber, 1954). Certain organic ions such as tetraethylammonium (TEA), histamine, piperidine, and others do not affect the tubular secretion of phenol red, but they may influence the secretion of each other (Sperber, 1960).

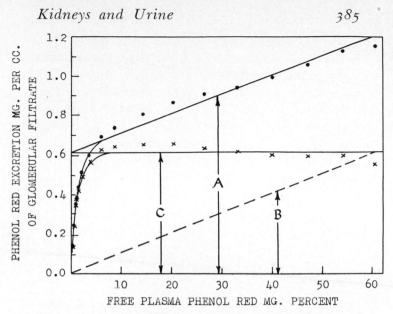

Figure 42. Excretion of phenol red by the chicken kidney in relation to concentration of free phenol red in plasma.

A, total excretion; B, that filtered; C, that excreted by tubules. The amount of phenol red filtered increases with plasma concentration, but this is not true for that excreted by tubules. (From Pitts, *J. Cell. & Comp. Physiol.*, 1938.)

Urea Clearance

Urea is the chief nitrogenous constituent of the urine of mammals and represents the end product of protein metabolism, but uric acid is the chief nitrogenous constituent of urine in birds. Urea is the end product of purine metabolism in birds, yet it is handled by the avian kidney in a way similar to that in most mammals; namely, it is completely filterable, but it is partially reabsorbed by the kidney tubules, independently of the plasma concentration (Pitts and Korr, 1938). The chicken kidney contains arginase and can produce urea from plasma arginine, as is demonstrated by the infusion experiments of Owen and Robinson (1964).

The average urea clearance in the chicken is 1.50 cc. per kg. of body weight per minute, and the clearance ratio of urea to inulin is 0.74 (Pitts and Korr). The fraction of filtered urea that is reabsorbed in the chicken (25 percent) is less than that in mammals (45 percent), according to these authors; but whether the species difference is significant is not known since in mammals urea reabsorption is known to be influenced by rate of urine formation (increasing with decreased flow). Whether or not this holds for the bird has not been determined (Pitts and Korr).

Korr (1939) concluded that the fraction of filtered urea that is reabsorbed is dependent upon the amount of filtered water that is reabsorbed, and not upon the actual volume of water excreted (urine flow). Reabsorption of urea from tubular urine is generally believed to be due to back diffusion rather than to active absorption.

Uric Acid Clearance

Uric acid is highly concentrated in the urine of birds, and constitutes from 60 to 80 percent of the total nitrogen. Studies of uric acid clearance by Shannon (1938b) demonstrated that 87 to 93 percent of the uric acid of the chicken is excreted by the tubules. The uric acid/inulin clearance ratio at moderate plasma uric acid concentrations (6 to 9 mg. percent) ranges from 7.5 to 15.8. These ratios are about the same as the phenol-red/inulin ratios at low plasma levels of the dye. As the plasma level of uric acid is raised, the ratio is depressed, until at a plasma uric acid level of 100 mg. percent the ratios range from 1.8 to 3.2

The absolute clearance of uric acid at plasma levels of 6 to 9 mg. percent is approximately 30 ml. per kg. per minute (Shannon). Gibbs (1928, 1929a, and 1929b) has shown that changes in renal blood flow and pressure, factors affecting filtration rate, do not appreciably affect the formation of uric acid in the urine, and this is further evidence of its secretion by the tubules. Sykes (1960a) reported the absolute clearance of uric acid in Sussex hens of 68.5 ml./minute, or approximately 25 ml. per kg. at plasma levels under 5 mg. percent. Clearances of about the same magnitude were reported by Nechay and Nechay (1959). The figures on uric acid reported by Sykes and by Nechay and Nechay are probably more reliable than some of the older data because they used a more reliable method (uricase) of uric acid determination. Most values (particularly on plasma) are lower with the uricase method (see Chapter 2). At similar plasma urate levels, the clearances of uric acid reported by Berger, Yü, and Gutman (1960) appear to be a bit lower than those reported by Sykes. The influence of plasma level of uric acid on clearance, and on the amounts of uric acid filtered and secreted, are shown from the data of Sykes (1960a) as follows:

Inulin clearance (ml./min.)	Plasma level (mg. percent)	Clearance (ml./min.)	Amount filtered (mg./min.)	Amount secreted (mg./min.)
5.6	2.5	63.0	0.14	1.41
6.4	2.8	43.5	0.18	1.03
2.2	31.0	16.1	0.67	4.31
2.4	47.7	12.5	1.13	4.86
4.4	124.0	4.7	5.42	0.48

It is seen from these data that as the plasma level of uric acid increases the amount filtered continues to increase, but that at very high plasma levels the ability of the tubules to secrete uric acid declines. The T max for uric acid is about 5 mg/min.

Recent work by Sykes (1960a) and by Berger *et al.* (1960) suggests that the same cellular mechanism is involved in the tubular transport of PAH and uric acid. Increasing the plasma concentration of PAH depresses the clearance of uric acid. Further evidence that these substances compete in tubular transport is based on studies with drugs that depress uric acid secretion. These drugs likewise depress PAH transport. Such drugs as probenecid, sulfinpyrazone, and zoxazolamine, and high dosages of phenylbutazone, all of which increase uric acid secretion in man, depress its secretion in chickens (Berger *et al.*; Nechay and Nechay, 1959). In chickens these drugs depress secretion of uric acid, but in man they inhibit tubular reabsorption of it. Probenecid likewise depresses the secretion of phenol red (Sanner, 1963).

Creatinine and Creatine Clearance

Creatinine is a normal constituent of the urine in mammals, but in birds the amount formed is negligible in relation to the amount of creatine. Clearance studies on birds, man, apes, and certain fishes indicate that the tubules of these species secrete creatinine. The creatinine/inulin ratio in the chicken at plasma concentrations of 9 to 12 mg. percent averages 1.54 (Shannon, 1938a). At higher concentrations the ratio is depressed, and at concentrations of 200 to 230 mg. percent the ratios are 1.09 and 1.07 respectively.

Sykes (1960b) reported that the absolute clearance of exogenous creatinine in hens is 3.90 ml./min. at plasma concentrations ranging from 3.2 to 57.0 mg. percent, with a creatinine/inulin ratio of 1.46. The clearance of endogenous creatinine averaged 2.25 ml./min., with a C/I ratio of 0.78. Thus, at normal or endogenous plasma levels (0.2 to 0.5 mg. percent) creatinine is not secreted but is reabsorbed. Thus the ability of the kidney to clear the plasma of creatinine is considerably lower than for uric acid, PAH, phenol red, and other substances.

The clearance of exogenous creatinine in hens averaged 6.70 ml./min., with a C/I ratio of 2.2, at plasma concentrations of 2.8 to 13.3 mg. percent (Sykes, 1960b). The mean clearance of endogenous creatine in hens is 3.90, with a C/I ratio of 1.41.

Clearance of Other Substances

A number of other substances are known to be secreted by the kidney tubules of chickens. These include glucuronides of menthol and phenol, sulfuric esters of phenol, resorcinol, and hydroquinone (Sperber, 1960); tetraethylammonium, TEA (Rennick *et al.,* 1954), thiamine and choline (Rennick, 1958); epinephrine (Rennick and Yoss, 1962); potassium (Rennick *et al.,* 1952; Orloff and Davidson, 1956; Sykes, 1961); histamine (Lindahl and Sperber, 1958); serotonin (Sanner and Wortman, 1962); and phosphate (Davidson and Levinsky, 1957).

TEA is excreted at a very rapid rate, histamine less rapidly. Lindahl and Sperber determined the apparent tubular excretion fraction (ATEF) of histamine by injecting histamine into the femoral vein and measuring the difference in the amounts excreted by the ipsilateral and contralateral kidneys. Thus,

$$\text{ATEF} = \frac{EXcI - EXcC}{INF} \times 100$$

with *EXcI* representing the total urinary excretion of the compound on the infused side, *EXcC* the rate of excretion on contralateral side, and *INF* the rate of infusion.

The ATEF for the different infusion rates of histamine ranges from 46 to 62 percent, and for phenol red is a little lower. The administration of certain organic bases (e.g. priscoline cyanine dye) depressed the secretion of histamine, suggesting that histamine has the same transport mechanism as these organic bases.

Serotonin (5-hydroxytryptamine) which is known to cause the release of histamine in chickens (see Chapter 3), appears to be secreted by the kidney tubules, but not at an appreciable rate (Sanner and Wortman, 1962). Since excretion of serotonin might be influenced by its simultaneous destruction by monoamine oxidase, the effects of catron, an inhibitor of this enzyme, on serotonin excretion were studied. The inhibitor significantly increased the excretion rate of serotonin. Another substance, d-1 epinephrine, is secreted at a rate of about 75 percent of the excretion of PAH, which is very high. The ATEF of d-1 Epinephrine averaged 38 percent. Sanner (1963) has reported that serotonin is transported in the kidney tubule by the organic base system, and is not influenced by pH. Reserpine did not influence the secretion of serotonin.

Probenecid, an inhibitor of the organic acid transport system, decreased the secretion of both epinephrine and PAH. The secretion of the former was more quickly affected (Rennick and Yoss).

Ferrocyanide and thiosulphate are also secreted by the tubules (Sykes, 1960b). The latter depresses the clearance of both inulin and uric acid.

Potassium is an inorganic constituent that is filtered, reabsorbed, and possibly secreted. Potassium is secreted in the fowl, but at a relatively low rate (Orloff and Davidson, 1956). The maximal rate of transport for one kidney (the one perfused) ranged from 60 to 85 micromoles per minute for a 2-kg. chicken. Reducing pCO_2 locally increases K excretion, and increasing pCO_2 decreases it. A mercurial diuretic inhibited excretion of K, and its virtual disappearance from the urine may indicate that the filtered K is entirely reabsorbed.

Hydrochlorothiazide belongs to the sulphonamyl group of compounds, and has been reported to have a diuretic action in turkeys. Sykes (1961) confirmed this, and also reported that it increased the excretion of sodium and potassium in the urine.

Strophanthidin, a cardiac aglycone, has been reported to act directly on the kidney tubules of chickens, and to inhibit the transport of potassium and hydrogen ions as well as of sodium (Orloff and Burg, 1960). Injection of the substance in the femoral vein caused an immediate increase in urine flow, and in sodium excretion in the ipsilateral kidney. In some instances K excretion increased; in others it decreased. The drug inhibits sodium reabsorption, and probably interferes with the secretion of potassium. Thus, the decrease in K excretion that occurred in some instances after administration of the drug is interpreted as interference with secretion; and it is proposed that in the chicken, as in other species, all or most of the filtered K is reabsorbed, and that subsequent secretion accounts for all or most of the K appearing in the urine.

URINE

Factors Affecting Amount of Urine Voided

The urine and feces of the bird are voided into the cloaca. In order to obtain urine free from fecal matter, it is necessary to cannulate the cloaca or the ureters or to separate the opening of the ureters or the rectum by surgery. Improved surgical techniques for exteriorizing the ureters (Dixon and Wilkinson, 1957) or the anus (Imabayashi, Kametaka, and Hatano, 1956; Fussell, 1960 Greuel, 1961) have been reported. Uncontaminated urine in the cloaca may also be obtained by plugging the anal opening. Most of the work relating to quantities of urine voided is based on short-period collections from which calculations were made on the output for 24 hours. Most of those who cannulated the ureters and collected urine for short periods (usually 30 to 100 minutes) estimated the output of the adult chicken (weight about 2 kg.) at from 500 to 1000 ml. per day (Davis, 1927; Coulson and Hughes, 1930; Sharpe, 1912; Mayrs, 1924; Hester, Essex, and Mann, 1940; and others). Short-period collections from exteriorized ureters gave similar estimates (Hester, Essex, and Mann). Thus the estimates of urine output based on short-period collections are unduly high. An estimated output of 1,000 ml. in 24 hours is considerably higher than water consumption for the same period (50 to 250 ml).

It was demonstrated by Hester, Essex, and Mann (1940), and by Hart and Essex (1942), that such estimates are in error, since the work of these authors showed the urine output from cannulated ureters to average 13.9 ml. for the first 30 minutes, but only 2.5 ml. during the second 30 minutes. Thus, estimates for 24 hours based on first collections gave an output of 667 ml. and on the second period one of 120 ml. The investigators concluded that cannulation and handling of the bird causes diuresis which persists for at least 30 minutes. In later experiments urine was collected in bags from exteriorized ureters for 24 hours; here the average output was 86.8 ml., with a range of 61 to 123.4 ml. In another experiment the output was as high as 180 cc. Urine collections made from exteriorized ureters, and after the rectum had been exteriorized by Dixon (1958), show urine flows of 132 and 155 ml. per 24 hours.

Role of ureters in control of urine flow. The ureters tend to force or milk the urine along by peristaltic action. The peristaltic waves move caudally; the pressure they exert is considerable, and the urine may be forced along against a pressure as high as 30 mm. of mercury (Gibbs, 1929c). The ureters, according to Gibbs, appear to be under sympathetic control.

Diuresis. Administration of water alone, and of hypertonic water solutions, increases urine output, whereas dehydration decreases it. Certain drugs influence the flow of urine. It is decreased by pituitrin or pitressin (Korr, 1939; Hester, Essex, and Mann, 1940), but increased by ether anesthesia and caffeine (Davis, 1927; Hester *et al.;* and others). The effects of ephedrine or adrenaline upon urine flow are inconstant. Mayrs (1924) reported an increase; Hester *et al.* reported no effect. Gibbs (1928) and Korr (1939) reported that a transient increase followed by a slight decrease, but the results were quite variable. Atropine and pilocarpine have no effect on urine flow, according to Gibbs (1929a). The antidiuretic hormone, arginine vasopressin in mammals, and arginine vasotocin, its counterpart in birds, both produce antidiuresis in chickens; the latter is considerably more potent than the former (Munsick, Sawyer, and Van Dyke, 1960). Removal of the neural lobe of the hypophysis, the principal source of the hormone caused polyuria in hens (Shirley and Nalbandov, 1956; see also Chapter 17).

Mercurial diuretics (Campbell, 1957) and hydrochlorothiazide, a different type of diuretic (Sykes, 1961), are effective in chickens and turkeys. Urine flow in the turkey increased approximately fivefold after administration of a single dose of 25 mg. of hydrochlorothiazide.

Role of the Cloaca in the Absorption of Water

Many of the early investigators believed that water from ureteral urine was absorbed in the cloaca and rectum, and that the cloaca served an important function in the conservation of water (for reveiw of some of the early work see Korr, 1939; Hester, Essex, and Mann, 1940; and Hart and Essex, 1942). Some of these workers observed an increase in the flow of urine collected from cannulated ureters, or from the cloaca after plugging the rectum. The urine was thin and watery, and had a low osmotic pressure. In one experiment, when the rectum was plugged with cotton approximately 22 ml. of urine were collected from the ureters in one hour, as contrasted with 9.8 ml. normally obtained (Korr, 1939; see also Sharpe, 1912). These findings, and other considerations, led Korr to estimate that from 10 to 30 ml. of ureteral urine per hour may be absorbed from the cloaca. Since the insertion of cannulae into the ureters, the plugging of the cloaca, handling the bird and anesthesia are all known to produce diuresis (Hester, Essex, and Mann), these results and estimates are subject to great error and appear unreasonably high.

Sharpe (1923) attempted to measure the amount of water absorbed directly into the cloaca by placing known amounts of solutions in the rectum and cloaca, which were separated from the ureters. He reported that from 1 to 3 ml. of water per hour was absorbed from the cloaca and rectum, depending upon the concentration of the solution and the pressure. Isotonic solutions were absorbed more slowly than hypo- or hypertonic ones.

Weyrauch and Roland (1957) attempted to measure water reabsorption in the cloaca of the chicken by introducing 10 ml. of a solution containing tracer isotopes into the cloaca, and measuring the content of isotope in the blood stream. The figures indicate that 7.6 percent of the isotope was absorbed within 4 hours. However, these studies really measure not cloacal absorption alone, but absorption into the anus and into the gut at a distance 10 cm. above the anus.

Experiments by Hart and Essex (1942), based on long-term urine collections, suggest that some water is reabsorbed into the cloaca, but not in appreciable amounts; the evidence for this conclusion is indirect. The investigators measured water consumption and urine flow in chickens whose ureters had been exteriorized, so that there could be no cloacal absorption, and in birds with an artificial anus, in which ureteral urine might still come into contact with the cloaca and water thus might be reabsorbed. Experiments by Dixon (1958), involving improved surgical techniques of exteriorizing the ureters and anus, leave no doubt that little or no water is reabsorbed in the cloaca of the chicken. In the hens with exteriorized ureters, reabsorption of water from urine in the cloaca and rectum was impossible. Reabsorption was possible in the cloaca but not in the rectum of the hens in which the anus was exteriorized. Dixon compared the water consumption and water voided in feces and urine of normal hens and surgically treated hens. His results follow:

Condition	Feed intake (gm.)	Water intake	Feces cc.	Feces % water	Urine cc.	Urine % water	Water recovered Total (cc.)	Water recovered Urine (cc.)	Water recovered Feces	Percentage of total water intake
Normal	106	325	248	88	—	—	218	—	—	67
Ex-ureters	105	326	115	78	132	95.5	215	125	90	66
Normal	117	343	262	88	—	—	230	—	—	67
Ex-rectum	119	342	109	74	155	96	229	148	81	67

Physical Characteristics of Urine

The urine of birds usually is cream-colored, contains thick, mucoid material, and is abundant in uric acid. However, under certain circumstances, such as diuresis, it may be thin and watery.

The pH of chicken urine ranges from 6.22 to 6.7, decreasing with increasing consistency.

Ureteral urine is usually hypotonic, with an osmotic pressure lower than blood, but under certain conditions it may be hypertonic (Mayrs, 1924, and Korr, 1939). An abnormally high intake of water, which increases the flow of urine decreases its osmotic pressure, whereas dehydration, which diminishes the flow, increases its osmotic pressure. Increasing the osmotic pressure of the blood by injections of sodium chloride or glucose increases the osmotic pressure of urine (Korr).

The specific gravity of duck urine is 1.0018, and of hen urine 1.0025 (Groebbels, 1932).

Acid-Base Balance in Urine

In mammals the renal regulation of H^+ and HCO^-_3 concentrations in the plasma is achieved partly by changes in the acidity of the urine and partly by changes in the amount of NH^+_4 excreted. Birds excrete considerable quantities of uric acid, and this exerts an additional load on the kidneys to conserve sodium ions (Sperber, 1960). When the base reserves of the chicken were depleted by the infusion of hydrochloric acid, the pH of the urine fell to a low limit of about 5.0. This was followed by an increased secretion of titratable acid, attributable to the excretion of phosphate and uric acid. Both of these are buffering agents at the pH of urine; however, uric acid is the more important of the two (Wolbach, 1955). Ammonia is also excreted in urine which is basic.

Nitrogenous Constituents of Urine

The principal difference in the chemical constituents of the urine in birds as compared with that of mammals is the preponderance of uric acid over urea, and of creatine over creatinine in the former. Creatinine exists only in minute amounts in bird urine (Paton, 1909; Davis, 1927; and others).

O'Dell et al. (1960) have reviewed the literature, and have presented new data on growing male chicks 5 to 6 weeks of age. Their results, and those of others, are presented in Table 60. In general, most of the investigators report a lower percentage of uric acid ni-

Table 60. Distribution of nitrogen in chicken urine as determined by various investigations, expressed as percentage of total urinary nitrogen (from O'Dell *et al.*, 1960)

Uric acid N	Possible allantoin N	Other purines	NH₃ N	Urea N	Creatine and creatinine	Amino acid N	Undetermined	Investigator
30	—	—	5.6	—	—	—	—	Sharpe (1912)
82	—	—	5.6	—	—	—	—	Katayama
66	—	—	—	—	6.0	—	—	Mayrs (1924)
63			17.3	10.4	8.0	—	1.4	Davis (1927)
66	3.8	9.6	7.6	6.5	4.6	—	2.8	Coulson & Hughes (1930)
60	—	20.0	—	—	—	10.0[a]		Edwards & Wilson (1954)
81	—	—	10.5	4.5	0.9	2.2	1.2⎫	Practical ration
76	—	—	15.4	5.6	0.2	1.7	1.2⎭	Purified diet O'Dell *et al.* (1960)

[a] Amino nitrogen.

trogen in the urine than O'Dell *et al.* The reason for the discrepancy is not clear, but certain differences did exist in the experiments performed. The results of O'Dell *et al.* are based on growing chickens that were well adapted to the conditions of urine collection, whereas most of the previous work had been conducted on mature birds, some of which were under physiological stress during the collection periods. The determination of uric acid by O'Dell *et al.* was by the uricase method, which is highly specific and which was not used by most of the other investigators.

Many investigators have determined the uric acid content of the excreta of birds, which contain both feces and urine. The uric acid per gram of air-dried excreta ranges from 53.8 to 89.5 mg. according to Bose (1944), and from 36.6 to 100.7 mg. according to Baker (1946). About 10 percent of the urates in bird blood are in solution, 18 percent are protein-bound, and about 70 percent exist as an ultrafilterable or colloidial fraction, according to Levine, Wolfson, and Lenel (1947).

The amount of urine water excreted per gram of uric acid varies with the amount of urine produced and ranges from 60 to 100 ml. according to Korr (1939), and from 30 to 165 ml. according to Hart and Essex (1942).

Uric acid is synthesized mainly in the liver of birds, as was indicated by Minkowski in 1886 and by others since (Milroy, 1904; Folin, Berglund, and Derick, 1924; Edson, Krebs, and Model, 1936). It is now generally agreed that the kidney is also concerned in the synthesis of uric acid in the pigeon. The livers of chickens and pigeons produce hypoxanthine, which is then oxidized to uric acid in the kidney of the pigeon, and in the liver of chickens by xanthine oxidase.

The uric acid content of blood, liver, and kidneys of birds (in milligrams per 100 ml. or 100 grams) is as follows:

Species	Whole blood	Muscle	Kidney	Liver	Author
Duck, normal	6.7	1.8	70.5	22.2	Folin *et al.* (1924)
Duck with ligated ureters	224.0	30.2	354.0	101.0	"
Chicken, normal	5.8	—	—	—	Levine *et al.* (1947)
Chicken with ligated ureters	304.0	—	—	—	"

Milroy (1904) reported that changes in the activity of the liver affected the amounts of uric acid excreted by the duck and goose. Electrical stimulation of the liver increased the excretion and synthesis of uric acid by the liver. Ligation of the ureters of birds caused marked increases in the concentration of uric acid in the blood and tissues, but not in the urine. Birds with ligated ureters usually died of uricemia within 12 to 24 hours (Folin *et al.*; Levine *et al.*).

ABNORMAL KIDNEY FUNCTION

Gross autopsy findings from a number of sources indicate that kidney disorders account for a large percentage of deaths. Siller (1959a) reported a 29.8 percent incidence of nephritis, and a 21 percent incidence of glomerulonephritiis. Apparently, from biopsy studies by Siller, the acute glomerular lesions may be completely reversible. Filtration and excretion in the kidneys of nephritic birds have not been studied.

Chickens, turkeys, and geese may suffer from visceral gout (see

Siller, 1959b), characterized by deposits of uric acid on the serous surface of such organs as the kidneys, heart, liver, lungs, and air sacs. Plasma urate levels may be elevated considerably, ranging as high as from 18 to 22 mg. percent (Siller, 1959b).

Histologically the kidney tubules are involved, and the lesions are considered typical for pyelonephritis (Siller). Apparently the tubules are unable to secrete uric acid, which becomes elevated in the blood and finally is deposited on the various organs. No filtration or excretion studies have been made on birds thus affected.

The disease of chickens known variously as pullet's disease, blue comb disease, and monocytosis, produces marked abnormalities in the structure and function of the kidney. The glomeruli and the convoluted tubules are involved. Clinically, the disease resembles uremia in mammals (Jungherr, 1948). The uric acid and nonprotein nitrogen in the blood are abnormally high, and the calcium may be low.

Disturbances in the renal structure and function of the chicken (nephrosclerosis) have been produced by large doses of desoxycorticosterone acetate (Selye, 1942) or excess sodium chloride (Selye, 1943).

Injury to the ureters, produced by sectioning, may lead to renal atrophy, according to Riddle (1930). The pressure developed in the ureters may be higher than the filtration or secretion pressure, according to Gibbs (1929c), who suggested that spasm of ureters might well be a cause of renal insufficiency in the bird.

Uricemia and tubular damage have been produced in chickens by feeding excessive amounts of galactose (Sondergaard *et al.,* 1957).

Different strains of White Leghorn chickens exhibited significant differences in susceptibility to kidney disorders (Biely and March, 1958).

EXTRARENAL SALT EXCRETION

It had long been suspected that marine birds might be able to consume and handle salt water, but only in recent years was the mechanism by which this is accomplished discovered (Schmidt-Nielsen *et al.,* 1958). Such birds have a specialized nasal gland that is able to secrete large quantities of NaCl. This gland has been reported and studied in several species, including cormorants (Schmidt-Nielsen *et al.*, 1958), the brown pelican (Schmidt-Nielsen and Fänge, 1958), the domestic duck (Scothorne, 1959a) the Aylesbury duck (Scothorne, 1959b), the herring gull (Fänge *et al.*, 1958), the Humboldt penguin (Schmidt-Nielsen and Sladen, 1958), and other species reported by Schmidt-Nielsen (1960).

Anatomy of Gland

The account that follows is from Schmidt-Nielsen (1960). The existence of a nasal gland, so called, has been known for centuries. It is not, however, always located in the nose. In most marine birds it is located on the top of the head, above the orbit of the eye; it has thus been called the supraorbital gland, although Schmidt-Nielsen prefers to call it the salt-secreting gland. On top of the skull of the gull are two flat, crescent-shaped glands, located in the shallow depressions in the bone. Two ducts run from each side down to the nose, where they open into the vestibular concha. From the anterior nasal cavity, the secretion flows out through the nares and drips off from the tip of the beak. The gland consists of longitudinal lobes, which in cross section show tubular glands radiating from a central canal. The gland receives its main arterial supply from the arteria ophthalmica interna. The arrangement of the blood vessels suggest a countercurrent mechanism; however, Schmidt-Nielsen does not believe that countercurrent flow accounts for the elaboration of the concentrated NaCl secreted. The gland is innervated from the ganglion ethmoidale, which is supplied by a relatively large branch of the ophthalmic nerve and a small one from the facial nerve, as well as by sympathetic fibers. Stimulation of the facial nerve branch causes secretion of a fluid rich in sodium. The nerve is apparently parasympathetic in nature. Injection of acetylcholine produces a copious secretion; but stimulation of the sympathetic causes no secretion, and injection of epinephrine blocks secretion.

Function of Gland.

The gland serves as an osmoregulator, for it responds to osmotic loads as well as to salt loads (Schmidt-Nielsen, 1960). A gull which had ingested 134 ml. of sea water containing 54 meq. of sodium, excreted most of the sodium through the salt gland—but some in the urine and feces—within 175 minutes, as follows:

Nasal Secretion		*Cloacal Secretion*	
Volume	*Sodium*	*Volume*	*Sodium*
(ml.)	*(meq.)*	*(ml.)*	*(meq.)*
56.3	43.7	75.2	4.41

The usual concentration of sodium in meq./liter for most species ranges from 500 to 700, and in some species approaches 1,000.

Recent work by Inoue (1963) suggests that two different mechanisms are involved in the secretion by the nasal gland. One is concerned with the handling of NaCl and the other with the water secreted.

There is some evidence that nasal secretion of salt is not restricted to marine birds, but occurs also in certain desert species, such as the partridge (*Ammoperdix heji*) and the ostrich. In these species, nasal secretion occurred without osmotic stimulation but in response to high temperature (Schmidt-Nielsen *et al.,* 1963). The chicken and pigeon do not have active salt-secreting nasal glands. Considerably more work should be conducted on the various avian species, from different habitats, as to the presence or absence of the nasal gland and the role it plays in the conservation of water and electrolytes.

Effects of drugs on nasal secretion. Fänge *et al.* (1958) demonstrated that the salt output of the glands could be lessened or abolished by carbonic anhydrase inhibition. Nechay, Larimer, and Maren (1960) also showed that the nasal secretion was influenced by alkalosis and acidiosis, which tend respectively to increase and to decrease secretion. Their evidence suggests that carbonic anhydrase, in an alkaline environment, is involved in the transport of NaCl.

Electrophysiological studies of the nasal gland by Thesleff and Schmidt-Nielsen (1962) show that the secretory activity is associated with electropotential changes, the duct of gland becoming positive relative to blood. The authors believe that an active sodium (cation) transport from the blood to the lumen of the gland is responsible for the gland's positivitiy. This view is supported by the fact that strophanthidin, a potent inhibitor of cation pumps in several systems, also blocks nasal secretion and the electropotential changes in the gland.

Recent results by Holmes, Phillips, and Butler (1961) and by Phillips, Holmes, and Butler (1961) suggest that although the normal triggering mechanism for nasal secretion may be osmoregulatory in nature, the final response is influenced or governed by adrenocortical hormones. The same authors have shown that in the adrenalectomized, salt-loaded duck, there is no nasal secretion of NaCl (Phillips *et al.*). After administration of cortisol to these birds, nasal secretion occurs as in an intact bird.

In normal ducks, salt-loaded, a diphasic response was noted (Holmes *et al.*), characterized by an initial diuresis (renal phase) during the first hour after salt-loading, and by the onset of nasal secretion at varying times during this interval. There was a progressive decline in renal sodium output coincident with the onset of nasal secretion. The authors state that also the concentrations of sodium and potassium in successive urine samples were compatible with an increased adrenocortical acitvity. However, nasal secretion was always preceded by a rise in serum sodium except in birds given aldosterone, cortisol, and ACTH, in which nasal secretion occurred before the rise in blood sodium. Thus, these data suggest that the increase in blood sodium normally triggers the release of the adrenal corticoids that are necessary for nasal secretion.

The authors presume that in birds the glucocorticoids, rather than aldosterone, are responsible for initiating nasal secretion. They believe the secretion of the latter, as in mammals, might be inhibited by salt-loading, although aldosterone was more effective than cortisol in increasing nasal secretion of sodium and potassium in the salt-loaded but not in the untreated duck. A need for further studies is indicated.

REFERENCES

Baker, C. J. L.   1946   A note on the estimation of the uric acid radical in avian excreta. Poultry Sci. 25:593.

Benoit, J. 1950 Traité de Zoologie, edited by P. P. Grasse. Tome XV: Oiseaux, p. 341. Masson & Co., Paris.

Berger, L., T. F. Yü, and A. B. Gutman 1960 Effects of drugs that alter uric acid excretion in man on uric acid clearance in the chicken. Am. J. Physiol 198:575.

Biely, J., and B. E. March 1958 Strain differences in susceptibility of chickens to renal disorders. Poultry Sci. 37:99.

Bose, S. 1944 An iodometric estimation of uric acid in poultry excreta. Poultry Sci. 23:130.

Campbell, D. 1957 Excretion and diuretic action of mercurial diuretics. Experientia 13:327.

Chambers, R., and R. T. Kempton 1933 Indications of function of the chick mesonephros in tissue culture with phenol red. J. Cell. & Comp. Physiol. 3:131.

Coulson, E. J., and J. H. Hughes 1930 Collection and analysis of chicken urine. Poultry Sci. 10:53.

Cuypers, Y. 1959 Étude de la sécrétion urinaire chez le coq. Arch. Int. Physiol. Biochem. 67:35.

Davidson, D. G., and N. Levinsky 1957 Effect of parathyroid extract on renal excretion of phosphate in the chicken. Fed. Proc. 16:28.

Davis, R. E. 1927 The nitrogenous constituents of hen's urine. J. Biol. Chem. 74:509.

Dixon, J. M. 1958 Investigation of urinary water reabsorption in the cloaca and rectum of the hen. Poultry Sci. 37:410.

Dixon, J. M., and W. S. Wilkinson 1957 Surgical technique for exteriorization of the ureters of the chicken. Am. J. Vet Res. 18:665.

Edson, N. L., H. A. Krebs, and A. Model 1936 The synthesis of uric acid in the avian organism: hypoxanthine as an intermediary metabolite. Biochem. J. 36:1380.

Fänge, R., K. Schmidt-Nielsen, and H. Osaki 1958 Salt gland of the herring gull. Biol. Bull. 115:162.

Folin, O., H. Berglund, and C. Derick 1924 The uric acid problem: an experimental study on animals and man, including gouty subjects. J. Biol. Chem. 60:361.

Fussell, M. H. 1960 Collection of urine and feces from the chicken. Nature 185:332.

Gibbs, O. S. 1928 The renal blood flow of the bird. J. Pharm. & Exp. Thera. 34:277.

Gibbs, O. S. 1929a The secretion of uric acid by the fowl. Am. J. Physiol. 88:87.

Gibbs, O. S. 1929b The effects of drugs on the secretion of uric acid in the fowl. J. Pharm. & Exp. Thera. 35:49.

Gibbs, O. S. 1929c The function of the fowl's ureters. Am. J. Physiol. 87:594.

Gilbert, A. B. 1961 The innervation of the renal portal valve of the domestic fowl. J. Anat. 95:594.

Gordeuk, S., Jr., and M. L. Grundy 1950 Observations on circulation in the avian kidney. Am. J. Vet. Res. 11:256.

Greuel, E. von 1961 Zur Technik der Anus praeternaturalis Operation beim Huhn. Arch. für Geflügelkunde 25:503.

Groebbels, F. 1932 Der Vogel. Erster Band: Atmungswelt und Nahrungswelt, Kot und Harn, p. 676. Verlag von Gebrüder Borntraeger, Berlin.

Hart, W. M., and H. E. Essex 1942 Water metabolism of the chicken with special reference to the role of the cloaca. Am. J. Physiol. 136:657.

Hester, H. R., H. E. Essex, and F. C. Mann 1940 Secretion of urine in the chicken. Am. J. Physiol. 128:592.

Holmes, W. N., J. G. Phillips, and D. G. Butler 1961 The effect of adrenocortical steroids on the renal and extra-renal responses of the domestic duck (Anas platyrhynchus) after hypertonic saline loading. Endocrinol. 69:483.

Imabayashi, K., M. Kametaka, and T. Hatano 1956 Studies on the digestion in the domestic fowl. I: "Artificial anus operation" for the domestic fowl and the passage of the indicator throughout the digestive tract. Tohoku J. Agr. Res. 6:99.

Inoue, T. 1963 Nasal salt gland: independence of salt and water transport. Science 142:1299.

Jungherr, E. 1948 Avian monocytosis, Chapter 29 in H. E. Biester and L. H. Schwarte, Diseases of Poultry. Iowa State College Press, Ames.

Korr, I. M. 1939 The osmotic function of the chicken kidney. J. Cell. & Comp. Physiol. 13:175.

Levine, R., W. Q. Wolfson, and R. Lenel 1947 Concentration and transport of true urate in the plasma of the azotemic chicken. Am. J. Physiol. 151:186.

Lindahl, K. M., and I. Sperber 1958 Some characteristics of the renal tubular transport mechanism for histamine in the hen. Acta Physiol. Scand. 42:166.

Liu, Hin-Ching 1962 The comparative structure of the ureter. Am. J. Anat. 111:1.

Marshall, E. K. 1934 Comparative physiology of vertebrate kidney. Physiol. Rev. 14:133.

Mayrs, E. B. 1924 Secretion as a factor in elimination by the kidneys. J. Physiol. 58:276.

Milroy, T. H. 1904 The formation of uric acid in birds. J. Physiol. 30:47.

Mouchette, R., and Y. Cuypers 1959 Study of the vascularization of the cock's kidney. Arch. Biol. 69:577.

Munsick, R. A., W. H. Sawyer, and H. B. Van Dyke 1960 Avian neurohypophysial hormones: pharmacological properties and tentative identification. Endocrinol. 66:860.

Nechay, B. R., J. L. Larimer, and T. H. Maren 1960 Effects of drugs and physiologic alterations on nasal salt excretion in sea gulls. J. Pharm. & Exp. Thera. 130:401.

Nechay, B. R., and L. Nechay 1959 Effects of probenecid, sodium salicylate, 2,4 dinitrophenol and pyrazinamide on renal secretion of uric acid in chickens. J. Pharm. & Exp. Thera. 126:291.

O'Dell, G. L., W. D. Woods, O. A. Laerdal, A. M. Jeffay, and J. E. Savage 1960 Distribution of the major nitrogenous compounds and amino acids in chicken urine. Poultry Sci. 39:426.

Orloff, J., and M. Burg 1960 Effect of strophanthidin on electrolyte excretion in the chicken. Am. J. Physiol. 199:49.

Orloff, J., and D. Davidson 1956 Mechanism of potassium excretion in the chicken. Fed. Proc. 15:452.

Owen, R. E., and R. R. Robinson 1964 Urea production and excretion by the chicken kidney. Am. J. Physiol. 206:1321.

Paton, N. 1909 Creatine excretion in the bird and its significance. J. Physiol. 39:485.

Phillips, J. G., W. N. Holmes, and D. G. Butler 1961 The effect of total and subtotal adrenalectomy on the renal and extra-renal response of the domestic duck (Anas platyrhynchus) to saline loading. Endocrinol. 69:958.

Pitts, R. F. 1938 The excretion of phenol red by chickens. J. Cell. & Comp. Physiol. 11:99.

Pitts, R. F., and I. M. Korr 1938 The exretion of urea by the bird. J. Cell. & Comp. Physiol. 11:117.

Rennick, B. R. 1958 The renal tubular excretion of choline and thiamine in the chicken. J. Pharm. & Exp. Thera. 122:448.

Rennick, B. R., D. M. Calhoon, H. Gandia, and G. K. Moe 1954 Renal tubular secretion of tetraethylammonium in the dog and chicken. J. Pharm. & Exp. Thera. 110:309.

Rennick, B. R., and H. Gandia 1954 Autonomic pharmacology of the smooth muscle valve in renal portal venous circulation in birds. Fed. Proc. 13:396.

Rennick, B. R., C. Latimer, and G. K. Moe 1952 Excretion of potassium by the chicken kidney. Federation Proc. 11:132.

Rennick, B. R., and N. Yoss 1962 Renal tubular excretion of dl-Epinephrine 2-C^{14} in the chicken. J. Pharm. & Exp. Thera. 138: 347.

Riddle, O. 1930 Complete atrophy of kidney in pigeons following section of the ureter. Proc. Soc. Exp. Biol. & Med. 27:1022.

Sanner, E. 1963 Studies on the excretion mechanism of serotonin (5-hydroxytryptamine) in the chicken kidney. Acta Physiol. Scand. 58:330.

Sanner, E. and Bernard Wortman 1962 Tubular excretion of serotonin (5-hydroxytryptamine) in the chicken. Acta Physiol. Scand. 55:319.

Saperstein, L. A. and F. A. Hartman 1959 Cardiac output and its distribution in the chicken. Am. J. Physiol. 196:751.

Schmidt-Nielsen, K. 1960 The salt secreting gland of marine birds. Circulation 21:955.

Schmidt-Nielsen, K., A. Borut, Ping Lee, and Eugene Crawford, Jr. 1963 Nasal salt excretion and possible function of the cloaca in water conservation. Science 142:1300.

Schmidt-Nielsen, K., and Ragnar Fänge 1958 The function of the salt gland in the brown pelican. Auk 75:282.

Schmidt-Nielsen, K., C. E. Jorgensen, and H. Osaki 1958 Extrarenal salt excretion in birds. Am. J. Physiol. 193:101.

Schmidt-Nielsen, K., and W. J. Sladen 1958 Nasal salt secretion in the Humboldt penguin. Nature 181:1217.

Scothorne, J. J. 1959a The nasal glands of birds: a histological and histochemical study of the inactive gland in the domestic duck. J. Anat. 93:246.

Scothorne, J. J. 1959b Histochemical study of succinic dehydrogenase in the nasal (salt-secreting) gland of the Aylesbury duck. Quart. J. Exp. Physiol. 44:329.

Selye, H. 1942 Production of nephrosclerosis by overdosage with desoxycorticosterone acetate. Canadian Med. Assoc. J. 47:515.

Selye, H. 1943 Production of nephrosclerosis in the fowl by NaCl. J. Am. Vet. Med. Assoc. 103:140.

Shannon, J. A. 1938a The excretion of exogenous creatinine by the chicken. J. Cell. & Comp. Physiol. 11:135.

Shannon, J. A. 1938b The excretion of uric acid by the chicken. J. Cell & Comp. Physiol. 11:135.

Sharpe, N. C. 1912 On the secretion of urine in birds. Am. J. Physiol. 31:75.

Sharpe, N. C. 1923 On the absorption from the cloaca in birds. Am. J. Physiol. 66:209.

Shirley, H. V., and A. V. Nalbandov 1956 Effects of neurohypophysectomy in domestic chickens. Endocrinol. 58:694.

Siller, W. G. 1959a The pathology of avian glomerulonephritis. J. Path. & Bacteriol. 78:57.

Siller, W. G. 1959b Avian nephritis and visceral gout. Lab. Investigation 8:1319.

Smith, H. W. 1951 The Physiology of the Kidney. Oxford University Press, New York.

Sondergaard, E., I. Prange, H. Dam, and E. Christensen 1957 Uricemia and kidney damage in galactose poisoned chicks. Acta Pathol. Microbiol. Scand. 40:303.

Spanner, R. 1925 Der Pfortaderkreislauf in der Vogelniere. Morph. Jahrb. 54:560.

Spanner, R. 1939 Die Drosselklappe der veno-venösen Anastomose und ihre Bedeutung für den Abkürzungskreislauf im portocavalen System des Vogels: zugleich ein Beitrag der epitheloiden Zellen. Z. Anat. Entwicklungsgeschichte 109:443.

Sperber, I. 1948 Investigations on the circulatory system of the avian kidney. Zoologiska Bidrag (Uppsala) 27:429.

Sperber, I. 1954 Competitive inhibition and specificity of renal tubular transport mechanisms. Arch. Int. Pharm. 97:221.

Sperber, I. 1960 Excretion, Chapter 12, Biology and Comparative Physiology of Birds, ed. A. J. Marshall. Academic Press, New York.

Sykes, A. H. 1960a The renal clearance of uric acid and P-amino hippurate in the fowl. Res. Vet. Sci. 1:308.

Sykes, A. H. 1960b The excretion of inulin, creatinine and ferrocyanide by the fowl. Res. Vet. Sci. 1:315.

Sykes, A. H. 1961 The action of hydrochlorothiazide in the turkey. Vet. Rec. 73:396.

Thesleff, S., and K. Schmidt-Nielsen 1962 An electrophysiological study of the salt gland of the Herring Gull. Mm. J. Physiol. 202:597.

Weyrauch, H. M., and S. I. Roland 1957 Electrolyte absorption from fowl's cloaca. Trans. Am. Assoc. Genito-Urinary Surgeons 49:117.

Wolbach, R. A. 1955 Renal regulation of acid base balance in the chicken. Am. J. Physiol. 181:149.

CHAPTER 14

The Special Senses

BY M. R. KARE

The Eye and Vision

THE optic lobes in the brain of the bird are unusually large and prominent. The eyes constitute a much greater volume of the head of the bird than do eyes in mammals. With a few interesting exceptions the bird is a vision-oriented animal, and it has been used extensively in research on vision.

The avian eye has structural components similar to that of the reptile. It also has unique features, some of which are probably adaptations for flight. The avian eye, unlike that of mammals, is not spherical, and its exact shape varies with the species (Figure 43). The shape is characterized by a concavity around the cornea. The resultant loss of strength in the structure is compensated for by a ring of scleral ossicles.

STRUCTURE

The bird has an upper and lower eyelid which close only in sleep. Underneath these is an additional eyelid, the nictitating membrane, which is present also in reptiles. This membrane covers the eye in flight and has a protective function. The eyes are moistened by secretions from the Harderian and lachrymal glands.

The outer layer of the eye, the sclera, contains cartilage, as it does in reptiles. The sclera is opaque except at its exposed surface, where it is transparent and unites with other tissue to form the cornea. The cornea is histologically similar to that of mammals except that Bowman's membrane is not always differentiated (Walls, 1942). The size of the cornea varies with species, being relatively

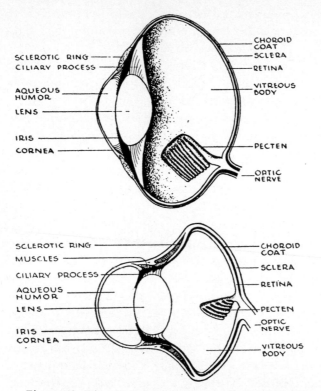

SCLEROTIC RING
CILIARY PROCESS

AQUEOUS
HUMOR

LENS

IRIS

CORNEA

CHOROID
COAT
SCLERA
RETINA

VITREOUS
BODY

PECTEN

OPTIC
NERVE

SCLEROTIC RING
MUSCLES
CILIARY PROCESS
AQUEOUS
HUMOR
LENS
IRIS
CORNEA

CHOROID
COAT
SCLERA
RETINA
PECTEN
OPTIC
NERVE
VITREOUS
BODY

Figure 43. Diagram of sections through the eyeball of a pigeon (upper), which has a flat eye, and of an owl (lower), which has a tubular eye. (From Atwood, *A Concise Comparative Anatomy,* C. V. Mosby Co., St. Louis, 1947.)

small in underwater swimmers and large in nocturnal birds. A ring of bone segments set around the cornea, the sclerotic ring, serves to offset extra- and intraocular pressures. These provide a firm origin for the muscles of accommodation.

Two layers of tissue inside the fibrous sclera are the choroid membrane and the retina. The intermediate choroid layer is highly vascular and serves to nourish the cells of the retina. The ciliary body is a thickened, folded anterior part of the choroid. The ciliary body in turn suspends the lens, which is a biconvex transparent body immediately behind the iris. The lens is chemically similar to that in mammals and has a comparable refractive index.

The iris is a pigmented continuous extension of the choroid and is pierced by the pupil, which controls the amount of light striking the lens.

The anterior cavity between the cornea and the lens is filled with a proteinaceous substance called the aqueous humor. The interior of the eye, the posterior cavity, contains a similar but more refractive material referred to as the vitreous humor. In chickens the vitreous humor is watery, whereas in predaceous birds such as the eagle and the owl it is more gelatinous. These fluids keep the eyeball distended and change the refractive index for the light passing through the eye. Changes in pressure in these fluids can cause disturbances in vision.

Pecten. The pecten projects from the retina at the base of the optic nerve into the vitreous humor. It is a highly vascular, pigmented structure with from 3 to 30 laminae folded accordion fashion. The number of folds and the size of the pecten vary greatly with the species. The domestic chicken has approximately 18 (Mann, 1924). The functions of the pecten are disputed, and many possible roles have been suggested. The evidence cited for its having a primarily nutritive function is that a similar structure in reptiles serves a nutritive purpose and that mammals, which lack the pecten, possess a highly vascular retina. However, Menner (1938) points out an apparent correlation of the size and shape of the pecten and the habits of the birds involved, which leads him to question whether it has an exclusively nutritional role. He suggests that the pecten increases the sensitivity of the eye to small moving images by casting a shadow on the retina, producing discontinuous images on localized areas of the retina. Crozier and Wolf (1943) provide evidence to support Menner's suggestion. The development and histochemistry of the pecten were described by O'Rahilly and Meyer (1960). They conclude that the functional significance of this organ remains an enigma.

Retina. The innermost layer of the eye is the retina (Figure 44). It arises during ontogenesis as a protrusion of each side of the anterior cerebrum. The retina of the bird is essentially like that of all vertebrates in its functional organization. Details on the histology of the avian retina are reported by Walls, 1942; Rochon-

Duvigneaud, 1950; and Polyak, 1957. The light is transmitted through the transparent retina and passes through most of it before forming an image at the pigmented epithelium. The light

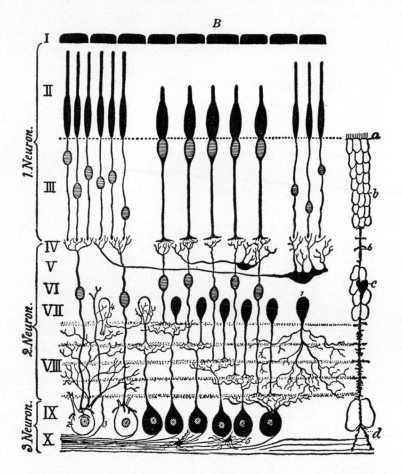

Figure 44. Schematic diagram of structure of the vertebrate retina. I, pigment layer; II and III, rod and cone cells extending into outer nuclear layer (III); IV, outer plexiform layer; V to VII, inner nuclear layer; V, horizontal correlation neurons; VI, bipolar cells; VII, amacrine cells (solid black); VIII, inner plexiform layer; IX, ganglion cells; X, axons of ganglion cells entering optic nerve. (After Greef, from *Fulton's Textbook of Physiology*, 16th ed., W. B. Saunders Co., Philadelphia, 1950.)

evokes a nervous response from the outer nuclear layer, which is made up of the rods and cones. These are imbedded in the pigment layer and point away from the lens toward the wall of the eye. The rods and cones are the photoreceptors which transduce the stimulus to nerve impulses and transmit the excitement to the bipolar cells. These in turn are connected to the ganglion cells, which traverse the inner surface of the retina and eventually converge to form the optic nerve.

The nerve system of the retina consists of small cellular groups, structurally well defined but with more or less distinct functions. Between these groups there are patterns of interconnection. In this they differ from such tissues as muscle, which have a more homogeneous pattern. The functional organization of the retina begins with the rod bipolar cells. Although a number of rod-nerve converge on a single rod-bipolar cell, in many instances the individual cone-nerve cells synapse with a single nerve fiber. This provides an exclusive pathway in the optic nerve, and suggests the more discriminative function of the cones as opposed to the integrative function of the rods. One ganglion cell may form a synapse with one or more bipolar cells. In the inner nuclear layer of the retina there is an abundance of nerve cells called amacrine cells, whose fibers run horizontally across the direction of the bipolar cells to form a synapse with the ganglion cells. A detailed presentation on neural activity in the retina has been made by Granit (1959).

Areae are places in the retina of diurnal birds where the cone density is highest, and within which there is usually a depression, forming a pit or fovea (Figure 45). Within and near the fovea, where the cones attain their highest density (a million per square millimeter in the larger hawks), is the place of maximum optical resolution.

Diurnal birds of prey and songbirds (Passeriformes) have very deep foveas. Most mammals have only one area or fovea; in some birds there are two (Polyak, 1957). Eagles, hawks, and swallows all have two foveas in each eye: one nasal or central, the other lateral or temporal. The eyes of the hawk and the falcon are so situated that each of the two central foveas may be directed to the side at separate objects and the temporal foveas directed ahead at one object (Figure 45). The eyes of chickens and turkeys have only central foveas (Rochon-Duvigneaud, 1950).

Photochemistry

Almost a century ago, Schultze (1866) suggested that the rods might be receptors of dim light (scoptopic vision) and the cones receptors of bright light (photopic vision). In all the photoreceptor cells the absorption of light employs a compound of the carotenoid class, conjugated with various proteins. The carotenoids consist of pigments ranging from yellow to red; they are fat soluble when unconjugated, highly unsaturated, and identifiable by their absorption spectra.

In birds the photosensitive portion of the rod cells consists of retinene. It is combined with a protein, opsin. The general term for this carotenoid-protein is rhodopsin (visual purple or scotop-

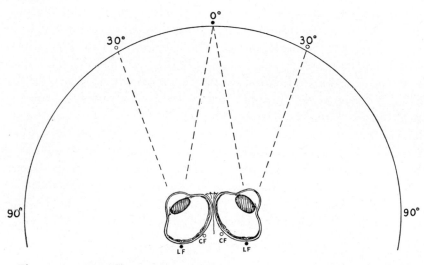

Figure 45. Foveal line of vision in falcon *(Falco tinnunculus).*

CF, central fovea and line of vision (30°); LF, lateral fovea and lines of vision (to 0°). The central foveas focus on two different objects simultaneously (monocular vision). The lateral foveas focus on one object (binocular vision). The four foveas can focus on three different objects at the same time. (Modified from A. Rochon-Duvigneaud, in *Traité de Zoologie,* edited by P. P. Grassé, Tome XV, Figure 184, Masson & Co., Paris, 1950.)

sin). The wavelength of maximum absorption of rhodopsin is near 500 mμ. (millimicrons) in most vertebrates, e.g. man 497, chicken 510.

The photosensitive pigment of the cone cells is referred to as iodopsin (photopsin). It was first extracted from the chicken retina by Wald and Zussman (1937). The carotenoids are identical to those from rhodopsin; only the opsin is different (see also Wald *et al.*, 1954). The maximum absorption of iodopsin in the chicken is 562 mμ. Recently Bridges (1962) isolated two pigments from the retina of dark-adapted pigeons. He was unable to extract a characteristic iodopsin from the retina of the pigeon, and questioned the reputed widespread occurrence of this pigment.

Central Mechanisms

The subcortical visual apparatus in the pigeon is almost entirely decussated. The optic nerve fibers originating in the retina of one eye terminate in the centers of the contralateral half of the mesodiencephalon. There is a point-to-point representation of the retina on the optic tectum in the pigeon. The upper visual field is represented on the dorsal surface (Hamdi and Whitteridge, 1954; see also Chapter 22).

Polyak (1957) commented on the remarkable complexity of the avian visual system. He noted that it involved a variety of subcortical centers directly related to the retinal fibers. The birds' optic lobes are relatively large; they possess an elaborate optic tectum which far exceeds the mammalian homologues, the superior colliculi, and equals the structure of the mammalian striate cortex. This would indicate a functional emphasis upon the midbrain in the birds' visual septum. An extensive account on the central mechanism of vision has been prepared by Bartley (1959).

FORMATION OF THE IMAGE

Focusing of light on the retina can be explained in terms of basic geometric optics. The image-forming mechanism of the eye has been discussed in detail by Fry (1959).

Refraction and Accommodation

As the light enters the eye it is refracted by the cornea, the aqueous humor, the lens, and the vitreous humor, and an inverted image is formed at the retina. The distance between the lens and the point of focus (principal focus) of the image is the focal length of the lens. For a given lens of fixed refractive index the focal length may be varied by varying the curvature of the lense. The combination of the curvature and refractive index of the lens determines the focal length of the lens. The refracting power of a lens (diopter) is traditionally expressed as the reciprocal of the focal length in meters. Thus a lens of one diopter, $1D = 1/\text{focal length} = 1$ meter.

The range or distance over which the lens can maintain a focus at the retina is known as the accommodation range. In mammals, birds, and most reptiles, accommodation is effected by changing the curvature of the posterior and anterior surfaces of the lens, by means of the ciliary muscles. Contraction of Brücke's muscle compresses the lens, shortening the focal length. The contraction of Crampton's muscle changes the shape of the cornea. In nocturnal birds these muscles are reduced and the focal length is virtually fixed. When the images of distant objects are focused in front of the retina, the condition is called myopia or nearsightedness; when the focus is behind or beyond the retina, the condition is called hypermetropia or farsightedness. When the distant image is focused correctly on the retina, the condition is known as emmetropia. Most birds are emmetropic or slightly hypermetropic, except the wingless kiwi (*Apteryx*), which is myopic (Walls, 1942; also Rochon-Duvigneaud, 1950).

In human beings, errors of refraction or accommodation are corrected with artificial lenses. The accommodation range in young children is 15 to 20 D; this decreases to about 4 D in middle age. Certain nocturnal birds such as the owl have accommodation ranges of from 2 to 4 D, whereas the domestic chicken and the pigeon are reported to have accommodation ranges of from 8 to 12 D. The close approach to their prey by insectivorous birds requires an ability about twice that of the pigeon. The diving cormorant has an accommodation range of from 40 to 50 D. The necessity for the cormorant to see in both air and water makes this ability essential.

Visual Field; Monocular and Binocular Vision

The angle or field through which the bird can see without moving its head is called the visual field. This field is determined by the position of the eyes in the head and by the shape of the eye. Birds with flat eyes (pigeons, chickens) have wider visual fields than those whose eyes are globose or elongated and tubular (birds of prey) (Figures 43 and 45). When the eyes are laterally situated as in the pigeon, the total visual field is about 300 degrees. In nocturnal raptors such as the barn owl (*Tyto alba*), whose eyes are frontally located, the total field is less than half that of the pigeon. Owls compensate for their more restricted visual field by frequently turning the head. The focusing of only one eye on one object, at a time is called monocular vision. When both eyes are focused on one object, the result is binocular vision. The chicken will often use only one eye while intently fixing on an object, but when picking up its food it employs binocular vision. The movement of the two eyes can be independent but becomes coordinated when binocular vision is involved. Many birds will follow a moving object with movement of the entire head and subsequently use monocular or binocular vision. Most birds are capable of binocular vision (penguins are not). The relative portion of the total visual field that is binocular is determined by the shape of the head, the shape of the eye, and the position of the eye in the head. Laterally placed eyes are capable of a smaller binocular field than frontally placed eyes. The binocular field of the homing pigeon is about 24 degrees wide (Walls), whereas owls and hawks with frontal tubular eyes have a binocular field of from 60 to 70 degrees extending straight ahead. Some birds have the added ability to see objects beneath them while their bills are in the normal vertical position. Depth perception is usually attained through binocularity; but in birds such as pigeons, where there is little overlap of visual fields, the typical back-and-forth movements of the head while walking, involving successive glances from different positions, may yield information on relative distance.

Visual Acuity

The sensitivity of the eye consists of an ability to respond to weak stimuli or a capacity for continuing to respond to light that is slowly being dimmed. The ability to distinguish details of visual objects as the details are made smaller and brought closer together is known as resolving power. Visual acuity reflects the degree of resolving power.

The acuity or resolving power of the retina depends upon the structure of the rods and cones, their spacing and concentration, and the number connected with each fiber of the optic nerve tract. The high resolving power attributed to avian vision is based upon the relatively large size of the eye, which permits a relatively large image to be cast on the retina. The bird also has a dense concentration of cone-nerve cells and a high ratio of optic nerve fibers to the visual cells.

The concentration of cones in the fovea of the sparrow averages 400,000 or more per square millimeter. In the hawk, the fovea may contain one million cones per square millimeter. Even outside the fovea, the hawk retina has nearly twice the number of cones of the human fovea (Sturkie, 1954). In the fovea or fundus of wagtails (*Motacilla*) and pipits (*Anthus*), cone density reaches 120,000 per square millimeter and the density of ganglion cells is about the same, indicating that every visual cell is individually represented in the optic nerve.

Pumphrey (1961) compares the visual acuity of birds and man, and concludes that the visual acuity of birds is not much greater than man's but that the rate of assimilation of detail is higher. The bird's vision is not sharper; rather, it is more rapid. The swiftness of flight makes rapid visual perception essential (Portmann, 1950).

Color Vision

All diurnal birds have color or chromatic vision. This attribute is associated with the preponderance of cone cells, whereas the rods are linked with the achromatic vision typical of nocturnal birds. The fundamental mechanism and the ability to discriminate colors in birds are probably similar to those in man.

A group of visual pigments, the carotenoid-proteins, is identified with the sensitivity of the retina to light and color. The dark-adapted rod-stimulated human eye responds maximally to

green light at a wavelength of about 510 mμ. The light-adapted
eye responds maximally at 560 mμ., or to yellow-green light. The
light-adapted eye therefore sees better in light of a longer wavelength than does the dark-adapted eye. This shift or change in response is known as the Purkinje phenomenon (Sturkie, 1954).

Electroretinograms of the chicken eye were found to exhibit
components typical of the eyes of other animals. Armington and
Thiede (1956) also demonstrated a Purkinje shift in this bird. The
eye of the pigeon, subjected to darkness for at least 45 minutes, becomes dark-adapted and responds maximally to light at 534 mμ.
and up to 664 mμ. The spectral range for the light-adapted eye is
424 to 704, with the maximum response to 564 mμ.

A comparison of the absorption spectra of visual pigments in
the chicken with the retinal spectral sensitivity of pigeons is illustrated in Figure 46. These results were obtained by inserting microelectrodes into the retina after removal of the lens and cornea.

Birds may be able to exceed man's capacity to discriminate between mixed colors because of the presence of colored oil droplets
in the cone cells. These droplets are orange, yellow, or red; they
act as intraocular color filters, intensifying similar colors but reducing discrimination of violet and blue (Walls and Judd, 1933;
Portmann, 1950).

A number of reports suggest that certain birds are sensitive to
extraspectral frequencies. There are also reports indicating a particular insensitivity to blue. Donner (1953), using a microelectrode technique, reported on the spectral sensitivity of the pigeon.
He supported the view that that photochemical substances involved in vision are the same in the avian eye as in other vertebrate eyes. The spectral threshold of starlings (*Sturnus vulgaris*)
was studied by Adler and Dalland (1959), using an operant conditioning technique. They reported that the dark-adaptation curve
of the starling differed considerably from what might be expected
of a human being under similar conditions.

Behavioral experiments for color vision in birds began with the
work of Hess (1912). He sprinkled grain on a floor and illuminated it with the six colors projected in a spectrum. He reported that
the chickens ate the grain illuminated by red, yellow, and green

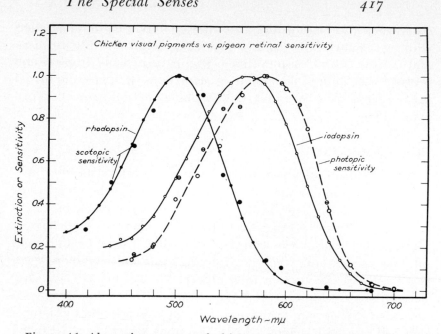

Figure 46. Absorption spectra of chicken rhodopsin and iodopsin, compared with the spectral sensitivities of dark- and light-adapted pigeons. The latter were measured electrophysiologically and are plotted in terms of the reciprocals of the numbers of incident quanta needed to evoke a constant electrical response. The scotopic data are from Donner, the photopic data from the same source (*barred circles*) and from Granit (*open circles*). The scotopic sensitivity agrees well with the absorption spectrum of rhodopsin. The photopic sensitivity is displaced about 20 mμ. toward the red from the absorption spectrum of iodopsin, owing in large part to the filtering action of the colored oil globules of the pigeon cones. (From G. Wald, Paul K. Brown, and Patricia H. Smith, Iodopsin., *J. Gen. Physiol.* 38: 62[1954–1955].)

light, but not the grain illuminated by the blue and violet light. Later, Honigmann (1921) and others, working with both stained and illuminated rice grains, observed that chickens did eat the blue and violet grains albeit less avidly than they did the others.

Watson (1915) and Lashley (1916) have shown that the chick's spectral limits are from 700 mμ. to 715 mμ. at one end of the spectrum and 395 mμ. to 405 mμ. at the other. The maximum sensitivity of the chick eye is at 560 mμ. and that of the adult fowl at 580 mμ. (Honigmann, 1921). This shift toward the red end of the spectrum was probably due to an increase in density of oil droplets with age. Some birds, such as hawks, woodpeckers (Piciformes), and parrots (Psittaciformes), have few or no red oil droplets and probably see blues and violets as man does. Strongly nocturnal birds such as owls have only faintly pigmented oil droplets (Portmann, 1950).

Behavior and Vision

Any discussion of vision in birds should consider specific function. For example, vision plays a primary role in the securing of food for the hawk whereas the owl uses hearing to locate prey.

Guhl (1953) studied the effect of limited light on bird behavior. He reported that chicks would start feeding when the light was one foot candle, and would begin to peck one another when it was two foot candles. Chickens were observed by Benner (1938) to use shadow to determine depth. They responded to photographs of peas with appropriate shadowing, but failed to respond to pictures that had peas with shadows in all directions. Chicks were reported by Hess (1956) to have a bimodal preference for color, with one peak occurring in the orange region of the spectrum and a second peak in the blue region. Pekin ducklings, on the other hand, he found to have a narrower range of preference, with a single sharp peak within the green and yellow-green region.

Perhaps the most commonly used bird for behavior studies involving vision is the pigeon. Largely with the use of operant conditioning techniques, a number of precise measurements of various psychophysical processes have been made. A general introduction to this research is contained in a review by Blough (1961).

Wood-Gush (1955) prepared a comprehensive review of the literature on the behavior of the domestic chicken. He concluded that chickens do not recognize form *per se* but can discern differences in shape and size. In discriminating between two figures they respond to an element of the figure rather than to the total configuration. Hens respond to optical illusions involving a purely subjective difference in size, in the same way that human subjects do.

The Ear and Hearing

Hearing is not uniformly developed, nor does it serve the same purpose in all birds. Hearing is used by owls to locate food, but in many passerine birds it functions primarily in relation to social behavior.

Hearing is generally conceded to be more highly developed in birds and mammals than in other classes of animals. However, the hearing apparatus of birds differs substantially from that of mammals.

STRUCTURE OF THE EAR

The avian ear is similar to that of reptiles. However, unlike most reptiles, birds have an external auditory meatus or canal (Figure 47), which leads from the body surface to the tympanic

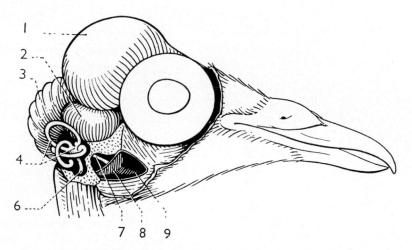

Figure 47. Diagram of lateral view of pigeon head, showing the location and parts of the ear.

1, cerebral hemisphere; 2, optic lobe; 3, cerebellum; 4, semicircular canals; 6, lagena or cochlea; 7, middle ear and columella; 8, tympanic membrane; 9, external auditory meatus. (From A. Portmann, in *Traité de Zoologie,* edited by P. P. Grassé, Tome XV, Figure 153, Masson & Co., Paris, 1950, after Krause.)

membrane or eardrum. This membrane is considered to be the boundary between the "outer" and the "inner" ear. A rod-shaped bone, the columella, extends from the inner surface of the tympanic cavity and joins the stapes, a bone that fits into a membranous oval window (fenestra ovalis) of the inner ear. The middle ear is situated in an air-filled cavity whose pressure is equilibrated with the oral cavity by the Eustachian tube. The bird's ear is almost inaccessible to bone-conducted sound (Schwartzkopff, 1955), since the inner bone structure is largely surrounded by air spaces. Unlike mammals, birds do not possess pinnae, and ceruminous (wax) glands are present only in some species.

Beyond the middle ear lies the inner ear, a fluid-filled complex of tubes and chambers whose tortuous shape has caused it to be known as the labyrinth. It consists of three functionally distinct structures. (1) The semicircular canals (Figure 47), which extend outward from the central bony casing, are concerned with maintaining equilibrium. (2) Closely related to the semicircular canals, and probably interconnected with them by nerves, are a pair of chambers called the utriculus and the sacculus (Figure 48).
These chambers contain stones or otoliths on slender supporting hairs; the information from these sensory elements concerns the vertical or upright posture. From the standpoint of evolution these are the oldest parts of the inner ear; they have been found in many vertebrates, including primitive fishes. (3) A third process, the cochlea, in the bird is an elongated structure extending from the labyrinth in a direction generally opposite to that of the semicircular canals. Mammals characteristically have a coiled cochlea with from 2 to 4 spirals; an interesting exception occurs in the egg-laying monotremes, where the cochlea is similar to that of birds. The avian cochlea (lagena) differs from the corresponding organ in mammals in being shorter and uncoiled (Figures 48 and 49). The cochlea of the chicken consists of a slightly bent tube, about 5 mm. long. Within the bony cochlear tube is another tube, the ductus cochlearis, with an elastic wall, the tegmentum vasculosum, forming a double canal with an elastic partition. This membrane is said to correspond to the membrane of Reissner in mammals.

The basilar membrane is a thin structure with its fibers running transversely, so that it is stronger and stiffer in the transverse direction than along its length. Together the basilar membrane and the tegmentum vasculosum divide the cochlear cavity into 3 tubes. The fingerlike central tube, the scala media, contains the fluid known as endolymph; the cavities above and below this tube, the

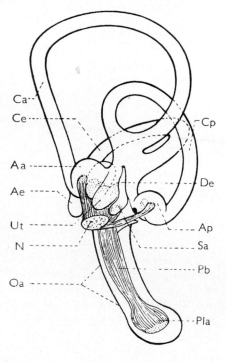

Figure 48. Diagram of inner ear of bird.

Aa and Ca, ampulla and anterior semicircular canal; Ae and Ce, ampulla and lateral semicircular canal; Ap and Cp, ampulla and posterior semicircular canal; De, endolymph duct; N, auditory nerve; Oa, papilla basilaris; Pb, basilar membrane; Pla, lagena; Sa, sacculus; Ut, utriculus. (From A. Portmann, in *Traité de Zoologie,* edited by P. P. Grassé, Tome XV, Figure 154, Masson & Co., Paris, 1950, after Satoh.)

scala vestibuli and scala tympani, contain a fluid, the perilymph. The exact composition of the perilymph and endolymph is still unknown. Facing the ductus cochlearis is a complex of structures, collectively referred to as the organ of Corti. These structures include the basilar membrane, hair cells, accessory supporting cells, nerve fibers, and tectorial membrane. In a manner not unlike that found in the retina, cylindrical cells lie in a long narrow row along the length of the basilar membrane. In any one cross section of the basilar membrane there are 30 to 50 of these cells. Each one is ciliated at the outer end, with numerous small rodlike hairlets whose roots enter the supporting haircells. The number of these cells in the bird's ear is considerably less than in man. The hairlets are covered over at their outer extremity by the tectorial membrane. The tectorial membrane is stiff with respect to vibrations, but lacks resistance to slow static displacements.

Unmyelinated terminal fibers of the auditory nerve enter the cochlear tunnel along its length and cross the membrane basilaris

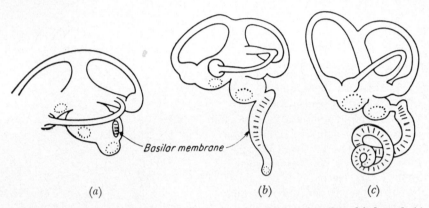

(a)   (b)   (c)

Figure 49. The membranous labyrinths of (*a*) a turtle, (*b*) a bird, and (*c*) a mammal.

The three canals at right angles to one another are concerned with the position of the head. The dotted circles represent small otolith organs, which serve in maintaining equilibrium. The auditory nerve endings are found in the regions indicated by cross-hatching; these regions are concerned with hearing. (From George von Békésy, *Experiments in Hearing; McGraw-Hill Book Co.,* 1960.)

to enter the organ of Corti; lying in a strip along the floor, they come into contact with the outer portion of the cylindrical hair cells at the roots of the hairlets. At the junction of the hairlets and the hair cells there is a stiff reticular membrane. At the site of the hair cells the mechanical sound energy is converted into nerve impulses.

Mechanism of Hearing

Several different theories have been offered to explain the mechanical aspects of hearing. One is that the number of nerve impulses reaching the brain corresponds exactly to the variations in pressure of the sound waves impinging on the ear. According to this theory, the analyses of the complexities of information carried by the sound is taken over completely by the nervous processes. A resonance theory was proposed by Helmholtz, namely that a series of separate structures, the arches of Corti, change dimensions progressively from one end of the cochlea to the other, and are probably capable of picking out the constituents of a complex sound and vibrating in sympathy with them. Helmholtz learned, however, that in the organ of Corti of the bird there are no arches or pillars to interrupt the continuous row of hair cells beneath the tectorial membrane, and accordingly changed his suggestions as to the resonating structure. Observing that the basilar membrane was composed of elastic parallel fibers along its whole length, like the cords of a venetian blind, he concluded that the basilar membrane must resonate in the manner of a reed frequency meter with the component frequencies of the sound. He observed that the variation in length of the basilar fibers would contribute to the frequency discrimination by the cochlea. There are many objections to this theory, including the absence of any clear-cut anatomical corroboration. Birds, cats, and rabbits have a basilar membrane made up of two layers of fibers, rather than only one layer as in man (Held, 1926).

Von Békésy (1960) has made stroboscopic observations of the actual vibration along the cochlea (Figure 50a and b), and reports that no structure of the cochlear partition exhibited movements corresponding to a system of resonant elements of the kind seen in a Frahm red frequency meter.

Electrical potentials recorded from the inner ear are of two types: one that is generated by the organ of Corti and is supposed to play a role in stimulating the nerve, and another that is produced by the nerve itself and is called the action potential. At low frequencies this electrical activity reproduces the form of the applied sound pressure. This electrical activity is the auditory counterpart of the retinal potentials, as revealed by the electroretinogram, and has become known as cochlear microphonics. The nerve action potentials generated at the level of the organ of Corti travel along the individual fibers of the acoustic nerve, to be projected to the cochlear nucleus and from there to several targets in the brain stem. In this function birds and mammals are similar. However, in mammals the brain stem paths terminate in the medial geniculate and thence to the neocortex. In birds the forebrain target is not the cortex, but is probably the corpus striatum. The peripheral end of the acoustic nerve diffuses itself along the path of the bony tube of the cochlea, and its ramifications pass through the bony

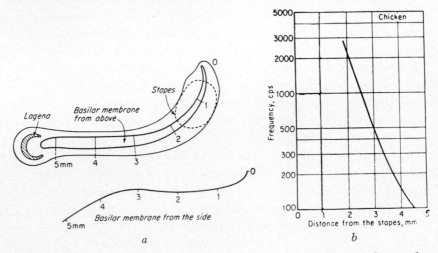

a   *b*

Figure 50. a. Form of the cochlea (above) and the basilar membrane (below) in the chicken. *b.* Positions of maximum stimulation along the cochlear partition of the chicken for various tones.

The basilar membrane of the chicken is represented as seen from above and somewhat to the side. The location of the stapedial footplate relative to the double canal is shown by the dotted circle. It can be seen that below 100 c.p.s. there can no longer be any mechanical frequency analysis in the chicken, because the cochlear partition vibrates as a whole, and the form of vibration is unaltered since the frequency is lower. (From George von Békésy, *Experiments in Hearing*, McGraw-Hill Book Co., 1960.)

wall which supports the cochlea. These ramifications have become known as the spiral ganglia, since in most higher animals the cochlea is a spiral. There are always two and sometimes three areas from which the responses are projected to the brain. Within each cerebral projection area there are specific smaller areas that correspond to specific places along the basilar membrane.

Von Békésy has contributed experimental evidence to support a suggestion that different frequencies are represented at different places along the basilar membrane of the cochlea. He has shown that a resonance theory is anatomically unsound; although spatial localization of frequencies along the basilar membrane does occur, it is not produced by a resonator mechanism.

Equilibrium

Pumphrey (1961) discusses at length the inner ear structures responsible for equilibrium in the bird. The semicircular canals provide continuous stimulation to the somatic musculature and are probably involved in the production of muscular tonus. Impulses arising in the semicircular canals, and their coordination with other stimuli, lead to compensatory body movement.

Hearing in Birds

There are two methods of measuring the distribution of sensitivity to sound in animals. The more difficult is the recording of cochlear potentials of the inner ear. A more convenient method is the use of behavioral tests with trained animals. A reflex movement produced by training can be a very successful index of the auditory capacity of the animal. An example is the pairing of an aversive stimulus, such as electric shock, to a sound that the experimenter wishes to investigate. The sound comes to have a biological value to the animal, and after a number of repetitions the animal will respond to the sound alone. Food can be used rather than shock, and some index of the animal's behavior toward the food can be obtained with sound alone after a number of pairings under the appropriate conditions.

Another approach, which might be called an ecological method, is implicit in the work of Payne (1962) with the barn owl (*Tyto alba*). His experiments demonstrated that the owl is capable of locating and striking a mouse in total darkness with a margin for error of less than one degree in both the vertical and horizontal planes. When recorded sounds of rustling leaves were substituted, the owl would strike with the same accuracy, except when frequencies above 8,500 cps were filtered out of the recorded signal; then the margin of error rose to about 5 degrees in both the vertical and the horizontal planes. When frequencies above 5,000 cps were absent, the owl made no attempt to strike upon hearing the sound. In owls the tympanum is exceptionally large, the inner ear is usually long, and there is a modification of the columella. In addition their ears, unlike those of other birds, are asymmetrical, and this aids in the localization of the sounds.

Hearing Range

The ranges of sound audible to various species of birds are shown in Table 61. The hearing range of birds does not extend as high as that of certain mammals, for example the dog, 35,000 cps; various mice and shrews, up to 30,000 cps; and whales and dolphins, up to 100,000 cps (Prosser and Brown, 1961).

The discrimination of frequencies within the range for birds seems to be about equal to that of man. Trained pigeons are able to discriminate between 300 cps and 365 cps, 387 cps and 500 cps, 800 cps and 1000 cps (Wever and Bray, 1936). Turtledoves and parrots have about equal discrimination (Jellinek, 1926a, 1926b; Knecht, 1940). Electrical potentials at the lagena show the ear of the pigeon to be less sensitive to loudness than that of the mammal.

Budgerigars (*Melopsittacus undulatus*) and crossbills (*Loxia curvirostra*) can discriminate frequencies differing by as little as 0.3 percent (Knecht, 1940) and are within the range of man's abilities. However, other species such as the pigeon have a lesser discriminatory ability (see Schwartzkopff, 1955).

Birds exceed many mammals, including man, in speed of response to sounds. Young chaffinches (*Fringilla coelebs*) can hear and learn details of song which would need to be slowed up at least tenfold before the human ear could detect the details (Thorpe, 1954). Oilbirds (*Steatornis caripensis*) find their way through the dark caves where they live by echolocation similar to that employed by bats. They emit a rapid series of sounds and respond to the resulting echoes (Griffin, 1953). Their speed of response is beyond that of man.

Behavior

The sight of an agitated chick under a bell jar will not attract the attention of the mother hen. Yet even out of sight, calls of distress from its offspring will immediately draw the hen to the place

Table 61. The hearing range of man and several birds (modified from Schwartzkopff, *Auk*, 1955)

Species	Lower limit cs./sec.	Highest sensitivity cs./sec.	Upper limit cs./sec.	Method	Author
Man (*Homo sapiens*)	16	1000–3000	20,000	—	—
Budgerigar (*Melopsittacus undulatus*)	40	—	14,000	D	Knecht, 1940
Starling (*Sturnus vulgaris*)	<100	2000	15,000	D	Granit, 1941
Crossbill (*Loxia curvirostra*)	—	—	20,000	D	Knecht, 1940
House sparrow (*Passer domesticus*)	—	—	18,000	D	Granit, 1941
European robin (*Erithacus rubecula*)	—	—	21,000	D	Granit, 1941
Greenfinch (*Chloris chloris*)	—	—	20,000	D	Granit, 1941
Bullfinch (*Pyrrhula pyrrhula*)	—	—	21,000	D	Granit, 1941
”	<100	3200	—	D	Schwartzkopff, 1949
”	<200	3200	20,000–25,000	C	Schwartzkopff, 1952
Chaffinch (*Fringilla coelebs*)	<200	3200	29,000	C	Schwartzkopff, 1955
Magpie (*Pica pica*)	<100	800–1600	21,000	C	Schwartzkopff, 1955
Crow (*Corvus sp.*)	<300	1000–2000	< 8,000	D	Trainer, 1946
Sparrow hawk (*Falco sparverius*)	<300	2000	<10,000	D	Trainer, 1946
Mallard (*Anas platyrhynchos*)	<300	2000–3000	< 8,000	D	Trainer, 1946
Domestic pigeon (*Columba livia*)	<300	1000–2000	—	D	Trainer, 1946
”	—	—	12,000	D	Wassiljew, 1933
”	50	1800–2400	11,500	C	Wever & Bray, 1936
Long-eared owl (*Asio otus*)	<100	6000	18,000	D	Schwartzkopff, 1955
Tawny owl (*Strix aluco*)	<100	3000–6000	21,000	C	Schwartzkopff, 1955
Great horned owl (*Bubo virginianus*)	60	1000	< 8,000	D	Trainer, 1946

D = conditioning.   C = cochlear potentials.

from which the sound emanates (Brückner, 1933). Klopfer (1962) discussed auditory imprinting in the Pekin duckling. The exposure of a duckling to a particular sound can lead to subsequent preference for that sound. However, this occurs only if the exposure has been during a specific and limited period after hatching, the so-called "critical period." Chicks hear almost nothing above 400 cps, a frequency which corresponds to the calls of the hen; but the hen responds to the calls (above 300 cycles) of the chick (Collias and Joos, 1953). Schwartzkopff (1955) suggests this may be related to a developmental stage in the middle ear of chicks during which the reception of higher frequencies is impeded.

The Chemical Senses

All animals respond to some chemical stimuli in their environment. Chemoreception in air-breathing animals is primarily associated with taste buds or olfactory epithelium.

The chemical senses are commonly divided into three classes: (1) olfaction or smell, (2) gustation or taste, and (3) the common chemical sense. Olfaction is characterized by a sensitivity to volatile substances in extreme dilution. This fact accounts for its having been described as a distance receptor. The gustatory receptors require more gross contact with the chemical stimulant. The common chemical sense is reserved for the nonspecific stimulants, often an irritant. The divisions between smell, taste, and the common chemical sense are arbitrary and can overlap, with a single chemical affecting all three categories. In some species, particularly among the less evolved forms, it is difficult if not impossible to distinguish among the chemoreceptor systems.

COMMON CHEMICAL SENSE

Moncrieff (1951) suggests that the common chemical sense is probably primitive, and that taste and olfaction are later differentiations. The prevalence of the common chemical sense in the lower vertebrates, and the diffuse and relatively unspecialized nature of the receptors both support this contention.

Irritants such as ammonia and acids stimulate the free nerve endings of numerous surfaces such as those in the nasal chambers, mouth, and eyelids of vertebrates. The nasal cavity of birds is innervated by the trigeminal as well as the olfactory nerves (Allison, 1953). Aquatic forms such as ducks and flamingoes have greater development of the trigeminal nerves than other birds; this may reflect a functional role in feeding, since aquatic birds might be expected to come into contact with chemical irritants more frequently than other birds.

The pigeon and the gray partridge (*Perdix perdix*) have been reported (Soudek, 1929) to be relatively insensitive to strong ammonia solutions. However, systematic studies have not been conducted on chemicals which stimulate the trigeminal nerves in birds.

SENSE OF SMELL

The question whether birds possess olfactory capabilities has long been debated. The nineteenth-century naturalists Audubon and Darwin carried out experiments to test the olfactory ability of vultures. They were preceded and followed by others whose works on smell in birds are as contradictory as they are numerous.

Structure of the Olfactory Organ

The typical avian olfactory system consists of external nares (nostrils), internal nares (choanae), nasal chambers, olfactory nerves, and the olfactory lobes of the brain. There are three nasal chambers, but only the turbinates of the posterio-superior chamber possess olfactory epithelium (Allison, 1953). Birds resemble reptiles in possessing three nasal conchae and in lacking the vomeronasal (Jacobson's) organ, although the latter has been identified in the very early embryonic life of birds (Mathes, 1934). In pelicans and their allies, the external nares are completely closed and there is a reduction of the size of other parts of the olfactory system. The comparative anatomy of the nose and the nasal air streams are discussed and illustrated by Bang and Bang (1959); see Figures 51 and 52.

The numerous negative reports on olfaction in birds probably have discouraged the use of this animal class in olfactory research, and may thus explain why so little work on the mechanism of ol-

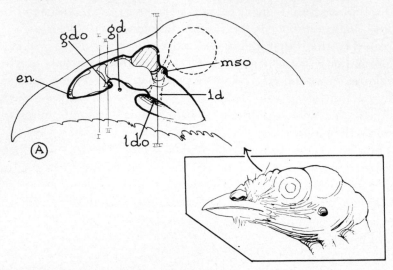

Figure 51. Diagrammatic sagittal section of right medial surface of nasal chambers of chicken. Not drawn to scale. Olfactory sensory area indicated by diagonal shading, position of eye and lachrymal duct by broken lines. Inserts of partially dissected head of chicken gives an idea of extent of fossa in relation to external landmarks.

en, external nares; gd, lateral nasal gland duct; gdo, lat. nas. gland duct orifice; ld, lachrymal duct; ldo, lachrymal duct orifice; mso, maxillary sinus ostium. (From Bang and Bang, *Bull. Johns Hopkins Hosp.*, 1959.)

faction deals with avian species. Current knowledge and theories of the peripheral olfactory receptors and central interpretation of stimuli are reviewed and discussed in depth by Adey (1959) and Ottoson (1963).

It is difficult to consider the olfactory system of birds collectively since there is so substantial a variation in development between species. The olfactory system is well developed in the kiwi, vulture, albatross, and petrels; moderately developed in the fowl, pigeon, and most birds of prey; and poorly developed in songbirds (Strong, 1911) Cobb, 1960).

Olfactory Development in Various Species

Vultures are carrion-eaters, and their ability to find food has been the subject of much speculation and anecdotal reporting in the early literature. Taber (1928) reported that they could not locate hidden carcasses, but Owre and Northington (1961) observed that vultures had some olfactory ability. The lack of uniform results has been explained on the basis of individual or species differences, minor visual cues, temperature, and many other factors.

Albatrosses and storm petrels possess tubular nostrils. They feed on a variety of marine animals and on animal refuse of all kinds. They seem to be attracted to fatty substances. Many of these birds eject an oil with a strong odor which appears to serve a social function (Murphy, 1936).

The kiwi, one of the flightless birds confined to New Zealand, is nocturnal and feeds largely on earthworms and other hidden food. Its vision is poor, and it is the only bird with nostrils at the tip of the beak; also unlike any other birds, the kiwi sniffs while foraging (Benham, 1906). Experimental evidence for olfaction in the

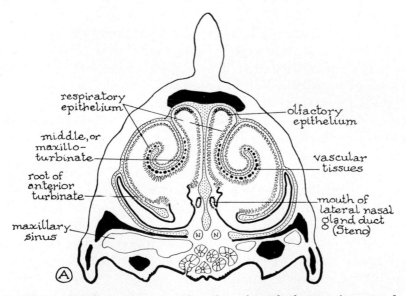

Figure 52. Diagram or map of sections through the anterior part of the respiratory portion of the nasal fossa of a chicken. Cartilage stippled; bone solid black; cornified squamous epithelium solid black line. (From Bang and Bang, *Bull. Johns Hopkins Hosp.,* 1959.)

kiwi is not unanimous; however, the anatomical and behavioral evidence is substantial.

Pigeons and doves have been used most frequently for studies on olfaction in birds. The emphasis on this group in unfortunate, since their olfactory development is only moderate as compared to the species already discussed. Olfactory sensitivity has been investigated using operant conditioning techniques. Calvin *et al.* (1957) reported that pigeons were not able to learn to use odor alone as a cue. Michaelsen (1959) reported discrimination in pigeons based upon olfactory stimuli. Cobb (1960), reporting further on Michaelsen's data, observed that this response was abolished after severing the olfactory nerves. In behavioral trials Soudek (1929), Zahn (1933), and others found that added odorants did not influence the acceptance of food and fluids.

Gallinaceous birds have been the subject of very little olfactory research. Although observation fails to suggest that the chicken is concerned with the odors of its environment, it does have moderately well developed olfactory lobes and nerve tracts leading from the turbinate bones.

When the olfactory lobes of chicks were destroyed by electric cautery, and the birds were exposed to a variety of compounds odorous to man, they showed no change in preference behavior that could be attributed to the surgery. Normal chicks were presented with two identical waterers, resting above screen-covered pans, only one of which contained an odorous material. The presence of the odor failed to exert a measurable effect on the preference between the waterers.

The olfactory system in a number of aquatic species, e.g. penguins, geese, and terns (Bang and Bang, 1959) has been described as well developed. Ducks and geese have been reported to respond to human odors (Phythian-Adams, 1953). However, Walter (1943) was unable to condition gastric juice secretion in domestic ducks in response to olfactory stimuli, although the birds were readily conditioned to visual stimuli.

The reports on olfactory behavior in songbirds are predominantly negative. Work has been carried out with thrushes, finches, siskins, robins, tits, and warblers.

Methods of Detecting Olfaction

The most common laboratory test of olfaction in birds has been based on the response to a choice situation. The innumerable variations in method make comparisons of the data from such tests almost impossible. The failure of a bird to respond to an odorant added to the feed raises the question of whether or not the odorant was carried to a receptor. Transport of the chemicals to the olfactory epithelium might be effected only in flight. Furthermore, it could well be that the perfumes or reagent-grade chemicals which have often been used simply did not correspond to the birds' spectrum of chemical sensitivity. Also, olfactory stimuli may perhaps be meaningful only in a specific context.

On the other hand, an apparent response to an added odorant might in actuality be the result of visual or tactile cues. In some of the reports the odorants employed were gaseous, and could thus have stimulated the sensitive receptors in the eyes.

Summary

The evidence available on the sense of smell in birds does not permit many generalizations. At one extreme is the kiwi, with anatomical development and "sniffing behavior" indicating that olfaction is functional in locating food. At the other extreme are the songbirds, for which there is little evidence of a functioning olfactory apparatus.

For most birds the evidence does not suggest a pre-eminent role for olfaction among their natural functions. Domesticated birds reveal no concern for the odors of their environment. However, the presence of neuroanatomical structures suggests that olfactory information can be transmitted even if it is not behaviorally meaningful.

TASTE

The function of taste in an animal is to encourage the ingestion of nutrients, perhaps to discriminate among foods that are available, and possibly to avoid those that are toxic. It is to be expected that the taste system in a particular species will serve to complement the metabolic and dietary requirements of that species.

Taste Receptors

Avian taste buds were first described by Botezat (1904). Taste receptors in chickens, 30 microns wide by 70 microns long, are found at the base of the tongue and the floor of the pharynx, commonly in close association with the salivary glands (Lindenmaier and Kare, 1959). As one might except, the highly cornified anterior part of the tongue is devoid of taste buds. Avian taste buds, intermediate in shape between those of fish and of mammals, resemble those of reptiles and are innervated by the glossopharyngeal nerve. Taste buds are composed of three types of cells, whose respective functions are sensory, supporting, and (to a small degree) basal. Engelmann (1957) suggests that taste acuity of the fowl is related to the total number of sensory cells.

Although birds have relatively few taste buds compared to other species, the significance, if any, of numbers and taste behavior has not been explained. The number of taste buds in the domestic fowl are reported to increase with age, whereas the converse has been found in the bullfinch (table 62).

Little use has been made of birds in neuroanatomical research

Table 62. Numbers of taste buds in various animals (from Kare and Ficken, in *Taste and Olfaction*, ed. Zotterman Pergamon Press, N.Y. 1963)

Chicken	24	(Lindenmaier & Kare, 1957)
Pigeon	37	(Moore & Elliott, 1946)
Bullfinch	46	(Duncan, 1960)
Starling	200	(Bath, 1906)
Duck	200	"
Parrot	350	"
Snake	0	(Payne, 1945)
Kitten	473	(Elliott, 1937)
Bat	800	(Moncrieff, 1951)
Human	9,000	(Cole, 1941)
Pig and goat	15,000	(Moncrieff, 1951)
Rabbit	17,000	"
Calf	25,000	(Weber, Davies, & Kare, 1961)
Catfish	100,000	(Hymen, 1942)

on taste. The reader is referred to Pfaffmann (1959) for a detailed discussion, based largely on mammalian research, of current knowledge and theories concerning central functions and peripheral mechanisms in taste.

Methods of Study

The early studies of taste in birds consisted of observing the behavior of birds as they consumed a food or fluid in their natural environment. The most common laboratory method used to measure the sensitivity of birds to taste stimuli is the preference test. Usually the material to be tested is placed in aqueous solution, and the animal is given a choice between the mixture and distilled water (Kare *et al.*, 1957). Duncan (1960), working with the feral pigeon, used a single stimulus method. The choices are presented singly at different times, thus eliminating possible position bias.

Electrophysiological studies involve the application of substances to the tongue of the subject and the measurement of subsequent discharges of the glossopharyngeal nerve. The results indicate whether or not the chemical has evoked a peripheral discharge, but not whether this chemical has had an appealing or offending taste to the animal. Although there are examples of close correlation between behavioral and electrophysiological response, there are also contradictions (Halpern, 1963). Using these techniques, Kitchell *et al.* (1959) demonstrated the water sense of the bird.

Operant conditioning techniques have been used to a very limited extent in taste research with birds, but such techniques have been extensively used in studies on vision in birds (Adler, 1963).

Research on taste in birds has been handicapped by the general assumption that they live in the human sensory world. The taste sensations experienced by man apparently are not the same as for birds. Nevertheless, in order to compare results obtained from birds with data for man or any other species, the classical taste categories of sweet, sour, bitter, and salty must be used.

Ability to Taste

Sweet. Contrary to the widely held supposition that sugars have a universal appeal, Kare and Medway (1959) observed that the

fowl was indifferent to the common sugars. Also indifferent to sucrose are the Japanese quail (*Coturnix*), jungle fowl, herring
gulls, redwinged blackbirds, starlings, finches, pigeons, geese, bob-
white, siskins, and laughing gulls. On the other hand, parrots,
budgerigars, and broad-tailed hummingbirds will select sugar solutions. There is unanimity in the literature that birds will reject
synthetic sweeteners such as saccharin or dulcin. Collectively, the
data suggest that nectar- or fruit-eating species such as hummingbirds or parrots respond to sugars, whereas insectivorous and granivorous birds are indifferent to them.

A number of factors other than taste might be involved, individually or collectively, in the response of a bird to a sugar solution, e.g. osmotic pressure, viscosity, melting point, nutritive
value, toxicity, and optical characteristics, among others. However, Kare and Medway (1959), using graded levels of sugar solutions up to a viscous 25 percent, reported that chicks accepted any
such solutions equally with water. These authors concluded that
no physical or chemical quality could be used to predict reliably
how a chick on an adequate diet would respond to the taste of a
solution. Visual properties and the surface texture of food have
been reported to take precedence over all other qualities (Morris,
1955; Kear, 1960) in the birds' selection of food.

Salty. The specific appetite for sodium chloride created by a
deficiency can be demonstrated with the chicken. Also, the domestic chick will delay drinking for extended periods in order to
avoid consuming a sodium chloride solution whose degree of concentration would exceed the ability of the chick's kidneys to handle it (Kare and Beily, 1948). In fact, where no alternative is available, many chicks will die of thirst rather than consume a toxic 2
percent salt solution. They will accept sodium chloride solutions
only up to about 0.9 percent (.15M; see Pick and Kare, 1962). Various other birds that have been studied have similar taste tolerance thresholds (Bartholomew and Cade, 1958; Bartholomew and
MacMillan, 1960, 1961; Hamrum, 1953). Mourning doves freely
drink any solution that is hypotonic to their body fluids.

Rensch and Neunzig (1925) investigated sodium chlorde thresholds (i.e., the lowest concentration at which solutions are rejected) for 58 species, and found that the thresholds ranged from 0.35 percent in a parrot to 37.5 percent in the siskin.

The domestic fowl on a diet very low in sodium or calcium will exhibit a specific appetite and select whatever is appropriate to its need in a choice situation. In the calcium-depleted birds Wood-Gush (1958) observed aggressive exploratory behavior with associated pecking. These birds were able to make the correct selection only from some of the presented calcium compounds.

The common tern has a high threshold for salt, which has been associated with the bird's intake of brackish water with its food. However, the herring gull, when given a choice, selects pure water over a saline solution.

The order of acceptability of ionic series by birds does not appear to fit into the lyotropic or sensitivity series reported for other animals. No physical or chemical theory has been offered to explain the responses to sodium salts and chlorides presented in Table 63.

Sour. Birds have a wide range of tolerance for acidity and alkalinity in their drinking water (Figure 53 and Table 63). Fuerst and Kare (1962) reported that over an 18-day period chicks would tolerate strong mineral acid solutions, i.e. pH 2 (Table 64). Organic acids were less acceptable, and the tolerance for hydrogen ion was not equally evident for the hydroxyl ion. The starling and the herring gull also readily accept hydrochloric acid solutions.

Bitter. A diversity of chemicals are offensive to taste at low concentrations. These include compounds that are bitter to man but quite acceptable to birds, some that are offensive to both man and birds, and a third category of those quite acceptable to man but rejected by some birds.

Sucrose octa acetate at a concentration bitter to man is readily accepted by the herring gull and the chicken. Quinine sulfate, which is used extensively as a standard bitter stimulus for man and rat, is also rejected by many species of birds. Both of these compounds evoked strong neural responses in the chicken.

An interesting compound is dimethyl anthranilate, which is

Table 63. The preference* for sodium and chloride metallic solutions at various concentrations over distilled water (chicks)

	Concentration (gm./100 ml.)				
	0.1	0.2	0.4	0.8	1.0
Na acetate	55*	52	56	52	51
Na sulfate	54	52	52	53	50
Na phosphate (monobasic)	52	53	52	52	54
Na succinate	49	52	54	50	56
Na citrate	54	52	54	47	35
Na phosphate (dibasic)	51	49	47	44	14
Na tungstate	50	46	48	—	—
Na bicarbonate	52	43	38	20	14
Na benzoate	49	41	23	15	10
Na bisulfate	38	23	35	17	23
Na pyrophosphate	46	37	20	3	4
Na perborate	42	29	10	9	6
Na carbonate	42	30	10	4	2
Na phosphate (tribasic)	46	20	4	1	2
Na cholate	4	20	3	—	3
Sodium Cl	50*	50	55	50	45
Magnesium Cl	49	51	51	53	45
Choline Cl	51	48	49	50	51
Manganese Cl	49	51	46	28	16
Strontium Cl	50	38	44	18	9
Ammonium Cl	49	46	35	12	6
Barium Cl	36	48	41	—	15
Calcium Cl	43	45	27	15	5
Zinc Cl	33	24	10	2	2
Cobalt Cl	26	12	6	5	6
Tin Cl	30	7	1	1	2
Copper Cl	6	11	3	8	4
Iron Cl	2	4	2	3	4
Cadmium Cl			lethal		
Lithium Cl			lethal		

* Preference $= \dfrac{\text{salt solution consumed} \times 100}{\text{total fluid intake}}$

Table 64. Percent intake of acids and bases at different pH levels

pH	1.0			2.0		3.0		4.0 —
Acids								
HCl	4	19	50			59		
H₂SO₄		15	35	54		56		
HNO₃	8			62		52		
Acetic						16		53
Lactic					15	61		

pH	— 10.0		11.0		12.0		13.0
Bases							
NaOH		45	47			33	2
KOH			48		36		3

Tabled values are the mean of replicate lots. The percent intake $= \dfrac{\text{volume of tested fluid}}{\text{total fluid intake}}$ ×100 (18 daily values were averaged). The position of the numbers is an indication of the pH of the test solution. For example at pH 1.5 the average daily consumption of HCl was 19 percent of the total fluid intake. Distilled water was the alternative in every instance.

used in the human food industry. At dilutions of 1 part to 10,000 it is offensive to starlings, Japanese quail, pigeons, redwinged blackbirds, jungle fowl, herring gulls, and finches.

The offensive taste quality of dimethyl anthranilate has been used to reduce food intake in growing chicks and turkey poults. The concentrations totally unacceptable in a choice situation had to be increased almost tenfold in a no-choice situation to effect a reduced intake over an extended period (Kare and Pick, 1960).

In many insects offensive secretions serve as a protective device against birds. Some of these have a caustic action on the eyes of the bird. The existence of mimicry in butterflies is explained on the basis of the distasteful quality of the model. Little is known about the chemistry of the offensive taste or its relation to human senses. Man's category of what tastes bitter does not always coincide with the birds' reaction.

Nutrition and Taste

The function of taste in nutrition is an enigma. When caloric

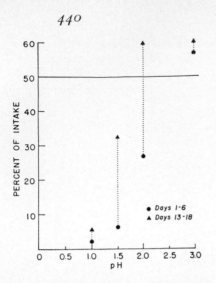

Figure 53. Daily consumption of HCl solutions for days 1–6 compared with daily consumption for days 13–18, expressed as percent of total fluid intake at four pH levels. Dot represents values for days 1–6. Triangle represents values for days 13–18. (From Fuerst and Kare, *Poultry Sci.* 41:71, 1962.)

intake is restricted, a chick will select a sucrose solution and increase its fluid intake to make up the deficiency (Kare and Ficken, 1963). A similarly correct nutritional choice was not made when the sugar was replaced with an isocaloric solution of fat or protein. Furthermore, a fowl acutely deficient in protein will avoid a casein solution and will select only water, apparently because of the taste.

In some experimental instances the bird's preference will complement its nutritional needs. However, the preference behavior of laboratory animals is not a reliable guide to the nutritional adequacy of a diet (Kare and Scott, 1962).

Temperature and Taste

The domestic fowl is acutely sensitive to the temperature of water. Acceptability decreases as the temperature of the water increases above the ambient. Fowl will discriminate when there is a temperature difference of only 5°F., rejecting the higher temperature. Chickens will suffer from acute thirst rather than drink water 10°F. above their body temperature.

At the other extreme, the chicken will readily accept water down to freezing temperatures. This pattern of sensitivity to temperature was also observed in electrophysiological studies. A sizable minority of chickens lack this sensitivity, however. Since the response to temperature may take precedence over all the chemical stimulants, it follows that in taste studies of the fowl, temperature should be eliminated as a variable.

Saliva and Taste

Saliva is involved in the normal phenomena of taste. Birds have been described as having a limited salivary flow. Using a technique that permitted continuous collection, Belman and Kare (1961) observed that the flow of saliva in the chicken was greater than that of man in terms of body weight, but less in terms of food consumed.

Individual Variation in Taste

Japanese quail and domestic chickens have been tested individually to measure their reactions to a variety of chemicals, including ferric ammonium, and calcium chlorides. Individuals showed markedly different thresholds. The distribution of thresholds was continuous, with reactions among birds to a single concentration of one chemical varying from preference to rejection. Chemical specificity was involved, since an individual which could taste one chloride at either unusually low or only very high concentrations would respond in an average manner to the others. It has been possible to select and breed for taste sensitivity to a specific chemical. This individual variation is not limited to birds (Kare, 1961).

That birds differ in their taste preferences as individuals, strains, or species has obvious ecological advantages. It would, for example, permit a population to utilize much more of the food in an environment than would be possible if all the birds competed for a limited group of nutrients.

Variation in response to taste is further compounded by possible seasonal changes. It is interesting to speculate as to whether taste directs or follows the abrupt changes in feeding pattern of birds that are insectivorous for part of the year and granivorous for the rest. A possible role for taste in the intensive feeding prior to migration is thus to be considered.

Summary

Birds have a sense of taste. However, no pattern, whether chemical, physical, nutritional or physiological, can be correlated consistently with the bird's taste behavior.

The observed responses, particularly to sweet and bitter, indicate that the bird does not share human taste experiences. On the other hand, the supposition that there is a difference in degree between individual birds, and an absolute difference between some species, appears warranted.

REFERENCES

Adey, W. R. 1959 The sense of smell, Chapter 21, Handbook of Physiology, ed. H. W. Magoun, Section 1, p. 535. Williams & Wilkins, Baltimore.

Adler, H. E. 1963 Psychophysical limits of celestial navigation hypothesis. Ergebnisse der Biologie 26:235.

Adler, H. E., and John Dalland 1959 Spectral thresholds in the Starling (Sturnis vulgaris). J. Comp. & Physiol. Psychol. 52:438.

Allison, A. C. 1953 The morphology of the olfactory system in the vertebrates. Biol. Rev. 28:195.

Armington, J. C., and F. C. Thiede 1956 Electroretinal demonstration of a Purkinje shift in the chicken eye. Am. J. Physiol. 186:258.

Atwood, W. H. 1947 A Concise Comparative Anatomy. C. V. Mosby Co., St. Louis.

Bang, B. G., and F. B. Bang 1959 A comparative study of the vertebrate nasal chamber in relation to upper respiratory infections. Bull. Johns Hopkins Hosp. 104:107.

Bartholomew, G. A., and T. J. Cade 1958 Effects of sodium chloride on the water consumption of house finches. Physiol. Zool. 31:304.

Bartholomew, G. A., and R. E. MacMillan 1960 The water requirements of mourning doves and their use of sea water and NaCl solutions. Physiol. Zool. 33:171.

Bartholomew, G. A., and R. E. MacMillan 1961 Water economy of the California quail and its use of sea water. Auk 78:505.

Bartley, H. S. 1959 Central mechanisms of vision, Chapter 30, Handbook of Physiology, ed. H. W. Magoun, Section 1, p. 713. Williams & Wilkins, Baltimore.

Belman, A. L., and M. R. Kare 1961 Character of salivary flow in the Chicken. Poultry Sci. 40:1377.

Benham, W. B. 1906 The olfactory sense in Apteryx. Nature 74:222.

Benner, J. 1938 Untersuchungen über die Raumwahrnehmung der Hühner. Z. f. Wissensch. Zool. 151:382.

Blough, D. S. 1961 Experiments in animal psychophysics. Sci. Am. 205:113.

Botezat, E. 1904 Geschmacksorgane und andere nervöse Endapparate im Schnabel der Vögel. Biol. Centralblatt. 24:722.

Bridges, C. D. B. 1962 Visual pigments of the pigeon (Columba livia). Vision Res. 2:125.

Brückner, G. H. 1933 Untersuchungen zur Tiersoziologie, insbesondere zur Auflösung der Familie. Z. Psychol. 128:1.

Calvin, A. D., C. M. Williams, and N. Westmoreland 1957 Olfactory sensitivity in the domestic pigeon. Am. J. Physiol. 188:255.

Cobb, S. 1960 Observations on the comparative anatomy of the avian brain. Perspectives in Biol. & Med. 3:383.

Collias, N., and M. Joos 1953 The spectrographic analysis of sound signals of the domestic fowl. Behav. 5:175.

Crozier, W. J., and E. Wolf 1943 Theory and measurement of visual mechanisms. J. Gen. Physiol. 27:401.

Donner, K. O. 1953 The spectral sensitivity of the pigeons's retinal elements. J. Physiol. 122:524.

Duncan, C. J. 1960 Preference tests and the sense of taste in the feral pigeon. Ani. Behav. 8:54.

Engelmann, C. 1957 So leben Hühner, Tauben, Gänse. Neumann Verlag.

Fry, G. A. 1959 The image forming mechanism of the eye, Chapter 27. In Handbook of Physiology, ed. H. W. Magoun, Section 1, p. 647.

Fuerst, F. F., and M. R. Kare 1962 The influence of pH on fluid tolerance and preferences. Poultry Sci. 41:71.

Granit, R. 1959 Neural activity in the retina, Chapter 29. In Handbook of Physiology, ed. H. W. Magoun, Section 1, p. 693.

Griffin, D. 1953 Acoustic orientation in the oil bird, Steatornis. Proc. Nat. Acad. Sci. 39:884.

Guhl, A. M. 1953 The social behavior of the domestic fowl. Kansas State College. Agr. Exp. Sta., Tech. Bull. 73:48.

Halpern, B. P. 1963 Gustatory nerve responses in the chicken. Am. J. Physiol. 203:541.

Hamdi, F. A., and D. Whitteridge 1954 The representation of the retina on the optic tectum of the pigeon. Quart. J. Exp. Physiol. 39:111.

Hamrum, C. L. 1953 Experiments on the senses of taste and smell in the bob-white quail (Colinus virginianus virginianus). Am. Midl. Nat. 49:872.

Held, H. 1926 Die Cochlea der Säuger und der Vögel, Chapter 2. Handbuch der Normalen und Pathologischen Physiologie, ed. A. Bethe, p. 467. Springer Verlag, Berlin.

Hess, E. H. 1956 Natural preferences of chicks and ducklings for objects of different colors. Psych. Reports 2:477.

Hess, V. C. 1912 Gesichtssinn. Handb. vergl. Physiol. 4:555.

Honigmann, H. 1921 Untersuchungen über Lichtempfindlichkeit und Adaptierung des Vogelauges. Arch. ges. Physiol. (Pflügers) 189:1.

Jellinek, A. 1926a Versuche über das Gehör der Vögel. I: Dressurversuche an Tauben mit akustischen Reizen. Arch. ges. Physiol. (Pflügers) 211:64. Cited by Wever and Bray, 1936.

Jellinek, A. 1926b Versuche über das Gehör der Vögel. II: Gehörprüfungen an Tauben nach Exstirpation des Mittelohres. Arch. ges. Physiol. (Pflügers) 211:73. Cited by Wever and Bray, 1936.

Kare, M. R. 1961 Physiological and Behavioral Aspects of Taste, p. 13. Univ. of Chicago Press.

Kare, M. R., and J. Beily 1948 The toxicity of sodium chloride and its relation to water intake in baby chicks. Poultry Sci. 27:751.

Kare, M. R., R. Black, and E. G. Allison 1957 The sense of taste in the fowl. Poultry Sci. 36: 129.

Kare, M. R., and M. S. Ficken 1963 Comparative studies on the sense of taste, in Olfaction and Taste, ed. Y. Zotterman. Pergamon, New York.

Kare, M. R., and W. Medway 1959 Discrimination between carbohydrates by the fowl. Poultry Sci. 38:1119.

Kare, M. R., and H. L. Pick 1960 The influence of the sense of taste on feed and fluid consumption. Poultry Sci. 39:697.

Kare, M. R., and M. L. Scott 1962 Nutritional value and feed acceptability. Poultry Sci. 41:276.

Kear, J. 1960 Food selection in certain finches with special reference to interspecific differences. Ph.D. Thesis in Cambridge Univ. Library.

Kitchell, R. L., L. Strom, and Y. Zotterman 1959 Electrophysiological studies of thermal and taste reception in chickens and pigeons. Acta Physiol. Scand. 46:133.

Klopfer, P. H. 1962 Behavioral Aspects of Ecology. Prentice-Hall, Englewood Cliffs, N.J.

Knecht, S. 1940 Über den Gehörsinn und die Musikalität der Vögel. Z. vergl. Physiol. 27:169.

Lashley, K. S. 1916 The colour vision of birds. I: The spectrum of the domestic fowl. Ani. Behav. 6:1.

Lindenmaier, P., and M. R. Kare 1959 The taste end-organs of the chicken. Poultry Sci. 38:545.

Mann, I. C. 1924 The pecten of Gallus domesticus. Quart. J. Microscop. Sci. (n.s.) 68:413.

Matthes, E. 1934 Geruchsorgan, Lubosch Handbuch der vergleichenden Anatomie der Wirbeltiere, Groppert, Kallius, Vol. 11. Urban & Schwarzenbeig.

Menner, E. 1938 Die Bedeutung des Pecten im Auge des Vogels für die Wahrnehmung von Bewegungen: nebst Bemerkungen über seine Ontogenie und Histologie. Zool. Jahrb. Abt. f. allg. Zool. u. Physiol. d. Tiere. 58:481. Cited by Walls, 1942.

Michaelsen, W. J. 1959 Procedure for studying olfactory discrimination in pigeons. Sci. 130:630.

Moncrieff, R. W. 1951 The Chemical Senses, p 172. Hill, London.

Morris, D. 1955 The seed preferences of certain finches under controlled conditions. Avic. Mag. 61:271.

Murphy, R. C. 1936 Oceanic Birds of South America. The Macmillan Co., New York.

O'Rahilly, R., and David Meyer 1960 The development and histochemistry of the pecten oculi. Dept. of Anatomy, Wayne State Univ. College of Med., Detroit, Mich.

Ottoson, D. 1963 Some aspects of the function of the olfactory system. Pharmacol. Rev. 15:1.

Owre, O. T., and P. O. Northington 1961 Indication of the sense of smell in the turkey vulture, Cathartes aura (Linnaeus), from feeding tests. Am. Midl. Nat. 66:200.

Payne, R. S. 1962 How the farm owl locates prey by hearing, in The Living Bird, Cornell Laboratory of Ornithology, 1:151.

Pfaffmann, C. 1959 The sense of taste, Chapter 20, Handbook of Physiology, ed. H. W. Magoun, Section 1, p. 507.

Phythian-Adams, E. G. 1953 Scenting power of birds. J. Bombay Nat. Hist. Soc. 51:750.

Pick, H. L., and M. R. Kare 1962 The effect of artificial cues on the measurement of taste preference in the chicken. J. Comp. Physiol. Psychol. 55:342.

Polyak, S. 1957 The Vertebrate Visual System. Univ. of Chicago Press.

Portmann, A. 1950 Traité de Zoologie, edited by P. P. Grassé. Tome XV: Les Organes des sens, p 213. Masson & Co., Paris.

Prosser, C. L., and F. A. Brown 1961 Comparative Animal Physiology. W. B. Saunders, Philadelphia.

Pumphrey, R. J. 1961 The Sensory Organs: Hearing in Birds, ed. A. J. Marshall, Vol. II. Academic Press, New York.

Rensch, B., and R. Neunzig 1925 Experimentelle Untersuchungen über den Geschmackssinn der Vögel. II J. Orn. 73:633.

Rochon-Duvigneaud, A. 1950 Traite dé Zoologie, edited by P. P. Grassé. Tome XV. Masson & Co., Paris.

Schultze, M. 1866 Zur Anatomie und Physiologie der Retina. Arch. mikr. Anatomie 2:175.

Schwartzkopff, J. 1955 On the hearing of birds. Auk 72:340.

Soudek, S. 1929 The sense of smell in the birds. Int. Cong. Zool. 10:755.

Strong, R. M. 1911 On the olfactory organs and the sense of smell in birds. J. Morphol. 22:619.

Sturkie, P. D. Avian Physiology (1st ed., 1954) Cornell University Press, Ithaca, N.Y.

Taber, W. B., Jr. 1928 A theory of how the turkey vulture finds its food. Wilson Bull. 35:221.

Thorpe, W. H. 1954 The process of song-learning in the chaffinch as studied by means of the sound-spectrograph. Nature 173:465.

Von Békésy, G. 1960 Experiments in Hearing. McGraw-Hill Book Co., New York.

Wald, G., Paul K. Brown, and Patricia H. Smith 1954-1955 Iodopsin. J. Gen. Physiol. 38:623.

Wald, G., and H. Zussman 1937 Carotenoids of the chicken retina. J. Biol. Chem. 122:445.

Walls, G. L. 1942 The Vertebrate Eye. Cranbrook Institute of Science, Bloomfield Hills, Mich.

Walls, G. L., and H. D. Judd 1933 The intraocular colour filters of vertebrates. Brit. J. Ophthalmol. 17:641. Cited by Pumphrey, 1961a.

Walter, W. G. 1943 Some experiments on the sense of smell in birds studied by the method of conditioned reflexes. Archiv. Neerland. Physiol. Homme et Animaux 27:1.

Watson, J. B. 1915 Studies on the spectral sensitivity of birds. Pap. Dept. Marine Biol. Carnegie Inst. Wash. 7:87.

Wever, E. G., and C. W. Bray 1936 Hearing in the pigeon as studied by electrical responses of the inner ear. J. Comp. Psychol. 22:353.

Wood-Gush, D. G. M. 1955 The behavior of the domestic chicken: a review of the literature. Brit. J. Anim. Behav. 3:81.

Wood-Gush, D. G. M. 1958 Personal communication.

Zahn, W. 1933 Über den Geruchssinn einiger Vögel. Z. vergl. Physiol. 19:785.

CHAPTER 15

Reproduction in the Female
and Egg Formation

ANATOMY AND HISTOLOGY OF THE FEMALE
REPRODUCTIVE SYSTEM

Ovary

THE ovary, or female gonad, is situated on the left side of the body at the cephalic end of the kidneys, and is attached to the body wall by the mesovarian ligament. The ovary consists of an outer cortex, made up of follicles containing ova, and an inner medulla. Before maturity the ovary of the chicken consists of a mass of small ova. Pearl and Schoppe (1921) counted 1,906 chicken ova which were visible to the naked eye (average among 24 birds) and about 12,000 in one bird which were microscopic in size. Others have estimated that the number of oöcytes in chicks may run into the millions (see Hutt, 1949). Only a few of these, however, reach maturity and are ovulated.

At sexual maturity the individual follicles in the chicken enlarge, to attain a diameter of approximately 40 mm. before ovulation (Figure 54). During embryonic development a right gonad and oviduct are formed, but usually these degenerate and only rudiments persist when the chick is hatched; however, some wild species have two ovaries, but usually only one oviduct (Witschi and Fugo, 1940). A persistent right ovary and oviduct have been reported in the chicken and duck (see Sturkie, 1954), and in rare instances both of the ovaries and oviducts are functional. Chap-

447

pelier (1913) reported such a case in a duck, which laid 2 eggs per day.

The incidence of persistent right oviducts varies and may be higher in inbred strains (Morgan and Kohlmeyer, 1957). Administration of estrogen to fertile eggs or embryos results in a high incidence of persistent but nonfunctional right oviducts (Burns, 1961).

The ovarian follicle is highly vascular except for the stigma, which to the naked eye appears avascular, although microscopic examination shows that small arteries and veins extend across it, according to Nalbandov and James (1949), (Figure 55). The ovary

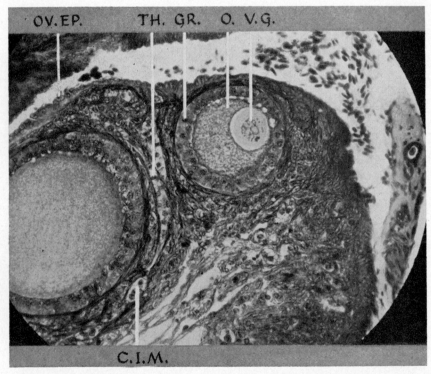

Figure 54. Cross section of ovary of chicken at two months of age.

OV.EP., ovarian epithelium; TH., theca; GR., granulosa; O., oöcyte; V.G., germinal vesicle; C.I.M., interstitial cells of medulla. (From Benoit, in *Traité de Zoologie,* edited by P. P. Grassé, Tome XV, Figure 279, Masson & Co., Paris, 1950.)

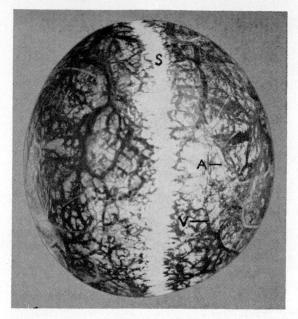

Figure 55. Mature ovarian follicle of the hen.

A, arteries; V, veins; S, stigma. (From Nalbandov and James, *Am. J. Anat.*, 1949.)

receives its blood supply from the short ovarian artery, which usually arises from the left renolumbar artery but may branch directly from the dorsal aorta (Figure 56) (see Nalbandov and James for details). The ovarian artery divides into many branches, and usually from 2 to 4 separate arterial branches lead to a single follicular stalk. A few arteries immediately surround the ovum; after branching, they pass through the theca, become arterioles, and form a capillary network peripheral to the basement membrane.

The venous system of the follicle is more prominent than the arterial system, and forms three layers or beds: 1) the innermost, located in the theca; 2) a middle layer; and 3) the outer or peripheral layer, consisting of a few large veins which encircle the follicle and leave via the stalk. Eventually all of the veins from the ovary unite into the two main, anterior, and posterior veins, which empty into the posterior vena cava.

Structure of Oviduct and Movement of Egg

The oviduct is the long, convoluted duct or tube through which the ovum is moved and where the albumen, shell membranes, and shell are formed. The oviduct consists of 5 distinct areas or parts

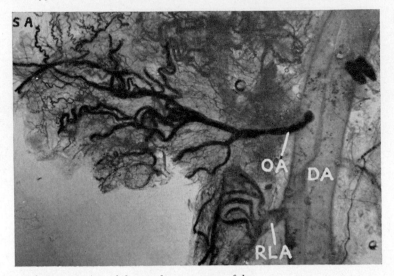

Figure 56. Arterial supply to ovary of hen.
DA, dorsal aorta; OA, ovarian artery; RLA, renolumbar artery;
SA, spiral artery. (From Nalbandov and James, *Am. J. Anat.,* 1949.)

(Figure 57), and varies in size depending on body size. The data that follow are concerned with the chicken.

Infundibulum. The infundibulum is the funnel-shaped anterior portion of the duct and is approximately 9 cm. long in the laying hen. The infundibulum engulfs the ovum when it is ovulated into the body cavity. The activity of the funnel is conditioned or initiated by the ovum, since it is normally quiescent until the ovum is liberated. If a foreign body is placed in the abdominal cavity at the time of ovulation and the ovum is removed, the infundibulum will engulf the foreign body. If this is done at some time before or after ovulation the funnel remains inactive. The ovum remains in the funnel, on the average, about 18 minutes (Warren and Scott, 1935). Occasionally the ovum is not picked up by the infundibulum, and the hen appears to be laying but never actually does so (Cole and Hutt, 1953, and others). The cause of the defective infundibulum is not known, but may be related to certain respiratory diseases. Sturkie (1955) demonstrated that the ovum (yolk), when not engulfed by the infundibulum, could be absorbed in the body cavity in 24 hours or less.

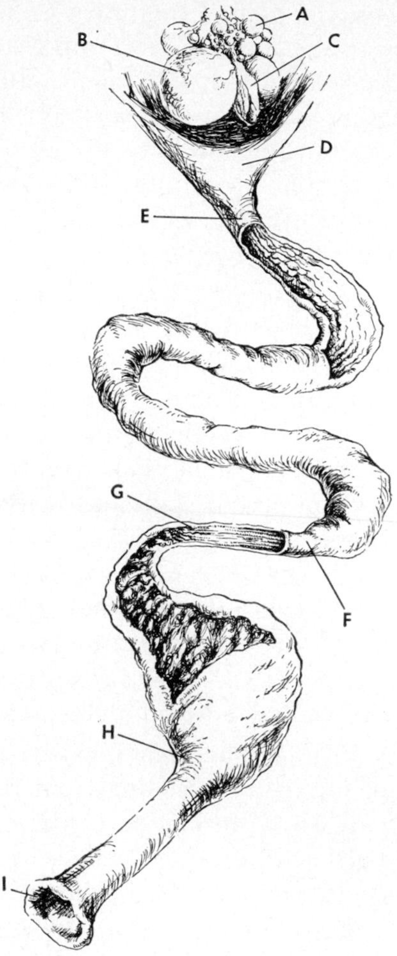

Figure 57. Reproductive tract of the laying hen.

A, immature ovum of ovary; B, mature ovum; C, ruptured ovarian follicle; D, infundibulum or funnel of oviduct; E, beginning of albumen-secreting region or magnum; F, end of magnum and beginning of isthmus; G, end of isthmus and beginning of uterus; H, end of uterus and beginning of vagina; I, opening of oviduct into cloaca.

Magnum. The ovum passes to the magnum, the largest single portion of the oviduct (hence its name), and measures 33 cm. in length. Here most of the protein of the egg (albumen) is formed. Histological studies by a number of workers reveal that the magnum is highly glandular and contains two types of glands, tubular and unicellular (see Romanoff and Romanoff, 1949). The tubular glands are composed of non-goblet cells which are not ciliated, but the unicellular glands are of the goblet type. The ovum remains in the magnum of the chicken an average of 2 hours and 54 minutes (Warren and Scott, 1935). Details on the formation of the various layers of albumen will be discussed later.

Isthmus. The peristaltic movements of the magnum force the ovum into the isthmus. In the laying female this region is approximately 10 cm. in length, and the line of demarcation between it and the magnum is distinct; the folds of the glands in the isthmus are not as large and numerous as in the magnum (Figure 57). The

inner and outer shell membranes are formed in the isthmus; some
workers, notably Pearl and Curtis (1912) and McNally (1934), believed that some albumen is added to the egg here, but the data of
other workers suggest that no albumen and only insignificant
amounts of water are added. The ovum remains in the isthmus 1
hour and 14 minutes and then moves into the uterus. Thus, the
time from the engulfing of the ovum by the funnel until it reaches
the uterus averages 4 hours and 26 minutes.

Uterus or shell gland. The uterus is the pouchlike portion of
the oviduct, which is approximately 10 to 12 cm. long in the laying hen. Its walls are thick and muscular. It contains tubular and
unicellular glands, whose function is unknown. It is presumed
that they form the watery uterine fluid which is added to the albumen through the shell membranes. Whether or not these glands
are concerned in shell formation is unknown. The ovum remains
in the uterus approximately 20 hours and 40 minutes (Warren and
Scott, 1935), where it receives the shell and where water and salts
are added to the albumen. The pigment of the shell is also formed
in the uterus, during the last 5 hours before laying (Warren and
Conrad, 1942). The brown pigment, porphyrin, is synthesized by
the shell gland from delta-amino levulinic acid (Polin, 1957).

Vagina. The vagina, which is about 12 cm. in length, is the part
of the oviduct leading from the uterus to the cloaca; it takes no
part in the formation of the egg, but may be involved in the expulsion of the egg. Details will be given later. A sphincter is situated at the border of the uterus and vagina.

Blood and Nerve supply. Little is known concerning the blood
supply and the innervation of the ovary and oviduct. Previous investigations on the anatomy of the avian oviduct and uterus have
been superficial. The early literature has been reviewed by Freedman and Sturkie (1963a,b). The reports of Mauger (1941) were
not detailed, and the drawings were very schematic. Bradley and
Grahame (1960) reproduced a number of drawings from the thesis
of Hseih (1951). These represented improvements over the older
work, but they showed nerve plexuses and blood vessels in the oviducal and cloacal regions without differentiation of the regions of
oviduct. Freedman (1961) and Freedman and Sturkie (1963a,b) re-

ported detailed studies on the blood vessels and nerves of the lower oviduct, particularly the uterus or shell gland. The principal blood vessels are shown in Figures 58 and 59, and the nerves are shown in Figures 59, 60, and 61.

Blood is supplied to the hen's uterus by three arteries, all of which originate from the left side of the body. The hypogastric artery, a branch of the left sciatic artery, carries blood to the anterior portion of the uterus. The hypogastric artery bifurcates into an anterior uterine and superior uterine artery. Lateral and inferior

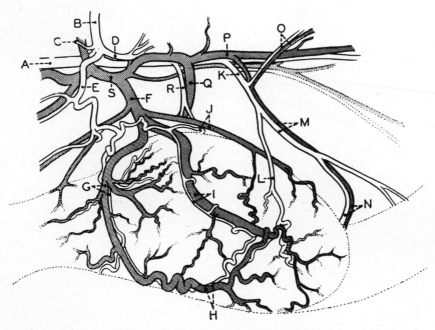

Figure 58. Lateral view of the blood vessels to the uterine portion of the hen's oviduct. The arterial system is in white and the venous system is shaded. Drawn to scale. From Freedman and Sturkie, *Am. J. Anat.* 113: 1 (1963a).

A, aorta; B, left sciatic artery; C, left middle renal artery; D, left posterior renal artery; E, hypogastric artery; F, hypogastric vein; G, anterior uterine artery and vein; H, inferior uterine artery and vein; I, lateral uterine artery and vein; J, superior uterine artery and vein; K, left internal iliac artery; L, middle uterine artery; M, left pelvic artery and vein; N, posterior uterine artery and vein; O, left pudendal artery and vein; P, coccygeal vein; Q, coccygeo-mesenteric vein; R, posterior mesenteric artery; S, left renal revehens (efferent) vein.

uterine arteries originate from the anterior uterine artery on both surfaces of the uterus.

The parasympathetic pelvic nerves originate from the pelvic visceral rami of spinal nerves 30–33 or lumbosacral nerves 8–11, but the principal contribution is from LSN 8 and 9. LSN 8 represents the first pelvic nerve in the chicken (see Figure 59). The pudendal

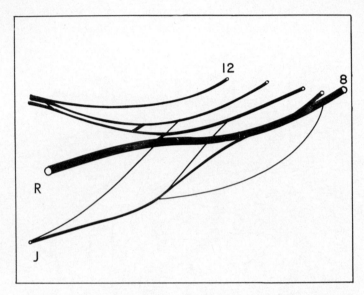

Figure 59. Diagrammatic representation of the formation of the left pelvic nerve from lumbosacral spinal nerves. See Figure 61 for abbreviations. (From Freedman and Sturkie, *Anat. Rec.* 147:431, 1963b.)

nerve, homologous to that in mammals, arises mainly from LSN 8 and 9. Only the left pelvic nerve innervates the uterus of the hen, via branches that accompany the middle and posterior uterine arteries (Freedman and Sturkie, 1963b); this is probably related to the fact that only the left mullerian duct persists in the chicken. Where the oviduct is bilateral, as in mammals, the pelvic plexus is also bilateral.

The sympathetic innervation to the uterus is from the hypogastric nerve, which represents a direct continuation of the aortic

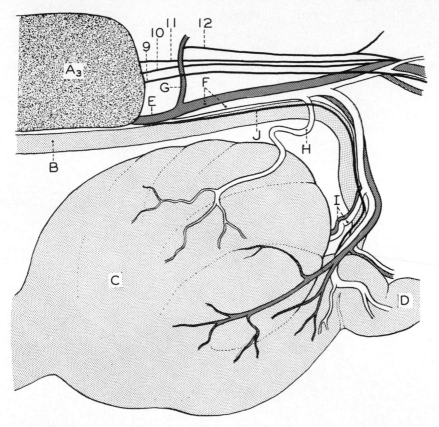

Figure 60. Semidiagrammatic drawing of the nerves and blood vessels supplying the posterior and lateral surfaces of the uterus.

The posterior lobe of the left kidney, pudendal vein, and spinal nerves have been reflected dorsally for a better exposure of the area depicted. Arteries are shown in white, veins are crosshatched, and nerves are solid black. X 2. See Figure 61 for abbreviations. (From Freedman and Sturkie, *Anat. Rec.* 147:431, 1963b.)

plexus. This nerve (present only on the left side) courses along with the hypogastric artery (Figure 61).

The pH of the different areas of the oviduct is highly variable (spanning almost 1 pH unit), but average values for certain areas are as follows: infundibulum 7.74, posterior magnum 7.17, uterovaginal junction 7.07, and vagina 7.70 (see Ogasawara, Van Krey, and Lorenz, 1964).

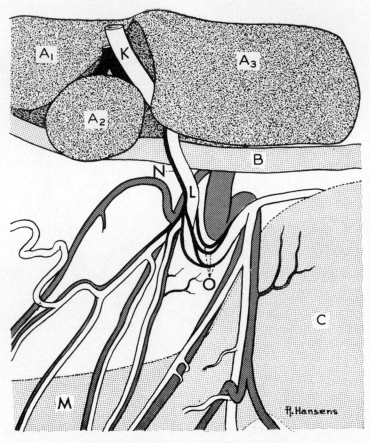

Figure 61. Semidiagrammatic drawing of the nerves and blood vessels supplying the anterior and lateral surfaces of the uterus. Arteries are shown in white, veins are crosshatched, and nerves are solid black. X2. (From Freedman and Sturkie. *Anat. Rec.* 147:431, 1963b.)

A₁, anterior lobe of the kidney; A₂, middle lobe of the kidney; A₃, posterior lobe of the kidney; B, left ureter; C, uterus or shell gland region of the oviduct; D, vaginal region of the oviduct; E, left internal iliac artery and vein; F, left pelvic artery and vein; G, left pudendal artery and vein; H, middle uterine artery; I, posterior uterine artery and vein; J, left pelvic nerve; K, left sciatic artery; L, hypogastric artery; M, isthmus region of the oviduct; N, hypogastric nerve; O, branches of the hypogastric nerve; R, left pudendal nerve; 8, 9, 10, 11 and 12, lumbosacral spinal nerves.

OVIPOSITION, LAYING AND BROODING HABITS OF BIRDS

In their laying and brooding habits birds vary in (1) the number of eggs laid in a given time, (2) the sequence in which the eggs are laid, (3) the intervals or breaks in the sequence, and (4) whether or not they incubate their eggs.

Wild birds usually lay one or more eggs in sequence, and then stop laying and sit on them (clutches). The number of clutches and the number of eggs in the clutch vary with the species and the season. Some birds, such as the auk and penguin, lay only one egg before sitting; the pigeon usually lays two, and the partridge as many as 12 to 20 eggs before sitting (Romanoff and Romanoff, 1949). Removal of eggs from the nests of some birds prolongs the laying time or number of eggs laid (indeterminate species), but is without effect in others (determinate species).

The interval between successively laid eggs of the pigeon is 40 to 44 hours, but the number of clutches and the interval between clutches varies with the season (Levi, 1941). Records from the New Jersey pigeon test (Platt, 1946) show that the number of clutches laid by pigeons averages 8 per year, and that the interval between clutches is approximately 45 days in the fall and winter and from 30 to 32 days in the spring and early summer. The laying and breeding seasons of some birds are influenced by climatic conditions, such as temperature and rainfall, and by the availability of food. For more details on the relation of behavior and reproduction in birds, consult Marshall (1961) and Lehrman (1961).

In some wild species mating or copulation is related to nest-building, which begins at about the time the female is sexually receptive. Nest-building in some species is also related to the time the first egg is laid, usually beginning a few days beforehand (Lehrman).

Laying Cycle and Rate of Laying

Many of the domesticated species, notably the chicken and duck, lay a number of eggs on successive days (a sequence); then the sequence is interrupted for one or more days before laying is resumed; such birds usually do not incubate their eggs. The terms "cycle" and "clutch" have been used to designate such behavior, but the Romanoffs (1949) state that only wild birds that incubate their eggs lay in clutches, whereas nonsitters lay in cycles. Neither of these terms, however, adequately describes the rate and rhythm of laying by domesticated birds. Strictly speaking, a cycle means a regularly recurring succession of events; applied to laying, it involves a sequence and the time intervals interrupting the sequence. Thus, a hen with a 3-egg laying cycle would lay 3 eggs on successive days before skipping a day or more and repeat the performance. According to the terminology of Romanoff and Romanoff, this is a regular cycle. For most chickens, however, the laying sequence and the interruptions in the sequence are not constant and regular; such behavior constitutes an irregular cycle, according to these authors.

Some of the variations in rhythm or pattern of laying exhibited by chickens may be illustrated as follows:

xx–xx–xx–	Two-egg cycle
xxx–xxx–xxx–	Three-egg cycle
xxx–xxx–xxx– – –	Regular sequence; irregular skip
xx–xxx–x–xxx–	Irregular sequence; regular skip
xx–xxx–x– – – –	Irregular sequence; irregular skip
xxxxxxxxxx–	Long sequence

The rate of lay, or laying frequency, represents the number of eggs laid in a given period of time, without regard to the pattern or rhythm of laying. Thus, a hen laying 15 eggs in 30 days lays at a rate of 50 percent. More details concerning sequences and cycles are reported by Fraps (1955). The frequency of oviposition within any cycle is indicated by $f = n/(n + z)$, in which n = number of days on which oviposition occurs singly or consecutively, and z = number of days intervening before resumption of oviposition.

Selected hens of the better laying breeds entered in the Random Egg Laying Contests laid between 250 and 260 eggs per bird per year. The number of successively laid eggs for most good laying hens ranges from 4 to 6, but some birds may lay for many days without an interruption in the sequence.

The interval between eggs laid on successive days by most hens ranges from 24 to 28 hours, depending on the length of the sequence (Warren and Scott, 1935; Scott and Warren, 1936; Heywang, 1938). This is illustrated in Figure 62, which shows the delay or lag in hours between successively laid eggs in a cycle. Thus, the lag or the interval between eggs is greater in short than in long sequences, and the intervals between the first two and the last two eggs of the sequence are greater than for intervening eggs, regardless of the length of the cycle. This difference in interval be-

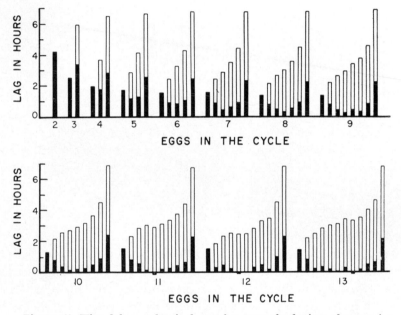

Figure 62. The delay or lag in hours between the laying of successive eggs in a cycle.

A 2-egg cycle is represented by 1 bar; a 3-egg cycle by 2 bars, etc. A lag of 0 hours means an interval of 24 hours between eggs. A lag of 4.2 hours occurs between the laying of the first and second egg of a 2-egg cycle (black bar). For the 3-egg cycle, the lag between the first and second eggs is about 2.5 hours, and between the second and third, about 3.4 hours (second black bar). The cumulative lag (white bar) is about 5.9 hours. In a sequence, the lag between the last egg and the preceding one is always greatest. (Courtesy of Dr. R. M. Fraps, based on data of Heywang, *Poultry Sci.,* 1938.)

tween eggs and the rhythm of lay of birds mainly represents differences in time of ovulation. Lag does not represent the interval between successive ovipositions, but the clockwise difference in time of day of one oviposition with respect to its predecessor (Fraps).

The actual time of day when eggs are laid depends on the length of the sequence and position of the egg in the sequence, and also on the length of the day (hours of daylight). Although hens may lay eggs during any of the daylight hours, most of them lay in the forenoon, and they tend to lay earlier when the days are longer. Birds laying three to four eggs in the sequence lay nearly all of them before noon, and most of them between the hours of 8 and 9:30 A.M. Birds laying one and two eggs in sequence lay mostly between the hours of 11 A.M. and 1:30 P.M., and between 9 and 10:30 A.M., respectively (Heywang, 1938).

The differences observed in the laying and brooding habits among different species of birds suggest that there may be temporal differences in the release of pituitary hormones concerned in the growth and maturation of the follicles, and in ovulation and broodiness. These will be discussed later in this chapter and in Chapter 17.

Control of Oviposition

The egg remains in the uterus of the hen for 18 to 20 hours, after which time the uterus contracts and forces the egg out through the vagina and cloaca. Little is known concerning the factors which normally initiate uterine contraction and oviposition, but there is evidence that the time of laying is influenced by the ruptured follicle from which the egg is ovulated (Rothchild and Fraps, 1944a and b).

Although recently ruptured follicles influence laying time, older ruptured follicles, and even unovulated ones, also influence it. Surgical removal of the recently ruptured, and all unovulated follicles retards oviposition for 9 to 36 hours. This might suggest that the ruptured follicle elaborates a hormone which normally initiates the oviposition; but attempts to isolate a hormone from the follicles have thus far been unsuccessful (Fraps, unpublished).

Later work by Conner and Fraps (1954) has indicated that removal of only a portion of a recently ruptured follicle actually caused premature oviposition, but that total removal still delayed oviposition time.

That light is not the main factor involved in the time of laying was demonstrated by McNally (1947) and by Fraps, Neher, and Rothchild (1947). Hens placed on a 14-hour light day and then on continuous lighting continue to lay out their cycles normally. When the birds on continuous lighting were fed from 8 A.M. through 4 P.M., most of the eggs were laid between 6 A.M. and 6 P.M. When, however, the hens were then fed from 8 P.M. to 4 A.M. under continuous lighting, the time of laying for most birds was during the hours of feeding. Body temperature also was highest during the feeding periods. However, later work involving changes in the feeding time, using automatic feeders, but involving no change in light regimen, did not change the time of laying (Wilson, 1963), nor did exposure of birds to noises at varying intervals (Morris, 1961).

Neurohypophysial hormones. Posterior pituitary preparations containing the pressor and the oxytocic fractions, particularly the latter, cause premature laying in the pigeon and chicken (Riddle, 1921; Burrows and Byerly, 1942; Burrows and Fraps, 1942). Obstetrical pituitrin (containing mainly oxytocin) injected at the rate of 0.1 to 0.2 cc. intravenously is effective in most birds within 3 or 4 minutes. More recent work by Munsick, Sawyer, and Van Dyke (1960), Sawyer (1961), and Heller and Pickering (1961) shows that the posterior lobe in the chicken contains arginine vasotocin instead of vasopressin, and also that the chicken uterus is very sensitive to vasotocin, fairly sensitive to vasopressin, and considerably less sensitive to pure oxytocin. That pituitrin causes contraction of the uterus was demonstrated in uterine strips *in vitro* by McKenney, Essex, and Mann (1932), and in the opened bird by Morash and Gibbs (1929).

Recently, Tanaka and Nakajo (1962) assayed the posterior pituitaries of laying hens and reported a decrease in vasotocin at the time of oviposition, suggesting that the decrease coincided with the release of the hormone and its effect on the uterus in causing oviposition. Douglas and Sturkie (1964) assayed the blood of laying hens for vasotocin, employing the frog bladder technique. They found that within 2 to 5 minutes before oviposition, the blood level of vasotocin increased many fold and then decreased to resting levels within 5 to 10 minutes after oviposition. These data indicate a causal relation between the release of neurohypophysial hormone and oviposition. However, there is some evidence which tends to militate against the view that vasotocin normally causes oviposition.

Shirley and Nalbandov (1956) showed that hens continue to lay normally after complete removal of the posterior lobe; these authors suggested that the operation inhibited the release of antidiuretic hormone (since the birds exhibited polyuria and polydipsia), and that possibly oxytocin was essential for oviposition, whereas in neurohypophysectomized hens oxytocin might come from the hypothalamus. It is now known that vasotocin is the principal oxytocic hormone and probably also the antidiuretic hormone in birds. Intracarotid injections of NaCl, which causes the release of neurohypophysial hormones in mammals was without effect on chickens; that is, the injection did not cause oviposition, as would be expected if it released the hormone (Sturkie, unpublished; see also Chapter 17).

Neural control. Since the shell gland receives sympathetic and parasympathetic innervations, one might expect the motility of the gland to be influenced by these nerves. However, transection of the pelvic nerves (Sturkie and Freedman, 1962), or hypogastric sympathetic nerves (Freedman and Sturkie, 1962) had no effect on oviposition. Studies involving cholinesterase stains indicate that the pelvic nerves are cholinergic. Administration of a cholinergic blocker (atropine) did not influence oviposition time (Sturkie and Freedman, 1962). The results of these studies indicate that the sympathetic and parasympathetic innervation of the uterus has little influence on oviposition.

Sykes (1953a,b; 1955a) made a study of nervous reflexes and oviposition, and reported that the "bearing down" reflex played an important role in oviposition. This reflex is initiated by cloacal or vaginal stimuli, such as occur when an egg enters the vagina, or can be evoked by other stimuli. Evocation of the reflex leads to an increase in respiratory rate and strong contraction of the abdominal muscles. Sectioning of the abdominal muscles (Sykes, 1953b) prevented normal laying in some of the birds even after administration of pituitrin, which usually causes premature expulsion. In others, oviposition was delayed. Sykes also reported that transection of the spinal cord at T5 and L4 (above the point where pelvic and hypogastric nerves leave the spinal cord) delayed oviposition considerably. He concluded that the contraction of both uterus and vagina is necessary for laying, and that "bearing down" aids greatly in the expulsion of the egg. Transection of the abdominal muscles is a drastic means of abolishing their activity. Sturkie, Joiner, and Freedman (1962) abolished the activity of abdominal and cloacal skeletal muscle by a less drastic means, namely the administration of curare, which paralyzes skeletal muscle but not smooth muscle. The results demonstrated that abolition of the abdominal press did not prevent oviposition although it delayed it slightly. Syke's evidence (1955a) for the belief that contraction of uterine muscle alone did not cause oviposition, and that the vagina must also contract, is based upon the *in vivo* administration of a local anesthetic, procaine. The drug prevented oviposition when applied locally to the vagina. Sykes did not think the uterine contractions were affected by this treatment.

Recently Opel (1964) has reported that electrical stimulation of certain areas of the brain, particularly the preoptic area, caused premature oviposition in a high percentage of birds, most of the eggs being laid 2 to 6 hours before the expected time of oviposition. Even insertion of electrodes without stimulation was effective, and the author presumed that the premature ovipositions were caused by immediate release of neurohypophysial hormone (vasotocin) following the stimulations.

Drugs and hormones. Morash and Gibbs (1929) demonstrated that histamine, acetylcholine, and ergotoxine produced contraction, and that epinephrine produced relaxation of the uterus. Atropine blocks the effects of acetylcholine. Acetylcholine and histamine cause premature oviposition, and ephedrine retards laying from 4 to 24 hours in the intact hen (Weiss and Sturkie, 1952).

Sykes (1955b) studied the effects of epinephrine upon oviposition in the intact bird and on uterine strips *in vivo*. Epinephrine retarded oviposition in the intact animal and inhibited motility of the strips. The muscles of the vagina exhibited variable responses. Epinephrine caused the circular muscles to contract, but the longitudinal muscle did not respond. Pituitrin likewise had no effect on the musculature of the vagina.

Recent experiments by Prasad, Davis, and Dale (1963) indicate that the response of avian uterine strips to epinephrine and isoproterenol depends upon estrogen. Uterine strips from nonlaying and presumably nonestrogenized hens may show a contractile response to epinephrine, and estrogenized muscle an inhibiting one.

Polin and Sturkie (1955) observed a hen that habitually laid soft-shelled eggs; when the hen was injected with ephedrine sulfate, which causes relaxation of uterine muscle, she laid normal, shelled eggs. Hypothermia causes hens to expel eggs prematurely from the uterus (Sturkie, 1946). Sutures (thread) placed in the uterus of hens caused the birds to expel the eggs prematurely (Sykes, 1953a).

Beta aminopropionitrile (BAP), the toxic substance of lathyrus odoratus, when administered to laying hens, decreases the number of eggs laid and increases the number of shell-less eggs laid (Barnett, Richey, and Morgan, 1957). The mechanism responsible for shell-less eggs is not known. They may be the result of a premature contraction of uterus and expulsion of egg before calcium deposition has occurred, or there may be some defect in the mechanism of calcium deposition (see later section).

Progesterone, desoxycorticosterone acetate, and certain estrogens and androgens may retard oviposition in the pigeon and dove, particularly if administered in large amounts (Dunham and Riddle, 1942). The mechanical properties of the avian shell gland have been studied by Hoover, Smith, and Abbott (1962).

Orientation of Egg in Oviduct

The orientation of the egg in the oviduct and its movement and rotation have been subjects of controversy. Early workers, including Purkinje in 1825 and Von Baer in 1828, and others since (see

Bradfield, 1951, for review), observed that the egg in the uterus of the opened hen lay with its pointed end caudad. However, a number of investigators observed that the blunt end of the egg emerged first (caudad) when the egg was laid. Olsen and Byerly (1932), however, in an extensive study, observed that the pointed end appeared first in from 66 to 82 percent of the eggs laid. Their method of study was to wait until the bird rose to its feet, apparently to lay, and then either to remove the bird from the nest and let it lay in the observer's hand, or else to place one hand under the cloaca and grasp the egg as it emerged. Bradfield, by fluoroscopic examinations of the egg in the uterus of the bird, showed that during most of the 18 to 20 hours that the egg was in the uterus it remained in the same position, with the pointed end directed caudally, but that just prior to laying the egg was rotated through 180° and was laid with the blunt end caudad.

Fistulation. A technique of fistulation of the hen's oviduct through the abdominal wall has been described by Gilbert and Wood-Gush (1963).

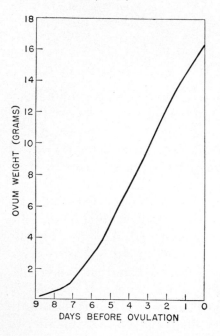

FORMATION AND GROWTH OF OVA

As the female approaches sexual maturity, the immature ova begin growing at a rapid rate; in the chicken they reach maturity within 9 or 10 days (see Figure 63). The weight of the yolk during the 7 days preceding maturity and ovulation increases

←◀◀◀

Figure 63. Changes in weight of the ovum of the chicken during the 9 days preceding ovulation. (From Warren and Conrad, *J. Agric. Res.,* 1939.)

approximately 16-fold, in a regular and straight-line fashion.

During the growth period the yolk material is laid down in concentric rings (Figure 64). The rate of growth and the amount of yolk deposited in a given time can be determined by feeding or by the injection of Sudan III, a fat dye which leaves marks on the yolk.

The rate of growth of the ovum in wild species is similar to that

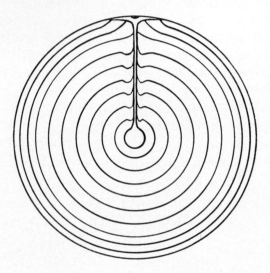

Figure 64. Diagram illustrating the growth and development of egg yolk.

The concentric rings represent daily growth of yolk, and their positions were determined by injecting into the hens a dye, Sudan III, which stains fat. (From Warren and Conrad, *J. Agric. Res.,* 1939).

in the chicken, with the final period of rapid growth ranging from 4 to 11 days preceding ovulation, depending on the species (Lehrman, 1961).

The growth and maturation of the ovarian follicles are caused by the action of the follicle-stimulating hormone, released from the pituitary (see Chapter 17).

The administration of gonadotrophic hormones (FSH and LH) affects the growth and development of ova, depending on age and sexual development. Until the age of about 120 days, the response of the chicken ovary to mammalian gonadotrophins consists mainly of increases in the secretion of estrogen and androgen and of hypertrophy of the ovarian medulla, which causes an increase in ovarian weight, but no appreciable change in size of ovarian follicles (see Van Tienhoven, 1961a, for review). When avian anterior pituitary extracts are administered there is some precocious ovarian development, and less hypertrophy of medulla than with mammalian hormones. However, the difference is attributable not entirely to the difference in type of avian and mammalian gonadotrophins (see also chapter on pituitary) but also in part to age. From 1 to 35 days of age the ovary exhibits no significant response to avian gonadotrophins, and from 35 days onward the response increases with age up to about 120 days (Taber *et al.,* 1958).

The injection of gonadotrophic hormones into intact laying hens (Fraps, Riley, and Olsen, 1942) or into hypophysectomized hens (Opel and Nalbandov, 1958 and 1961), does not produce ovarian follicles of graded size such as are observed in normal laying hens; either the follicles are not stimulated or all are stimulated similarly (about same size). This is in contrast to the response of certain wild avian species whose ovaries are stimulated to develop by gonadotrophins, and that can be made to lay eggs in the nonbreeding season. The follicles of such birds show normal gradations in size (Van Tienhoven, 1961a).

The rate of growth of the ovum is not related to rate of laying or ovulation, according to Warren and Conrad (1939). The yolk size of the first egg of a sequence is larger than in succeeding ones. This is due not to differences in rate of ovum growth, but apparently to a difference in the period of growth (Warren and Conrad), or to differences in the time and amounts of the ovulating and follicular-stimulating hormones from the pituitary. Later studies indicate that the number of follicles varies constantly with time, and that the time required for an individual follicle to attain maturity is dependent upon the number of follicles growing in sequence.

The administration of certain drugs, hormones, and chemicals is known to reduce yolk size. Among these are quinine sulfate (Riddle and Anderson, 1918); alcohol (Riddle and Basset, 1916); the vermifuge Kamala (Maw, 1934); and thyroxine (Asmundson and Pinsky, 1935). High environmental temperature also decreases yolk size.

The mature ovum may consist of alternate layers or rings of yellow and white yolk; the yellow layer is wider than the white. Riddle (1911) suggested that these bands were formed as a result of diurnal variation in metabolic rate, but Conrad and Warren (1939) showed that the alternate white and yellow bands are not formed when the birds are fed a uniform diet ad libitum, but only when the birds are supplied with feeds differing in xanthophyl content at irregular intervals.

OVULATION

Ovulation is the release of the ovum from the ovarian follicle, and normally occurs within 15 to 75 minutes after laying in the chicken, and four to five hours after laying of the first egg by the pigeon. Successive ovulations in a cycle are of about the same magnitude as that between laid eggs, with certain exceptions that have already been discussed. The mechanics of ovulation in the chicken have been studied in detail by Warren and Scott (1934), Phillips and Warren (1937) and Warren (1949). Rupture of the follicle takes place at the stigma, which is relatively avascular. The immediate causes and factors concerned in the rupture have been discussed by Phillips and Warren. They conclude that ovulation appears to be independent of stimuli from the ovary or other organs of the hen, since clamping the follicular stalk just prior to ovulation, or complete excision of the follicle from the ovary, does not prevent ovulation. They suggested that tension of the fibers of the follicular membrane may cause ovulation. Olsen and Neher (1948) demonstrated that excised ova can be made to ovulate *in vitro* by placing them in Ringer's solution at a temperature of 107°F. Ovulation occurred within one hour. Nalbandov believed that ovulation was preceded by local ischemia of the follicular wall, but Van Tienhoven (1961a), who reviewed the subject, suggests that other factors may be involved.

Hormones involved. Fraps and co-workers, in a series of reports, demonstrated that ovulation is induced by the cyclic release of the luteinizing hormone (LH) from the pituitary (see also Chapter 17). Ovulation can be induced prematurely, in some instances by as much as 17 to 30 hours, by injecting extracts containing LH (Fraps, Olsen, and Neher, 1942; Fraps, Riley, and Olsen, 1942 and later). Further evidence on the behavior of the ovulating hormone was supplied by hypophysectomizing laying hens 3 to 8 hours prior to their normal time of ovulation (Rothchild, 1946;

Rothchild and Fraps, 1949). Of those hens operated upon 8 or more hours prior to ovulation all failed to ovulate, but 73 percent of those hypophysectomized 3 to 4 hours before ovulation time, ovulated. These data indicate that the ovulating hormone is released by the pituitary 6 to 8 hours prior to time of ovulation, and the same conclusion is borne out by the fact that injections of LH, or progesterone, also induce ovulation within the same period. Very small amounts of progesterone applied directly to the pituitary or to the muscles of the leg are also effective in inducing ovulation (Rothchild, 1949). Opel and Nalbandov (1961a, b) demonstrated that shortly after hypophysectomy the ovarian follicles become atretic and increase in sensitivity to the ovulating hormone (LH). When LH of mammalian origin was injected into hens 3 to 15 hours after hypophysectomy, a higher incidence of premature ovulations occurred; the percentage of hens ovulating two or more ova (87) was greatest when LH was injected 6 hours after hypophysectomy.

Progesterone, however, is ineffective in the hypophysectomized chicken, indicating that it normally stimulates the pituitary to release LH (Rothchild and Fraps, 1949). Progesterone may inhibit or retard ovulation in the pigeon and dove, according to Dunham and Riddle (1942).

The first ovarian follicle of a sequence is more sensitive to given quantities of ovulating hormone than succeeding ones (Fraps, 1946).

Neher and Fraps (1950), by injecting progesterone or LH, were able to increase the number of eggs laid in a 12-day period by an average of 2.7 eggs per bird; but the yolk size of the laid eggs was smaller than normal, suggesting that ovulation was taking place before the ova were mature (see also Chapter 17).

Desoxycorticosterone acetate (DCA), in doses of 1 mg. per bird, is about as effective in inducing premature ovulation in chickens as is progesterone (Fraps, 1955). Larger dosages (5 mg.) inhibited ovulation and laying, according to Höhn (1960), but cortisone (2 mg.) had no effect.

More recent work by Van Tienhoven (1961b) indicates that corticosterone, the principal adrenal corticoid of birds, at levels of

0.5, 1, and 5 mg. per hen do not influence ovulation, but that a
dose of 10 mg. blocks ovulation in some and induces ovulation in
other chickens. Larger dosages (20 mg.) consistently blocked spontaneous or progesterone-induced ovulations. Cortisone did not
influence ovulation. Large doses (100 IU) of adrenocorticotrophin
(ACTH) cause premature ovulation and most probably lead to the
release of corticosterone.

Injections of small amounts (5 to 10 micrograms) of progesterone into the preoptic region of the hypothalamus cause premature ovulation, but this amount injected into the anterior pituitary had no effect (Ralph and Fraps, 1960). Certain of the barbitu-
rates (diallyl barbituric acid, nembutal, calcium ethylisoproply-
barbiturate) induce premature ovulation (increase of 15 to 30
percent) when administered 12 to 16 hours before the expected
time of ovulation (Fraps and Case, 1953). This is in contrast to the
effects of phenobarbital, which blocks ovulation induced by progesterone (Fraps, 1955). No satisfactory explanation for this
difference has been adduced.

Time of laying apparently does not influence ovulation time.
Premature laying (Warren and Scott, 1935) or retarded laying
(Weiss and Sturkie, 1952), induced experimentally, has no effect
upon time of subsequent ovulation.

Mechanism of ovulation. Considerable evidence is at hand to
indicate that progesterone acts through a neural mechanism to release LH or the ovulating hormone from the anterior pituitary.
Various hypotheses have been proposed to explain the asynchronous ovulatory cycle of the chicken. Fraps (1955) proposed a variation or diurnal rhythm in neural threshold to excitation hormones.
Bastian and Zarrow (1955) postulated fluctations in threshold of
response of ovary to LH, and Nalbandov (1959) proposed that
after ovulation the egg in the oviduct might inhibit gonadotrophic
secretion until the egg had passed from the isthmus to the shell
gland, and that then the pituitary would require time to recover
and produce enough gonadotrophins to induce the next ovulation.
These hypotheses have been reviewed in detail by Van Tienhoven
(1961a), who stated that "judgment as to the correctness of each
hypothesis must be withheld."

Interruption of ovulation. Ovulation is more easily interrupted or inhibited than induced; this applies to birds more than to mammals. It may be inhibited in a number of ways. Subcutaneous injections of such substances as ovalbumin, casein, peptone, desiccated brain, muscle, and other tissues, delay ovulation in the fowl from 6 to 10 hours when small dosages are administered, but large doses produce prompt and extensive follicular atresia (Fraps and Neher, 1945).

Abdominal operations usually cause a temporary cessation of ovulation in the fowl. Rothchild and Fraps (1945) found that the incidence of follicular atresia and the time before resumption of ovulation following operations were inversely proportional to the rate of ovulation preceding the operation. Huston and Nalbandov (1953) reported that injury to, or a foreign body in, the oviduct above the uterus would inhibit ovulation. When loops of thread were suspended in the oviduct, ovulation was inhibited but not the growth or ripening of the follicles. The authors postulated that injury to the oviduct must in some way inhibit or alter the release of certain pituitary hormones. It would appear that the release of the luteinizing, but not the follicle-stimulating hormone is inhibited. Further experiments by Van Tienhoven (1953) revealed that a thread placed in the isthmus inhibited ovulation for a longer time than one placed in the infundibulum or magnum. These results, however, have not been confirmed by Sykes (1962), or by Lake and Gilbert (1964). Large dosages of progesterone interrupt egg-laying in hens, presumably by causing follicular atresia.

Progesterone-induced ovulation can be blocked by administration of adrenergic blocking agents such as SKF 501 and dibenamine, and atropine, an anticholinergic agent (see Van Tienhoven, 1961a).

Extracts from a plant, *Lithospermum ruderale,* inhibit ovulation in mice and also in hens, presumably by inhibiting the secretion of LH (Zeller, Breneman, and Carmack, 1958).

Electrical stimulation of the hypothalamus of certain mammals causes a release of LH, but such attempts have been unsuccessful in the fowl.

Lesions produced in the preoptic region of hypothalamus prevent progesterone-induced ovulation in the hen (Ralph, 1959; Ralph and Fraps, 1959; Opel and Fraps, 1961). The latter workers showed that stimulation with stainless steel electrodes was effective but that stimulation with platinum electrodes was ineffective, as has been reported in mammals.

Effects of Light upon Ovulation

The stimulating effect of light on ovulation and laying is well known, and has been reviewed by Romanoff and Romanoff (1949), Benoit (1950), Bissonnette (1936), Van Tienhoven (1961a), and Quisenberry (1963). It is known that lights cause birds to start laying earlier than usual, and to lay more intensely during the fall and early winter months. However, lights do not usually increase average annual egg production.

For many years light was thought to stimulate egg production directly by increasing the hours of daylight and the feeding periods; but ample experimental work has shown that the principal effect of light is its stimulating effect upon the pituitary and the release of gonadotrophins, which in turn stimulate the ovary (see also Chapter 17).

Rowan and others believed that light merely permitted birds to remain awake, causing them to exercise and to eat more, and that this was the primary sexually activating stimulus.

Most workers are agreed that 12 to 14 hours of light are required to produce maximum stimulation (see Byerly and Moore, 1941; Carver, 1941; and others). Continuous lighting is no more effective than 12 to 14 hours of light.

Little work on the effect of different wavelengths upon ovulation has been reported. Platt (unpublished) reported that red light of a given intensity was more effective than white light of the same intensity in stimulating egg production.

Light and dark periods and ovulation. In recent years attempts have been made to increase ovulating and laying rates in chickens by various combinations of light and darkness. Although 13 to 14 hours of continuous light are considered optimum for ovulation, it is known that less light is necessary if it is interspersed with darkness (intermittent light; Wilson and Abplanalp, 1956). Some hens continue to lay, but usually at a reduced rate, even when kept in complete darkness (Wilson and Woodward, 1958). Intermittent light and flashing light have been used, but no significant increase in laying rate has been achieved (Lanson and Sturkie, 1961).

Lanson (1959) demonstrated that a minimum of $1\frac{1}{4}$ hours of darkness in 24 hours was sufficient to alter the time of ovulation and oviposition greatly. Birds on 24 hours of light laid at all hours during the 24, but those subjected to darkness could be made to lay at a given time of day. When $1\frac{1}{4}$ or more hours of darkness were imposed from 5 P.M. to midnight, most of the birds laid between 5 and 7 A.M. Darkness imposed in the period from midnight to 7 A.M. caused most of the hens to lay their eggs in the afternoon (2 to 3 P.M.). Similar results have been obtained by Wilson, Woodward, and Abplanalp (1963).

Up until recent years the belief persisted that the amount of light above 14 hours per day did not increase egg production, and most of the data supported this view. Recent experiments by King (see review by Morris and Fox, 1961, and bibliography by Quisenberry, 1963) suggested that increasing day length a given amount per week (18 minutes) over an extended period of time would increase egg production for those receiving a standard 14 hours of light. However, interpretation of the results was complicated by the fact that King had raised the birds up to sexual maturity on 6 hours of light instead of normal daylight. The results of Bowman and Jones (1963) tend to confirm King's. Even when the birds are reared on normal daylight, and then subjected to increasing light increments per week, there appears to be some increase (3 to 5 percent) in egg production over those birds receiving a constant amount of light (Morris and Fox, 1961). These authors state that "there is some reason to doubt whether the day-length increments are themselves responsible for the increased yield. It will be necessary to investigate the effects of light increments applied at different rates and starting from different initial day lengths with all the appropriate constant day controls before a generalized quantitative model can be constructed."

FORMATION OF ALBUMEN, SHELL
MEMBRANES, AND SHELL

The components of the egg are shell, shell membranes, albumen, and yolk. The proportionate part of the total of each of these components is shown in Table 65. A number of investigators have studied the formation of the egg components. The subject is reviewed by Warren (1949) and by Romanoff and Romanoff (1949).

Formation of Albumen

There are 4 distinct layers of albumen in the laid egg: (1) the chalaziferous layer attached to the yolk; (2) the inner liquid layer; (3) the dense or thick layer; and (4) the outer thin or fluid layer. Approximately one-fourth of the total albumen is found in the outer layer, and one-half in the dense, thick layer. The inner layer comprises 16.8 percent, and the chalaziferous layer 2.7 percent of the total (Table 65).

An egg taken from the hen just before it enters the isthmus contains only one layer of albumen, thick and jellylike in consistency. At this time the egg contains approximately one-half the amount of albumen of the laid egg and about twice the amount of protein

Table 65. Composition of the hen's egg (Romanoff and Romanoff, 1949)

| | Yolk | Albumen layers | | | | Shell |
		Outer	Middle	Inner	Chalazi-ferous	
Weight (grams)	18.7	7.6	18.9	5.5	0.9	6.2
Water (percent)	48.7	88.8	87.6	86.4	84.3	1.6
Solids (percent)	51.3	11.2	12.4	13.6	15.7	98.4
		All layers				
Proteins (percent)	16.6		10.6			3.3
Carbohydrates	1.0		0.9			—
Fats	32.6		trace			0.03
Minerals	1.1		0.6			95.10

per given volume (Pearl and Curtis, 1912; McNally, 1934; Scott, Hughes, and Warren, 1937). Thus, the presence of the different strata of albumen and the relative decrease in the proteins and solids of the laid egg suggest that after the egg leaves the magnum mainly water is added to the albumen and that this change, plus other physical changes resulting from rotation and movement of the egg down the oviduct, is responsible for the stratification of the albumen. Smith *et al.* (1957) concluded that the weight loss of dry matter in the magnum was the same as the dry weight of secreted albumen. They concluded that the albumen was secreted within the cells during the period when an egg was not in the magnum, and that water was added to the material in the cells when an egg was in the magnum.

Pearl and Curtis (1912) and McNally (1934) concluded from studies of laid eggs, and of eggs taken from the isthmus, that about 10 percent of the total nitrogen of the albumen was added while the egg was in the isthmus. This would mean that the proteins were added before the shell membranes were formed, because it appears physically impossible for the protein molecules to pass through the semipermeable shell membranes. Scott (1938), however, showed no increments of protein (nitrogen) to the egg in the isthmus. Burmester (1940), who studied the volume of albumen of the egg as it entered and left the isthmus, showed that water was added, but in insignificant amounts. Asmundson (1939) also demonstrated that water was added to turkey eggs in the isthmus. Pearl and Curtis, and also McNally, based their conclusions upon nitrogen determinations of the laid egg, which was the first egg of the cycle, and of the uterine egg, which was the second egg of the cycle. Scott, Hughes, and Warren (1937) demonstrated that the second laid egg of the cycle contained about 10 percent less nitrogen than the first egg, owing to the fact that the second egg was usually smaller than the first egg; and this could account for the discrepancy in results.

The latter investigators also compared the nitrogen content of the laid egg (first egg of the cycle) with the uterine egg (second egg) and found that the latter contained 96.2 percent as much nitrogen as the laid egg. The actual amounts of albumen and nitrogen in the uterine and laid egg are as follows:

	Albumen in gms.	Nitrogen in gms.
Uterine egg	16.60	0.509
Laid egg	32.84	0.529

Beadle, Conrad, and Scott (1938), who determined the chemical composition of uterine fluid, found that it contained only 0.06 percent nitrogen. They also compared the chemical composition of the albumen of the laid egg with the uterine solution and concluded that the principal additions to the albumen were potassium and bicarbonate ions, with smaller amounts of sodium and chloride ions.

Hoover and Smith (1958), who described a method for collecting fluid secreted by the shell gland or uterus, reported that mechanical stimulation of the organ by glass catheters of varying size did not appreciably influence the secretion rate, but that highest rate of secretion coincided with the first 5 hours the egg was in the uterus, and that fluid was added to the albumen (plumping). Calculations indicate that fluid collected from the uterus has a different ionic composition from that added to the albumen, suggesting that osmotic work is performed during plumping.

Types of Proteins in Albumen

Hughes and Scott (1936) determined the amounts of mucin, globulin, and albumin in the different layers of albumen of laid and oviducal eggs and the percentage of the total nitrogen contributed by the different types as follows, when the oviducal eggs had been in the uterus about 4 to 5 hours and most of the albumen had been formed.

Mucin is highest in the middle thick layer and lowest in the inner thin of both laid and oviducal eggs, but is higher in all layers of the oviducal egg than in the laid egg. The amount of mucin is responsible for the higher viscosity of the thick white, yet this layer contained slightly more water than the outer thin white. Globulin, however, is higher in all layers of the laid eggs than that in oviducal eggs. Globulin is highest in the inner thin and lowest in the outer thin layers. There is little or no difference in the relative amounts of albumin in the laid and oviducal eggs with respect to a given layer of albumen, but the highest amount is found in the outer thin white. The authors state that their analysis of ovomucin was not entirely satisfactory, and later workers (Forsythe and Berquist, 1951) have indicated that present methods of analysis of ovomucin are inadequate.

Formation of Albumen Layers

The chalazae are the paired twisted strands of albumen attached at opposite poles of the yolk, and parallel to the long axis of the egg. It is well known that the mucin content of inner thin white is less than thick white, and this suggested to Conrad and Phillips (1938) that the chalazae are formed by the mechanical twisting and segregation of the mucin fibers from the inner layer of albumen; histological evidence supports this view (Scott and Huang, 1941). That the decrease in mucin was not due to its chemical destruction was determined *in vitro*. That the chalazae are twisted clockwise and counterclockwise at the large and small ends of the egg respectively suggests that the egg is rotated on its long axis, so as to produce the twisting of the strands. Conrad and Phillips were able to produce chalazae artificially by placing isthmian eggs in a mechanical rotater.

There is good evidence that stratification of the albumen is effected by physical and chemical changes in the uterus. Sturkie and Polin (1954) removed oviducal eggs from the uterus 2 to 3 hours after they had left the magnum and compared the condition of the albumen with that of freshly laid eggs, which varied greatly in albumen quality. It was concluded, from differences in height, viscosity, and visual scores of albumen in laid and uterine eggs, that albumen deteriorates in quality (becomes thinner) after the egg leaves the magnum and enters the uterus. It was concluded that poor quality in the albumen (thinness of the white) is caused mainly by changes taking place in the uterus rather than by secretory activity in the magnum.

Rate of Formation of Albumen

The rate at which fluid is added to the albumen in the isthmus and uterus is shown in Figure 65 (Burmester, 1940), where the egg albumen totals of oviducal and laid eggs of the same hens are compared. This graph shows that the weight of albumen of the egg entering the uterus is approximately one-half that of the laid egg. After the first hour in the uterus, and up to the 6th or 8th hour, the rate of increase in albumen weight is rapid and fairly constant, but not quite a straight-line function. After the 8th hour in the

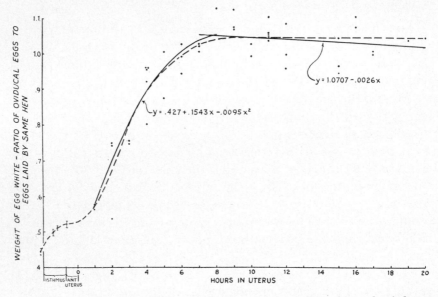

Figure 65. Relative weight of albumen in eggs taken from the isthmus and uterus (oviducal eggs).

The broken line is the curve drawn freehand, which represents the data throughout the whole period. The solid lines between 1 and 8 hours and between 7 and 20 hours represent the functions of the curvilinear and linear regression equations respectively. (From Burmester, *J. Exp. Zool.,* 1940.)

uterus there is little change in weight, since most of the albumen has been formed.

The rates of formation of the inner thin and outer thin white are shown in Figure 66. The slope of the curves for inner and outer thin are quite similar, and reveal that the increase in volume during the first 4 to 5 hours in the uterus is rapid, then slows and is fairly constant up to 18 hours. The graphs show that for the egg held 20 hours in the uterus, or the freshly laid egg, the volumes of outer and inner thin albumen approximate 5 and 9 cc. respectively. In studying a large number of freshly laid eggs of varying albumen quality, Sturkie and Weiss (1950) found the weights of the outer and inner albumen to average 5.8 and 7.3 grams respectively.

The curve for the formation of thick white (Figure 67) shows a rapid decrease in volume (percentage of thick white) during the first 4 to 6 hours the egg is in the uterus. There is little change up to 12 hours, and then there is a gradual but persistent decrease in

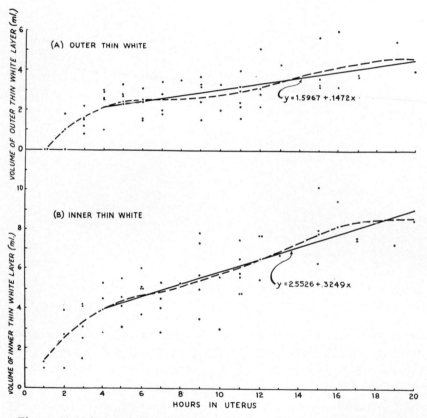

Figure 66. Volume of the outer thin white (A) and inner thin white (B) in eggs from the uterus.

In each graph, the broken line is the curve drawn freehand, which represents the data throughout the whole period, and the solid line between 4 and 20 hours represents the function of the linear regression equation. (From Burmester, *J. Exp. Zool.*, 1940.)

volume up to 17 hours, after which there is no appreciable change. This curve is approximately the reciprocal of the combined curves for inner and outer thin white.

After the egg has been in the uterus for 20 hours, the volume of thick albumen is approximately 58 percent of what it was when the egg left the magnum.

The great decrease in thick albumen occurring during the first 5 to 6 hours in the uterus is due mainly to the addition of water

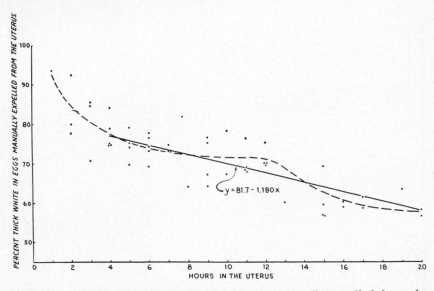

Figure 67. Percentage of thick white in eggs manually expelled from the uterus of the hen at different periods. (From Burmester, *J. Exp. Zool.,* 1940.)

(see also Figure 68); however, the slight but progressive decrease thereafter, particularly after shell is formed, is due mainly to the breakdown of mucin, the constituent that makes albumen thick. With the addition of water through the shell membranes to the thick albumen, there is a corresponding decrease in the percentage of solids, mainly protein, during the first 4 to 6 hours, but no change thereafter (Figure 68). The changes in percentages of solids for the inner thin albumen parallel those for the thick layer.

The decrease in percentage of solids of the inner thin and thick albumen begins as the egg enters the isthmus. No outer thin albumen is formed at this time, but it is first evident after the egg reaches the isthmus. The percentage of solids then decreases and reaches a low at 7 hours, after which the solids increase continuously but gradually (Figure 68). An increase in the outer thin layer implies a decrease in the volume of the thick layer, but such a decrease does not occur until about the 12th hour (see Figure 67). This suggests that while the egg is in the uterus, water is added at a more rapid rate than its diffusion into and through the thick white. The curve for the percentage of solids in the outer thin white is not the reciprocal of the volume curve of the same layer; it would thus appear that the relation between the volume of the layer and protein concentration is not close (Burmester, 1940).

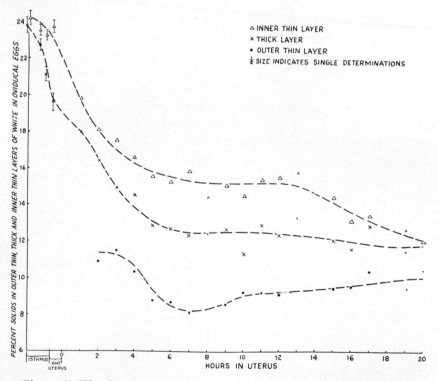

Figure 68. The decrease in percent solids of the inner thin, thick, and outer thin layers of white while the egg is in the isthmus and uterus. (From Burmester, *J. Exp. Zool.*, 1940.)

Effects of Resection of Magnum on Albumen Formation

Surgical removal of different areas of the magnum by a number of investigators (see Warren, 1949, for review) demonstrates that the amount and quality of albumen formed in the laid egg are reduced. On the basis of such experiments, Asmundson and Burmester (1938) interpreted their results to mean that most of the thick albumen was produced by the posterior half of the magnum. Scott and Burmester (1939) found that the amount of thin albumen was reduced most when the anterior and posterior sections of the magnum were removed. Removal of the middle and posterior areas reduced the amount of thick albumen most.

Mechanical Stimulation of Albumen Formation

Stimulation of the magnum and other parts of the oviduct to elaborate albumen, shell membranes, and shell is believed by many to be a reflex reaction to the passage of a body or object through the oviduct. The pressure of the yolk stimulates the magnum to secrete albumen, and the amount formed is believed to be related to the size of the yolk. There are cases on record, however, of the secretion of albumen by isolated loops of the oviduct while an egg passed through the intact portion of the tract, and of yolkless eggs containing albumen (Burmester and Card, 1939 and 1941). Thus, stimuli other than mechanical would appear also to be concerned in the secretion of albumen.

Nervous Control of, and the Effects of Drugs on, Albumen Formation

That the ovary and oviduct are innervated by the autonomic system has been noted, but the role of these nerves in albumen secretion has not been determined. Some of the nerve plexuses described by Mauger (1941) were located in the hen by Sturkie and Weiss (unpublished), but their position and size were such that direct stimulation could be accomplished in the open bird only after considerable manipulation of the viscera. In view of these difficulties the direct approach was abandoned in favor of the indirect approach, utilizing drugs which mimic the effects of the autonomic nerves. It was hoped that by using sympathomimetic and parasympathomimetic drugs, information could be obtained concerning the type of innervation, and the effect of such nerves upon the secretion of albumen. A similar procedure was followed by Riddle and King (1921) on the ringdove. They used atropine, cocaine, pilocarpine, and nicotine. None of these drugs produced significant changes in albumen secretion. Among the drugs used by Sturkie, Weiss, and Ringer (1954) were ephedrine sulfate (sympathomimetic) and acetylcholine (parasympathomimetic). The drugs were injected, usually subcutaneously in oil, during a period of 4 to 8 hours from the time of ovulation and the formation of albumen in the magnum. The laid eggs were then broken open, and the volume, viscosity, and total solids in the outer thin, inner thin, and thick layers of albumen were measured, and compared with those of control eggs from the same birds.

When the drugs were injected during a 4-hour period from the time of ovulation when the egg is in the magnum, there were slight but no significant changes observed in the albumen. But when the injections were made over the first 8-hour period—which meant that the eggs were in the isthmus and uterus for 3 to 4 hours of the injection period—significant but not appreciable changes in albumen were observed in most instances.

Acetylcholine significantly increased the viscosity of the outer and thin albumen, but there were no appreciable changes in the volume or the total solids. Since changes in viscosity reflect changes in mucin, the increase was in the mucin content with no changes in water content. Ephedrine usually decreased the viscosity of all albumen layers, and particularly that of the middle thick and inner thin; but other changes were not significant.

When acetylcholine or ephedrine was injected after the egg had left the magnum and entered the uterus, similar changes were produced in the albumen.

These results suggest that the magnum is innervated by sympathetic and parasympathetic nerves which govern its motility; but the insignificant effects of the drugs on the secretion of albumen suggest that these nerves play a minor role in the formation of albumen in the magnum.

Effects of Diseases, Environment, and Heredity on Formation and Deterioration of Albumen

High environmental temperature decreases the amount and viscosity of the albumen of laid eggs. Respiratory ailments such as Newcastle disease and bronchitis cause deterioration of the thick albumen in laid eggs (Hill and Lorenz, 1955; Sevolan and Levine, 1957). The duration of the effect of bronchitis virus on albumen quality apparently depends on the type and virulence of the strain, since some birds recover fairly soon after an attack of bronchitis, while others persist in laying poor eggs indefinitely.

Heredity also influences the amount of thick white in the egg. Strains of chickens have been developed by selective breeding, differing markedly in the amount of thick and thin white produced in the egg (see Hutt, 1949, and first edition of this book for review). It is well known that the thick albumen of normal freshly laid eggs deteriorates with age, length of storage, temperature, and other factors. This suggests that freshly laid eggs containing albumen of low viscosity (thin, watery albumen) may result also from the breakdown of mucin in the isthmus and uterus. Results obtained by Sturkie and Polin (1954), previously discussed, support this view.

Formation of Avidin by the Magnum

The albumen of eggs contains a factor, avidin, which when fed to chickens or rats produces a deficiency of biotin, since it inactivates the latter. Avidin is produced by the oviducts of birds and amphibians (Hertz and Sebrell, 1942), and by the magnum only of the laying hen (Fraps, Hertz, and Sebrell, 1943). The magna of nonlaying hens with atrophic ovaries do not contain avidin, indicating that avidin production is correlated closely with ovarian and oviducal functions. Avidin formation, however, can be induced in the nonlaying or immature hen by administration of stilbestrol and progesterone (Hertz, Fraps, and Sebrell, 1943).

FORMATION OF SHELL MEMBRANES

There are two shell membranes, an inner and an outer, each made up of a network of protein fibers, keratin (Romanoff and

Romanoff, 1949). The inner membrane is formed first. An egg partly extending into the isthmus can be observed to have the membrane (inner) formed on that part of the egg. By the time all of the egg is in the isthmus, the outer membrane is believed to have been formed. Data from other sources tend to support this view.

The amount of membrane formed in relation to the time the egg moves into, and the time it remains in, the isthmus has been studied by a number of workers. The relation of the rate of formation of the protein in the membranes to the distance that the center of the egg has traversed in the isthmus is a linear one, according to Burmester (1940).

EGGSHELL FORMATION AND
SKELETAL METABOLISM

BY T. G. TAYLOR AND D. A. STRINGER

The structure of the eggshell of the hen has been reviewed by Stewart (1935) and more recently by Simkiss (1961). The shell is bounded on the inside by two membranes which are closely attached to each other except at the broad end of the egg, where they separate to form the air space. The outer membrane is attached to the shell itself by the mammillae, which are hemispherical masses of calcite containing a core of organic material. As shell calcification proceeds more calcium carbonate becomes deposited to form the main body of the shell, known as the spongy layer, which also contains an organic matrix (Simkiss and Tyler, 1957). Figure 69 is a diagrammatic representation of a radial section through an eggshell.

The "true shell" (the part remaining after the membranes and cuticle have been removed) consists almost entirely of calcite, with small amounts of magnesium, phosphate, and citrate and traces of sodium and potassium.

Factors Affecting Shell Formation

The ability to produce an egg with a thick shell is strongly hereditary. Taylor and Lerner (1939), for example, were able to establish two strains of chickens by selective breeding, one of which laid eggs with predominantly thick and the other with thin shells. Shell formation is, however, influenced by many other factors such as nutrition, environment, age, season, and disease. Impairment of the shell-forming process is most easily recognized in the production of thin-shelled eggs.

A deficiency of calcium in the diet brings about a progressive thinning of the shell followed by a complete cessation of laying,

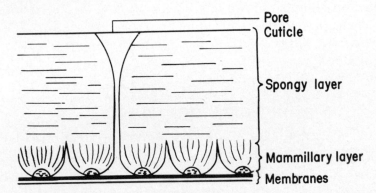

Figure 69. Diagrammatic representation of a transverse section through the decalcified eggshell of a domestic fowl. The entire shell is about 330 μ thick.

probably as the result of an inhibition of pituitary gonadotrophin secretion, (Taylor, Morris and Hertelendy, 1962). A dietary deficiency of vitamin D, a factor which impairs calcium absorption, also causes hens to cease to lay (Hertelendy and Taylor, 1960). On rations low in manganese, egg production is reduced (Gallup and Norris, 1939); Golding, Schaible, and Davidson, 1940), and the shells are of lower breaking strength than normal (Gutowska and Parkhurst, 1952).

The Mechanism of Shell Calcification

Eggs recovered from the distal region of the isthmus are surrounded by membranes but contain no calcareous deposits. Those removed from the shell gland, on the other hand, are invariably found to possess calcified mammillae, even though they are still in an unplumped condition, showing that they have been in the gland for only a short time. Our own observations suggest that formation of the mammillae may be initiated in the tubular region between the uterus and the isthmus, the so-called isthmo-uterine junction of Richardson (1935). In the lining of this region there is a gradual transition from cells typical of the isthmus to those typical of the uterus, and there is no definite histological boundary between these two parts of the oviduct (Bradley, 1927–1928).

The main process of shell calcification, namely the laying down of calcium in the spongy layer, occurs in the thick muscular shell gland, and it is thought to have important features in common with the calcification of bone (Simkiss and Tyler, 1958; Simkiss, 1958). These workers believe that the process of calcification involves a "seeding" mechanism followed by crystal growth—rather than a precipitation, as was formerly assumed—and involving the formation of calcium carbonate from calcium and carbonate ions.

The source of the CO_3^{2-} ions is thought to be the HCO_3^- ions of the blood, and investigations designed to throw light on the mechanism by which the supply of CO_3^{2-} ions is provided, have centered on the enzyme carbonic anhydrase. The epithelial lining of the uterus contains relatively large amounts of this enzyme, and the concentration is greater in hens that lay well than in those that lay poorly or not at all (Common, 1941a; Gutowska and Mitchell, 1945). Carbonic anhydrase has also been demonstrated by histochemical techniques to be present on the mammillae of soft-shelled eggs (Robinson and King, 1963).

Carbonic anhydrase is inhibited by sulfanilamide. Administration of this drug results in the production of thin, pitted, or shell-less eggs (Benesch, Barron, and Mawson, 1944; Scott, Jungherr, and Matterson, 1944; Gutowska and Mitchell, 1945). Scott *et al.* (1944) found that the decrease in shell thickness which resulted from feeding sulfanilamide at low concentration was directly proportional to the level at which it was fed, but that egg production ceased when 0.25 percent of the drug was included in the diet.

Gutowska and Mitchell (1945) have suggested that the role of carbonic anhydrase is to break down the carbonic acid formed in the reaction

$$2HCO_3^- \rightarrow H_2CO_3 + CO_3^{2-}$$

$$\downarrow \quad \text{carbonic anhydrase}$$

$$CO_2 + H_2O$$

thus favoring production of a continuous supply of CO_3^{2-} ions, and that the effect of sulfanilamide on eggshell formation is brought about by a decline in the production of these ions, due to the inhibiting effect of the drug on carbonic anhydrase.

Only unsubstituted sulfonamides of the type $R \cdot SO_2 \cdot NH_2$ inhibit carbonic anhydrase (Krebs, 1948). Bernard and Genest (1945) found that, whereas two unsubstituted sulfonamides caused hens to lay thin rough-shelled eggs similar to those obtained by feeding sulfanilamide itself, substituted sulfonamides such as sulfamerazine and sulfadiazine had a negligible effect beyond a slight pitting of the shell.

There is evidence from balance experiments that sulfanilamide deranges the normal metabolic processes in bone (Tyler, 1950, 1954a), and this may be an important factor in the shell-thinning caused by the drug. Another possibility is that the effect of sulfonamides on shell formation is related to their diuretic action (Mueller, 1962).

Rate of Shell Calcification

Warren and Scott (1935) and Burmester, Scott, and Card (1939) found that the rate of calcium carbonate deposition on the shell increased within 4 hours after the egg had entered the uterus, after which time the rate remained constant for the subsequent 16 hours (Figure 70). The initial slow rate of calcification coincides with the period during which the egg is being plumped.

The radiographic studies of Bradfield (1951) on the rate of shell deposition gave results essentially similar to those of Burmester *et al.* (1939).

Blood Changes during Shell Formation

Calcium. The majority of normal eggshells contain from 1.6 to 2.4 grams of calcium, the actual amount depending on the size of the egg and the thickness of the shell. Most of this calcium is deposited during the rapid phase of shell deposition, which lasts 15 to 16 hours. It has been shown that the shell gland itself contains very little calcium (Common, 1938; Taylor and Hertelendy, 1960), so that the immediate source of calcium for shell formation must be the blood (see Chapter 2 for a table of values). This has been demonstrated by Winget, Smith, and Hoover (1958), who showed that the calcium concentration of the efferent blood supply from the uterus was less than that of the afferent vessels leading to the uterus during shell calcification. Bearing in mind the calcium content of the shell, it is therefore clear that this ion is withdrawn from the blood at a rate of 100–150 mg./hour during

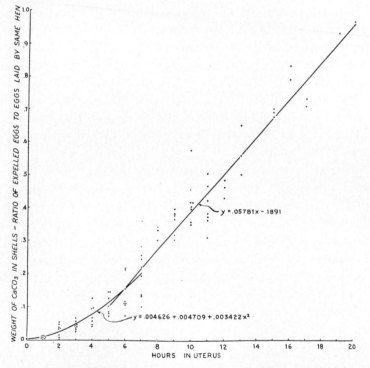

Figure 70. Rate of calcium carbonate deposition on the egg in the uterus of the hen.

The curved and straight lines represent the functions of the curvilinear and linear regression equations respectively. (From Burmester, *J. Exp. Zool.,* 1940.)

the main period of shell calcification. A 2-kg. hen has a plasma volume of approximately 100 ml. and taking 25 mg./100 ml. as an average figure for the level of total calcium in the plasma of a laying hen, it may be calculated that a weight of calcium equal to the total amount circulating at any one instant is withdrawn from the blood every 10 to 15 minutes during periods of shell calcification.

The effect on the level of blood calcium of this exceptionally high rate of calcium withdrawal has been studied by several groups of workers, and their results show no general agreement (See Sturkie, 1954, for earlier work; Winget and Smith, 1958; Polin and Sturkie, 1957).

However, these discordant results have to a large extent been reconciled by the work of Hertelendy and Taylor (1961), who, by studying large numbers of individual birds at different stages of the laying cycle, showed that there were very large differences between individual birds in the changes in blood calcium which occurred during the egg cycle. In some birds, the fall in total calcium during shell calcification was found to be as great as 10 mg./100 ml.; in others it was only 1 mg./100 ml. When mean values were considered, it was invariably found that there was a significant fall in total plasma calcium associated with shell calcification.

During their study of the changes in plasma-diffusible calcium which occur during the egg cycle, Taylor and Hertelendy (1961) observed that shell calcification was almost always associated with a fall in the diffusible calcium level of 0.1 to 2.6 mg./100 ml.

Phosphorus. Feinberg *et al.* (1937), Peterson and Parrish (1939), and Hunsaker (1959) have shown that the level of plasma inorganic phosphorus increases during shell calcification. This may be related to the fact that when bone mineral is mobilized during shell calcification, the rate at which calcium is removed from the circulation by the uterus is relatively greater than the rate at which phosphorus is excreted by the kidney (see also Chapter 2).

Magnesium. The available evidence suggests that there is a slight decrease in the total magnesium level of the plasma during shell formation in the domestic fowl (Taylor and Hertelendy, 1961).

Phosphatases. Cyclic changes occur in the plasma levels of alkaline and acid phosphatase during shell formation (Taylor and Williams, 1964).

Sources of Calcium for Shell Formation

Although the immediate source of calcium for shell formation is the blood, it is clear that the ultimate source must lie elsewhere. Since there are no large stores of calcium in the soft tissues (including the blood), the only possible sources of shell calcium are the food and the skeleton.

The skeletons of laying hens fed a calcium-deficient diet become progressively depleted of minerals; Taylor and Moore (1954a) found that the mean skeletal loss of calcium after laying 6 eggs on a deficient diet was 38 percent. Great variations were found in the extent to which the different bones had been affected. Whereas the skull, metatarsi, and toes lost only small amounts of calcium, the ribs, sternum, ilia, ischia, and pubis suffered severely. In the birds that laid 6 eggs on the deficient diet, these latter bones lost over 50 percent of the mineral matter originally present. Mineral depletion was associated with increases in the magnesium, sodium, potassium, and phosphate of the bone ash, and with decreases in the calcium, carbon dioxide, and citrate (Taylor and Moore, 1956).

Experiments on the daily calcium and phosphorus balance of laying hens (Common, 1932; Tyler, 1940; Common and Hale, 1941) showed that the amount of phosphorus excreted in the droppings varied greatly from day to day, and that calcium deposition was associated with the excretion of large amounts of phosphorus. This was particularly marked when a low calcium diet was fed (Common, 1932), but it was clear that some degree of mobilization of skeletal reserves was a normal feature of eggshell formation, even when a high calcium ration was fed. Whereas the calcium liberated as a result of bone absorption is utilized for shell formation, the phosphorus released simultaneously is largely excreted in the urine (Fussell, 1960).

Tyler (1954b) prepared autoradiographs of tangential sections of the shells of eggs laid by hens that were fed Ca^{45} continuously for a week. In the first few eggs laid after introducing the isotope into the diet, concentric dark rings on the films represented areas of shell calcium derived from the food, and light rings represented areas derived from skeletal calcium. Autoradiographs prepared from the shells of eggs laid after the Ca^{45} had been withdrawn showed dark rings produced by radiocalcium derived now from the bones and lighter rings produced by the inactive food calcium diluting the labeled calcium of the blood (Figure 71).

Comar and Driggers (1949) and Driggers and Comar (1949), also using Ca^{45}, showed that 60 to 75 percent of the calcium in the eggshell comes from the food.

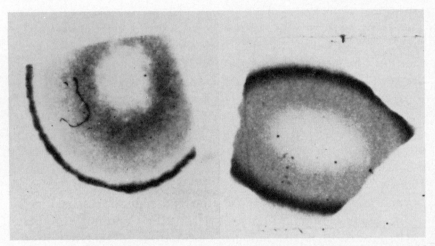

Figure 71. Autoradiographs of tangential sections of shells from eggs laid by hens fed radioactive calcium (Tyler, 1954b)

Left, egg laid 3.25 P.M. on the day after Ca^{45} was included in the diet. Shell calcification would have begun about 7.30 P.M. on the previous day, and the dark inner ring shows that radiocalcium from the current day's food was providing calcium for shell formation at this time. The dark outer ring represents Ca^{45} derived from the food fed at 9.30 A.M., on the day of laying, and the clear zone immediately inside, laid down between 7 A.M. and noon (approx.), was calcified by skeletal calcium (unlabeled).

Right, egg laid 9.30 A.M. some days after Ca^{45} had been withdrawn from the diet. Radiocalcium was now supplied by the skeleton, and the dense outer zone laid down early in the morning during the final period of shell formation was calcified largely by skeletal calcium.

Medullary Bone

It is generally accepted that the vertebrate skeleton acts as a store of minerals, particularly of calcium and phosphorus, which can be drawn upon when the requirements of the animal are in excess of the amounts absorbed from the food (Duckworth and Hill, 1953). In laying birds the calcium requirements for shell formation are so great that a special mechanism has been evolved. During the period of reproduction the marrow cavities of many of the bones of the female bird are invaded by a whole new system of secondary bone, and it seems probable that this bone is largely responsible for the provision of calcium for shell formation when absorption from the gut is insufficient. This physiological ossification within the marrow cavities of the long bones of female pigeons during the breeding season was first noted by Kyes and Potter (1934), and this tissue has since come to be known as medullary bone. It seems probable that medullary bone development is a normal physiological feature associated with reproduction in all birds. It does not occur naturally in male birds, although it may be induced in males by estrogen.

The microscopic anatomy of medullary bone has been studied in great detail in the pigeon by Bloom, Bloom, and McLean (1941). These workers showed that medullary bone grows out from the endosteal surface of the shaft in the form of fine interlacing trabeculae which advance between the sinuses and blood vessels of the red marrow tissue, apparently leaving the vascular pattern untouched. The chemical nature of the mineral matter (Taylor and Moore, 1956, 1958) and of the collagen matrix of medullary and cortical bone are very similar, but the two types of bone differ in their reaction to histochemical tests for acid and neutral mucopolysaccharides, these substances being present in higher concentrations in medullary than in cortical bone (Simkiss and Tyler, 1958; Stringer and Taylor, 1961).

Changes in medullary bone during the egg cycle. Bloom *et al.* (1941) have described the histological changes which occur in the medullary bone during the reproductive cycle in the female pigeon. Formation of the new bone begins after mating, and it in-

creases in amount with the increase in size of the developing follicles in the ovary, until it has invaded the entire marrow cavity at
the time when the first ovulation occurs.

Soon after the formation of the first eggshell a phase of bone
destruction is initiated, and this becomes more intense as
calcification proceeds. Osteoclasts surround the trabeculae in increasing numbers, and toward the end of shell formation the
amount of medullary bone present is considerably reduced. The
osteoclastic reaction continues for 4 to 5 hours after the egg is laid,
and subsequently gives way to a period of intense bone formation
which lasts for 20 hours. This is followed once more by a period of
intense bone destruction while the second egg, which is laid 2 days
after the first, is being calcified. The marrow cavity returns to its
resting condition in about 10 days. These changes in bone are
under the influence of the parathyroid hormone and of estrogen
(see also Chapter 20).

Medullary bone requires a constant stimulus from estrogen for
its maintenance, and it has been suggested (Riddle, Rauch, and
Smith, 1945; Urist, 1959; Urist, Deutsch, Pomerantz, and McLean,
1960) that fluctuations in the blood level of estrogen rather than
of parathyroid hormone are responsible for the changes which
occur in the cell population during the egg cycle.

The changes which occur in the medullary bone of the domestic
fowl during the laying cycle are less clear-cut than in the pigeon.
This is probably because hens lay many eggs in a clutch instead of
two, and because the eggs of a clutch are laid daily instead of on
alternate days as in the pigeon. It seems probable also that during
centuries of domestication the ability of the domestic fowl to absorb calcium from the gut has increased, so that it is somewhat
less dependent on medullary bone than pigeons. Nevertheless,
Bloom, Domm, Nalbandov, and Bloom (1958) have shown that in
high-producing hens the medullary bone undergoes sequences of
bone formation and destruction during the egg cycle. In the early
stages of shell formation (which occur during the afternoon and
evening when calcium is being absorbed from the gut in large
amounts) both osteoblasts and osteoclasts are abundant, whereas in
the advanced stages of shell calcification (when supplies of dietary

calcium may not be so plentiful) the bone trabeculae are surrounded by huge numbers of osteoclasts, and the osteoblasts are rare. When shell calcification was not in progress, Bloom *et al.* (1958) found that the cell population was very variable.

Figure 72 shows the gross structure of the medullary bone in the femur of a laying hen as contrasted with that of a nonlayer.

Distribution of Medullary Bone

In the domestic fowl medullary bone is not present in all the bones of the skeleton but is restricted to those bones which possess an efficient blood supply (Landauer and Zondek, 1944; Clavert, 1948; Taylor and Moore, 1953, 1956). It is absent from the humerus (a pneumatic bone), metatarsus, and toes, while the skull and cervical vertebrae contain only small amounts. The importance of the vascular supply in determining the distribution of medullary bone was shown experimentally by Taylor, Moore, and Loosmore (1958), who found that medullary bone developed in the metatarsus of hens after the blood supply had been augmented as a result of fracture, but not in the unfractured homologous bone. It seems probable, however, that bones vary in their ability to respond to humoral conditions favoring medullary bone induction (Benoit and Clavert, 1945b; Taylor *et al.*, 1958).

Hormonal Control of Medullary Bone

Since the development of medullary bone accompanies the onset of sexual maturity in the female bird, it is not surprising that this development is associated with the secretion of estrogens; a great deal of work has been done on the experimental induction of medullary bone with these hormones (see Gardner and Pfeiffer, 1943; and Simkiss, 1961, for reviews). The results of some of these experiments are conflicting, in large measure because of the varying experimental conditions employed by different workers. In particular, there is disagreement as to the role of androgens in medullary bone formation. Type and dosage of hormone, duration of treatment, age, sex, species and breed of bird, season, and whether the birds are castrated or intact, all influence the bone response (Clavert, 1948).

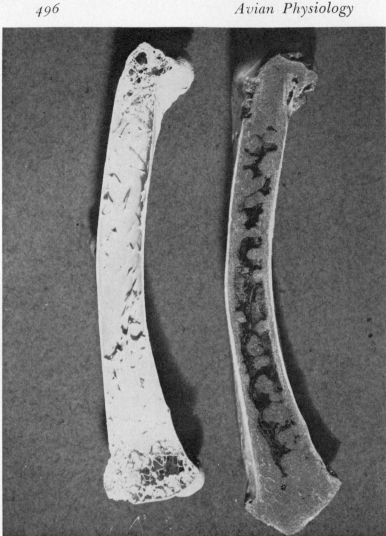

Figure 72. Longitudinal sections (X2) of the ethylene diamine extracted femur of (left) a nonlaying hen and (right) a laying hen, showing the massive development of secondary (medullary) bone in the marrow cavity of the latter.

The weight of evidence suggests that estrogens and androgens act synergistically in the development of medullary bone, and our own (unpublished) experiments using immature pullets (4 to 6 weeks of age) strongly support this view. No secondary bone was produced with either estrogen or androgen alone, but combinations of both hormones over a wide range of doses gave positive results. The maximum response, however, was considerably less than in a pullet coming into lay naturally; it was associated with excessively high levels of plasma calcium, often greater than 50 mg./100 ml. There can be little doubt that the experimental induction of medullary bone formation in the domestic fowl is less readily achieved than in the pigeon or duck, and it is possible that hormones additional to estrogens and androgens are required for the normal development of medullary bone. Further experiments with immature birds seem more likely to yield information on the hormone complex involved than experiments with sexually mature birds, in which endogenous production of hormones is likely to be greater.

The work of Benoit and Clavert (1947) suggests that the thyroid gland may be concerned in the normal development of medullary bone. The microscopic structure of the bone induced in thyroidectomized drakes by estrogen appeared to be normal, although it developed more slowly than in intact birds. Microscopic examination revealed that the newly formed bone was osteoporotic, although we have not been able to confirm this feature by using thyroid inhibitors (unpublished observations).

The effect of parathyroidectomy on medullary bone formation under the influence of estrogens has been investigated by Riddle *et al.* (1945) and by Benoit and Clavert (1945a). The former group, using pigeons, maintained the blood calcium levels of their birds after the operation by feeding aluminum hydroxide (to prevent phosphate absorption), or by feeding calcium gluconate in conjunction with dihydrotachysterol, and they were successful in keeping their birds alive for months by these treatments. They found that the formation of new bone proceeded equally as well as in unoperated birds and that its calcification was normal. Benoit and Clavert (1945a) on the other hand, using drakes, took no steps to prevent the death of their birds by tetany. Some lived for only 10 hours after the operation, others for 36 hours, when they were killed. The formation of new bone matrix occurred normally, but it failed to calcify. From these experiments the formation of the bone matrix and its calcification appear to be independent processes.

Source of Minerals for Medullary Bone Formation

Clavert and Benoit (1942) found that a single injection of estradiol dipropionate led to an increased retention of calcium and phosphorus within 24 hours, and that the effect continued for 10 days. Common, Rutledge, and Hale (1948) reported that in immature pullets treated with both estrogen and androgen the retention of calcium and phosphorus increased to levels comparable to those observed in normal pullets during the prelaying period (Common, 1933, 1936, 1938; Taylor and Moore, 1954a). Neither hormone alone caused increased retention of calcium or phosphorus.

We have examined the amount of medullary bone that is normally present in pullets at points of lay and have observed that the spicules of medullary bone invade the marrow cavity of the femur to a depth of from 150 to 1200μ., varying with the individual bird and with the breed. The maximum depth which we have been able to induce experimentally by the administration of sex hormones in pullets approaching sexual maturity is 100μ. Newly formed trabeculae of medullary bone, whether produced naturally or experimentally, are much thicker than those observed in birds which have been in lay for 6 weeks or more. Thus, the marrow cavities of pullets, unlike those of pigeons, are not filled with medullary bone at the start of lay, as was assumed by Common *et al.* (1948) and Simkiss (1961). The trabeculae gradually advance into the marrow cavity as laying progresses, becoming thinner as they do so, and the greater surface area of medullary tissue thus exposed probably facilitates bone resorption and formation during the laying cycle. It is generally recognized (Hurwitz and Griminger, 1960) that pullets are in negative calcium balance for the first few weeks of lay; this may be due to the relatively poor development of medullary bone at this time.

Physiological Significance of Medullary Bone

Formation of medullary bone may be related to the need to provide large amounts of calcium for eggshell formation in a short space of time. At one time there was a tendency to regard the hypercalcemia that is associated with laying hens as an adaptation for the provision of calcium for the alternate functions of forming shell and medullary bone. However, female frogs, fish, and snakes, which do not lay eggs with calcified shells, also exhibit hypercalcemia during the reproductive period; the phenomenon must therefore be related primarily to the laying of yolky eggs and to the transport of the yolk proteins in the blood (Urist, 1959). It is the ionic calcium of the blood that is immediately concerned in shell calcification, and although the ionic calcium is in equilibrium with the protein-bound calcium of the blood, the amount of the latter released when the ionic calcium falls is negligible compared with the requirements for shell calcification (see also Chapters 2 and 20).

Other factors also have a bearing on skeletal physiology. The amount of calcium absorbed from the intestine and taken up by the body calcium pool is of vital importance. Laying colostomized pullets fed 3 grams of calcium per day have been shown to retain 1.83 grams of calcium and in addition to excrete 0.22 grams of calcium in the urine, so that the net daily intestinal absorption rates would be of the order of 2.05 grams per day (Hurwitz and Griminger, 1961). Assuming that intestinal calcium absorption occurs at a constant rate, as it almost certainly does not, this would be equivalent to a mean absorption rate of 85 mg. calcium/hour. There is little doubt that this figure will be exceeded during feeding periods; but late at night intestinal absorption is likely to be reduced, and this is the period when shell formation is occurring at its maximal rate. It has already been suggested that calcium is being removed from the blood at a rate of 100 to 150 mg./hour to meet the demands of shell formation, and it may therefore be assumed that the difference between the rates of intestinal absorption and of shell deposition provides a measure of the rate at which calcium is supplied by the skeleton (i.e., 100 to 150 minus 85 mg./hour, which is 15 to 65 mg./hour). During shell deposition urinary calcium is negligible, whereas in the absence of this phenomenon it may rise to a maximum of 50 mg./hour (Fussell, 1960). Thus the difference between intestinal absorption (85 mg./hour), and urinary excretion (50 mg./hour) represents a possible bone formation rate of 35 mg. calcium/hour. This figure is in close agreement with the bone accretion rate of 30 mg./hour calculated from the maximum daily retention rate of 0.75 grams of calcium observed by Taylor and Moore (1954b) for pullets just prior to the onset of lay. These concepts are illustrated in Figure 73. In addition, small amounts of calcium are bound by the yolk

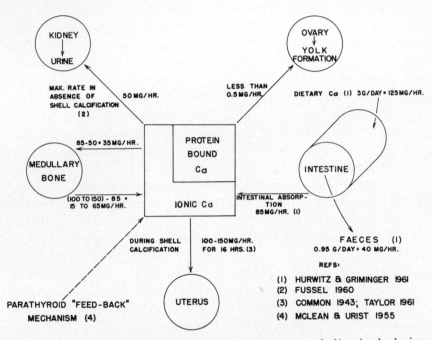

Figure 73. Diagrammatic representation of calcium metabolism in the laying fowl (for details concerning the rates at which these processes occur, see text).

proteins, although the amount is so small by comparison that it could almost be ignored.

Thus with a better understanding of the role of the skeleton, and in particular of that played by medullary bone, the rigid distinction between "food" and "bone" calcium can no longer be made in relation to shell formation. A more fruitful concept is that of a dynamic equilibrium between blood, bone, and calcifying shell. When active absorption of dietary calcium is occurring the amount entering the blood may be sufficient to allow both bone and shell calcification to occur. It may be assumed that the calcifying eggshell has priority for available calcium, so that bone calcification falls with a decline in the rate of absorption of calcium from the gut. When this rate falls below the rate of removal of calcium by the shell gland the deficit is made good by bone resorption. Thus food calcium laid down in the bone at one time might be liberated into the blood and deposited on the shell within 12 hours or even sooner. The skeleton of the bird, and especially the medullary bone, may therefore be looked upon as a buffer, which removes calcium from the blood when it is absorbed at a rate greater than that at which it is required for shell calcification, and which releases it when the rate of absorption is less than the rate of utilization by the uterus.

REFERENCES

Asmundson, V. S.   1939   The formation of the egg in the oviduct of the turkey (Meleagris gallopavo). J. Exp. Zool. 82:287.

Asmundson, V. S., and B. R. Burmester   1938   The effect of resecting a part of the uterus on the formation of the hen's egg. Poultry Sci. 17:126.

Asmundson, V. S., and P. Pinsky   1935   The effect of the thyroid on the formation of the hen's egg. Poultry Sci. 14:99.

Barnett, B. D., D. J. Richey, and C. L. Morgan   1957   Effect of beta-aminopropionitrile on reproduction of chickens. Proc. Soc. Exp. Biol. & Med. 95:101.

Bastian, J. W., and M. X. Zarrow   1955   A new hypothesis for the asynchronous ovulatory cycle of the domestic hen (Gallus domesticus). Poultry Sci. 34:776.

Beadle, B. W., R. M. Conrad, and H. M. Scott   1938   Composition of uterine secretion of the domestic fowl. Poultry Sci. 17:498.

Benesch, R., N. S. Barron, and C. A. Mawson   1944   Carbonic anhydrase, sulphonamides, and shell formation in the domestic fowl. Nature 153:138.

Benoit, J.   1950   Traité de Zoologie, edited by P. P. Grassé. Tome XV: Oiseaux, p. 459. Masson & Co., Paris.

Benoit, J., and J. Clavert   1945a   Rôle indispensable des parathyroïdes dans la calcification de l'os folliculinique chez le canard. C. R. Soc. Biol., Paris 139:743.

Benoit, J., and J. Clavert 1945b Hypercalcémie et osteogenèse médullaire folliculiniques chez le canard domestique soumis à un régime acalcique. C. R. Soc. Biol., Paris, 139:737.

Benoit, J., and J. Clavert 1947 Action de la thyroidectomie sur l'ossification folliculinique chez le canard. C. R. Soc. Biol., Paris, 141:1258.

Bernard, R., and P. Genest 1945 Sulfonamides and egg shell formation in the domestic fowl. Science 101 (2633):617.

Bissonnette, T. H. 1936 Sexual photoperiodicity. Quart. Rev. Biol. 11:371.

Bloom, W., M. A. Bloom, and F. C. McLean 1941 Calcification and ossification: Medullary bone changes in the reproductive cycle of female pigeons. Anat. Rec. 81:443.

Bloom, M. A., L. V. Domm, A. V. Nalbandov, and W. Bloom 1958 Medullary bone of laying chickens. Am. J. Anat. 102:411.

Bowman, J. C., and R. H. Jones 1963 Lighting techniques for the domestic fowl. Brit. Poultry Sci. 4:27.

Bradfield, J. R. G. 1951 Radiographic studies on the formation of the hen's egg shell. J. Exp. Biol. 28:125.

Bradley, D. C. 1927–1928 Notes on the histology of the oviduct of the hen. J. Anat., London 62:339.

Bradley, O. C. 1960 The Structure of the Fowl, 4th ed. revised by T. Grahame. Oliver & Boyd, Edinburgh.

Burmester, B. R. 1940 A study of the physical and chemical changes of the egg during its passage through the isthmus and uterus of the hen's oviduct. J. Exp. Zool. 84:445.

Burmester, B. R., and L. E. Card 1939 The effect of resecting the so-called "chalaziferous region" of the hen's oviduct on the formation of subsequent eggs. Poultry Sci. 18:138.

Burmester, B. R., and L. E. Card 1941 Experiments on the physiology of egg white secretion. Poultry Sci. 20:224.

Burmester, B. R., H. M. Scott, and L. E. Card 1939 Rate of egg shell formation in the hen. Proc. VII World's Poultry Cong. Cleveland, Ohio, p. 99.

Burns, R. K. 1961 Role of hormones in the differentiation of sex, in Sex and Internal Secretions, edited by W. C. Young, Volume I, p. 76. Williams & Wilkins, Baltimore.

Burrows, W. H., and T. C. Byerly 1942 Premature expulsion of eggs by hens following injection of whole posterior pituitary preparations. Poultry Sci. 21:416.

Burrows, W. H., and R. M. Fraps 1942 Action of vasopressin and oxytocin in causing premature oviposition by domestic fowl. Endocrinol. 30:702.

Byerly, T. C., and O. K. Moore 1941 Clutch length in relation to period of illumination in the domestic fowl. Poultry Sci. 20:387.

Carver, J. S. 1941 Light requirements of laying hens. Fiftieth Annual Report, Wash. Agr. Exp. Sta. (Abs.).

Chappelier, A. 1913 Persistance et développement des organes génitaux droits chez les femelles adults des oiseaux. Bull. Sci. France Belg. 47:361.

Clavert, J. 1948 Contribution à l'étude de la formation des oeufs telolecithiques des oiseaux: Mécanismes de l'édification de la coquille. Bull. Biol. 82:290.

Clavert, J., and J. Benoit 1942 Action de la folliculine sur le métabolisme du calcium chez les oiseaux. IV: Rétention du calcium alimentaire déterminée chez le pigeon par le dipropionate d'oestradiol. Bull. Soc. Chim. Biol., Paris 24:1469.

Cole, R. K., and F. B. Hutt 1953 Normal ovulation in non-laying hens. Poultry Sci. 32:481.

Comar, C. L., and J. C. Driggers 1949 Secretion of radioactive Ca in the hen's egg. Science 109:282.

Common, R. H. 1932 Mineral balance studies on poultry. J. Agric. Sci. 22:576.

Common, R. H. 1933 Observations on the mineral metabolism of pullets, I. J. Agric. Sci. 23:555.

Common, R. H. 1936 Observations on the mineral metabolism of pullets, II. J. Agric. Sci. 26:85.

Common, R. H. 1938 Observations on the mineral metabolism of pullets, III. J. Agric. Sci. 28:347.

Common, R. H. 1941a The carbonic anhydrase activity of the hen's oviduct. J. Agric. Sci. 31:412.

Common, R. H. 1941b Observations on the mineral metabolism of pullets. V: Acid base equilibrium and reproductive activity. J. Agric. Sci. 31:281.

Common, R. H., and R. W. Hale 1941 Observations on the mineral metabolism of pullets. VI: The mobilization of body calcium for shell formation. J. Agric. Sci. 31:415.

Common, R. H., N. A. Rutledge, and R. W. Hale 1948 Observations on the mineral metabolism of pullets. VIII: The influence of gonadal hormones on the retention of calcium and phosphorus. J. Agric. Sci. 38:64.

Conner, M. K., and R. M. Fraps   1954   Premature oviposition following sub-total excision of the hen's ruptured follicle. Poultry Sci. 33:1051.

Conrad, R. M. and R. E. Phillips   1938   The formation of the chalazae and inner white in the hen's egg. Poultry Sci. 17:143.

Conrad, R. M., and D. C. Warren   1939   The alternate white and yellow layers of yolk in the hen's ova. Poultry Sci. 18:220.

Douglas, D. S., and P. D. Sturkie   1964   Plasma levels of antidiuretic hormone during oviposition in the hen. Fed. Proc. 23:150.

Driggers, J. C., and C. L. Comar   1949   The secretion of radioactive calcium (Ca^{45}) in the hen's egg. Poultry Sci. 28:420.

Duckworth, J., and R. Hill   1953   The storage of elements in the skeleton. Nutrit. Abst. Rev. 23:1.

Dunham, H. H., and O. Riddle   1942   Effects of a series of steroids on ovulation and reproduction in pigeons. Physiol. Zool. 15:383.

Feinberg, J. G., J. S. Hughes, and H. N. Scott   1937   Fluctuations in calcium and inorganic phosphorus in the blood of the laying hen during the cycle of one egg. Poultry Sci. 16:132.

Forsythe, R. S., and D. H. Berquist   1951   The effects of physical treatments on some properties of egg white. Poultry Sci. 30:302.

Fraps, R. M.   1946   Differential ovulatory reaction of first and subsequent follicles of the hen's clutch. Anat. Rec. 96:573.

Fraps, R. M.   1955   Egg production and fertility in poultry, Chapter 15, Progress in Physiology of Farm Animals, ed. John Hammond. Butterworth, London.

Fraps, R. M., and J. F. Case   1953   Premature ovulation in the domestic fowl under barbiturate sedation. Proc. Exp. Biol. & Med. 45:810.

Fraps, R. M., R. Hertz, and W. H. Sebrell   1943   Relation between ovarian function and avidin content in the oviduct of the hen. Proc. Soc. Exp. Biol. and Med. 52:140.

Fraps, R. M., and B. H. Neher   1945   Interruption of ovulation in the hen by subcutaneously administered non-specific substances. Endocrinol. 37:407.

Fraps, R. M., B. H. Neher, and I. Rothchild   1947   The imposition of diurnal ovulatory and temperature rhythms of periodic feeding of hens maintained under continuous light. Endocrinol. 40:241.

Fraps, R. M., M. W. Olsen, and B. H. Neher   1942   Forced ovulation of normal ovarian follicles in the domestic fowl. Proc. Soc. Exp. Biol. & Med. 50:308.

Fraps, R. M., G. M. Riley, and M. W. Olsen 1942 Time required for induction of ovulation following intravenous injection of hormone preparations in the fowl. Proc. Soc. Exp. Biol. & Med. 50:313.

Freedman, S. L. 1961 Innervation and blood vessels of chicken's uterus. Thesis, Rutgers University.

Freedman, S. L., and P. D. Sturkie 1962 Disruption of the sympathetic innervation of the fowl's uterus. Poultry Sci. 41:1644.

Freedman, S. L., and P. D. Sturkie 1963a Blood vessels of the chicken's uterus (shell gland). Amer. J. Anatomy 113:1.

Freedman, S. L., and P. D. Sturkie 1963b Extrinsic nerves of the chicken's uterus. Anat. Rec. 147:431.

Fussell, M. H. 1960 Studies on calcium and phosphorus metabolism in the hen. Ph.D. Thesis, University of Cambridge.

Gallup, W. D., and L. C. Norris 1939 The effects of a deficiency of manganese in the diet of the hen. Poultry Sci. 18:83.

Gardner, W. V., and C. A. Pfeiffer 1943 Influences of estrogens and androgens on the skeletal system. Physiol. Rev. 23:139.

Gilbert, A. B., and D. G. M. Wood-Gush 1963 A technique for the fistulation of the hen's oviduct through the abdominal wall with recovery of the ovum. J. Reprod. Fertility 5:451.

Golding, W. V., P. J. Schaible, and J. A. Davidson 1940 A breed difference in the manganese requirements of laying hens. Poultry Sci. 19:263.

Gutowska, M. S., and C. A. Mitchell 1945 Carbonic anhydrase in the calcification of the egg shell. Poultry Sci. 24:159.

Gutowska, M. S., and R. T. Parkhurst 1942 Studies in mineral nutrition of laying hens. I: The manganese requirement. Poultry Sci. 21:277.

Heller, J., and B. T. Pickering 1961 Neurohypophysial hormones of nonmammalian vertebrates. J. Physiol. 155:98.

Hertelendy, F., and T. G. Taylor 1960 On the interaction between vitamin D and parathyroid hormone in the domestic fowl. Biochim. Biophys. Acta 44:200.

Hertelendy, F., and T. G. Taylor 1961 Changes in the blood calcium associated with eggshell calcification in the domestic fowl. 1: Changes in the total calcium. Poultry Sci. 40:108.

Hertz, R., R. M. Fraps, and W. H. Sebrell 1943 Induction of avidin formation in the avian oviduct by stilbestrol and progesterone. Proc. Soc. Exp. Biol. & Med. 52:142.

Hertz, R., and W. H. Sebrell   1942   Occurrence of avidin in the oviduct and secretions of the genital tract of several species. Sci. 96: 257.

Heywang, B. W.   1938   The time factor in egg production. Poultry Sci. 17:240.

Hill, R. W., and F. W. Lorenz   1955   Some effects of respiratory diseases on oviduct function. Poultry Sci. 34:1201.

Höhn, E. O.   1960   Action of certain hormones on the thymus of the domestic hen. J. Endocrinol. 19:282.

Hoover, G. N., and A. H. Smith   1958   Secretion of fluid by the shell gland of the laying hen. Poultry Sci. 37:467.

Hoover, G. N., A. H. Smith, and V. K. Abbott   1962   Some mechanical properties of the avian shell gland. Poultry Sci. 41:1137.

Hseih, T. M.   1951   The sympathetic and parasympathetic nervous systems of the fowl. Doctoral dissertation, University of Edinburgh.

Hughes, J. S., and H. M. Scott   1936   The change in the concentration of ovoglobulin in egg white during egg formation. Poultry Sci. 15:349.

Hunsaker, W. C.   1959   Blood flow and calcium transfer through the uterus of the chicken. Ph.D. Thesis, Rutgers University.

Hurwitz, S., and P. Griminger   1960   Observations on the calcium balance of laying hens. J. Agric. Sci. 54:373.

Hurwitz, S., and P. Griminger   1961   Partition of calcium and phosphorus excretion in the laying hen. Nature 189:759.

Huston, T. M., and A. V. Nalbandov   1953   Neurohumoral control of the pituitary in the fowl. Endocrinol. 52:149.

Hutt, F. B.   1949   Genetics of the Fowl. McGraw-Hill Book Co., Inc., New York.

Krebs, H. A.   1948   Inhibition of carbonic anhydrase by sulphonamides. Biochem. J. 43:525.

Kyes, P., and T. S. Potter   1934   Physiological marrow ossification in female pigeons. Anat. Rec. 60:377.

Lake, P. E., and A. B. Gilbert   1964   The effect on egg production by a foreign object in the lower oviduct regions of the domestic hen. Res. [British] Vet. Sci. 5:39.

Landauer, W., and B. Zondek   1944   Observations on the structure of bone in estrogen treated cocks and drakes. Am. J. Path. 20:179.

Lanson, R. K.   1959   A study of the influence of light and darkness upon the reproductive performance of the fowl. Thesis, Rutgers University.

Lanson, R. K., and P. D. Sturkie 1961 The influence of light and darkness upon the reproductive performance of the fowl. Poultry Sci. 40:1751.

Lehrman, D. S. 1961 Hormonal regulation of parental behavior in birds and infrahuman mammals, Chapter 21, Sex and Internal Secretions, ed. W. C. Young. Williams & Wilkins, Baltimore.

Levi, W. M. 1941 The Pigeon. R. L. Bryan Company, Columbia, S.C.

McKenney, F. D., H. E. Essex, and F. C. Mann 1932 The action of certain drugs on the oviduct of the domestic fowl. J. Pharm. & Exp. Thera. 45:113.

McNally, E. 1934 Passage of ovoglobulins through the shell membrane. Proc. Soc. Exp. Biol. & Med. 31:946.

McNally, E. 1947 Some factors that affect oviposition in the domestic fowl. Poultry Sci. 26:396.

Marshall, A. J. 1961 Biology and Comparative Physiology of Birds. Vol. II, Chapters 21, 23, 24. Academic Press, New York.

Mauger, H. M., Jr. 1941 The autonomic innervation of the female genitalia in the domestic fowl and its correlation with the aortic branchings. Am. J. Vet. Res. 2:447.

Maw, A. J. G. 1934 The effect of kamala on egg production and egg weight. Poultry Sci. 13:131.

Morash, R., and O. S. Gibbs 1929 The effect of pituitary on the bird. J. Pharm. & Exp. Thera. 37:475.

Morgan, W., and W. Kohlmeyer 1957 Hens with bilateral oviducts. Nature 180:98.

Morris, J. A. 1961 The effect of continuous light and continuous noise on pullets held in a sealed chamber. Poultry Sci. 40:995.

Morris, T. R., and S. Fox 1961 Increasing versus constant day length for laying pullets. British Poultry Sci. 2:59.

Mueller, W. J. 1962 Carbonic anhydrase, diuretics and eggshell formation. Poultry Sci. 41:1792.

Munsick, R. A., W. H. Sawyer, and H. B. Van Dyke 1960 Avian neurohypophysial hormones: Pharmacological properties and tentative identification. Endocrinol. 66:860.

Nalbandov, A. V. 1959 Neuro-endocrine reflex mechanisms: bird ovulation, in Comparative Endocrinology, ed. A. Gorbman, p. 161. John Wiley & Sons, New York.

Nalbandov, A. V., and M. F. James 1949 The blood-vascular system of the chicken ovary. Am. J. Anat. 85:347.

Neher, B. H., and R. M. Fraps 1950 The addition of eggs to the hen's clutch by repeated injections of ovulation-inducing hormones. Endocrinol. 46:482.

Ogasawara, F. X., H. P. Van Krey, and F. W. Lorenz 1964 Hydrogen ion concentration of the oviduct of the laying domestic fowl. Poultry Sci. 43:3.

Olsen, M. W., and T.C. Byerly 1932 Orientation of the hen's egg in the uterus and during laying. Poultry Sci. 11:266.

Olsen, M. W., and B. H. Neher 1948 The site of fertilization in the domestic fowl. J. Exp. Zool. 109:355.

Opel, H. 1964 Premature oviposition following operative interference with the brain of the chicken. Endocrinol. 74:193.

Opel, H., and R. M. Fraps 1961 Blockade of gonadotrophin release for ovulation in the hen following stimulation with stainless steel electrodes. Proc. Soc. Exp. Biol. & Med. 108:291.

Opel, H., and A. V. Nalbandov 1958 A study of hormonal control of growth and ovulation of follicles in hypophysectomized hens. Poultry Sci. 37:1230.

Opel, H., and A. V. Nalbandov 1961a Ovulability of ovarian follicles in the hypophysectomized hen. Endocrinol. 69:1029.

Opel, H., and A. V. Nalbandov 1961b Follicular growth and ovulation in hypophysectomized hens. Endocrinol. 69:1016.

Pearl, R., and M. R. Curtis 1912 Studies on the physiology of reproduction in the domestic fowl. V: Data regarding the physiology of the oviduct. J. Exp. Zool. 12:99.

Pearl, R., and W. F. Schoppe 1921 Studies on the physiology of reproduction in the domestic fowl. XVIII: Further observations on the anatomical basis of fecundity. J. Exp. Zool. 34:101.

Peterson, W. J., and D. B. Parrish 1939 Fluctuations of phosphatase and inorganic phosphorus in the blood of the laying hen during the period of egg formation. Poultry Sci. 18:54.

Phillips, R. E., and D. C. Warren 1937 Observations concerning the mechanics of ovulation in the fowl. J. Exp. Zool. 76:117.

Platt, C. S. 1946 Report of the New Jersey Pigeon Breeding Test, Millville, N.J.

Polin, D. 1957 Formation of porphyrin from delta amino-levulinic acid by uterine and liver tissue from laying hens. Proc. Soc. Exp. Biol. & Med. 94:276.

Polin, D., and P. D. Sturkie 1955 Prevention of premature oviposition and shell-less egg with ephedrine. Poultry Sci. 34:1169.

Polin, D., and P. D. Sturkie 1957 The influence of the parathyroids on blood calcium levels and shell deposition in laying hens. Endocrinol. 60:778.

Prasad, A., L. E. Davis, and H. E. Dale   1963   Adrenergic response of the avian uterus. Science (in press).

Quisenberry, J. H.   1963   Light control for growing pullets and laying hens. Compilation of publications appearing in Poultry Science and British Poultry Science 1959 to date. Mimeographed material from Texas A & M College.

Ralph, C. V.   1959   Some effects of hypothalamic lesions on gonadotrophin release in the hen. Anat. Rec. 134:411.

Ralph, C. V., and R. M. Fraps   1959   Long term effects of diencephalic lesions on the ovary of the hen. Am. J. Physiol. 197:1279.

Ralph, C. L., and R. M. Fraps   1960   Induction of ovulation in the hen by injection of progesterones in the brain. Endocrinol. 66:269.

Richardson, K. C.   1935   The secretory phenomena in the oviduct of the fowl, including the process of shell formation examined by the micro-incineration technique. Phil. Trans. Roy. Soc. London, Series B, 225:149.

Riddle, O.   1911   On the formation, significance and chemistry of the white and yellow yolk of ova. J. Morph. 22:455.

Riddle, O.   1921   A simple method of obtaining premature eggs from birds. Science 54:664.

Riddle, O., and C. E. Anderson   1918   Studies on the physiology of reproduction in birds. VIII: The effects of quinine on the production of egg yolk and egg albumen. Am. J. Physiol. 47:92.

Riddle, O., and G. C. Basset   1916   The effect of alcohol on the size of the yolk of the pigeon's egg. Am. J. Physiol. 41:425.

Riddle, O., and C. B. King   1921   Studies on the physiology of reproduction in birds. XII: The relation of nerve stimuli to oviducal secretions as indicated by effects of atropine and other alkaloids. Am. J. Physiol. 57:275.

Riddle, O., V. M. Rauch, and G. C. Smith   1945   Action of estrogen on plasma calcium and endosteal bone formation in parathyroidectomized pigeons. Endocrinol. 36:41.

Robinson, D. S., and N. R. King   1963   Carbonic anhydrase and formation of hen's egg shell. Nature 199:497.

Romanoff, A. L., and A. J. Romanoff   1949   The Avian Egg. John Wiley & Sons, Inc., New York.

Rothchild, I.   1946   The time of release of the ovulating hormone from anterior pituitary of domestic hen. Anat. Rec. 96:542 (Abs.).

Rothchild, I. 1949 An indication that the ovulating hormone release inducing action of progesterone is an indirect one. Fed. Proc. 8:135.

Rothchild, I., and R. M. Fraps 1944a Relation between light-dark rhythms and hour of lay of eggs experimentally retained in the hen. Endocrinol. 35:355.

Rothchild, I., and R. M. Fraps 1944b On the function of the ruptured ovarian follicle of the domestic fowl. Proc. Soc. Exp. Biol. & Med. 56:79.

Rothchild, I., and R. M. Fraps 1945 The relation between ovulation frequency and the incidence of follicular atresia following surgical operation in the domestic fowl. Endocrinol. 37:415.

Rothchild, I., and R. M. Fraps 1949 The induction of ovulating hormone release from the pituitary of the domestic fowl by means of progesterone. Endocrinol. 44:141.

Sawyer, W. H. 1961 Neurohypophysial hormones. Pharmacol. Rev. 13:225.

Scott, H. M. 1938 The physiology of egg size in the domestic fowl. Thesis, University of Illinois.

Scott, H. M., and B. R. Burmester 1939 Effect of resection of the albumen tube on secretion of egg white. Proc. VII World's Poultry Congress, Cleveland, Ohio. p. 102.

Scott, H. M., and W. Huang 1941 Histological observations on the formation of the chalaza in the hen's egg. Poultry Sci. 20:402.

Scott, H. M., J. S. Hughes, and D. C. Warren 1937 Augmentation of nitrogen to the egg white after the formation of the shell membranes in the fowl. Poultry Sci. 16:53.

Scott, H. M., E. Jungherr, and L. D. Matterson 1944 The effect of feeding sulfanilamide to the laying fowl. Poultry Sci. 23:446.

Scott, H. M., and D. C. Warren 1936 Influence of ovulation rate on the tendency of the fowl to produce eggs in clutches. Poultry Sci. 15:381.

Sevolan, M., and P. P. Levine 1957 Effects of infectious bronchitis on the reproductive tracts, egg production and egg quality of laying chickens. Avian Diseases 1:136.

Shirley, H. V., and A. V. Nalbandov 1956 Effects of neurohypophysectomy in domestic chickens. Endocrinol. 58:477.

Simkiss, K. 1958 The structure of the eggshell with particular reference to the hen. Ph.D. Thesis, University of Reading.

Simkiss, K. 1961 Calcium metabolism and avian reproduction. Biol. Rev. 36:321.

Simkiss, K., and C. Tyler 1957 A histochemical study of the organic matrix of hen eggshells. Quart. J. Micr. Sci. 98:19.

Simkiss, K., and C. Tyler 1958 Reactions between eggshell matrix and metallic cations. Quart. J. Micr. Sci. 99:5.

Smith, A. H., G. N. Hoover, J. O. Nordstrom, and C. M. Winget 1957 Quantitative changes in the hen's oviduct associated with egg formation. Poultry Sci. 36:353.

Stewart, G. F. 1935 The structure of the hen's eggshell. Poultry Sci. 14:24.

Stringer, D. A., and T. G. Taylor 1961 The calcification mechanism as exemplified by a histochemical study of the avian medullary bone. Biochem. J. 78:19P.

Sturkie, P. D. 1946 The effects of hypothermia upon the reproductive tract of the hen. Poultry Sci. 25:369.

Sturkie, P. D. Avian Physiology (1st ed., 1954) Cornell University Press, Ithaca, N.Y.

Sturkie, P. D. 1955 Absorption of egg yolk in body cavity of the hen. Poultry Sci. 34:736.

Sturkie, P. D., and S. L. Freedman 1962 Effects of transection of pelvic and lumbosacral nerves on ovulation and oviposition in fowl. J. Reprod. & Fertility 4:81.

Sturkie, P. D., P. Joiner, and S. L. Freedman 1962 Role of the "bearing down" reflex on oviposition in the chicken. Endocrinol. 70:221.

Sturkie, P. D., and D. Polin 1954 Role of magnum and uterus in the determination of albumen quality of laid eggs. Poultry Sci. 33:9.

Sturkie, P. D., and H. S. Weiss 1950 The effects of sympathomimetic and parasympathomimetic drugs upon egg formation. Poultry Sci. 29:781 (Abs.).

Sturkie, P. D., H. S. Weiss, and R. K. Ringer 1954 Effects of injections of acetylcholine and ephedrine upon components of the hen's egg. Poultry Sci. 33:18.

Sykes, A. H. 1953a Premature oviposition in the hen. Nature 172:1098.

Sykes, A. H. 1953b Some observations on oviposition in the fowl. Quart. J. Exp. Physiol. 38:61.

Sykes, A. H. 1955a Further observations on reflex bearing down in the fowl. J. Physiol. 128:249.

Sykes, A. H. 1955b The effect of adrenaline on oviduct motility and egg production in the fowl. Poultry Sci. 34:622.

Sykes, A. H. 1962 Effect of uterine irritant on egg formation in the fowl. J. Reprod. & Fertility 4:214.

Taber, E., M. Claytor, J. Knight, D. Gambrell, J. Flowers, and C. Ayers 1958 Ovarian stimulation in the immature fowl by desiccated avian pituitaries. Endocrinol. 62:84.

Tanaka, K., and S. Nakajo 1962 Participation of neurohypophysial hormones in oviposition in the hen. Endocrinol. 70:453.

Taylor, L. W., and I. M. Lerner 1939 Inheritance of egg-shell thickness in White Leghorn pullets. J. Agric. Res. 58:386.

Taylor, T. G., and F. Hertelendy 1960 Parallel distribution of calcium and citric acid in the oviduct of the hen. Nature 187:244.

Taylor, T. G., and F. Hertelendy 1961 Changes in the blood calcium associated with eggshell calcification in the domestic fowl. 2: Changes in the diffusible calcium. Poultry Sci. 40:115.

Taylor, T. G., and J. H. Moore 1953 Avian medullary bone. Nature 172:504.

Taylor, T. G., and J. H. Moore 1954a Skeletal depletion in hens laying on a low-calcium diet. Brit. J. Nutrit. 8:112.

Taylor, T. G., and J. H. Moore 1954b Unpublished observations.

Taylor, T. G., and J. H. Moore 1956 The effects of calcium depletion on the chemical composition of bone minerals in laying hens. Brit. J. Nutrit. 10:250.

Taylor, T. G., and J. H. Moore 1958 The effect of high and low levels of dietary inorganic phosphate on the pre-laying storage of calcium and phosphorus and on the composition of the medullary and cortical bone in pullets. Brit. J. Nutrit. 12:35.

Taylor, T. G., J. H. Moore, and R. M. Loosmore 1958 Some effects of bone fracture in hens. Zentralblatt für Veterinarmedizin 5:579.

Taylor, T. G., T. R. Morris, and F. Hertelendy 1962 The effect of pituitary hormones on ovulation in calcium deficient pullets. Vet. Rec. 74:123.

Taylor, T. G., and Ann Williams 1964 Cyclic changes in plasma acid- and alkaline-phosphatase concentration associated with eggshell calcification in the fowl. Biochem. J. 91:21.

Tyler, C. 1940 Studies of calcium and phosphorus metabolism in relation to chemical structure of bone. 1: Experiments with laying birds. Biochem. J. 34:202.

Tyler, C. 1950 The effect of sulfanilamide on the metabolism of calcium, carbonate, phosphorus, chloride and nitrogen in the laying hen. Brit. J. Nutrit. 4:112.

Tyler, C. 1954a A further study of the effect of sulfanilamide on the metabolism of calcium and phosphorus in the laying hen. J. Agric. Sci. 45:156.

Tyler, C. 1954b Studies on eggshells. IV: The site of deposition of radioactive calcium and phosphorus. J. Sci. Fd. Agric. 5:335.

Urist, M. R. 1959 The effects of calcium deprivation upon the blood, adrenal cortex, ovary and skeleton in domestic fowl. Recent Prog. Hormone Res. 15:455.

Urist, M. R., N. M. Deutsch, G. Pomerantz, and F. McLean 1960 Interaction between actions of parathyroid hormone and estrogens on bone and blood in avian species. Am. J. Physiol. 199:851.

Van Tienhoven, A. 1953 Further study of the neurogenic blockade of LH release in the hen. Anat. Rec. 115:374.

Van Tienhoven, A. 1961a Endocrinology of reproduction in birds. Chapter 28, Vol. II, Sex and Internal Secretions, William C. Young, Williams & Wilkins Company, Baltimore.

Van Tienhoven, A. 1961b The effect of massive doses of corticotrophin and of corticosterone on ovulation of the chicken. Acta Endocrinol. 38:407.

Warren, D. C. 1949 Fertility and hatchability of chicken and turkey eggs, Chapter 2 in Formation of the Hen's Egg. John Wiley & Sons, Inc., New York.

Warren, D. C., and R. M. Conrad 1939 Growth of the hen's ovum. J. Agric. Res. 58:875.

Warren, D. C., and R. M. Conrad 1942 Time of pigment deposition in brown-shelled hen eggs and in turkey eggs. Poultry Sci. 21:515.

Warren, D. C., and H. M. Scott 1934 Ovulation in the domestic hen. Science 80:461.

Warren, D. C., and H. M. Scott 1935 The time factor in egg production. Poultry Sci. 14:195.

Weiss, H. S., and P. D. Sturkie 1952 Time of oviposition as affected by neuromimetic drugs. Poultry Sci. 31:227.

Wilson, W. O. 1963 Photocontrol of oviposition in gallinaceous birds. Conference on photo-neuro-endocrine effects in circadian systems, with particular reference to the eye.

Wilson, W. O., and Hans Abplanalp 1956 Intermittent light stimuli in egg production of chickens. Poultry Sci. 35:532.

Wilson, W. O., and A. E. Woodward 1958 Egg production of chickens kept in darkness. Poultry Sci. 37:1054.

Wilson, W. O., A. E. Woodward, and H. Abplanalp 1963 Exogenous regulation of oviposition in chickens. Poultry Sci. 42:1319.

Winget, C. M., and A. H. Smith 1958 Changes in plasma calcium concentration during egg formation. Poultry Sci. 37:509.

Winget, C. M., A. H. Smith, and G. N. Hoover 1958 Anterio-venous differences in plasma calcium concentration in the shell gland of the laying hen during shell formation. Poultry Sci. 37:1325.

Witschi, E., and N. W. Fugo 1940 Response of sex characters of adult female starling to synthetic hormones. Proc. Soc. Exp. Biol. & Med. 45:10.

Zeller, F. J., W. R. Breneman, and M. Carmack 1958 Action of Lithospernum ruderale on ovulation in the hen. Poultry Sci. 37:455.

CHAPTER 16

Reproduction in the Male, Fertilization, and Early Embryonic Development

ANATOMY AND HISTOLOGY OF THE REPRODUCTIVE SYSTEM

THE reproductive system of the male consists of paired testes, the epididymi, the vasa deferentia (which transport the spermatozoa to the penis), and the penis (Figure 74). The testes are near the cephalic end of the kidneys and ventral to them. The weight of the testes comprises about 1 percent of the total body weight (Parker, 1949). The epididymi in birds are small in comparison to those in mammals. The bird, unlike mammals, has no Cowper's gland or seminal vesicle. The avian testis is without septa and lobules, and consists of seminiferous tubules, the rete tubules, and vas efferentia.

From the seminiferous tubules, the sperm pass to the rete tubules and then to the vas efferentia, epididymis, and vas deferens. Normally, at least in the chicken, sperm are not stored in the epididymis, nor in any of the other accessory organs (Lake, 1957).

In passerine birds, the terminal part of the vas deferens is enlarged, and is often referred to as the seminal vesicle; however, Marshall (1961) states that structurally this organ has nothing in common with the seminal vesicle of mammals, hence he prefers the designation "seminal sac." Sperm, however, may be stored here.

515

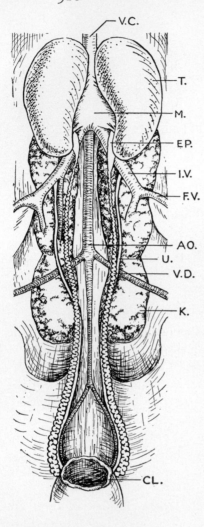

Figure 74. Urogenital system of the male chicken.

V.C., posterior vena cava; T., testes; M., mesorchium; EP., epididymis; I.V., iliac vein; F.V., femoral vein; AO., aorta; U, ureter; V.D., vas deferens; K, kidney; CL., cloaca.

Cocks have a small phallus, which on erection becomes engorged not with blood but with lymph from the lymph folds (Nishiyama, 1955). This lymph fluid is added to the semen in the vas deferens, and both are ejected simultaneously along the longitudinal groove of the phallus (Figure 75). The genital apparatus of the turkey is similar to that of the chicken (Lorenz, 1959). Duck and geese have well developed phalli, which are spirally twisted and which serve as intromittent organs (Benoit, 1950).

The seminiferous tubules of prepuberal males are small, and are lined with a single layer of cells (Figure 76A). The mature testis has a multilayered epithelium representing the various stages of spermatogenesis. From the wall of the tubule to the lumen may be found spermatogonia, primary spermatocytes, secondary spermatocytes, spermatids, the nutritive cells (cells of Sertoli) to which the spermatids are attached, and the spermatozoa. The connective tissue stroma between the tubules contains the interstitial cells (Leydig) and blood vessels. The follicle-stimulating hormone from the pituitary,

FSH, is responsible for the growth of the tubules. The interstitial cell-stimulating hormone (ICSH) stimulates the growth and development of the Leydig cells, or the luteinizing hormone (LH) causes these cells to secrete androgen (see Chapters 17 and 18).

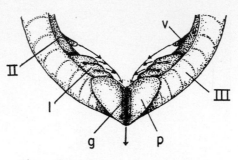

Figure 75. Diagram showing the ejaculation of the semen of the cock. *g*, longitudinal groove of the erected phallus; *l*, swollen lymphfold; *p*, erected phallus; *v*, papillary process of vas deferens; *II*, 2nd fold of cloaca; *III*, 3rd fold of cloaca, i.e. anus; denotes the ejection of vas deferens semen from *v*, and outflow of transparent fluid from *l*, as well as the ejaculation of the semen (the mixture of vas deferens semen with transparent fluid) along *g* to the outside of anus. (From Nishiyama, *J. Faculty of Agric., Kyushu Univ.* 10:277, 1955.)

Development of the Testes and Spermatogenesis

The growth and development of the testes and spermatogenesis have been studied in detail by a number of workers (see reviews by Lorenz, 1959, and Van Tienhoven, 1961). Kumaran and Turner (1949a and b), who studied the histology of the testes of White Plymouth Rock chickens at various ages (see also Blivaiss, 1947) reported their observations as follows: During the first 5 weeks the tubules are organized, and multiplication of the basal layer of cells, the spermatogonia, occurs. The primary spermatocytes begin to appear at about the 6th week. During the next 2 or 3 weeks, growth of the primary spermatocytes takes precedence over the further multiplication of the spermatogonial layer.

The secondary spermatocytes begin to appear at about 10 weeks of age as a result of the reduction division of the primary spermatocytes (Figure 76B). Spermatids (immature spermatozoa) begin to appear in the seminiferous tubules at about 12 weeks of age, and by the 20th week are usually present in all of the tubules (Figure 76C). The weight of the testes of the Plymouth Rock cockerels at 20 weeks averaged 9.11 grams, and at 16 weeks, 2.7 grams.

In White Leghorns, which are more precocious sexually, the average weight of the testes at 20 weeks is 16.7 grams (Jones and La-

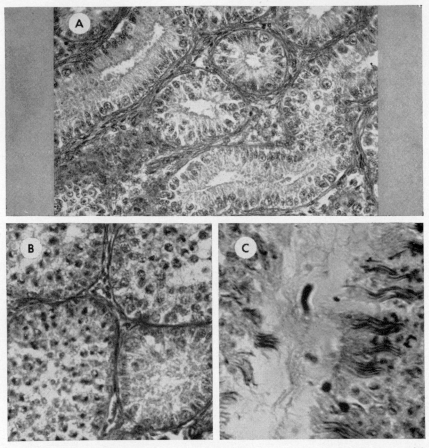

Figure 76. Cross sections of testes of cockerels at 42 days of age (A), at 70 days of age (B), and at six months of age (C), showing different stages of spermatogenesis.

A shows beginning of formation of primary spermatocytes in some tubules. In many areas, however, there is one layer of cells. In B, primary and secondary spermatocytes are abundant. In C, spermatids, spermatozoa, and sertoli cells are present. Between the tubules are the interstitial cells. (Figures A and B from Kumaran and Turner, *Poultry Sci.,* 1949. Figure C from Blivaiss, *Physiol. Zool.,* 1947.)

moreux, 1942). In older males, testes weight may reach 30 grams. Although histologically the testes may show spermatozoa at 16 to 20 weeks, and in Leghorn cockerels even at 12 weeks, fertility is not good until the males are 24 to 26 weeks of age (Hogue and

Schnetzler, 1937; Parker, Mc-Kenzie, and Kempster, 1942). Enheptin (2-amino, 5 nitrothiazole) inhibits testicular and comb development by inhibiting pituitary gonadotrophin secretion (Pino, Rosenblatt, and Hudson, 1954).

In the absence of the thyroid gland, the development of the testes is subnormal and spermatogenesis does not proceed beyond the formation of secondary spermatocytes (Blivaiss, 1947).

Detailed studies of spermatogenesis in ducks have been made by Clermont (1958).

Mature spermatozoa of birds exhibit a great deal of variation in size and shape, depending on the species. Romanoff (1960) has described and shown photographs of spermatozoa from many avian species. Electron-microscopic studies of fowl spermatozoa have been conducted by Grigg (1951) and Bonadonna (1954). In the chicken, the spermatozoon has a long headpiece with a pointed acrosome, and a short midpiece, to which is attached the long tail (Figure 77).

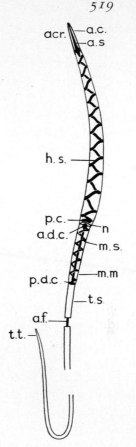

Figure 77. Diagram of the spermatozoon of the chicken.

a.c., apical cap; acr., acrosome; a.d.c., anterior distal centriole; a.f., axial filament; a.s., apical spine; h.s., head; m.m., midpiece membrane; m.s., midpiece spiral; n, neck; p.c., proximal centriole; p.d.c., posterior distal centriole; t.s., tail sheath; t.t., tip of tail. (Modified slightly from Grigg, *Proc. IX World's Poultry Congr.,* 1951.)

FACTORS AFFECTING FERTILITY IN THE MALE

Maturing of spermatozoa. Munro (1938a) demonstrated that spermatozoa of the chicken must be ripened or matured in the epididymis before they are capable of fertilization. Spermatozoa taken directly from the testes do not fertilize ova, and those taken from the epididymis fertilized only 13 percent of the females inseminated. When semen was taken from the lower vas deferens, 74 percent of the females inseminated laid fertile eggs. The motility of the spermatozoa from these sites was directly proportional to their fertilizing capacity. The duration of the ripening period apparently is not long, because it was shown that spermatozoa could pass from the testes through the vas deferens to the cloaca within 24 hours. Since ligation of the vas deferens, or castration, had no effect upon the spermatozoa in the vas deferens, Munro (1938b) believed that hormones from the testes were not concerned in the process of maturing.

Number of Spermatozoa and Amount of Semen Produced

Semen from the cock is usually white and opaque, but may be clear and watery, particularly when the concentration of spermatozoa is low. The pH of cock semen is 7.04 according to Wheeler and Andrews (1943), and 7.27 according to Parker, McKenzie, and Kempster (1942).

The volume of semen of a given ejaculation has been measured by a number of workers; some of the variation reported may be attributable to the methods of collection. Some have collected the semen from the cloaca of the hen after a normal mating, and some have collected it directly from the male, obtaining it artificially by massaging the abdomen after a technique of Burrows and Quinn (1937, 1939).

Parker (1949), who reviewed the subject, compiled the results of a number of investigators, including his own. The volumes reported (averages) range from 0.11 (collected from the cloaca of the hen) to 1 cc. (collected from the male directly). Spermatozoa per cubic millimeter of semen average about 3.5 million. Thus, in a given ejaculate (0.5 to 1 cc. volume) the number of spermatozoa ranges from 1.7 to 3.5 billion. Lake (1957) reported averages of 7 billion and a maximum of 8.2 billion in Brown Leghorn cocks.

Turkeys produce less semen than chickens, but the concentration of spermatozoa is much greater. The amounts average about 0.2 ml. per collection, and the concentration varies from 6 to 11 billion per ml. (Lorenz, 1959).

The amount of semen obtained from pheasants (*Phasianus colchicus*) is 0.1 ml. or less (Shaklee and Knox, 1954).

There is little correlation between the concentration of spermatozoa and fertility when the semen contains from 825,000 to 7 million spermatozoa per cu. mm., according to Hutt (1929). A minimum of 100 million spermatozoa must be inseminated to obtain optimum fertility (Munro, 1938c; Parker, McKenzie, and Kempster, 1942). Weakley and Shaffner (1952), however, reported little change in fertility when semen was diluted 1:10, and each insemination supplied less than 100 million sperm.

Abnormal spermatozoa may cause sterility, but apparently very few males produce sufficient numbers of abnormal spermatozoa to produce this effect (Sampson and Warren, 1939).

The number of matings or ejaculations per day influences the volume of semen produced and the concentration of spermatozoa. Both decrease with the frequency of mating, and after three or four successive ejaculations the concentration of spermatozoa is very low in some males (Parker, McKenzie, and Kempster, 1940).

The number of times a male chicken mates per day may range from 25 to 41, according to Heuser (1916) and Philips (1918). More recent work by Guhl (1951) suggests that males may mate still more frequently than the figures given above. Guhl made studies on individual males placed in pens with from 30 to 40 females, where mating behavior was observed for 21 minutes per day for periods as long as 84 days. The observations were made during the first 21 minutes that the males were introduced to the females. The actual observation time was 29 hours and 24 minutes. The number of treadings for three males during this period were 410, 788, and 853, or 13.9, 26.7, and 29.0 matings per hour, respectively. It was shown, however, that when males are first introduced into a pen, they mate most frequently during the first 3 to 6 minutes. Guhl, Collias, and Alee (1945) and Guhl and Warren (1946) demonstrated that the social order or "peck order" of the hens to which males are introduced affects their mating behavior. Males, regardless of their social standing, tend to mate most frequently not with the highest- or lowest-ranking hens, but with the "middle-class" hens. When three or more males are introduced together in a pen of females, both the frequency of matings and the fertility are highest for the top-ranking male. The lowest-ranking male mates with few females because of interference from the higher-ranking males.

Other factors affecting the production of semen and fertility of the male and female are age, season, amount of light, state of nutrition, and health (see Lorenz, 1959).

There is a diurnal variation in the production of spermatozoa by the fowl, with the greatest spermatogenic activity at 3 A.M. according to Riley (1940) and at midnight according to Macartney (1942).

It is generally conceded that fertility declines in males and females in the second and third years of life. Male chickens vary in their production of semen and fertility with season (Parker and McSpadden, 1943; Wheeler and Andrews, 1943). These workers found that the amount of semen and number of spermatozoa increase from December through April and then decline, to reach a low in July and August. Fertility also declines in the summer.

Effects of Light

It is well known that lights stimulate the pituitary to elaborate FSH and LH, which in turn activate the gonads (see also Chapter 17). When young cockerels receive 12 or more hours of light, growth of testes and production of semen are maximal. Maximum response to light is observed in about one month. With less than 9 hours of light, stimulation is at a minimum (Lamoreux, 1943).

Different wavelengths of light vary in their stimulating effect on the testes (Bissonnette, 1936; Benoit and Ott, 1938; Benoit *et al.,* 1950; Burger, 1943). Only that portion of the spectrum visible to man, between 4,000 and 7,000 angstroms, has a stimulating effect on spermatogenesis in the starling (Burger). Red light is slightly more effective than white, and blue-green light is least effective. Benoit and Ott (1938) reported the order of effectiveness of colored lights in stimulating the pituitary and testes of ducks as follows: (1) red, (2) orange, (3) yellow, (4) green, (5) blue. Blue had a slight stimulating effect and infrared was ineffective.

Experiments by Benoit, Walter, and Assenmacher (1950), in which the heads of ducks were exposed to lights where the wavelengths covered a narrower and more specific spectral range, show that only red and orange (708 and 617 mμ.) are very effective stimulators of the pituitary and gonads. Stimulation begins with yellow (577 mμ.) reaches a maximum at 617 to 708, and decreases at 740 mμ.

Flashing light may also activate the testes. Burger, Bissonnette, and Doolittle (1942) subjected starlings to uninterrupted light, but not enough to be sexually activating, plus flashing light. The exposure to both types of light equaled 14 hours. The workers found that to be effective, the interval of light must be more than 0.9 seconds, and the interval of darkness must be less than 15 seconds. Farner (1959) lists in his review a number of species that respond to artificial light (see also Van Tienhoven, 1961).

Chemical Composition of Semen

The composition of seminal plasma of chickens is similar to blood plasma, except that it is much higher in potassium than the latter, averaging 12.6 meq. per liter as compared to 4.9 for blood plasma (Lake *et al.*, 1958). The average composition of semen in meq./l. is as follows:

Na	*K*	*Ca*	*Cl*	*Mg*	*Cu**	*Zn**
171	11	4	59	7	10	0.57

* Gamma equivalents per liter.

By comparison with bull semen, the concentration of most of these in chicken semen is lower, except for Na and Zn (see Van Tienhoven, 1961, for further details; also Lorenz, 1959).

Storage of Semen

Unlike mammalian semen, avian semen retains its fertilizing capacity *in vivo* for as long as 30 days; however, attempts to store chicken semen (*in vitro*) without impairing fertility have been generally unsuccessful. Burrows and Quinn (1939), who stored semen at 4.4°C. or lower, found that the spermatozoa lost their fertilizing capacity in a short time. Semen can be stored at –79°C. for 14 months, and then thawed, but fertility is very low (Shaffner, Henderson, and Card, 1941). The length of life of spermatozoa in the unfrozen state is greatest at 0 to 1°C. Semen can be quick-frozen to a solid state at –6°C., and then thawed immediately at 42° to 45°C., without apparent damage to motility and fertility. But if it is stored for more than one minute after quick freezing, fertility decreases greatly (Shaffner, 1942). For further details, see Lorenz (1959). The reasons for the difference in the behavior of avian and mammalian semen are still being sought; the question has been discussed by Lorenz (1959) and Van Tienhoven (1961). One of the main differences in the composition of bull and of avian semen is the very high concentration of glutamate in the latter. Van Tienhoven (1959, 1961) presents evidence which suggests that avian spermatozoa are very sensitive to chloride ions; at least this was true when sperm diluents were used. Replacement of Cl ions in the diluent by glutamate did not decrease metabolic rate as did chloride ions, nor did it produce sperm abnormalities. Lake (1958) reported that a diluent containing a high concentration of glutamate extended the fertilizing capacity of chicken semen somewhat, but it appears that other unknown factors must also be involved. The metabolism of fowl spermatozoa in different diluents has been studied, by Van Tienhoven (1960).

Artificial Insemination

Burrows and Quinn (1937, 1939) and Parker (1939) developed a technique for obtaining semen artificially from the male. It is thus possible to dilute semen as much as ten times and inseminate a large number of females. To ensure good fertility, inseminations should be made every 4th or 5th day in the chicken, according to Warren and Gish (1943). They revealed that fertility declines rapidly after the 4th day following insemination. Turkey hens remain fertile after matings much longer than do chickens. Burrows and Marsden (1938) obtained good fertility in turkeys (83 percent) when the hens were inseminated every 30 days.

In a more recent review of the subject, Lorenz (1959) stated that the most satisfactory results (fertility) had been obtained with freshly collected and undiluted semen, 0.05 ml. per insemination at 5- to 7-day intervals for chickens, and 0.025 ml. at 3-week intervals for turkeys. However, difficulty is often experienced in successfully inseminating such small quantities.

Fertility and Time of Mating

The time elapsing between copulation and the first fertile egg obtained in chickens has been reported by many investigators (see review by Parker, 1949). The time averages about 72 hours, but may be as low as 19.5 hours, according to one report. The latter figure, if correct, means that the egg may be fertilized while it is in the magnum or isthmus.

Mimura (1939) studied the movement of spermatozoa through the oviduct of the fowl and showed that when spermatozoa were introduced into the uterus, they reached the upper part of the oviduct or ovary within as short a time as 26 minutes. Under normal conditions, with an egg in the oviduct, the time may be different.

A number of workers have studied the relation of time of insemination to fertility. Moore and Byerly (1942) reported that fertility was lowest when females were inseminated while a hard-shelled egg was present in the uterus, and highest when inseminations were made after the egg had been laid. Other workers have reported that fertility was significantly higher if inseminations or matings were restricted to the afternoon, when usually a soft-shell egg is in the uterus (Gracewski and Scott, 1943; Malmstrom, 1943; Parker, 1945). When matings were restricted to the afternoon, fertility was 80.9 percent, as compared to 54.8 percent with morning matings, and 71 and 74 percent with unrestricted matings (Gracewski and Scott).

Later work by Parker (1950) and by Schindler, Volcani, and Weinstein (1958), however, showed only a slight or insignificant difference in fertility between matings restricted to the morning (hard shell in uterus) and afternoon (soft shell).

Maximum fertility in chickens is usually obtained 2 or 3 days after matings. Good fertility is obtained as long as 5 or 6 days after the last matings, and then declines rapidly, but a few fertile eggs may be obtained as late as 35 days after the last mating. Seventy-two hours after the last mating, however, spermatozoa are found only in the infundibulum, according to Van Drimmelen (1945, 1951). This finding was based upon mucous scrapings from various parts of the oviduct. In turkeys, high fertility is obtained 20 days after insemination, and then decreases slowly with some fertile eggs being obtained 10 weeks after insemination (Lorenz, 1959).

FERTILIZATION AND EARLY EMBRYONIC DEVELOPMENT

Site of Fertilization

Early workers expressed the belief that fertilization in birds occurred in the ovary before ovulation. This belief was based upon the results of the experiments of Ivanoff (1924) and Walton and Whetham (1933), who washed out the oviduct of inseminated hens with a spermicide and still obtained fertile eggs. However, it has been suggested by later work that the spermicide may have not reached the spermatozoa because of the numerous folds and crypts in the oviduct.

Olsen and Neher (1948) proved conclusively that fertilization occurs after ovulation and before the egg reaches the magnum. They removed mature ovarian follicles from the ovaries of sterile nonmated hens just before ovulation. These follicles then ovulated *in vitro,* and were transferred to the oviducts of fertile, mated hens. Eighty-two percent of the eggs laid subsequently were fertile.

The same workers also removed ovarian follicles from fertile females, and after ovulation *in vitro* these were transferred to the oviducts of sterile, nonmated hens. All of these eggs were sterile. These workers, and Van Drimmelen (1951), also reported that ova could be fertilized by placing fresh semen in the infundibulum of the abdominal cavity.

Maturation, Cleavage, and Gastrulation

Approximately 24 hours before ovulation, the wall of the germinal vesicle of the hen's ovum begins to distintegrate and the inner surface of the vesicle becomes flattened (Olsen, 1942). The first maturation division, and the formation of the first polar body, occur while the ovum is still attached to the ovary. The spindle for the second maturation division is then formed, after which ovulation occurs.

The egg is then fertilized, usually within 15 minutes after ovulation. Three or four spermatozoa normally enter the egg at the time of fertilization, but the female pronucleus is fertilized by only one spermatozoon. The second polar body is extruded following the penetration of the spermatozoa, and before or simultaneously with the fusion of the male and female pronuclei. The first cleavage division occurs as the egg enters the isthmus, approximately 5 hours after ovulation. Within 20 minutes the second division occurs. The 4- and 8-cell cleavage stages occur while the egg is in the isthmus. Within 4 hours after the egg has entered the uterus, cleavage of the blastodisc has progressed from the 16-cell to approximately the 256-cell stage.

Since the maturation changes in the ovum can be induced prematurely with the ovulating hormone, it would appear that this hormone normally initiates the growth and maturation division of the ovum (Olsen and Fraps, 1950).

Neher and Fraps (1946) studied the effects of premature ovulation upon subsequent fertility and embryonic development. They forced hens to ovulate 6, 14, 22, and 30 hours prematurely, by intravenous injections of male chicken anterior pituitary extract. There was practically no difference in the fertility and hatchability of normally ovulated eggs and those ovulated 6 and 14 hours prematurely. When the ovulations were 22 hours premature, 9 out of 13 eggs were fertile.

Gastrulation in the pigeon occurs from 5 to 7 hours before laying, according to Patterson (1909). It has been assumed that the chicken egg has reached the gastrula stage by the time it is laid. However, Butler (1935), Jacobson (1948), and Sturkie and Williams (1945), have shown that this is not necessarily true. Many of the eggs have not reached the gastrula stage.

From the work of Stockard (1921) it has been assumed that twinning and monstrosities in chicks were due to an interruption of development in eggs which had not reached the gastrula stage when they were laid. Sturkie and Williams believe this assumption has little foundation. They removed eggs from the hen 5 to 10 hours before such eggs would have been laid normally, and cooled them. After cooling for several hours (development interrupted long before gastrulation) the eggs were incubated. The percentage of duplicate embryos obtained was higher than the normal incidence, but was still very low (1.5 percent).

Sturkie (1946) showed that twinning and duplicity could be produced in 8 percent of the embryos if normal development was interrupted during the early cleavage stages by lowering the body temperature of the hens.

Parthenogenesis in the domestic turkey has been reported by Olsen and co-workers in a series of papers, and by Kosin and Nagra (1956). The latter authors reported that the frequency of parthenogenesis varied between different breeds of turkeys, and was higher in the Beltsville white breed. Olsen (1960) reviewed much of his older work and presented new data on turkeys. The results show that 32.4 percent of infertile turkey eggs underwent parthenogenesis. In most of these eggs, the embryos died very early; 4.9 percent were recognizable as embryos. As of 1960, 67 parthenogenetic eggs had been hatched and a few of the chicks survived to sexual maturity. All have been males with the diploid number of chromosomes, and some have sired offspring. It was later shown (Olsen, 1961) that the incidence of parthenogenesis could be increased by inoculation of hens with Rous sarcoma virus.

REFERENCES

Benoit, J.   1950   Traité de Zoologie, edited by P. P. Grassé. Tome XV: Oiseaux, p. 350. Masson & Co., Paris.

Benoit, J., and L. Ott   1938   Action de lumières de différentes longueurs d'onde sur la gonadstimulation chez le canard impubère. Compt. Rend. Soc. Biol. 127:906.

Benoit, J., F. X. Walter, and I. Assenmacher   1950   Contribution à l'étude du réflexe opto-hypophysaire gonadostimulant chez le canard soumis à des radiations lumineuses de diverses longueurs d'onde. J. de Physiologie (Bordeaux) 42:537.

Bissonnette, T. H.   1936   Sexual photoperiodicity. Quart. Rev. Biol. 11:371.

Blivaiss, B. B.   1947   Interrelationships of thyroid and gonad in the development of plumage and other sex characters in Brown Leghorn roosters. Physiol. Zool. 20:67.

Bonadonna, T. 1954 Observations on the submicroscopic structures of Gallus gallus spermatozoa. Poultry Sci. 33:1151.

Burger, J. W. 1943 Some effects of colored illumination on the sexual activation of the male starling. J. Exp. Zool. 94:161.

Burger, J. W., T. H. Bissonnette, and H. D. Doolittle 1942 Some effects of flashing light on testicular activation in the male starling. J. Exp. Zool. 90:73.

Burrows, W. H., and S. J. Marsden 1938 Artificial breeding of turkeys. Poultry Sci. 17:408.

Burrows, W. H., and J. P. Quinn 1937 The collection of spermatozoa from the domestic fowl and turkey. Poultry Sci. 16:19.

Burrows, W. H., and J. P. Quinn 1939 Artificial insemination of chickens and turkeys. U. S. Dept. of Agr. Cir. 525.

Butler, E. 1935 The developmental capacity of the unincubated chick blastoderm. J. Exp. Zool. 70:357.

Clermont, Y. 1958 Structure de l'épithélium seminal et mode de renouvellement des spermatogonies chez le canard. Arch. Anat. Microscop. et. Morphol. Exp. 47:47.

Farner, D. S. 1959 Photoperiodic control of annual gonadal cycles in birds; in Photoperiodism, ed. R. B. Withrow. A.A.A.S. Pub. 55:717.

Gracewski, J. J., and H. M. Scott 1943 The influence of time of mating on fertility. Poultry Sci. 22:264.

Grigg, G. W. 1951 The morphology of fowl spermatozoa. IX World's Poultry Cong. 3:142.

Guhl, A. M. 1951 Measurable differences in mating behavior of cocks. Poultry Sci. 30:687.

Guhl, A. M., N. E. Collias, and W. C. Allee 1945 Mating behavior and the social hierarchy in small flocks of White Leghorns. Physiol. Zool. 18:365.

Guhl, A. M., and D. C. Warren 1946 Number of offspring sired by cockerels related to social dominance in chickens. Poultry Sci. 25:460.

Heuser, G. F. 1916 A study of the mating behavior of the domestic fowl. Thesis, Cornell University.

Hogue, R. L., and E. E. Schnetzler 1937 Development of fertility in young Barred Rock males. Poultry Sci. 16:62.

Hutt, F. B. 1929 On the relation of fertility in fowls to the amount of testicular material and density of sperm suspension. Proc. Roy. Soc. Edinburgh 49:102.

Ivanoff, E. 1924 Recherches expérimentales à propos du processus de la fécondation chez les poules. Compt. Rend. Soc. Biol. 91:54.

Jacobson, W. 1948 The early development of the avian embryo. I: Endoderm formation. J. Morph. 62:415.

Jones, D. G., and W. F. Lamoreux 1942 Semen production of White Leghorn males from strains selected for high and low fecundity. Poultry Sci. 21:173.

Kosin, I. L., and H. Nagra 1956 Frequency of abortive parthenogenesis in the domestic turkey. Proc. Soc. Exp. Biol. & Med. 93:605.

Kumaran, J. D. S., and C. W. Turner 1949a The normal development of the testes in the White Plymouth Rock. Poultry Sci. 28:511.

Kumaran, J. D. S., and C. W. Turner 1949b Endocrine activity of the testes of the White Plymouth Rock. Poultry Sci. 28:636.

Lake, P. E. 1957 The male reproductive tract of the fowl. Jour. Anat. 91:116.

Lake, P. E. 1958 *In vitro* storage of fowl spermatozoa. Proc. XI World's Poultry Cong.

Lake, P. E., E. J. Butler, J. W. McCallum, and I. J. MacIntyre 1958 A chemical analysis of the seminal and blood plasmas of the cock. Quart. J. Exp. Physiol. 43:309.

Lamoreux, W. F. 1943 The influence of different amounts of illumination upon the production of semen in the fowl. J. Exp. Zool. 94:73.

Lorenz, F. W. 1959 Reproduction in domestic fowl: physiology of the male, Chapter 11 in Reproduction in Domestic Animals, ed. H. H. Cole and P. T. Cupps. Academic Press, New York.

Macartney, E. L. 1942 Diurnal rhythm of mitotic activity in the seminiferous tubules of the domestic fowl. Poultry Sci. 21:130.

Malmstrom, M. V. 1943 Factors influencing fertility in the domestic fowl. Master's Thesis, University of Connecticut.

Marshall, A. J. 1961 Biology and Comparative Physiology of birds. Vol. II, Chapter 18: Reproduction. Academic Press, New York.

Mimura, H. 1939 On the mechanism of travel of spermatozoa through the oviduct in the domestic fowl, with special reference to artificial insemination (trans. Moore and Byerly, 1942). Sonderabdruck aus Okajimas Folia Anatomica Japonica, Band. 17, Heft 5.

Moore, O. K., and T. C. Byerly 1942 Relation of time of insemination to percent fertility. Poultry Sci. 21:253.

Munro, S. S. 1938a Functional changes in fowl sperm during their passage through the excurrent ducts of the male. J. Exp. Zool. 79:71.

Munro, S. S. 1938b The effect of testis hormone on the preservation of sperm life in the vas deferens of the fowl. J. Exp. Biol. 15:186.

Munro, S. S. 1938c The effect of dilution and density on the fertilizing capacity of fowl sperm suspensions. Canadian J. Res., Sec. D, 16:281.

Neher, B. H., and R. M. Fraps 1946 Fertility and hatchability of the prematurely ovulated hen's egg. J. Exp. Zool. 101:83.

Nishiyama, H. 1955 Studies on the accessory reproductive organs in the cock. J. Faculty of Agr., Kyushu Univ. 10:277.

Olsen, M. W. 1942 Maturation, fertilization and early cleavage in the hen's egg. J. Morph. 70:513.

Olsen, M. W. 1960 Nine year summary of parthenogenesis in turkeys. Proc. Soc. Exp. Biol. & Med. 105:279.

Olsen, M. W. 1961 Rous sarcoma virus associated with parthenogenesis in turkey eggs. Nature 190:191.

Olsen, M. W., and R. M. Fraps 1950 Maturation changes in the hen's ovum. J. Exp. Zool. 114:475.

Olsen, M. W., and B. H. Neher 1948 The site of fertilization in the domestic fowl. J. Exp. Zool. 109:355.

Parker, J. E. 1939 An avian semen collector. Poultry Sci. 18:455.

Parker, J. E. 1945 Relation of time of day of artificial insemination to fertility and hatchability of hen's eggs. Poultry Sci. 24:314.

Parker, J. E. 1949 Fertility and hatchability of chicken and turkey eggs, Chapter III, Fertility in Chickens and Turkeys. John Wiley & Sons, Inc., New York, ed. L. W. Taylor.

Parker, J. E. 1950 The effect of restricted matings in flocks of New Hampshire chickens on fertility and hatchability of eggs. Poultry Sci. 29:268.

Parker, J. E., F. F. McKenzie, and H. L. Kempster 1940 Observations on the sexual behavior of New Hampshire males. Poultry Sci. 19:191.

Parker, J. E., F. F. McKenzie, and H. L. Kempster 1942 Fertility in the male and domestic fowl. Mo. Agric. Exp. Sta. Res. Bull. 347.

Parker, J. E., and B. J. McSpadden 1943 Seasonal variation in semen production in domestic fowls. Poultry Sci. 22:142.

Patterson, J. T. 1909 Gastrulation in the pigeon's egg: A morphological and experimental study. J. Morph. 20:65.

Phillips, A. G. 1918 A brief study of the mating habits of fowls with a test of the value of a single mating. J. Am. Inst. & Invest. Poultry Husb. 4:30.

Pino, J. A., L. S. Rosenblatt, and C. B. Hudson 1954 Inhibition of pituitary gonadotrophin secretion in domestic fowl by enheptin. Proc. Soc. Exp. Biol. & Med. 87:201.

Riley, G. M. 1940 Diurnal variations in spermatogenic activity in the domestic fowl. Poultry Sci. 19:360.

Romanoff, A. L. 1960 The Avian Embryo. The Macmillan Co., New York.

Sampson, F. R., and D. C. Warren 1939 Density of suspension and morphology of sperm in relation to fertility in the fowl. Poultry Sci. 18:301.

Schindler, H., R. Volcani, and S. Weinstein 1958 Changes in pH during storage, buffering capacity and glycolysis of cock and bull semen. Poultry Sci. 37:21.

Shaffner, C. S. 1942 Longevity of fowl spermatozoa in frozen condition. Science 96:337.

Shaffner, C. S., E. W. Henderson, and C. G. Card 1941 Viability of spermatozoa of the chicken under various environmental conditions. Poultry Sci. 20:259.

Shaklee, W. E., and C. W. Knox 1954 Hybridization of the pheasant and fowl. J. Hered. 45:183.

Stockard, C. R. 1921 Developmental rate and structural expression: An experimental study of twins, double monsters, and single deformities, and the interaction among embryonic organs during their origin and development. Am. J. Anat. 28:115.

Sturkie, P. D. 1946 The production of twins in Gallus domesticus. J. Exp. Zool. 101:51.

Sturkie, P. D., and A. G. Williams 1945 Studies on pregastrular development, early embryonic development and hatchability of prematurely laid eggs of the hen. Poultry Sci. 24:546.

Van Drimmelen, G. C. 1945 The location of spermatozoa in the hen by means of capillary attraction. J. S. Afr. Vet. Med. Assoc. 16:97 (Abs.).

Van Drimmelen, G. C. 1951 Artificial insemination of birds by the intraperitoneal route: A study in sex physiology of pigeons and fowls with reports upon a modified technique of semen collection, a new technique of insemination, and observations on the spermatozoa in the genital organs of the fowl hen. Onderstepoort J. Vet. Res., Suppl. N. 1:212.

Van Tienhoven, A. 1959 Reproduction in the domestic fowl: physiology of the female, in Reproduction in Domestic Animals, ed. H. H. Coles and P. T. Cupps, Vol. II, p. 305. Academic Press, New York.

Van Tienhoven, A. 1960 The metabolism of fowl sperm in different diluents. Jour. Agr. Sci. 54:67.

Van Tienhoven, A. 1961 Endocrinology of reproduction in birds, Chapter 28, Sex and Internal Secretions, ed. William C. Young, Vol. II. Williams & Wilkins Co., Baltimore.

Walton, A., and E. O. Whetham 1933 The survival of the spermatozoon of the domestic fowl. J. Exp. Biol. 10:204.

Warren, D. C., and C. L. Gish 1943 The value of artificial insemination in poultry breeding work. Poultry Sci. 22:108.

Weakley, C. E., and C. S. Shaffner 1952 The fertilizing capacity of diluted chicken semen. Poultry Sci. 31:650.

Wheeler, N. C., and F. N. Andrews 1943 The influence of season on semen production in the domestic fowl. Poultry Sci. 22:361.

CHAPTER 17

Hypophysis

INTRODUCTION

THE endocrine organs secrete substances which have important physiological effects upon certain organs and processes of the body. These glands are ductless and discharge their hormones into the blood stream, where they are transported to the organs concerned. Some of the endocrine glands of the body produce only hormones (internal secretions); others elaborate hormones and other substances (external secretions).

The endocrine glands or organs of the bird are: (1) hypophysis or pituitary; (2) thyroids; (3) parathyroids; (4) adrenals; (5) pancreas; (6) testes and ovary (gonads); and (7) the intestine. The first four of these are strictly endocrine organs, whereas the last three exhibit both endocrine and exocrine functions. The thymus and pineal bodies, which are sometimes classified as endocrine organs, are present in the bird, but their functions are not clear.

The hypophysis is a master endocrine organ because it elaborates a number of hormones which in turn stimulate other glands to secrete hormones. The testes and ovary secrete androgen and estrogen respectively; these are discussed in Chapters 15 and 16, on reproduction in the female and the male, and in Chapter 18, on gonadal hormones. The hormones of the thyroids, the parathyroids and pancreas, and the adrenals are considered in Chapters 19, 20, and 21 respectively. A brief account of the intestinal hormone, secretin, is given in Chapter 11.

ANATOMY OF HYPOPHYSIS

The hypophysis, or pituitary gland, is situated in the saddlelike depression of the sphenoid bone (sella turcica), just posterior to the optic chiasma at the floor of the diencephalon. The gland comprises an anterior lobe (which consists of two distinct areas cytologically) and a posterior lobe, but no intermediate lobe, such as is present in mammals. There is, as in mammals, a pars tuberalis. See reviews by Wingstrand (1951), Legait and Legait (1955), Mi-

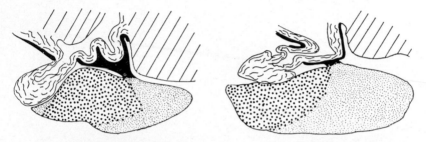

Figure 78. Diagrams of the pituitaries of the chicken (left) and duck (right); sagittal sections.

Large dots and small dots represent caudal and cephalic areas respectively of the anterior lobe. Solid black area, pars tuberalis; wavy lines, posterior lobe; parallel lines, area of third ventricle of brain. (From Rahn and Painter, *Anat. Rec.*, 1941.)

kami (1958), and Herlant *et al.* (1960). The extensive study by Wingstrand covers the anatomy and histology of pituitaries of a number of avian species.

The anterior lobe (adenohypophysis) is separated from the posterior lobe (neurohypophysis) by a distinct connective tissue sheath. The infundibulum and stalk communicate with the third ventricle of the brain (see Figures 78, 79, 80, 81). Both the anterior lobe—which is derived from Rathke's pouch as it is in mammals —and the posterior lobe are ectodermal in origin.

Cytology

The cytology of avian pituitaries has been studied by a number of investigators, including Rahn and Painter (1941), Wingstrand

(1951), Payne (1946, 1961), Legait and Legait (1955), Mikami (1958), and Herlant *et al.* (1960). All are agreed that there are two distinct areas cytologically, namely the caudal and cephalic areas. The avian adenohypophysis contains at least three cell types: chromophobes, acidophils, and basophils. There are at least two types

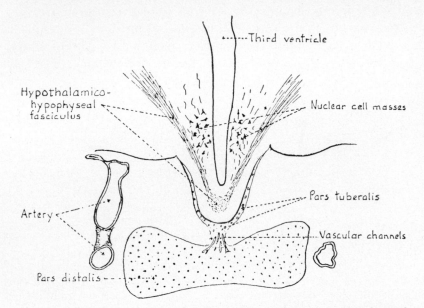

Figure 79. A composite drawing constructed from frontal sections of the chicken hypophysis, showing innervation. (From Drager, *Endocrinol.*, 1945.)

of acidophils; those occupying the caudal area (A_1 cells) are cytologically like those of anterior lobe of mammals (Payne; Rahn and Painter; Mikami). The A_1 cells are larger than the A_2 cells and contain coarse granules which stain deeply with azocarmine and orange G (Mikami). The cephalic area is distinguished by the absence of A_1 cells and the presence of V cells. According to Mikami, since the V cells are stained orange by the azan method and reddish purple by the trichrome method, and have a specific affinity for acid violet, they are identical with the light-staining acidophils of Rahn (1939) and may correspond to the A_2 cells of Payne and Wingstrand and the cephalic acidophils of many investigators

(Mikami, 1958). Since the granules of V cells are also stainable with basic dyes, they are not true acidophils, according to Mikami.

Most investigators are agreed that there are also at least two types of basophils, the thyrotrophs (see also Chapter 19) and the gonadotrophs (Mikami, 1958), and some believe that two or more gonadotrophs exist. Herlant *et al.* (1960) claim to be able to distinguish 6 distinct cell types in the adenohypophysis of the duck, 5 of which are homologous to those described in mammals. The same workers describe two acidophils and three types of basophils, two of which are gonadotrophic. One of them, the gamma basophil cell, is located exclusively in the caudal lobe; it stains carmine with azan and purple with Herlant's stain, and is positive periodic acid–Schiff (PAS). Such cells are most numerous during testicular growth, particularly during development of interstitial tissue; they undergo involution during testicular regression and are believed to secrete LH. The beta cells located in the cephalic lobe are also PAS positive but show other staining reactions different from the gamma cells, and are believed by Herlant to secrete FSH. Another type described by Herlant *et al.* (an acidophil cell) is thought to produce the hormone prolactin.

Schooley and Riddle (1938) and Rahn (1939) also believed that the acidophils produced prolactin. During periods of broodiness, when the greatest amount of prolactin is produced by the pituitary, the numbers of basophil cells decrease greatly in the pituitary and are replaced by small acidophils or "broody cells" (Payne, 1947). Yasuda (1953) observed that the caudal lobe of broody hens exhibited an increase in number of acidophils, while the cephalic lobe showed a decrease in basophils and an increase in chromophobes. This suggested that the A_1 cells might elaborate prolactin, and that the caudal lobe of broody hens should have a higher potency of prolactin; and this has been demonstrated by Nakajo and Tanaka (1956). These workers also showed, however, that the cephalic lobe also contained prolactin, and in nonbroody birds contained as much as the caudal lobe, thus suggesting that the A_2 cells may also produce prolactin.

The evidence is good that a special type of basophil (beta), a large polygonally shaped cell, secretes thyrotrophic (TSH) hormone (see also Chapter 19). Mikami (1958) reports that the basophils that produce TSH are confined largely to the cephalic lobe. After thyroidectomy there is a marked hypertrophy of the cephalic lobe, and the "thyroidectomy cells" increase in size and number. The cells are large and are round, oval or polygonal in shape, and they develop directly from cephalic basophils (Mikami, 1958). Mikami assayed the cephalic and caudal lobes of pituitaries of normal and thyroidectomized cockerels for thyrotrophic potency. The cephalic lobe was very potent in TSH, but the caudal lobe had a low potency. TSH potency of the cephalic lobe decreased slightly after thyroidectomy.

The V cells reported by Mikami to be restricted to the cephalic lobe are amphophilic cells which have an affinity for both acid and basic dyes. After adrenalectomy the V cells increased in number and exhibited a chromophobic appearance owing to loss of granules. Thus Mikami concluded that "adrenalectomy cells" develop from V cells and that they probably secrete ACTH. Adrenalectomy cells are considered by Mikami to be a completely new type of cell, which differs from other types in such respects as morphology, stainability, distribution, and origin.

Castration cells which are found in the pituitaries of some castrated mammals were reported not to be present in castrated chickens by Payne (1940, 1947), but were reported by Mikami (1958). There is an increase in size and number of basophils in both caudal and cephalic lobes after castration, and these are believed to be gonadotrophs.

Payne (1961 and earlier), who has done extensive work on pituitary cytology, does not attempt to ascribe a different secretory function to each cell type. In fact, he believes that different pituitary hormones may be secreted by the same cell type, and he cites evidence for his view.

Size

The anterior lobe of birds is small. Most of the studies on pituitary weights have been made on chickens. The weights of pituitaries of White Leghorn female chickens at different ages are as follows (Breneman, 1955):

Age in days	20	40	60	80	100	110	126
Weight in mg.	1.6	3.85	5.00	5.25	6.50	6.40	8.23

Weights of male pituitaries at similar ages were reported by Breneman (1950). His data indicate that the glands of the males up to 120 days of age are larger but not greatly so. According to Oakberg (1951), however, there appears to be no difference in the gland weights of normal males and females of comparable body weights, before 120 days of age, but at this age the male gland is heavier. Data from Oakberg follow:

Sex and age	No.	Body weights gm.	Pituitary Weight mg.
White Leghorn males 120 days	59	1672	10.3
White Leghorn females 120 days	99	1226	8.4

The pituitary weights (mg.) of hens at various stages of reproduction are shown as follows (Nakajo and Imai, 1961):

Breed	Reproductive stage	Anterior lobe	Caudal part	Cephalic part
Nagoya	Nonlaying	6.9	2.4	4.4
"	Laying	7.8	2.9	4.4
"	Early broody	8.1	2.2	5.5
"	Late broody	8.9	2.9	5.9
White Leghorn	Nonlaying	8.4	2.8	5.3
"	Laying	9.0	3.1	5.4

The wet weights of anterior lobes of pituitaries of female turkeys (20 to 21 weeks) were 16.5 mg., and for male turkeys 24 weeks old, 23 mg. (Munsick, 1964).

Hypothalamo-hypophysial Complex and Neurosecretory System

In recent years the structure and physiology of this complex have received much attention, which has served to explain many puzzling aspects of pituitary function. For more details on the structure of this system in several species, including chicken, pigeon, duck, Japanese quail, zebra finch, and white-crowned sparrow, consult the works of Farner and Oksche (1962), Benoit (1962), Wingstrand (1951), Grignon (1956), Legait (1959), Mosier (1955),

Duncan 1956), Oksche (1962), Oksche *et al.* (1959, 1964), and others.

Most of this work in recent years has come from the laboratories of Farner and co-workers in the United States, and Benoit and co-workers (notably Assenmacher) in France.

The integral parts of this system are the neurosecretory cells in the hypothalamus (the supraoptic nuclei, paraventricular nuclei and infundibular nuclei) and the axons of these cells which make up certain fiber tracts (the supraoptic hypophysial, paraventriculo-hypophysial and tubero-hypophysial tracts). These three tracts also have branches into the median eminence. Most of the fibers of the supraoptico-hypophysial tract end in the posterior lobe of the pituitary; see Figure 80 (Farner and Oksche).

The supraoptic and paraventricular nuclei vary considerably in their morphologic characteristics among different species of birds (Farner and Oksche). The first neurosecretory granules appear in chick embryos between the 12th and 14th days, according to Wingstrand (1951) and Grignon (1956), but as early as the 4th according to Mosier (1955), and as early as 68 hours according to Duncan. In the duck embryo such material is observed in 14 to 16 days (Assenmacher, 1957).

The neurosecretory cells produce a secretion which migrates down the axons (fibers) to reach the posterior lobe directly; on the other hand, the secretory fibers do not extend into the anterior pituitary (Drager, 1945; Benoit, 1962; and others), but end in the pars tuberalis and median eminence. However, evidence will be presented later that hypothalamic neurosecretory material of birds does reach the anterior lobe, and stimulates it to release hormones as it does in mammals. It is now abundantly clear that it does so by way of the hypothalamo-hypophysial portal blood vessels. In birds, some of the fiber tracts form loops which approach the blood vessels of the primary capillary plexus in the median eminence (Okamoto and Ihara, 1960). These blood vessels transport the secretion to the anterior lobe; see Figure 81 (Green, 1951).

The neurosecretory material has an especial affinity for certain stains, such as chromic hematoxylin-phloxin or fuchsin aldehyde (Gomori's stain). Okamoto and Ihara believe that neurosecretory

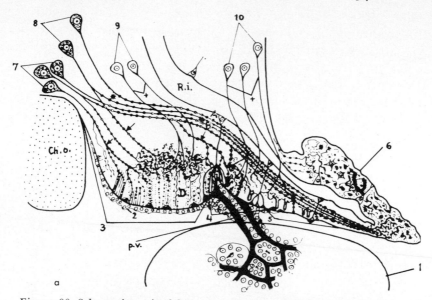

Figure 80. Schematic sagittal lateral section through the infundibulum and the hypophysis of *Zonotrichia leucophrys gambelii* (white-crowned sparrow). *Ch.o.,* optic chiasma; *R.i.,* infundibular recess.

Adenohypophysis: *1,* pars distalis; *2,* pars tuberalis (infundibularis).

Median eminence: *3,* anterior division; *4,* posterior division; *A,* zona interna, ependymal layer; B, zona interna, fiber layer; *C,* zona externa, reticular layer; *D,* zona externa, palisadic layer; *p.v.,* portal vessels; *5,* infundibular stem, *6,* neural lobe.

Nuclei: *7,* supraoptic nucleus; *8,* paraventricular nucleus; *,* tractus supra-optico-hypophyseus; ↑, beaded neurosecretory fibers penetrating the median eminence; *9,* anterior; *10,* posterior division of the infundibular nucleus; +, tractus tubero-hypophyseus. (From Farner and Oksche, *Gen. and Comp. Endocrinol.* 2:113, 1962; after Oksche, 1962.)

material may also reach the adenohypophysis from the neural lobe by a direct path.

Hypophysial Portal Blood Vessels

Detailed studies on the blood vessels of the bird pituitary have been conducted by Green (1951), Wingstrand (1951), Benoit and Assenmacher (1951 and later, on ducks), and by others. Green's account of the blood supply in the chicken gland is as follows: The superior hypophysial arteries supply the primary capillary net on the median eminence. The portal vessels collect the blood from this plexus and pass downward to the anterior lobe. On reaching the latter, they fan out in all directions (secondary capillary network) and drain into the venous sinuses surrounding the gland (Figure 81). The neural lobe receives an independent blood supply from a superficial plexus of vessels, which penetrates it in the form of regular arcades. These vessels project inward toward the

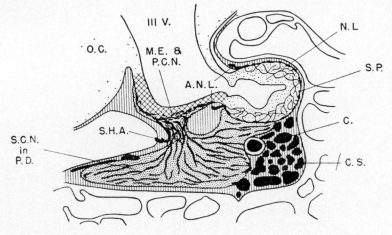

Figure 81. Pituitary of *Gallus Domesticus* showing blood supply. N.L., neural lobe; M.E., median eminence; P.C.N., primary capillary net of portal vessels; S.H.A., superior hypophysial artery; S.C.N., secondary capillary net of portal vessels; III V., third ventricle; P.D., pars distalis; O.C., optic chiasma; A.N.L., artery of neural lobe; C.S., cavernous sinus; C., carotid artery; S.P., superficial plexus. (From Green, *Am. J. Anat.,* 1951.)

infundibular recess. In all of the birds studied by Green, the carotid arteries anastomosed behind the anterior lobe, indenting the caudal lobe.

HORMONES OF THE ANTERIOR LOBE

The anterior lobe of the bird pituitary produces all of the known hormones found in the pituitaries of mammals. These are adrenocorticotrophic (ACTH), thyrotrophic (TSH), follicle-stimulating (FSH), Luteinizing (LH), prolactin, and growth hormone. Three general techniques are used to determine the presence and action of pituitary hormones: (1) administration of hormones to intact animal; (2) ablation of pituitary (hypophysectomy); and (3) replacement therapy. The hypophysis is surgically removed and the effects on the various organs and physiological behavior observed. Replacement therapy can follow several lines. The normal or hypophysectomized animal can be implanted or injected with whole pituitaries, pituitary extracts, or separate fractions from the glands, or with pure hormones of known composition to the same or other species, and the response of the animal observed. Quantitative estimation of the potency of the glands can be made this way, providing the preparation of the extracts is standardized.

ACTH and TSH Hormones

The actions of ACTH, TSH, and some of the gonadotrophic hormones are discussed in Chapters 21, 19, and 15 and 16 respectively.

Chemically pure ACTH has been isolated from the pituitaries of a number of mammalian species, and although there is good evidence (Chapter 21) for its presence in avian pituitaries, little or nothing is known of the chemical nature of avian ACTH. In fact, little or no work has been conducted upon the chemical purification and identification of avian hypophysial hormones.

Gonadotrophic Hormones

The anterior pituitary of birds, like that of mammals, produces the ovarian follicle-stimulating hormone (FSH), the luteinizing hormone (LH), and prolactin. FSH and LH are present in the pituitary of chick embryo by the 18th day of development (see Moszkowski, 1949, and later section). Although the avian ovary does not produce corpora lutea, which in mammals develop as a result of LH, the presence of FSH and LH in the avian pituitary has been demonstrated by implants or injections of pituitary material from avian species in young chicks or into the immature hypophysectomized mouse or rat. Hypophysectomy results in a decrease in size of gonads (Benoit, 1950; Nalbandov and Card, 1942, 1943). FSH stimulates tubular growth of testes and spermatogenesis in the male, and ovarian-follicle growth in the female (see also

Chapters 15 and 16). LH causes ovulation in the female (Chapter 15) and stimulates the interstitial cells of the testes, as it does in mammals (Chapter 16). Hypophysectomized hens can be made to ovulate by injection with mammalian LH, but the ova are not of graded size, as is usual in an intact bird (see Chapter 16).

Nalbandov, Meyer, and McShan (1951), have suggested that the chicken hypophysis contains either a third gonadotrophic hormone, avian ICSH, or LH possessing different properties from mammalian LH. Their conclusion was based on the following results: The combs of male chickens, which atrophy after hypophysectomy, can be made to grow for 10 to 12 days by administering mammalian LH, but regression of comb size ensues thereafter in spite of continued administration of LH. Continuous comb growth, however, can be produced by administering chicken pituitary material. These conclusions have, nevertheless, been questioned by Knobil and Sandler (1963), who point out that other factors may have influenced their results, such as "immunological inactivation," the propriety of the ratio of mammalian FSH and LH administered and the completeness of the replacement, in that a full complement of pituitary hormones was given in one instance and purified fractions in another."

Release of LH from the chicken pituitary occurs 6 to 8 hours before ovulation (see Chapter 15, and later in this section).

Assays for LH and FSH. Total gonadotrophins may be assayed by several methods. One of the most sensitive and common methods is the change in testes size of young chicks (Breneman, Zeller, and Beekman, 1959; Nakajo and Imai, 1956, 1961; Herrick, Mc-Gibbon, and McShan, 1962; and others). Injections are usually made subcutaneously at 12-hour intervals; the chicks are killed after about 5 injections, and the testes weights are compared with testes weights of control chicks. Linear responses to PMS, FSH, and LH are observed when weight increases are plotted against log dose. A minimum dose of 5.0 I.U. of PMS, 5.0 micrograms of FSH, and 5.0 micrograms of LH produced significant increases in testes weights (Breneman *et al.*).

Avian pituitaries have also been assayed by determining the effects on ovarian weights or vaginal epithelial changes in rats (Riley and Fraps, 1942a, b; Fraps, 1943; Phillips, 1942).

The weaver finch test, a sensitive assay for LH, is not affected by presence of FSH, prolactin, and other pituitary hormones (Witschi, 1955). An area of the body of the bird is deplumed and the new emerging feathers show definite color changes (a colored bar) following administration of LH.

Herrick *et al.* (1962) compared the gonadotrophic potency of pituitaries from chickens, turkeys, and rats by assaying 10 mg. of gland tissue from each of the three animals in the immature female rat, the 3-day-old turkey poult, and the 3-day-old chick. The chick testes were sensitive to pituitaries from all species, but more so to chicken pituitaries (see also Nakajo and Imai, 1956). The ovaries of the immature rat responded only to gonadotrophin from the rat.

Factors affecting pituitary gonadotrophins. All workers employing the rat and chick assay methods have reported a sex difference in gonadotrophic potency (FSH and LH) of the pituitaries, with a much higher potency in the glands of adult males, and higher in young males after 60 days of age (see Figure 82).

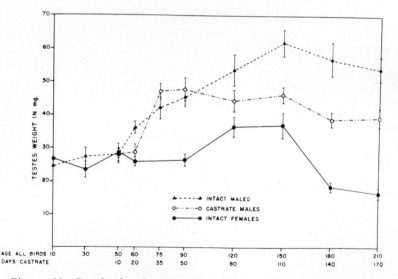

Figure 82. Graph showing gonadotrophic activity as measured by chick testes weight response to 10 mg. of anterior glands from intact and castrate male, and intact female crossbred chickens, at different ages. (From Herrick *et al., Endocrinol.* 71:487, 1962.)

Male pituitaries contain 11 times as much FSH as those of laying hens, and 7 times as much as those of nonlayers. The LH potencies in terms of ovulating units for the pituitaries of males, nonlaying and laying hens are 200, 25, and 17 units respectively (Fraps, 1943). The ovulating unit is the least amount of dry pituitary tissue required to produce ovulation in 50 percent of the females treated. These results suggest that estrogen secreted by the ovary of the hen cuts down on the production of gonadotrophins by the pituitary.

Phillips (1942) assayed unfractionated pituitaries of birds of different ages and conditions for gonadotrophins. He used the rat as the assay animal, and determined the effects of the extracts upon ovarian growth and epithelial changes in the vagina. He ranked the birds in descending order of pituitary potency as follows: (1) capons; (2) springers, 2.5 to 3.5 pounds; (3) roasters, 3.5 to 6 pounds; (4) turkeys; (5) pullets approaching sexual maturity; (6) laying hens, poor to medium production; and (7) laying hens, good production.

A deficiency of vitamin E in the diet of male chickens decreases the size of the testes and reduces both spermatogenesis and the gonadotrophic potency of the pituitary (Herrick, Eide, and Snow, 1952).

The gonadotrophic potency of the serum in immature males, immature females, and nonlaying hens is about the same, and is higher than in laying females and adult males, according to Bailey and Phillips (1952).

Breneman (1955) reported the gonadotrophic potency of female chick pituitaries of varying ages as follows:

Age (days)	20	40	60	80	100	110	115	126
Chick units*	0.4	1.1	3.1	4.6	6.4	6.4	7.3	14.4

* Chick unit represents a 35 percent increase in testes weight over control testes.

The gonadotrophic content of the cephalic and caudal lobes of anterior pituitaries of chickens of different reproductive stages has been reported by Nakajo and Imai (1961) as follows:

Breed	Reproductive stage	Gonadotrophic content in chick units		
		Cephalic lobe	*Caudal lobe*	*Anterior lobe*
Nagoya	Nonlaying	2.1	1.1	3.2
"	Laying	1.5	1.0	2.5
"	Late broody	0.7	0.3	1.0
White Leghorn	Nonlaying	2.5	1.1	3.6
"	Laying	1.5	1.0	2.5

Prolactin

Prolactin, the hormone which causes milk secretion in mammals and crop-sac secretion in pigeons, causes broodiness in chickens. It has been isolated and crystallized. The pituitaries of broody chickens contain more prolactin than those of nonbroody ones (Saeki and Tanabe, 1955); the same thing has been demonstrated also in pigeons, the gull (Bailey, 1952), and the pheasant (Breitenbach and Meyer, 1959). Riddle, Bates, and Lahr (1935) first demonstrated that prolactin injected into hens caused broodiness and that the full expression of broodiness (clucking and nesting) was induced only in those breeds showing a natural tendency to go broody.

Nalbandov and Card (1942), working with the chicken, and Riddle and Bates (1939), with the pigeon, showed that different breeds and strains vary in the response to prolactin. Leghorn males (a nonbroody breed) require 4 to 5 times as much prolactin to produce broodiness as the Cornish, a naturally broody breed.

The prolactin content of the cephalic and caudal areas of anterior pituitaries of broody hens is about the same, but it is much higher in the cephalic lobe of the nonbroody hen, where, however, it remains fairly constant. The changes in the prolactin content of the caudal lobe are closely related to broodiness (Nakajo and Tanaka, 1956). Interruption of broodiness by electrical stimulation of the head decreased the prolactin content of the caudal area.

Assays. The crop-sac method has been widely used in assays for prolactin. There are a number of techniques, but all are based on stimulation and growth of the gland of the pigeon. Three of these methods involve (1) the gross weight, (2) minimum stimulation, and (3) local stimulation (see Riddle and Bates, 1939, and Meites and Turner, 1950).

The first is an objective method; the second is a subjective one, based upon observed changes in the excised crop as examined by transmitted light. Positive stimulation is indicated by the presence of parallel strands of thickened mucosa. In the local-stimulation method prolactin is injected intracutaneously over the crop sac, and only the small area at the site of the injection is affected. A single injection is made and the birds are autopsied after 48 hours. The excised crop is examined as in the minimum-stimulation method. This method is very sensitive. As little as 0.1 gamma of the pure hormone produces a response. A recent very sensitive modification of this method has been described by Grosvenor and Turner (1958). An international unit of prolactin is equal to 1/10 mg. of pure prolactin.

Action of prolactin. The antigonadal action of prolactin has been demonstrated in pigeons (Riddle and Bates, 1939) and chickens (Nalbandov, Hockhauser, and Dugas, 1945). The testes and ovaries of sexually mature pigeons regress following prolactin administration, but the change can be prevented by simultaneous administration of FSH. Thus, prolactin acts by suppressing the output of FSH, which is necessary for gonad stimulation.

Nakajo and Imai (1961) have shown that the prolactin content of the pituitary tends to be inversely proportional to the level of FSH and LH.

Riddle and Lahr, (1944) induced broodiness in pigeons and doves by administration of testosterone or progesterone. These hormones caused the pituitary to release prolactin, according to these workers.

That broodiness in chickens can be terminated by estrogen administration (discussed in Chapter 18) suggests that this hormone prevents the release of prolactin by the pituitary. Although prolactin causes broodiness in hens, it does not in ringdoves (Lehrman and Brody, 1961). These workers found, however, that progesterone induced incubation behavior, and they suggested that this behavior stimulated the secretion of prolactin.

Prolactin may produce molting in the chicken, male, female, or capon (Juhn and Harris, 1958). The effect of prolactin on carbohydrate metabolism is discussed in Chapter 12.

Growth Hormone

Hypophysectomy in the growing chicken retards growth (Nalbandov and Card, 1943). Solomon and Greep (1959), who made comparative assays of pituitaries of a number of species, reported that the chicken pituitary possessed very little growth-promoting activity in the epiphyses of the immature hypophysectomized rat; however, in these studies only one pituitary dose was used, on only a small number of rats.

Hazelwood and Hazelwood (1961) assayed rat and chicken pituitaries in immature hypophysectomized rats, and found that for equal amounts of dried pituitary, the rat hypophysis contained 8 times as much growth hormone. The chicken extract not only produced growth but also decreased the hematocrit in the rat.

Moudgal and Li (1961) have also reported growth hormone in the chick pituitary, as based on the rat assay. The effect of avian or mammalian pituitary extracts on growth in hypophysectomized chickens has not been determined.

Growth hormone of mammalian origin had no effect on growth of young chickens, according to Libby, Meites, and Schaible (1955) and Glick (1960). This hormone did increase the growth of the long bones in chick embryos (Blumenthal, Hsieh, and Wang, 1954). Injections of mammalian growth hormone into laying hens caused a decrease in egg-laying and, in some instances, molting and broodiness (Carter *et al.*, 1955; Burmester and Waters, 1955).

There is some evidence that prolactin acts to promote growth in pigeons and in chickens (Hüblé, 1956). Schooley, Riddle, and Bates (1941) claim to have obtained adequate growth in hypophysectomized pigeons with prolactin.

Although the chicken appears not to be responsive to mammalian growth hormone, the same is not true of certain other avian species, notably the parakeet. Schlumberger and Rudolph (1959) have studied pituitary tumors of parakeets, and have found that the tumors contained an active growth hormone that increased growth in rats and in parakeets. Moreover, mammalian growth hormones are effective in producing changes in the plasma proteins of parakeets (Rudolph and Pehrson, 1961).

HYPOPHYSECTOMY

Hypophysectomy has been performed in the pigeon, duck, and chicken. See Benoit, 1950; Schooley, 1939; Hill and Parkes, 1934; Mitchell, 1929; Nalbandov and Card, 1943; and Rothschild, 1948a & b, for details of the technique. The account in this section will deal with the technique of hypophysectomy and its general effects. The specific effects of pituitary removal on reproductive organs, thyroids, and adrenals are considered in Chapters 15 and 16, 19, and 20 respectively.

There are two principal approaches to the hypophysis: through the orbit, which entails removal of the eye (Benoit), and through the roof of the mouth and pharynx. Some workers have made the incision through the floor and roof of the mouth with beak and mouth closed (transbuccal); others have made the incision only through the roof of the mouth, with mouth opened and beak pulled backward (oral approach, Rothchild). The mortality following the operation is usually higher when the transbuccal approach is employed. The injury to the lower beak and mandible makes eating difficult, and increases the chances for infection. These complications are avoided or minimized by employing the oral or parapharyngeal approach (Schooley, 1939). With the latter approach, the incision is made below the mouth, around the trachea, and through the palate. After the incision is made, the area is exposed and preparations are made for drilling through the bone. Burrs of suitable size and drill are necessary. After the gland is exposed, it may be removed by suction and/or destroyed by cautery. Nalbandov and Card (1943) first removed the gland by suction and then cauterized the opening. Rothchild and Schooley used suction alone in removing the gland. In these experiments only the anterior lobe was removed.

Mortality after Hypophysectomy

The mortality rates of adult chickens hypophysectomized by the transbuccal and oral routes, without replacement therapy, are shown in percentages as follows (Rothchild, 1948b):

Weeks after operation	1	2	3	4	6	8	10
Oral method (42 birds)	12	14	45	62	83	90	95
Transbuccal method (130 birds)		40	48	55	62	74	81	93

The mortality for those undergoing the oral operation was considerably less during the first and second weeks (less trauma), but from the third week onward there was little or no difference for the two groups of birds. Mitchell (1929) stated that none of his birds survived longer than 11 days after the operation. The mortality for growing chicks, completely hypophysectomized at 60 days of age, is 70 percent, 30 days after the operation (Nalbandov and Card, 1943). Hill, Corkill, and Parkes (1934), using the transbuccal technique, reported that 24 out of 30 birds died within 48 hours after the operation. Schooley (1939) reported an early mortality of only 2 percent from the operation in pigeons.

Hypophysectomy and Growth

Data relating to growth and hypophysectomy are meager, mainly because of the excessive early mortality reported by some workers, and because most of the operations on chickens were performed on the adult.

Nalbandov and Card (1943 and earlier) found that when the gland was completely removed in growing chicks, the body weight continued to increase for as long as 60 days or more, even above that of the control birds. However, the increase in weight was due to abnormal deposition of fat (from 5 to 7 times that found in the controls), rather than true growth. Increase in length of the bones, particularly the metatarsals, in the operated birds is only 10 percent, as compared to 50 percent in the control birds during the same period. The extreme obesity observed in their birds by these investigators, who used the cautery in the operation, suggests that the hypothalamus was injured, but the authors did not think so.

Rothchild (1948b) reported that hypophysectomized hens did

not develop obesity or undergo marked changes in body weight. During the first three weeks after the operation body weight dropped by from 10 to 15 percent and remained at this level until the 9th or 10th week, at which time body weight increased to about 110 percent of the original weight, and remained at this point until death at 52 weeks.

Immature hypophysectomized pigeons lose weight rapidly following the operation: approximately 10 percent during the first 10 days (Schooley, 1939). Part of this loss is due to loss of appetite, since fasted pigeons lose as much weight as the operated birds. It was shown that when the hypophysectomized birds were force-fed they maintained normal body weight.

Ablation of the pituitary in chickens decreases food consumption by one-half to two-thirds of normal and reduces metabolic rate (Nalbandov and Card, 1942). Restriction of food intake by normal birds reduces metabolic rate to about the same level.

Hypophysectomy and Organ Weights

It has been amply demonstrated that hypophysectomy decreases the size of many of the endocrine organs, such as the thyroids, adrenals, and gonads, and of some nonendocrine organs. The effects upon the endocrine organs are as expected and have been discussed in detail under the organs concerned. Hypophysectomy in pigeons reduced the length of the intestines by 20 percent and the weights of (1) the liver, 18 percent; (2) pancreatic tissue, 54 percent; (3) crop sac, 14 percent; (4) adrenals, 27 percent; (5) thyroids, 50 percent; and (6) testes, 66 percent (Schooley, Riddle, and Bates, 1941).

POSTERIOR LOBE OF HYPOPHYSIS

The avian posterior lobe contains the hormones oxytocin and arginine vasotocin (Munsick, Sawyer, and Van Dyke, 1960; Sawyer, 1961; Chauvet, Lenci, and Acher, 1960; Munsick, 1964). In addition to detecting vasotocin in their material, Chauvet *et al.* reported the presence of vasopressin, although Munsick *et al.*, and Heller and Pickering (1961) could not detect vasopressin in their material. Munsick (1964) subjected neurohypophysial extracts from chickens and turkeys to ion exchange chromatography on CMC columns, and fractions obtained by gradient elution were examined pharmacologically. Only oxytocin and arginine vasotocin were consistently found.

Arginine vasotocin has the ring structure of oxytocin and the side chain of arginine vasopressin:

1	2	3	4	5	6	7	8	9
CYS.	Tyr.	Ileu	Glu(NH$_2$).	Asp(NH$_2$).	CYS.	Pro.	Arg.	Gly(NH$_2$)

Arginine vasotocin

CYS.	Tyr.	Ileu	Glu(NH$_2$).	Asp(NH$_2$).	CYS.	Pro.	Leu.	Gly(NH$_2$)

Oxytocin

It has extraordinary potency when assayed for its oxytocic activity in the hen (contraction of hen's oviduct; see also Chapter 15), and its antidiuretic activity in chickens. It is also very potent in increasing the water permeability of the frog bladder. The relative potencies of fowl neurohypophysial extracts and pure arginine vasotocin, based on 11 different assays, are shown in Figure 83.

Tanaka and Nakajo (see Chapter 15) have demonstrated that the content of vasotocin in the posterior lobe is associated with the stage of reproduction, and that the amount in the posterior lobe decreases just prior to laying. At this same time the amount of hormone in the blood increases (Douglas and Sturkie; see Chapter 15).

The effects of vasopressin and oxytocin on uterine contraction and on the cardiovascular system are discussed in Chapters 15 and 3 respectively.

Removal of posterior lobe has been performed by Shirley and Nalbandov (1956a). The operation had no adverse effect on egg-laying (see Chapter 15); this may indicate that oxytocin and vasotocin are not essential for oviposition, or that these hormones come from the hypothalamus. The operation caused polydipsia and polyuria (Chapter 13).

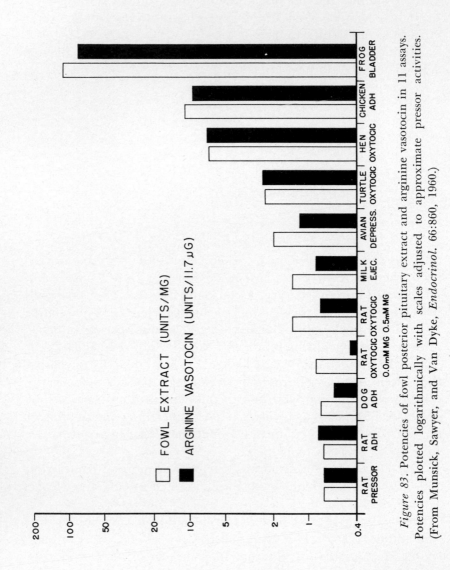

Figure 83. Potencies of fowl posterior pituitary extract and arginine vasotocin in 11 assays. Potencies plotted logarithmically with scales adjusted to approximate pressor activities. (From Munsick, Sawyer, and Van Dyke, *Endocrinol.* 66:860, 1960.)

INTERMEDIN

The chicken pituitary has no intermediate lobe, but the presence of intermedin in the anterior lobe has been demonstrated (Kleinholz and Rahn, 1940). The cephalic portion of the lobe is considerably more potent than the caudal portion (20 times). Chen, Oldham, and Geiling (1940) report that this hormone is present in the chick's hypophysis as early as the 5th day of embryonic development; they used the hypophysectomized frog as the assay animal. Intermedin causes an expansion of melanophores in the skin of the frog, chameleon, lizard, and fish. Kleinholz and Rahn used the hypophysectomized lizard, *Anolis carolinensis,* to assay the potencies of the pituitaries of several species for intermedin. They found that the cephalic portion of the anterior lobe of chickens was more potent in intermedin than equal weights of pituitary from the intermediate lobes of cattle.

CONTROL OF PITUITARY SECRETION

It is now well established that the neurosecretory mechanism plays an important role in the control and regulation of pituitary function in many lower and higher vertebrates (see Harris, 1955, 1960; also Greep, 1961, for review of situation in mammals; see Gorbman and Bern, 1962, for comparative account). The situation in birds has been reviewed thoroughly by Farner and Oksche (1962), and by Benoit (1962).

The neurosecretory cells of the hypothalamus produce the hormones oxytocin and arginine vasopressin found in many mammals, and oxytocin and arginine vasotocin in birds (see earlier section). The hormones migrate via the neurosecretory tracts to the posterior lobe, where they are stored. Recent evidence (Ishii, Hirano, and Kobayashi, 1962) indicates that the median eminence of birds (pigeons and *Zosterops*) also contains mainly arginine vasotocin, and that the pars nervosa contains oxytocin and vasotocin. Moreover, exposing the birds (*Zosterops*) to long daily periods of artificial light, which activates the gonads, increased the amount of vasotocin in the median eminence, but had no effect on that in the pars nervosa. Conversely, dehydration reduced the level of vasotocin in the pars nervosa considerably but had no effect on the level in the median eminence. Likewise Oksche, Laws, Kamemoto, and Farner (1959) and Legait (1959) reported that dehydration decreased the amount of neurosecretory substance in the pars nervosa of sparrows and of chickens respectively. Dehydration also caused an increase in acid phosphatase in the pars nervosa of pigeons, but had no effect on that in median eminence (Kobayashi, Oota, and Hirano, 1962). These data suggest an intimate relation between the content of neurohypophysial hormones in the median eminence and the release of gonadotrophins in the adenohypophysis, and also that the activities of the pars nervosa and median eminence are controlled independently. Some other factors affecting the release of neurohypophysial hormones are discussed in Chapters 13 and 15.

Neurosecretion and Release of Gonadotrophins

It is well known that light stimulates the pituitary to release gonadotrophins (see also Chapters 15 and 16). A body of evidence accumulated in recent years shows that there is some factor within the neurosecretory substance that reaches the median eminence and ultimately the adenohypophysis via the portal blood vessels.

One common method employed in determining the relation between hypothalamus and adenohypophysis is to disrupt the connection between them by transecting the hypophysial stalk or by transplanting the pituitary to some other site, such as the kidney (Ma and Nalbandov, 1963). Shirley and Nalbandov (1956b) demonstrated that stalk sectioning in chickens completely disrupted reproductive function and release of gonadotrophins but had no appreciable effect upon the release of TSH or ACTH. Similar results were obtained following transplantation of the pituitary (Ma and Nalbandov). Thyroid and adrenal weights were approximately normal, and the authors suggest that the adrenal gland must have considerable autonomy (see also Chapter 21).

The transplanted avian pituitary did not produce any more or less prolactin than in the normal *in situ* gland. Sixteen-day-old embryonic chicken pituitaries cultivated for 3 days with hypothalamic tissue produced more gonadotrophins than when cultured alone (Moszkowski, 1958).

Similar results have been obtained from stalk transection in ducks by Benoit and Assenmacher (1953), and by Assenmacher (1958 and earlier; see review by Benoit, 1962). Transection of the hypophysial stalk so that the portal blood vessels were cut, or transecting the median eminence, prevented both the release of gonadotrophic hormones and the growth of gonads (see Figure 84). Moreover, it was found that when vascular regeneration was prevented the testes remained atrophic but that where some vascular regeneration occurred, the gonads were not atrophied.

Similar results were obtained in the duck when the pituitary was transplanted and moved away from its normal site. Thus,

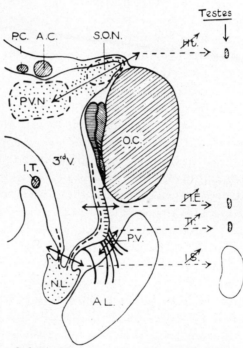

Figure 84. Schema of the different operations performed on the hypothalamo-hypophysial region of the duck, with their effect on the testes. Ht. (with arrow), lesion of the anterior hypothalamus; M.E. (with arrow), section of the hypothalamo-hypophysial tract in the median eminence; Tr (with arrow), section of the portal veins in the portotuberal tract; LS (with arrow), section of the hypothalamo-hypophysial tract in the infundibular stalk; A.C., anterior commissure; A.L., anterior lobe; I.T., infundibular tract; N.L., neural lobe; O.C., optic chiasm; P.C., posterior commissure; P.V., portal veins; P.V.N., paraventricular nucleus; S.O.N., supraoptic nucleus; 3rd V., third ventricle. (From Benoit, *Gen. and Comp.* Endocrinol. Supplement 1:254, 1962; after Assenmacher, 1958.)

these results demonstrate that the hypophysial tissue of birds when deprived of its intimate association with the median eminence or portal blood vessels is not capable of maintaining normal gonadotrophic function. When large lesions were made (electrolytically) in the supraoptic and paraventricular nuclei, testicular atrophy occurred (figure 84). LH release and ovulation in the hen could be blocked by placing electrolytic lesions in this area (Ralph and Fraps; see Chapter 15). Attempts to induce premature ovulation by stimulating the same area were unsuccessful (Chapter 15).

Legait (1959 and earlier) has reported changes in neurosecretory cell activity associated with changes in the reproductive cycle of hens. Farner and Oksche reviewed in detail the effects of light on the neurosecretory system of several species of wild birds, and found a similar effect in all of them.

The earlier classical work of Benoit and associates (see Benoit, 1950, 1962, for reviews) dealt with the mechanism in the duck by which light stimulates the pituitary to release gonadotrophins. Irradiation of the head and eyes stimulated the pituitary and growth of the testes, but when the head and eyes were covered and other parts of the body were irradiated, the hypophysis was not stimulated (Benoit, 1937). When the eyes were enucleated and light was introduced through the orbit by way of a quartz rod, the pituitary was stimulated. The hypophysis can also be stimulated by irradiating the head even when the optic nerves are cut, and by directly stimulating the hypothalamus with light (Benoit, 1938, 1950). Moreover, when areas of the central nervous system (rhinencephalon) adjacent to the hypothalamus are stimulated with light, the pituitary is stimulated indirectly by way of the hypothalamus, according to Benoit and Kehl (1939).

Later, Benoit, Walter, and Assenmacher (1950) reported that various lengths of light within the visible spectrum were quite effective in stimulating the pituitary by way of the hypothalamus, when the latter was irradiated directly. When only the duck's head was irradiated however, some of the colored lights were ineffective in stimulating the hypophysis. Red and orange lights stimulated the gland maximally, but the yellows, greens, and blues (wave lengths of 577, 546, and 436 mμ.) were relatively ineffective (see Chapter 16; also Benoit and Ott 1938, and Benoit and Assenmacher, 1959). The difference in effect of the various lights, according to the authors, may be explained as follows: (1) The retina of the duck eye is less sensitive to yellow, green, and blue, and reflex stimulation of the pituitary through the eye by these colors is at a minimum; (2) the tissues surrounding the eye and orbital region absorb some of the colored light rays, which do not reach the central nervous system, another avenue by which the pituitary is stimulated. The authors reported that red and orange rays penetrated these tissues readily, but blue rays only slightly.

Visual (reflex) stimulation of the pigeon pituitary has been reported by Matthews (1939). The pigeon's own reflected image in a mirror, or seeing other pigeons, is sufficient to stimulate follicular growth and ovulation by the release of FSH and LH from the pituitary.

It is not clear whether the control of the anterior pituitary involves other neurosecretory cells than those which produce the posterior lobe hormones (see earlier section). It is likely that there are a number of central nervous system neurohumors that influence the release of anterior pituitary hormones; but considerably more work is needed on the isolation, purification, and chemical identification of these in mammals and birds.

There is evidence that the release of anterior pituitary hormones in birds is influenced less by the central nervous system than it is in mammals; in particular this is true of ACTH and possibly TSH and prolactin (see also Chapters 19 and 21).

When mammalian pituitaries are transplanted, there is usually a significant decrease in the production of all hypophysial hormones except prolactin, whose output actually increases. The results obtained by Meites, Nicoll, and Talwalker (1963), who cultured mammalian pituitaries *in vitro,* are in general agreement with those obtained by transplantation. Nicoll and Meites (1962) and Meites (unpublished) have reported, however, that the pigeon pituitary, when cultured, does not produce more prolactin than the pituitary does in its normal location. This suggests that the hypothalamus of birds does not produce an inhibitor of prolactin release as does the mammalian gland. However, Nakajo (1952), who interrupted broodiness in hens by electrical stimulation of the head, believed that suppression of prolactin secretion by the pituitary was mediated by way of the hypothalamus. Lefranc (1958) reported that the administration of reserpine to pigeons caused proliferation of crop-sac epithelium, and that the drug which affected the central nervous system increased the secretion of prolactin.

Hormone Feedback

This is another mechanism by which the output of anterior pituitary hormones is regulated. An increase in the circulating levels of certain target-organ hormones either directly, or indirectly via the hypothalamus, causes the pituitary to decrease its output of the appropriate trophic hormones. This is particularly true of the adrenal cortical hormones (see Chapter 21), thyroxine, (Chapter 19), and the gonadal hormones (Chapter 18).

REFERENCES

Assenmacher, I. 1957 Évolution de la neurosécrétion hypothalamo-neurohypophysaire au cours de l'organogénèse du canard domestique. Comp. Rend. Soc. Biol. 41:1301.

Assenmacher, I. 1958 Recherches sur le contrôle hypothalamique de la fonction gonadotrope préhypophysaire chez le canard. Arch. Anat. Microscop. Morphol. Exp. 47:447.

Bailey, R. E. 1952 The incubation patch of passerine birds. Condor 54:121.

Bailey, R. L., and R. E. Phillips 1952 Gonadotrophic potency of avian blood serum. Poultry Sci. 31:68.

Benoit, J. 1937 Facteurs externes de l'activité sexuelle. II: Étude du mécanisme de la stimulation par la lumière de l'activité testiculaire chez le canard domestique: Rôle de l'hypophyse. Bull. Biol. France, Belg.: 71:394.

Benoit, J. 1938 Action de divers éclairements localisés dans la région orbitaire sur la gonadostimulation chez le canard mâle impubère: Croissance testiculaire provoquée par l'éclairement direct de la région hypophysaire. Comp. Rend. Soc. Biol. 127:909.

Benoit, J. 1950 Traité de Zoologie, edited by P. P. Grassé. Tome XV: Oiseaux, p. 316, Masson & Co., Paris.

Benoit, J. 1962 Hypothalamo-hypophyseal control of the sexual activity in birds. Gen. & Compar. Endocrinol. Suppl. 1:254.

Benoit, J., and I. Assenmacher 1951 Étude préliminaire de la vascularisation de l'appareil hypophysaire du canard domestique. Arch. Anat. Microsc. Morphol. Exp. 40:27.

Benoit, J., and I. Assenmacher 1953 Rapport entre la stimulation sexuelle préhypophysaire et la neurosécrétion chez l'oiseau. Arch. Anat. Microsc. Morphol. Exp. 42:334.

Benoit, J., and I. Assenmacher 1959 The control by visible radiations of the gonadotrophic activity of the duck hypophysis. Recent Prog. Hormone Res. 15:143.

Benoit, J., and R. Kehl 1939 Nouvelles recherches sur les voies nerveuses photoréceptrices et hypophysostimulantes chez le canard domestique. Comp. Rend. Soc. Biol. 131:89.

Benoit, J., and L. Ott 1938 Action de lumières de différentes longueurs d'onde sur la gonado-stimulation chez le canard mâle impubère. Comp. Rend. Soc. Biol. 127:906.

Benoit, J., F. X. Walter, and I. Assenmacher 1950 Contribution à l'étude du réflexe opto-hypophysaire gonadostimulant chez le canard soumis à des radiations lumineuses de diverses longueurs d'onde. J. de Physiologie (Bordeaux) 42:537.

Blumenthal, H. T., K. Hsieh, and T. Wang 1954 The effect of hypophyseal growth hormone on the tibia of the developing chick embryo. Am. J. Pathol. 30:771.

Breitenbach, R. P., and R. K. Meyer 1959 Pituitary prolactin levels in laying, incubating and brooding pheasants. Proc. Soc. Exp. Biol. & Med. 101:16.

Breneman, W. R. 1950 A study of the pituitary-gonad-comb relationship in normal, unilaterally castrated, and caponized chicks. J. Exp. Zool. 114:115.

Breneman, W. R. 1955 Reproduction in birds: the female. Mem. Soc. Endocrinol. No. 4. Cambridge University Press, London.

Breneman, W. R., F. Z. Zeller, and B. E. Beekman 1959 Gonadotrophin assay in chicks. Poultry Sci. 38:152.

Burmester, B. R., and N. F. Waters 1955 Some effects of growth hormone preparations in pullets and mature hens. Poultry Sci. 34:1415.

Carter, R. D., R. N. Risner, and H. Yacowitz 1955 Some effects of growth hormone preparations in pullets and mature hens. Poultry Sci. 34:1407.

Chauvet, J., M. T. Lenci, and R. Acher 1960 Présence de deux vasopressines dans la neurohypophyse du poulet. Biochim. Biophys. Acta 38:571.

Chen, G., F. K. Oldham, and E. M. K. Geiling 1940 Appearance of the melanophore-expanding hormone of the pituitary gland in developing chick embryo. Proc. Soc. Exp. Biol. & Med. 45:810.

Drager, G. A. 1945 The innervation of the avian hypophysis. Endocrinol. 36:124.

Duncan, D. 1956 An electron microscope study of the neurohypophysis of a bird, Gallus domesticus. Anat. Rec. 125:457.

Farner, D. S., and A. Oksche 1962 Neurosecretion in birds. Gen. and Comp. Endocrinol. 2:113.

Fraps, R. M. 1943 Potencies of anterior pituitary glands of mature chickens in the induction of ovulation in the hen. Anat. Rec. 87: 443.

Glick, B. 1960 The effect of bovine growth hormone, DCA, and cortisone on the weight of the bursa of Fabricius, adrenal glands, heart and body weight of young chickens. Poultry Sci. 39:1527.

Gorbman, A., and H. A. Bern 1962 A Textbook of Comparative Endocrinology. John Wiley & Sons Inc., New York.

Green, J. D. 1951 The comparative anatomy of the hypophysis with special reference to its blood supply and innervation. Am. J. Anat. 88:225.

Greep, R. O. 1961 Physiology of anterior hypophysis in relation to reproduction, in Sex and Internal Secretions, ed. W. C. Young and G. W. Corner, Vol. 2, p. 240. Williams & Wilkins Co., Baltimore.

Grignon, G. 1956 Développement du complexe hypothalamo-hypophysaire chez l'embryon de poulet. Société d'impressions typographiques, Nancy.

Grosvenor, C. E., and C. W. Turner 1958 Assay of lactogenic hormone. Endocrinol. 63:530.

Harris, G. W. 1955 Neural control of pituitary gland. Physiological Society Monograph, No. 3. Arnold, London.

Harris, G. W. 1960 Central control of pituitary secretion, in Handbook of Physiology, Vol. 2. Section 1: Neurophysiology. Am. Physiol. Soc., Washington, D.C.

Hazelwood, R. L., and B. S. Hazelwood 1961 Effects of avian and rat pituitary extracts on tibial growth and blood composition. Proc. Soc. Exp. Biol. & Med. 108:10.

Heller, H., and B. T. Pickering 1961 Neurohypophysial hormones of non-mammalian vertebrates. J. Physiol. 155:98.

Herlant, M., J. Benoit, A. Tixier-Vidal, and I. Assenmacher 1960

Modifications hypophysaires au cours du cycle annuel chez le canard Pekin. Comp. Rend. Acad. Sci., Paris, 250:2936.

Herrick, E. H., I. M. Eide, and M. R. Snow 1952 Vitamin E in pituitary gland function of fowls. Proc. Soc. Exp. Biol. & Med. 79:441.

Herrick, R. B., W. H. McGibbon, and W. H. McShan 1962 Gonadotrophic activity of chicken pituitary glands. Endocrinol. 71:487.

Hill, R. T., A. B. Corkill, and A. S. Parkes 1934 Hypophysectomy of birds. II: General effects of hypophysectomy of fowls. Proc. Roy. Soc. London, Series B, 116:208.

Hill, R. T., and A. S. Parkes 1934 Hypophysectomy of birds. I: Technique, with a note on results. Proc. Roy. Soc. London, Series B, 115:402.

Hüblé, J. 1956 Gonadal and hypophyseal interactions on the young fowl. Acta Endocrinol. 23:101.

Ishii, S., T. Hirano, and H. Kobayashi 1962 Neurohypophyseal hormones in the avian median eminence and pars nervosa. Gen. and Comp. Endocrinol. 2:433.

Juhn, M., and P. C. Harris 1958 Molt of capon feathering with prolactin. Proc. Soc. Exper. Biol. & Med. 98:669.

Kleinholz, L. H., and H. Rahn 1940 The distribution of intermedin: A new biological method of assay and results of tests under normal and experimental conditions. Anat. Rec. 76:157.

Knobil, E., and R. Sandler 1963 The physiology of adenohypophyseal hormones, in Comparative Endocrinology, ed. U. S. von Euler and H. Heller, Vol. 1, p. 447. Academic Press, New York.

Kobayashi, H., Y. Oota, and T. Hirano 1962 Acid phosphatase activity of the hypothalamo-hypophyseal system of dehydrated rats and pigeons in relation to neurosecretion. Gen. & Comp. Endocrinol. 2:495.

Lefranc, G. 1958 Influence de la réserpine sur le jabot du pigeon. Comp. Rend. Soc. Biol. CLII:1495.

Legait, E., and H. Legait 1955 Modifications du lobe distal de l'hypophyse et de la neuro-hypophyse chez le poussin ou la poule Rhode Island après injection d'intermedia. Comp. Rend. Soc. Biol. CXLIX:2207.

Legait, H. 1959 Contribution à l'étude morphologique et expérimentale du système hypothalamo-neurohypophysaire de la poule Rhode-Island. Thèse, Louvain-Nancy.

Lehrman, O. S., and P. Brody 1961 Does prolactin induce incubation behavior in the ring dove. J. Endocrinol. 22:269.

Libby, D. A., J. Meites, and J. Schaible 1955 Growth hormone effects in chickens. Poultry Sci. 34:1329.

Ma, R. E. S., and A. V. Nalbandov 1963 Discussion on the transplanted hypophysis, in Advances in Neuroendocrinology, ed. A. V. Nalbandov, p. 306. University of Illinois Press, Urbana.

Matthews, L. H. 1939 Visual stimulation and ovulation in pigeons. Proc. Roy. Soc. London, Series B, 126:557.

Meites, J., C. S. Nicoll, and P. K. Talwalker 1963 The central nervous system and the secretion and release of prolactin, in Advances in Neuroendocrinology, ed. A. V. Nalbandov, p. 238. University of Illinois Press.

Meites, J., and C. W. Turner 1950 Lactogenic hormone. In Hormone Assay, ed. C. W. Emmens, p. 237. Academic Press, New York.

Mikami, S. I. 1958 The cytological significance of regional patterns in the adenohypophysis of the fowl. J. Fac. Agric., Iwate University.

Mitchell, J. B. 1929 Experimental studies of the bird hypophysis. I: Effects of hypophysectomy in the Brown Leghorn fowl. Physiol. Zool. 2:411.

Mosier, H. D. 1955 The development of the hypothalamo-neurohypophyseal secretory system in the chick embryo. Endocrinol. 57:661.

Moszkowski, A. 1949 Pouvoir corticotrope et gonadotrope de l'hypophyse de l'embryon de poulet. Comp. Rend. Soc. Biol. 143:1332.

Moszkowski, A. 1958 Étude in vitro de l'hypothalamus et de l'activité préhypophysaire gonadotrope chez l'embryon du poulet. Comp. Rend. Soc. Biol. 152:725.

Moudgal, N. R., and C. H. Li 1961 Immunochemical studies of bovine and ovine pituitary growth hormone Arch. Biochem. & Biophys. 93:122.

Munsick, R. A. 1964 Neurohypophyseal hormones of chickens and turkeys. Endocrinol. 75:104.

Munsick, R. A., W. H. Sawyer, and H. B. Van Dyke 1960 Avian neurohypophyseal hormones: Pharmacological properties and tentative identification. Endocrinol. 66:860.

Nakajo, S. 1952 Effect of electrical stimulation of the head on broodiness of chickens. Poultry Sci. 31:337.

Nakajo, S., and K. Imai 1956 Investigation on chick assay method for avian gonadotrophins. Endocrinol. Jap. 3:197.

Nakajo, S., and K. Imai 1961 Gonadotrophin content in the cephalic and the caudal lobe of the anterior pituitary in laying, non-laying and broody hen. Poultry Sci. 40:739.

Nakajo, S., and K. Tanaka 1956 Prolactin potency of the cephalic and the caudal lobe of the anterior pituitary in relation to broodiness in the domestic fowl. Poultry Sci. 35:990.

Nalbandov, A., and L. E. Card 1942 Hormonal induction of broodiness in roosters. Poultry Sci. 21:474 (Abs.).

Nalbandov, A., and L. E. Card 1943 Effect of hypophysectomy of growing chicks. J. Exp. Zool. 94:387.

Nalbandov, A., M. Hockhauser, and M. Dugas 1945 A study of the effect of prolactin on broodiness and on cock testes. Endocrinol. 36:521.

Nalbandov, A., R. K. Meyer, and W. H. McShan 1951 The role of a third gonadotrophic hormone in the mechanism of androgen secretion in chicken testes. Anat. Rec. 110:475.

Nicoll, C. S., and J. Meites 1962 Prolactin secretion in vitro: Comparative aspects. Nature 195:606.

Oakberg, E. F. 1951 Genetic differences in quantitative histology of the adrenal, organ weights, and inter-organ correlations in White Leghorn chickens. Growth 15:57.

Okamoto, S., and Y. Ihara 1960 Neural and neurovascular connections between the hypothalamic neurosecretory center and the adenohypophysis. Anat. Rec. 137:485.

Oksche, A. 1962 The fine nervous neurosecretory and glial structure of median eminence in white-crowned sparrow. Proc. Third Internat. Conference on Neurosecretion, Bristol (in press).

Oksche, A., D. F. Laws, F. I. Kamemoto, and D. S. Farner 1959 The hypothalamo-hypophyseal neurosecretory system of the white-crowned sparrow. Z. Zellforsch. 51:1.

Oksche, A., W. O. Wilson, and D. S. Farner 1964 The hypothalamic neurosecretory system of Coturnix japonica. Z. f. Zellforschung 61:688.

Payne, F. 1940 Signet-ring or castration cells in the chick pituitary. Anat. Rec. 76:29.

Payne, F. 1946 The cellular picture in the anterior pituitary of normal fowls from embryo to old age. Anat. Rec. 96:77.

Payne, F.   1947   The effects of gonad removal on the anterior pituitary of the fowl from ten days to six years. Anat. Rec. 97:507.

Payne, F.   1961   The pituitary of the fowl: A correction and addition. Anat. Rec. 140:321.

Phillips, R. E.   1942   Comparative gonadotrophic potency of unfractionated extracts of poultry pituitaries. Poultry Sci. 21:161.

Rahn, H.   1939   The development of the chick pituitary with special reference to the cellular differentiation of the pars buccalis. J. Morph. 64:483.

Rahn, H., and B. T. Painter   1941   The comparative histology of the bird pituitary. Anat. Rec. 79:297.

Riddle, O., and R. W. Bates   1939   The preparation, assay, and actions of lactogenic hormones, in Sex and Internal Secretions, ed. Edgar Allan, 2d ed., pp. 1088-1117. Williams & Wilkins Co., Baltimore.

Riddle, O., R. W. Bates, and E. L. Lahr   1935   Prolactin induces broodiness in the fowl. Am. J. Physiol. 111:352.

Riddle, O., and E. L. Lahr   1944   On broodiness of ring doves following implants of certain steroid hormones. Endocrinol. 35:255.

Riley, G. M., and R. M. Fraps   1942a   Relationship of gonad-stimulating activity of female domestic fowl anterior pituitaries to reproductive activity. Endocrinol. 30:537.

Riley, G. M., and R. M. Fraps   1942b   Biological assays of the male chicken pituitary for gonadotrophic potency. Endocrinol. 30:529.

Rothchild, I.   1948a   A simplified technique for hypophysectomy of domestic fowl. Endocrinol. 43:293.

Rothchild, I.   1948b   Notes on survival and body weight changes of adult hens following hypophysectomy. Endocrinol. 43:298.

Rudolph, H. J., and N. C. Pehrson   1961   Growth hormone effect on the blood plasma proteins in the parakeet. Endocrinol. 69:661.

Saeki, Y., and Y. Tanabe   1955   Changes in prolactin content of fowl pituitary during broody periods and some experiments on the induction of broodiness. Poultry Sci. 34:909.

Sawyer, W. H.   1961   Neurohypophyseal hormones. Pharmacol. Rev. 13:225.

Schlumberger, H. G., and H. J. Rudolph   1959   Growth promoting effect of a transplantable pituitary tumor in parakeets. Endocrinol. 65:902.

Schooley, J. P.   1939   Technique for hypophysectomy in pigeons. Endocrinol. 25:373.

Schooley, J. P., and O. Riddle 1938 The morphological basis of pituitary function in pigeons. Am. J. Anat. 62:314.

Schooley, J. P., O. Riddle, and R. W. Bates 1941 Replacement therapy in hypophysectomized juvenile pigeons. Am. J. Anat. 69:123.

Shirley, H. V., and A. V. Nalbandov 1956a Effects of neurohypophysectomy in domestic chickens. Endocrinol. 58:477.

Shirley, H. V., and A. V. Nalbandov 1956b Effects of transecting hypophyseal stalks in laying hens. Endocrinol. 58:694.

Solomon, J., and R. O. Greep 1959 The growth hormone content of several vertebrate pituitaries. Endocrinol. 65:335.

Wingstrand, K. G. 1951 The structure and development of the avian pituitary. C. W. K. Gleerup, Lund, Sweden.

Witschi, E. 1955 Vertebrate gonadotrophins in comparative physiology of reproduction. Mem. Soc. Endocrinol. 4:149.

Yasuda, M. 1953 Cytological studies of the anterior pituitary of broody fowl. Proc. Japan Acad. 29:586.

CHAPTER 18

Gonadal Hormones

PRODUCTION AND METABOLISM OF
GONADAL HORMONES

THE principal gonadal hormones include androgen, estrogen, and progesterone. Structural formulas of certain of these are shown in Figure 85. In the mammalian ovary progesterone is produced by the corpora lutea, but the avian ovary does not form these bodies, although progesterone has been isolated from the chicken ovary (Layne, Common, Maw, and Fraps, 1957), and from the blood of laying and nonlaying hens and cocks (but not capons). This suggests that either the male or female gonad is concerned in its production (Fraps, Hooker, and Forbes, 1948, 1949; Hooker and Forbes, 1949). The main metabolic pathway is by way of the liver, which can convert progesterone into as many as 7 different pregnane compounds, but other tissues are also capable of metabolizing progesterone.

The principal naturally occurring estrogens in the chicken which have been isolated from the ovaries and excreta are estradiol 17-beta, estriol, and estrone (Layne, Common, Maw, and Fraps, 1958; MacRae, Layne, and Common, 1959). Following the injection of radioactive estradiol 17-beta, estriol, estrone, and 16-epi-estriol were detected in the excreta (MacRae and Common, 1960). The ratio of estriol of 16-epi-estriol in the excreta is considerably higher than the corresponding ratio in human pregnancy urine, and indicates, according to these authors, that 16-epi-estriol is an important metabolite of estradiol 17-beta. Ainsworth and Common (1963) suggest that radioactive estriol is converted in the

COMPOUND

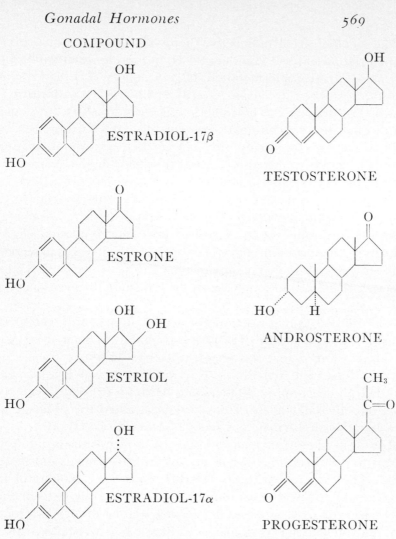

Figure 85. Structural formulas of certain gonadal hormones.

fowl to 16-oxoestradiol-17 beta and to 16-epi-estriol, and that the equilibrium conditions in the fowl are such that 16-epi-estriol tends to be formed at the expense of estriol.

A number of synthetic estrogens are available, including diethylstilbestrol, dianisylhexene and dienestrol, among many others. These estrogens have been used extensively for fattening chickens; this and their relative potencies will be discussed later.

The metabolism of radioactive diethylstilbestrol (DS) has been studied (Hopwood and Gassner, 1962a, b) and the results indicate that DS is excreted and metabolized very rapidly. The half life of the hormone was 2 to 3 days. As early as 6 hours after administration of DS, most of the hormone existed not as a free substance but in the form of a conjugate, presumably a glucuronide.

The liver is the main site of estrogen metabolism. The 16-hydroxylation of estradiol-17 beta to estriol in the avian liver has recently been demonstrated by Mitchell and Hobkirk (1959).

It is generally conceded that the thecal cells of the ovarian follicles, as in mammals, secrete estrogen; however, there is no real proof for, and some evidence against this view. Immature chickens, after gonadotrophins have been administered, begin to secrete estrogen long before there is any increase in size of ovarian follicles, although there is some increase in ovarian medulla (see Chapter 15).

It is also known that the testes of mammals and birds secrete estrogen, but the exact site of secretion is unknown. Some investigators have assumed that the Sertoli cells are the source because it has been observed that excess secretion of estrogen is associated with Sertoli cell tumors. Siller (1956) has reported Sertoli cell tumors in a Brown Leghorn chicken which caused the plumage to look like that of a female (evidence of estrogen secretion).

Androgen. The principal androgen of most mammals is testosterone, and this is probably true also of birds (Gorbman and Bern, 1962). The principal pathway of synthesis is from cholesterol to progesterone to androstenedione to testosterone. The testis of the white-crowned sparrow can convert progesterone into testosterone and androstenedione (Gorbman and Bern). It is well known that testosterone can be converted to estrogens *in vivo*.

The site of the production of androgen is the interstitial (Leydig) cells of the testis (see review by Taber, 1951). Kumaran and Turner (1949a), Benoit (1922 and later), and others have demonstrated that the great increase in interstitial tissue coincides with the growth and development of the comb, an indication of androgenic activity. Kumaran and Turner (1949b) observed the first birefringent material in the testes of young cockerels at anywhere from 12 to 16 weeks of age, when comb growth begins. This material was observed only in the interstitial cells. This birefringence technique is a means of identifying androgen and other steroid hormones.

Experiments by Nalbandov, Meyer, and McShan (1946), who studied the growth of the comb and testes of hypophysectomized males following injections of a number of pituitary preparations containing FSH and LH, leave little doubt that the Leydig cells are the principal, if not the only, source of androgen. They found that pituitary preparations free of LH (pure FSH) did not cause growth in the combs of hypophysectomized males, but did in the testes. Pure LH produced growth in both combs and testes. There was a synergistic effect between FSH and LH. FSH contaminated with minute amounts of LH stimulated the growth of both combs and testes. Some of the pituitary preparations tested by these workers, reputedly free of LH, gave comb growth, indicating the presence of LH.

X-rays, which destroy practically all tubular tissue, have no effect upon interstitial tissue, except possibly to increase it (Benoit, 1924; Essenberg and Karrash, 1940). Sturkie, Pino, Weatherwax, Donnelly, and Dorrance (1949) demonstrated that sterilizing doses of X-rays, 2,100 to 5,600 roentgen units, did not affect comb growth or sexual libido of males, even though testis size was decreased considerably.

SECONDARY SEXUAL CHARACTERISTICS

Secondary sexual characteristics which differentiate male and female birds include differences in comb size, plumage color, structure of feathers, voice, and temperament. The gonadal hormones are responsible for many of these (see Witschi, 1961, for a review). Androgen produces comb growth in males and females. In the latter, where the comb is smaller, the androgen is produced by the interstitial cells of the medulla of the ovary (Taber, 1949, 1951).

The size and shape of the feathers is influenced by the gonadal hormones and the thyroid hormone (see Chapter 19). The hackle and saddle feathers of the male chicken are elongated and tapering in form, and those of the female are shorter and more blunt. This difference is due not to androgen but to estrogen. Castrated males (capons) and females (Poulards) develop feathers resembling those of the cock in structure except that the feathers are longer (neutral type plumage).

The response of hen-feathered breeds to sex hormones is different. Males of this breed have the same type of feather structure as females. Henny feathering is dominant over normal feathering. When hen-feathered males are castrated, their plumage reverts to the neutral type. The plumage of the castrated female of the henny breed also reverts to the male or neutral type, as does that of normal females. It has been demonstrated, by testicular grafts and hormone injections, that the gonads of the hen-feathered male produce androgen as do the gonads of normal males. Thus the gene for henny feathering acts directly on the feather follicle but requires androgen for its expression (for details see Witschi).

Color Changes in Plumage and Bill

Certain breeds and species of birds exhibit plumage dimorphism, and certain others do not; the plumage color is controlled by genes and may be independent of gonadal hormones. In such species the plumage color of both sexes may be hen-feathered (chicken hawk, song sparrow, hen-feathered chickens) or cock-feathered (herring gull, blue jay).

In many of the species whose plumage is influenced by gonadal hormones, the male plumage is more brilliantly colored than the female. The plumage of the castrate female chicken (Brown Leghorn) reverts to that of the male in color, but the plumage color of castrate males is unchanged. Thus, the difference in male and female plumage color is due to the action of estrogen. In the African weaver finches the neutral type is the hen plumage; the cock plumage is the result of pituitary hormones (Brown, 1950). In the herring gull, the cock type of plumage depends upon the action of androgens (Boss, 1943). The color of the beak of the weaver finch and the sparrow (Witschi and Woods, 1936) is intensified when androgen is injected. In certain other species (e.g. the common starling) the bills of both sexes are black during the eclipse and bright orange-yellow during the breeding season. Castration in both sexes produces black bills, and administration of androgen produces the yellow color (Witschi, 1961).

In black breeds of chickens, the intensity of the black pigment in the feathers is usually greater in the female; this effect is due to estrogen. In certain crosses involving black and spangled birds, the female offspring may show more black and less spangling than the males.

Comb Growth

The dramatic effect of androgen upon comb growth has been demonstrated by a number of workers. Breneman (1938, 1939) injected day-old chicks with testosterone propionate and dihydro-androsterone (0.6 to 2.5 mg. per day) over a period ranging from 5 to 10 days. The increase in comb size was tremendous, and some of the chicks began crowing as early as 7 days of age. Testis size was decreased. Kumaran and Turner (1949b) also demonstrated that treatment of the male with androgen decreased the size of the testes and inhibited spermatogenesis by depressing the output of pituitary FSH. Dorfman and Dorfman (1948a) revealed that the comb of the White Leghorn is 15 times as sensitive to androgen as the combs of Rhode Island Reds and Barred Plymouth Rocks. Because of the variation in the response of comb growth in different breeds (Dorfman and Dorfman, 1948b) and even in strains within a breed (Campos and Shaffner, 1952) to androgens, the use of the chick comb as an assay technique is subject to considerable error. The route of administration of androgen also influences the response. Intraperitoneal injections are less effective, particularly at lower dosages, than subcutaneous injections (Bernstorf, 1957). Munson and Sheps (1958) reviewed much of the earier work on assays of androgen and reported on an improved method of direct application of androgen to the chick's comb. Their experiments involved 162 assays and 20,000 chicks. They concluded that $\log \frac{\text{comb weight}}{\text{body weight}}$ yielded a linear log dose response curve and minimized the variance.

Androgen administered to female chicks (Breneman, 1956) or adult females (Brard and Benoit, 1953a) increased comb growth; however, the effect was less pronounced in females than in males, suggesting an antagonistic effect of estrogen, as was demonstrated by ovariectomizing the females. Following the operation, comb response to androgen was like that in the capon (Brard and Benoit, 1953b).

The response of comb growth to androgen is influenced by exercise (Wong, Lavenda, and Hawthorne, 1954). Forced exercise reduces the response to androgen. It has long been observed that normal males kept confined have larger combs than males allowed to run free. Exercise is a factor here, but light and temperature may also be involved.

Earlier workers reported that light tended to decrease the response of the comb to a given dose of androgen, but more recent and better-controlled experiments (Lamoreux, 1943; Wong and Hawthorne, 1954) ruled out light as a factor showing that increased environmental temperature increased the comb response to androgen.

Castration in the Male and Female

Castration in the male, or caponization, produces capons which grow more slowly and put on more fat than the uncastrated male, particularly after 5 months of age. Androgen tends to increase the amount of hemoglobin and the number of erythrocytes in the blood (see Chapter 1). The rate of metabolism in capons is about 13.5 percent lower then in cocks, according to Mitchell, Card, and Haines (1927).

Burmester and Nelson (1945) reported that the female chicken is more susceptible to lymphomatosis than the male, and that capons are more susceptible than normal males. The results obtained by these workers suggest that androgen is responsible for the increased resistance of normal males. When the capons were treated with androgen their susceptibility was the same as that of normal males. Later work by Davis, Andrews, and Doyle (1951) suggests that androgen is not the sole factor in the lower incidence of the disease in males, but that hormone imbalance and possibly other factors may be involved. These workers injected certain females with estrogen and others with androgen; in both the incidence of the disease was practically the same as in the untreated females.

Castration in the female is termed ovariectomy or ovariotomy. The effects of sinistral and bilateral ovariectomy are different. Usually two operations are required for bilateral ovariectomy. In the first operation, the left ovary is removed (sinistral). Then a hypertrophy of the rudimentary right gonad produces an ovotestis. Soon after the sinistral operation, and following the next molt, the new plumage is like that of the male in color and structure; but later, after the right gonad has developed and begun to secrete estrogen, the new plumage following the next molt may revert to the female type. The right gonad is then removed, and the plumage reverts to the male type, which is retained.

Development of the rudimentary right gonad in the sinistral castrate can be inhibited by the administration of estrogen or, to a lesser extent, of androgen (Kornfeld and Nalbandov, 1954; Taber and Salley, 1954). Estrogen secretion by the left ovary normally inhibits the growth of medullary tissue in the right gonad. If this inhibition is removed before 30 days of age by sinistral ovariectomy, then medullary tissue proliferates; after 30 days of age, however, estrogen has destroyed the potential of the medulla to develop and no proliferation occurs (see review by Van Tienhoven, 1961).

The experiments of Kornfeld (1958), and Taber *et al.* (1958), show that the action of estrogen is mainly responsible for the suppression of the rudimentary gonad by a direct action.

Hormones and differentiation of sex

In recent years a number of reports have appeared concerning the effects of androgen and estrogen on the sexual development of the embryo (see reviews by Benoit, 1950, and Burns, 1961). The hormones are injected into the egg before differentiation of the gonads (6 to 7 days). When estrogen is injected into zygotic females, the left ovary and the Wolffian ducts are usually not affected. The right oviduct, which normally is very small or degenerated at hatching time, persists and is hypertrophied, and so is the left oviduct. The zygotic male injected with estrogen develops an ovotestis on the left side, and sometimes on the right side, if the dose injected is large enough. With large doses, ovarian follicles with oöcytes may be present on the left side; also, the left and sometimes the right oviduct may be present. The right testis is much less responsive, and requires very large doses of estrogen. The response of the testis to estrogen varies with the breed or strain (Kondo, 1963).

Testosterone injected into zygotic males has little effect except to increase the size of the Wolffian ducts and to decrease slightly the size of the testes. In zygotic females the effects of testoterone are pronounced. The normal left ovary is transformed into an ovotestis (with medullary tissue predominating), and the right gonad (which normally degenerates) forms a testis as the result of proliferation by the medullary tissue. Development of the left oviduct (Mullerian duct) is partially inhibited, but the right one is stimulated.

Estrogen injected into incubating eggs has pronounced effects upon the hatched and growing chick. Greenwood and Blyth (1938) found that most such females raised to maturity failed to lay eggs, and that most of what few eggs were laid were devoid of shell or shell membranes. At autopsy these birds showed two incompletely formed oviducts. Van Tienhoven (1957) introduced gonadal hormones into incubating eggs by dipping the eggs into solutions containing the hormones; after allowing the eggs to hatch, he made observations on the chicks up to 6 months of age. He reported that estrogenized genetic males had extensive ovarian cortex at hatching time, but that it decreased with age. At 6 months, the testes were smaller than normal and spermatogenesis was retarded. In estrogenized genetic females at 6 months of age and after, egg-laying was reduced because of a high incidence of ovulations into the body cavity and of the small and poorly developed left oviduct.

Hutt (1937) reported a case of gynadromorphism in the fowl, wherein the structure of the left side of the body was female, and that of the right side was male. The male side contained an ovotestis, and the female side a nearly normal ovary. Hutt believed that this bird was originally a male, but that there had been the loss of a sex chromosome in the 2-cell cleavage stage, such that the female half of the bird developed from the cells which had lost the chromosome.

EFFECTS OF ESTROGEN AND PROGESTERONE ON THE OVIDUCT

The tremendous increase in the size of the oviduct of the hen coincident with sexual maturity is due to the effects of estrogen, elaborated by the maturing ovary. The sensivity of the avian oviduct is such that growth of the immature oviduct has been used as an assay method for estrogens (Hertz, 1945; Kar, 1947; Dorfman and Dorfman, 1948c; Breneman, 1956; and Lorenz *et al.*, 1962).

The size of the chick oviduct may increase by as much as 40 times following continued estrogen administration when the birds are fed a normal ration; however, the response to estrogen is diminished if the ration is deficient in folic acid (Hertz, 1945). The diminished response is not due mainly to inanition, although this is a factor; rather, it may be the effect of the folic acid involved in the enzyme system through which estrogen exerts its effect (Kline and Dorfman, 1951). The latter investigators demonstrated that a deficiency of thiamine in the ration increases the response of the chick oviduct to all levels of estrogen, and that so does a deficiency of nicotinic acid when moderate to low doses of estrogen are administered. But at very high levels the oviduct response is reversed. Chicks deficient in riboflavin show a diminished oviduct response to estrogen; but this is evidently due principally to inanition, for when the control birds are starved there is little difference in the response of the two groups. Thiamine deficiency appears to interfere with estrogen inactivation and to produce an increased oviduct response, regardless of the effect of inanition (Kline and Dorfman).

The response of the chick oviduct to estrogen is not affected appreciably by deficiencies in riboflavin, pantothenic acid, choline, or vitamins A and D, but is influenced by a deficiency of folic acid (Haque, Lillie, Shaffner, and Briggs, 1949).

The response of the immature avian oviduct to estrogen may be influenced by progesterone and testosterone. Some investigators have reported a synergistic effect of the latter hormones, and some have not. The variation in response appears to be related to dosage and species; it is discussed at length by Van Tienhoven (1961). Thyroxine and thiouracil, even though they inhibit the rise in serum calcium, phosphorus, and some other constituents of the plasma induced by estrogens, do not inhibit the hypertrophy of the oviduct produced by estrogens (Fleischmann and Fried, 1945; Common, Keefe, and Maw, 1950). The latter workers disclosed that thiouracil slightly enhances the effects of estrogens in stimulating growth of the oviduct.

Zarrow, Greenman, and Peters (1961) studied the effects of a number of steroids on weight increase of the oviduct produced by estrogen. Many of these, including progesterone, certain cortical hormones, and certain androgens, inhibited or decreased the estrogen effect on oviduct weight.

Assays for estrogen. Most biological assays are based on oviduct weight, but treatments of the data vary among investigators (see Lorenz *et al.*, 1962). Among others, these include simple comparisons of mean oviduct weights, the 4-point method of Bliss, and its modifications. To be really accurate the Bliss method would require a linear response to the log dose, but since logarithms of oviduct weights are not employed, this condition is not met (Lorenz *et al.*).

Lorenz and his colleagues demonstrated that the log dose response curves were linear when the log dose was plotted against log oviduct weights over a range of 30 to 600 mg.

Burger and Lorenz (1962) showed also that the size of cloaca is influenced by estrogens, and that the change in cloacal weight of chicks represented a fairly accurate assay technique for estrogens, although the method was not as sensitive as that involving oviduct weight.

EFFECTS OF ESTROGEN ON PLASMA AND TISSUE CONSTITUENTS

Blood calcium and phosphorus. Most investigators are agreed that the total calcium and phosphorous increases as birds begin laying. The increase in calcium is principally in the nondiffusible fraction (see also Chapters 2 and 20). Most of the phosphorus fractions are increased, particularly the lipid and protein phosphorus (Common, Bolton, and Rutledge, 1948; Fleischmann and Fried, 1945, on the chicken; Urist, 1959; McDonald and Riddle, 1945,

Table 66. Effects of estrogens (injected for 5 or more days) on serum calcium and phosphorus

Species, age, and treatment	Total serum calcium mg./100 ml.		Inorganic serum phosphorus mg./100 ml.	
	Control	Treated	Control	Treated
(a) Duck, mature Pekin male; estradiol; 1 mg. per day	10.4	52.4	2.4	9.9
(b) Pigeon, males and females, immature; estradiol, 0.25 to 5 mg. per day	10.5	28.9	4.3	6.6
(c) Chicken, immature, both sexes; estradiol, 1 mg. per day	11.9	30.4	7.6	16.3
(d) Chicken, immature females; estradiol	12.5	49.8	7.3	16.0
(e) Hen, +125 mg. estrogen per week	11.4	137.0	5.4	22.0
(f) Mature cock, +125 mg. estrogen per week	10.0	97.0	6.2	20.0

(a) Landauer, Pfeiffer, Gardner & Shaw, 1941; (b) McDonald, Riddle, & Smith, 1945; (c) Fleischmann & Fried, 1945; (d) Common, Bolton, & Rutledge, 1948; (e) and (f) Urist, 1959.

on the pigeon; and others). That these increases are due mainly to the effects of estrogen has been demonstrated by a number of workers with pigeons, chickens, and ducks. Examples of the effects of estrogens on total calcium and inorganic phosphorus are shown in Table 66. The role of the parathyroids in causing these increases is discussed in Chapter 20.

Blood Lipids. The lipids of the blood increase with laying (see also Chapter 2); this increase is governed mainly by estrogen, and has been demonstrated in the chicken, duck, and pigeon (Table 67).

Lorenz (1938), and Entenmann, Lorenz, and Chaikoff (1940), who injected estradiol benzoate (3.8 to 6.9 mg./kg.) into immature males and female chickens, reported tremendous increases in all of the lipid fractions, approaching or exceeding the values they reported in laying females (see also Chapter 2). Similar results have been obtained in cocks, capons, pigeons, and ducks (see Riddle, 1942; Benoit, 1950). Different estrogens vary in their lipogenic potencies (Lorenz and Bachman, 1947; and Lorenz *et al.*, 1962).

Plasma proteins are increased by estrogen, and the effect is mainly on the globulins, as illustrated in Table 67 (see also Chapter 2).

Estrogen and tissue constituents. Estrogen increases plasma riboflavin, vitamin A, liver fat, and liver protein in the chicken (Common, Rutledge, and Bolton, 1947; Common, Bolton, and Rutledge, 1948). The liver weight of the pigeon is also increased by estrogen, by approximately 80 percent (depending upon dosage); the increase is due mainly to the increase in the number and size of the liver cells (Clavert, 1944; see also Chapter 2).

Fleischmann and Fried (1945) asserted that estrogen does not increase ̖the amount of cholesterol in the tissues, and that the increase observed in the plasma is due not to changes in synthesis or to destruction of cholesterol, but to alterations in the distribution of cholesterol between plasma and tissues. Stamler, Bolene, Dudley and Levinson (1950) found, on the contrary, that diethylstilbestrol pellets implanted into 6-week-old cockerels increased the cholesterol and fatty acids not only in the plasma but also in the tissues. They studied the liver, kidneys, heart, adrenals, gut, and lungs, all of which showed an increased cholesterol content. All of the visceral organs had increased amounts of lipid phosphorus, and all except the heart showed significant increases in total lipids and fatty acids. The investigators concluded that estrogen increases lipid synthesis in the liver, but has little effect upon the destruction of lipids (see Chapter 2).

Thyroxine administered to the pigeon or chicken prevents the increases in plasma lipids, vitamin A, phosphorus, liver protein,

Table 67. Effects of estrogens on lipids and proteins of blood

Species and treatment	Total lipids serum mg./100 ml.		Author
	Control	Treated	
Duck, male, estradiol, 1 mg./day	448	3136	Landauer *et al.* (1941)
Pigeon, both sexes, immature, 0.25–0.5 mg. estradiol/day	468	1775	McDonald & Riddle (1945)
Chicken, cock, 4 mg. stilbestrol/day for 6 days	125	5430	Zondek & Marx (1939)
Chicken, immature, 3.8 to 6.9 mg. estradiol/kg.	415	2261	Entenmann *et al.* (1940)
Chicken, laying hen	1689	3417*	Lorenz & Bachman (1947)
Chicken, laying hen	2060	12,830	Urist (1959)

	Phospholipids mg./100 ml. serum		
Chicken, cock	191	4264	Urist (1959)
Chicken, hen	1530	5515	Urist (1959)

	Proteins g./100 ml. serum						
	Total		Albumin		Globulin		
	Control	Treated	Control	Treated	Control	Treated	
Chicken, cock	3.90	7.40	1.00	0.60	2.90	6.80	Urist, (1959)
Chicken, hen	6.60	8.90	1.90	0.90	4.70	8.00	"

* Neutral fat.

plasma proteins, and liver weight induced by estrogen injections, by either decreasing the synthesis or increasing the destruction of the latter (see Chapter 2 for more details). Thiouracil appears to have the same effect as thyroxine, except that it does not decrease liver weight and liver protein, but actually increases them, even though it depresses serum proteins (Common, Keefe, and Maw, 1950).

That the liver is the principal organ concerned in the increased synthesis of lipids induced by estrogen was proven by Ranney and Chaikoff (1951), who demonstrated that estrogen does not induce lipemia in the hepatectomized fowl. The liver is also the principal site for the formation of phospholipids in the fowl (Ranney, Chaikoff, and Entenmann, 1951), as it is in the mammal (Chaikoff, Lindsay, Lorenz, and Entenmann, 1948).

Estrogen and medullary bone formation are discussed in detail in Chapters 15 and 20.

EFFECTS OF GONADAL HORMONES ON OUTPUT OF PITUITARY HORMONES

Administration of estrogen and androgen usually depresses the output of the pituitary gonadotrophins FSH and LH (Nalbandov and Baum, 1948; Kumaran and Turner, 1949a); however, estrogen may influence the release of LH (see Chapters 15 and 17).

The influence of estrogen on the output of other pituitary hormones is not clear (see also Chapter 21, on the adrenals) but there is some evidence that at certain dose levels dienestrol diacetate may increase the secretion of thyrotrophic hormone (Burger, Lorenz, and Clegg, 1962).

Estrogen-induced depression of the release of pituitary gonadotrophin may be mediated via the hypothalamus. Legait (1959) has reported changes in the neurosecretory granules and cells of the paraventricular nucleus of the hypothalamus following estrogen administration in chickens. Estrogen suppresses the output of gonadotrophin in mammals by way of hypothalamus (Flerko, 1957).

That estrogen depresses the secretion of prolactin by the pituitary is suggested by the results of Godfrey and Jaap (1950) demonstrating that broodiness can be interrupted by the administration of estrogen.

The ovulation and release of LH induced in the chicken by progesterone have been discussed in Chapter 15. Large doses of progesterone interrupt ovulation and egg-laying, presumably by causing follicular atresia and molting (see Van Tienhoven, 1961).

Kar (1949) reported that progesterone injected into immature male pigeons for 30 days increased testicular weight and changed the epithelium of the tubules from the one layer of cells found in the prepuberal state to the multilayered condition. The Leydig cells were also increased. Kar concluded that progesterone stimulated the pituitary to release FSH and LH. These results, however, are contrary to those reported for chickens, where large doses decreased testis size and inhibited spermatogenesis (see Van Tienhoven, 1961).

Administration of testosterone caused ovulation in about 40 percent of the treated hens (see also Van Tienhoven, 1961).

EFFECTS OF ESTROGEN ADMINISTRATION ON GROWTH, FAT DEPOSITION, AND STORAGE IN TISSUES

The blood lipids of the laying female are considerably higher than in nonlaying females and males, and most of the surplus fat is deposited in the egg to form the yolk. That the blood lipids of males receiving estrogen are also increased, suggests that the surplus blood fat in males might be stored in the tissues, thus making the bird fatter and more desirable as a meat-producer. The feasibility of this proposal has been tested by a number of investigators, with varying results. The subject was reviewed in the first edition of this book, and by Lorenz (1954); Hill, Carew, and Van Tienhoven (1958); and others.

Most of the work has been done with synthetic estrogens such a diethylstilbestrol, or its dimethyl ether (dianisylhexene), and dienestrol diacetate. Diethylstilbestrol (DS) is effective when injected or implanted, but relatively ineffective when given orally (Jaap and Thayer, 1944; Jaap, 1945; Lorenz, 1945b). Lorenz (1945b) showed that when DS was implanted, about 2 mg. per week had to be absorbed to give satisfactory results. Treatment for 4 to 6 weeks was found in most cases to be optimum. The size of the pellet implanted ranges from 15 to 25 mg., depending on the size of the bird. The pellet is usually implanted in the skin, high on the neck or head, with an implanter, a trocar and plunger device, especially designed for the operation. Diethystilbestrol may also be implanted in the form of a paste.

Dianisylhexene and dienestrol are effective orally when fed at the level of 0.01 percent or less of the feed for 3 to 6 weeks. Lorenz and Bachman (1947) found that these estrogens gave satisfactory results when fed at levels of 0.0033 percent, but that more time was required to produce results than at higher levels. At a level of 0.01 or above, lipemia was produced, but not at the 0.0033 level.

Fat deposition. Nearly all investigators have reported that estrogen increased the amount of fat deposited in the tissues, particularly abdominal fat, and improved the grade of the carcass of males. This has been demonstrated in broilers, roasters, cock chickens, and turkeys.

The improvement in grade is due to increased fat deposits and to changes in the skin. The skin of the treated birds is smoother and softer. Estrogen increases the deposits of abdominal and liver fat, with lesser increases in other organs. (Lorenz, 1945b).

The results of earlier experiments were variable. Although most estrogenized birds exhibited some increase in body weight, in most instances the differences were not statistically significant. In the slightly heavier treated birds the increase was mainly in abdominal fat. Under some conditions estrogen administration depresses growth and body weight.

Although it has long been known that some of the variation in results is caused by the dose of the hormone and the method and duration of its administration, more recent experiments indicate that the protein content and caloric intake of the diet fed influence the response to estrogen significantly. Estrogenized chickens (Camp, Couch, and Quisenberry, 1957) and turkeys (Miner, Marsden, and Denton, 1959) fed diets low in protein (13 to 16 percent) gained more weight than those receiving higher levels of protein, and birds eating a diet containing 21 percent protein showed no gain in weight.

Increased fat production following the administration of estrogen is due primarily to increased energy consumption and to a lesser extent to preferential synthesis of fat at the expense of protein (Hill, Carew, and Van Tienhoven, 1958).

Storage of estrogen in tissues. The liver and fatty tissues tend most readily to store estrogen. Thus the possibility exists that sufficient quantities of estrogen may be stored in the tissues to produce undesirable physiological effects when such flesh is eaten, and thus to render the meat unsafe for human consumption. Early attempts to detect and measure residual estrogens in the edible tissues of treated animals by chemical and biological methods were reviewed by Lorenz (1954), and a sensitive biological assay technique was described by Umberger, Gass, and Curtis (1958). The administration of certain estrogens to animals to improve gains and market quality of the meat is approved by the appropriate authorities and is practiced commercially.

EFFECTS OF GONADAL HORMONES ON BURSA OF FABRICIUS

It is known that adrenal corticoids cause involution of lymphatic tissue such as the thymus and bursa of Fabricius. Androgen also causes involution of the bursa in chicks (Glick, 1957; Zarrow, Greenman, and Peters, 1961) and in chick embryos (Aspinall, Meyer, and Rao, 1961). Zarrow *et al.* reported that estradiol was also effective, but that progesterone had no effect on the bursa.

REFERENCES

Ainsworth, L., and R. H. Common 1963 Urinary and fecal conversion products of 16-oxoestradiol-17 beta 16-C^{14} in the domestic fowl. Canad. J. Biochem. Physiol. 41:2045.

Aspinall, R. I., R. K. Meyer, and M. A. Rao 1961 Effect of various steroids on the development of the bursa Fabricii in chick embryos. Endocrinol. 68:944.

Benoit, J. 1924 Action des rayons X sur le testicule du coq domestique. Comp. Rend. Soc. Biol. 90:802.

Benoit, J. 1950 Traité de Zoologie, edited by P. P. Grassé. Tome XV: Oiseaux, p. 419. Masson & Co., Paris.

Bernstorf, E. C. 1957 Difference in response of the capon comb to intraperitoneally and subcutaneously injected testosterone propionate. Endocrinol. 60:173.

Boss, W. R. 1943 Hormonal determination of adult characters and sex behavior in herring gulls (Larus argentatus). J. Exp. Zool. 94:181.

Brard, E., and J. Benoit 1953a Action de la testosterone sur des poules en ponte. Comp. Rend. Soc. Biol. 147:1943.

Brard, E., and J. Benoit 1953b Action de la testosterone sur la crête de la poule avant et après ovariectomie. Comp. Rend. Soc. Biol. 147:1940.

Breneman, W. R. 1938 Relative effectiveness of testosterone-propionate and dihydroandrosterone-benzoate in the chick as indicated by comb growth. Endocrinol. 23:44.

Breneman, W. R. 1939 Effect of androgens on the chick. Proc. VII World's Poultry Cong., pp. 91–95.

Breneman, W. R. 1956 Steroid hormones and the development of the reproductive system in the pullet. Endocrinol. 58:262.

Brown, F. A. 1950 Chapter 22, Comparative Animal Physiology, ed. C. L. Prosser. W. B. Saunders Co., Philadelphia.

Burger, R. E., and F. W. Lorenz 1962 Cloacal weight stimulation by estrogen in chicks. Endocrinol. 71:669.

Burger, R. E., F. W. Lorenz, and M. T. Clegg 1962 The effect of estrogen on the pituitary thyroid axis in the immature domestic fowl. Poultry Sci. 41:1703.

Burmester, B. R., and N. M. Nelson 1945 The effect of castration and sex hormones upon the incidence of lymphomatosis in chickens. Poultry Sci. 24:509.

Burns, R. K. 1961 Role of hormones in the differentiation of sex, in Sex and Internal Secretions, ed. W. C. Young, Vol. 2, p. 76. Williams & Wilkins, Baltimore.

Camp, A. A., J. R. Couch, and J. H. Quisenberry 1957 Response to diethylstilbestrol injections of growing chicks fed various protein levels. Poultry Sci. 36:171.

Campos, A. C., and C. S. Shaffner 1952 The genetic control of chick comb and oviduct response. Poultry Sci. 20:387.

Chaikoff, I. L., S. Lindsay, F. W. Lorenz, and C. Entenmann 1948 Production of atheromatosis in the aorta of the bird by administration of diethylstilbestrol. J. Exp. Med. 88:373.

Clavert, J. 1944 Action de la folliculine sur le foie du pigeon: Variation de poids du foie. Comp. Rend. Soc. Biol. 138:928.

Common, R. H., W. Bolton, and W. A. Rutledge 1948 The influence of gonadal hormones on the composition of the blood and liver of the domestic fowl. J. Endocrinol. 5:263.

Common, R. H., T. J. Keefe, and W. A. Maw 1950 Some biochemical effects of thiouracil on the response of the immature pullet to estrogen. Canadian J. Res. 28 (D):272.

Common, R. H., W. A. Rutledge, and W. Bolton 1947 The influence of gonadal hormones on serum riboflavin and certain other properties of blood and tissues of the domestic fowl. J. Endocrinol. 5:121.

Davis, O. S., F. N. Andrews, and L. P. Doyle 1951 Studies in avian leucosis. V: An investigation of the possible relationship of sex hormones to visceral lymphomatosis. Amer. J. Vet. Res. 11:428.

Dorfman, R. I., and A. S. Dorfman 1948a Studies on the bioassay of hormones: The assay of testosterone propionate and androsterone by a chick comb inunction method. Endocrinol. 42:1.

Dorfman, R. I., and A. S. Dorfman 1948b Studies on the bioassay of hormones: The relative reactivity of the comb of various breeds of chicks to androgen. Endocrinol. 42:7.

Dorfman, R. I., and A. S. Dorfman 1948c Studies on the bioassay of hormones: The comparative oviduct response of various breeds of chicks to stilbestrol. Endocrinol. 42:102.

Entenmann, C., F. W. Lorenz, and I. L. Chaikoff 1940 The endocrine control of lipid metabolism in the bird. III: Effects of crystalline sex hormones on blood lipids of birds. J. Biol. Chem. 134:495.

Essenberg, J. M., and R. J. Karrasch 1940 An experimental study of the effects of roentgen rays on the gonads of the sexually mature domestic fowl. Radiology 34:358.

Fleischmann, W., and I. A. Fried 1945 Studies on the mechanism of the hypercholesterolemia and hypercalcemia induced by estrogen in immature chicks. Endocrinol. 36:406.

Flerko, B. 1957 Le rôle des structures hypothalamiques dans l'action inhibitrice de la folliculine sur la sécretion de l'hormone folliculostimuline. Arch. Anat. Microscop. Morphol. Exp. 46:159.

Fraps, R. M., C. W. Hooker, and T. R. Forbes 1948 Progesterone in blood plasma of the ovulating hen. Science 108 (2795):86.

Fraps, R. M., C. W. Hooker, and T. R. Forbes 1949 Progesterone in blood plasma of cocks and non-ovulating hens. Science 109 (2837):493.

Glick, B. 1957 Experimental modification of the growth of the bursa of Fabricius. Poultry Sci. 36:18.

Godfrey, E. F., and R. G. Jaap 1950 Estrogenic interruption of broodiness in the domestic fowl. Poultry Sci. 29:356.

Gorbman, A., and H. A. Bern 1962 A Textbook of Comparative Endocrinology. John Wiley & Sons, New York.

Greenwood, W. W., and J. S. S. Blyth 1938 Experimental modification of the accessory sexual apparatus in the hen. Quart. J. Exp. Physiol. 28:61.

Haque, M. F., R. J. Lillie, C. S. Shaffner, and G. M. Briggs 1949 Response of vitamin-deficient chicks to the sex hormones. Poultry Sci. 28:914.

Hertz, R. 1945 The quantitative relationship between stilbestrol response and dietary folic acid in the chick. Endocrinol. 37:1.

Hill, F. W., L. B. Carew, Jr., and A. Van Tienhoven 1958 Effect of diethylstilbestrol on utilization of energy by the growing chick. Am. J. Physiol. 195:654.

Hooker, C. W., and T. R. Forbes 1949 Specificity of the intrauterine test for progesterone. Endocrinol. 45:71.

Hopwood, M. L., and F. X. Gassner 1962a Metabolism of C[14] diethylstilbestrol in the chicken: Retention and excretion. Endocrinol. 70:880.

Hopwood, M. L., and F. X. Gassner 1962b Metabolism of C[14] diethylstilbestrol in the chicken: Conversion in vivo. Endocrinol. 70:886.

Hutt, F. B. 1937 Gynandromorphism in the fowl. Poultry Sci. 16:354.

Jaap, R. G. 1945 Activity of synthetic estrogens on oral administration in the domestic fowl and turkey. Endocrinol. 37:369.

Jaap, R. G., and R. H. Thayer 1944 Oral administration of estrogens in poultry. Poultry Sci. 23:249.

Kar, A. B. 1947 Responses of the oviduct of immature female fowl to injection of diethylstilbestrol and the mechanism of perforation of the oviduct in the domestic fowl. Poultry Sci. 26:352.

Kar, A. B. 1949 Testicular changes in the juvenile pigeon due to progesterone treatment. Endocrinol. 45:346.

Kline, I. T., and R. I. Dorfman 1951 Estrogen stimulation of the oviduct in vitamin deficient chicks. Endocrinol. 48:345.

Kondo, K. 1963 The effect of estrogen treatment on male embryos from reciprocal crosses between breeds of fowl with high and low response. J. Exp. Zool. 154:329.

Kornfeld, W. 1958 Endocrine influences upon the growth of the rudimentary gonad of the fowl. Anat. Rec. 130:619.

Kornfeld, W., and A. V. Nalbandov 1954 Endocrine influences on the development of the rudimentary gonad of fowl. Endocrinol. 55:751.

Kumaran, J. D. S., and C. W. Turner 1949a The endocrinology of spermatogenesis in birds. I: Effect of estrogen and androgen. Poultry Sci. 28:593.

Kumaran, J. D. S., and C. W. Turner 1949b The endocrinology of spermatogenesis in birds. II: The effect of androgens. Poultry Sci. 28:739.

Lamoreux, W. F. 1943 Effect of difference in light and temperature upon the size of combs on White Leghorns. Endocrinol. 32:497.

Landauer, W., C. A. Pfeiffer, W. U. Gardner, and J. C. Shaw 1941 Blood serum and skeletal changes in two breeds of ducks receiving estrogens. Endocrinol. 28:458.

Layne, D. S., R. H. Common, W. A. Maw, and R. M. Fraps 1957 Presence of progesterone in extracts of ovaries of laying hens. Proc. Soc. Exp. Biol. & Med. 94:528.

Layne, D. S., R. H. Common, W. A. Maw, and R. M. Fraps 1958 Presence of estrone, estradiol and estriol in extracts of ovaries of laying hens. Nature 181:351.

Legait, H. 1959 Contribution à l'étude morphologique et expérimentale du système hypothalamoneuro-hypophysaire de la poule Rhode-Island. Thèse D, Agrégation de l'enseignement supérieur, Louvain.

Lorenz, F. W. 1938 Effects of estrin on blood lipids of the immature fowl. J. Biol. Chem. 126:763.

Lorenz, F. W. 1945a The influence of diethylstilbestrol on fat deposition and meat quality in chickens. Poultry Sci. 24:128.

Lorenz, F. W. 1945b The fattening action of orally administered synthetic estrogens as compared with diethylstilbestrol pellet implants. Poultry Sci. 24:91.

Lorenz, F. W. 1954 Effects of estrogens on domestic fowl and applications in the poultry industry. Vitamins & Hormones 12:235.

Lorenz, F. W., and G. H. Bachman 1947 Lipemia and fat deposition in response to oral administration of synthetic estrogens. Poultry Sci. 26:419.

Lorenz, F. W., R. E. Burger, E. B. Bennett, and W. Reimann 1962 Hepatic and renal effects on potency of estrogenis stilbene derivatives in chicken. Endocrinol. 71:649.

McDonald, M. R., and O. Riddle 1945 The effect of reproduction and estrogen administration on the partition of calcium, phosphorus and nitrogen in pigeon plasma. J. Biol. Chem. 159:445.

McDonald, M. R., O. Riddle, and G. C. Smith 1945 Action of thyroxine on estrogen-induced changes in blood chemistry and endosteal bone. Endocrinol. 37:23.

MacRae, H. F., and R. H. Common 1960 Formation of 16-epiestriol from estradiol 17, beta in the laying hen. Poultry Sci. 39:701.

MacRae, H. F., D. S. Layne, and R. H. Common 1959 Formation

of estrone, estriol and an unidentified steroid from estradiol in the laying hen. Poultry Sci. 38:684.

Miner, J. J., S. J. Marsden, and C. A. Denton 1959 The effect of diethylstilbestrol, methimazole and dienestrol diacetate on turkey broilers. Poultry Sci. 38:750.

Mitchell, H. H., L. E. Card, and W. T. Haines 1927 The effect of age, sex and castration on the basal heat production of chickens. J. Agric. Res. 34:945.

Mitchell, J. E., and R. Hobkirk 1959 Conversion of 16-14C-Estradiol-17beta to 14C-labelled Estriol by avian liver slices. Biochem. Biophys. Res. Comm. 1:72.

Munson, P. L., and M. C. Sheps 1958 An improved procedure for the biological assay of androgens by direct application to the combs of baby chicks. Endocrinol. 62:173.

Nalbandov, A. V., and G. J. Baum 1948 The use of stilbestrol-inhibited males as test animals for gonadotrophic hormones. Endocrinol. 43:371.

Nalbandov, A. V., R. K. Meyer, and W. H. McShan 1946 Effect of purified gonadotrophes on the androgen secreting ability of testes of hypophysectomized cocks. Endocrinol. 39:91.

Ranney, R. E., and I. L. Chaikoff 1951 Effect of functional hepatectomy upon estrogen-induced lipemia in the fowl. Amer. J. Physiol. 165:600.

Ranney, R. E., I. L. Chaikoff, and C. Entenmann 1951 Site of formation of phospholipids in the bird. Am. J. Physiol. 165:596.

Riddle, O. 1942 Cyclic changes in blood calcium, phosphorus and fat in relation to egg laying and estrogen production. Endocrinol. 31:498.

Siller, W. J. 1956 A Sertoli cell tumor causing feminization in a Brown Leghorn capon. J. Endocrinol. 14:197.

Stamler, J., C. Bolene, M. Dudley, and E. Levinson 1950 Effect of prolonged exhibition of diethylstilbestrol on plasma and tissue lipids in the chick. Endocrinol. 46:375.

Sturkie, P. D., J. A. Pino, J. S. Weatherwax, A. J. Donnelly, and G. M. Dorrance 1949 Effect of X-rays on fertility in White Leghorn male chickens treated before puberty. Radiology 52:112.

Taber, E. 1949 Androgen production in the female Brown Leghorn fowl. Anat. Rec. 105:561.

Taber, E. 1951 Androgen secretion in the fowl. Endocrinol. 48:6.

Taber, E., M. Clayton, J. Knight, J. Flowers, D. Gambrell, and C.

Ayers 1958 Some effects of sex hormones and homologous gonadotrophins on the early development of the rudimentary gonad
in the fowl. Endocrinol. 63:435.

Taber, E., and K. W. Salley 1954 The effects of sex hormones on
the development of the right gonad in female fowl. Endocrinol.
54:415.

Umberger, E. J., G. H. Gass, and J. M. Curtis 1958 Design of a
biological assay method for the detection and estimation of estrogenic residues on the edible tissues of domestic animals treated
with estrogens. Endocrinol. 63:806.

Urist, M. R. 1959 The effects of calcium deprivation upon the
blood adrenal cortex, ovary and skeleton in domestic fowl. Recent
Prog. in Hormone Res. 15:455.

Van Tienhoven, A. 1957 A method of controlling sex by dipping
of egg in hormone solutions. Poultry Sci. 36:628.

Van Tienhoven, A. 1961 Endocrinology of reproduction in Birds,
Chapter 18, Sex and Internal Secretions, ed. W. C. Young.
Williams & Wilkins, Baltimore.

Witschi, E. 1961 Sex and secondary sexual characters, Chapter 17,
Biology and Comparative Physiology of Birds, ed. A. J. Marshall
Vol. II. Academic Press, New York.

Witschi, E., and R. P. Woods 1936 The bill of the sparrow as in-
dicatory of the male sex hormone. J. Exp. Zool. 73:445.

Wong, H. Y. C., and E. W. Hawthorne 1954 Influence of filtered
and no sunlight on weight and comb response in androgen treated
cockerels. Am. J. Physiol. 179:419.

Wong, H. Y. C., N. Lavenda, and E. W. Hawthorne 1954 Effect of
exercise on comb response of androgen treated capons. Am. J.
Physiol. 178:269.

Zarrow, M. X., D. L. Greenman, and L. E. Peters 1961 Inhibition
of the bursa of Fabricius and the stilbestrol stimulated oviduct of
the domestic chick. Poultry Sci. 40:87.

Zondek, B., and L. Marx 1939 The induction of lipemia and cal-
cemia in the cock by means of oestrogenic hormone. Arch. Int.
Pharm. Thera. 41:77.

CHAPTER 19

Thyroids

BY ROBERT K. RINGER

ANATOMY

Location; Blood and Nerve Supply

THE thyroid glands in avian species are paired organs, oval in shape and dark red in color, with a glistening appearance. They are located on either side of the trachea on the ventral-lateral aspect of the neck just exterior to the thoracic cavity. The thyroids may be readily located by tracing the major blood vessels, and can be found adhering to the common carotid just above the junction of the common carotid with the subclavian artery. They are situated medial to the jugular vein.

The vascular supply to the thyroid is by the cranial and caudal thyroid arteries, which originate from a branch directly off the common carotid artery. Return circulation is through veins emptying into the jugular vein. The thyroid epithelium has an ill-defined basement membrane; thus, the vascular endothelium is in virtual contact with the follicular epithelium.

Nothing is known about the innervation of the thyroid in birds; it may stem from the cervical sympathetic ganglion, as in mammals. In man the nerves accompany the blood vessels in the thyroid and mostly end in the perivascular plexus; occasionally they end on the follicular cells.

Embryology and Histology

Embryologically the thyroid appears on the second day of incubation of the chick as a midline outgrowth (median anlage) from the ventral pharyngeal wall at the level of the first and second branchial pouches. The median anlage becomes cuplike and bilobed, with a narrow stalk attached to the pharyngeal wall. The stalk ruptures, and the lobes separate and migrate laterally as crescent-shaped structures. The glands ultimately develop their definitive shape and position (for complete review see Romanoff, 1960).

The cells within the thyroid are arranged in chordlike rows. Intracellular impregnation by blood vessels and connective tissue occurs. Colloid secretion commences and displaces the epithelium peripherally, forming spherical vesicles known as follicles. At 7 days of incubation the thyroid of the embryonic chick can concentrate radioactive iodine (I^{131}) many times over the amount present in the blood, yet no follicles or colloid are visible. On the 9th day of incubation, droplets of colloid are visible and radioiodine uptake is protein-bound. On the 13th day the thyroid abruptly increases radioiodine accumulation upon injection of I^{131}, suggesting that the pituitary may be exerting some control (Waterman, 1959). From the in-

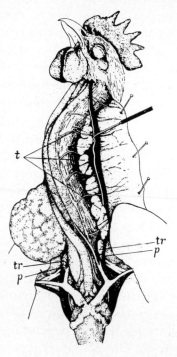

Figure 86. Location of thyroids *(tr)*, parathyroids *(p)*, and thymus *(t)* in the chicken. (From Nonidez and Goodale, *Am. J. Anat.,* 1927.)

corporation of radioiodine in the follicular colloid, Hansborough and Khan (1951), and Stoll and Blanquet (1953), concluded that the embryonic chick thyroid becomes functional and secretes thyroxine after 10 to 11 days of incubation. Just prior to hatching the activity of the thyroid increases, as measured by greater radioiodine uptake (Rogler, Parker, Andrews, and Carrick, 1959a) and by morphological feature changes indicating a turbulent outflow of secretion (Kraicziczek, 1956).

Radioiodide administered to hens concentrates in the ovary (yolk) as thyroxine and triiodothyronine (Roche, Michel, and Volpert, 1956); however, Okonski, Lengemann, and Comar (1961) reported that only a small fraction of the I^{131} was protein-bound; the largest segment was in the form of iodide. The iodide is utilized by the developing embryo. At the start of incubation the major portion of radioiodide is concentrated in the yolk, but by the 9th day of incubation, when vascularization has taken place, the first iodide appears concentrated in the embryo thyroid. Concentration within the thyroid continues until at the 19th day 40 percent of the I^{131} is in the thyroid, 40 percent is elsewhere in the embryo, and 20 percent remains in the egg (Stoll and Blanquet, 1953; also see Wollman and Zwilling, 1953; and Okonski, Lengemann, and Comar, 1960). Functional differentiation of the embryonic thyroid gland is not due to the elaboration of thyrotrophin by the hypophysis, since the thyroid gland will develop both morphologically and functionally in chorioallantoic grafts or *in vitro*. The thyroid gland of the embryo possesses an intrinsic ability to develop autonomously. Both *in vitro* and *in vivo* studies of the thyroid show the same schedule of I^{131} concentration (Waterman, 1959).

Histologically the thyroid is encapsulated by reticular connective tissue. The follicles are composed of entodermal epithelium of varying height, depending upon the state of activity (secretory rate). The epithelial type may vary from squamous to columnar. Depending upon the secretory state, the follicles may be filled with, or completely devoid of, colloid. The colloid is a homogeneous fluid. Between the follicles are connective tissue stroma, interfollicular cells, and a rich blood supply (see Thommes, 1958).

Size

The size of the thyroid is influenced by several variables such as age, sex, climatic conditions, diet, activity, species, and hypophysectomy. In proportion to the total body weight the thyroid in the domestic fowl does not vary markedly with increasing age, but its absolute weight increases with age. Growth rate of the thyroid is almost constant from hatching until about 50 to 60 days after hatching. The rate of thyroidal growth is then accelerated until between 100 and 120 days, at which time a pronounced slowing occurs (Breneman, 1954).

Species	Thyroid Wt.; Percent of B.W.	Investigator
Domestic fowl	0.004–0.007	Schultze & Turner (1945)
Domestic pigeon	0.01–0.025	Riddle (1947)
Rouen duck	0.006	Benoit (1950)
Pekin duck	0.011	Benoit (1950)
Mallard duck	0.01	Höhn (1949)

The correlation between thyroid weight and body weight of 4-week-old New Hampshire chicks was +0.59, and the linear regression coefficient was 9.85 mg. of thyroid per 100 gm. of body weight (Shaklee and Knox, 1956). The heritability of thyroid weight has been shown to be extremely high. Shaklee and Knox (1956) reported heritabilities of 77 and 92 percent, depending on the method of estimate used.

Female White Plymouth Rocks have a greater thyroid weight than males (Schultze and Turner, 1945). The same is true of White Leghorns (Latimer, 1924) and New Hampshires (Shaklee and Knox, 1956). Castration of the Pekin duck results in marked increases in thyroid weight (Tixier-Vidal and Assenmacher, 1961a, 1961b); however, Benoit and Aron (1934) could not show differences in the duck or rooster. Capons, males, and females show no differences in average thyroid weights from hatching until 90 days of age, at which time the thyroid weights of capons start to exceed those of both cockerels and pullets (Breneman, 1954). Breneman also reported that administration of estradiol-dipropionate (0.2 to 40.0 mg./day for 20 days) had no effect on the thyroid weight of either males or capons. Burger, Lorenz, and Clegg (1962) fed 100 ppm. dienestrol diacetate to cockerels and found that thyroid weight was unaffected up to 12 days, but that from the 12th to 16th day the thyroids were enlarged compared to those of the controls. These workers suggest that estrogen increases the destruction of circulating hormone, and is thus a secondary influence on thyroid weight through increased thyrotrophic hormone output.

That diet has an influence upon thyroid size is widely known. Since iodine is essential in the biosynthesis of the thyroid hormones, a deficiency of iodine in chickens produces goiter or enlargement of the thyroid (Patton, Wilgus, and Harshfield, 1939). Feeding of soybean oil meal tended to enlarge the thyroid of chicks (Wilgus, Gassner, Patton, and Gustavson, 1941), apparently because of its low iodine content. Van Tienhoven *et al.* (1956) demonstrated that 0.1 and 0.2 percent sulfamethazine in the feed increased the thyroid weight, probably through action, either direct or indirect, upon the pituitary. Antibiotics, when fed to growing chickens, have been reported to increase thyroid weight in relation to body weight (Mellen and Waller, 1954; Menge and Conner, 1955). Other workers have shown no consistent enlargement of the thyroid with growth stimulation by penicillin (Libby and Meites, 1954; Maghrabi and Turner, 1953; Kneeling *et al.,* 1955; Draper and Firth, 1957) or chlortetracycline Maghrabi and Turner, 1953; Kneeling *et al.,* 1955).

In chicks, the feeding of 10 to 14.5 percent fat produced smaller thyroids than did the feeding of 2.5 percent fat (March and Biely, 1957); however, thyroxine secretion rate was not always reduced by the higher levels. Restricted caloric intake does not influence thyroid weight even though the metabolic rate is lowered (Mellen, Hill, and Dukes, 1954), as is the thyroid secretion rate (Premachandra, 1962).

According to Cruickshank (1929) and Galpin (1938), the thyroid weight of chickens is greater in the fall and winter than in the summer, and according to Riddle (1927) this is also true of pigeons; however, Turner (1948a) did not confirm these findings. An increased metabolism in cool weather coincides with an increase in thyroid weight and activity (to be discussed later). Exposure to cold probably causes an increase in TSH secretion from the anterior pituitary. Tixier-Vidal (1957) observed histological changes in the chick embryo thyroid brought about by cold, suggestive of increased TSH secretion.

An increase in the size of the thyroid may be due to an increase in cell size (hypertrophy) and/or number of cells (hyperplasia), associated with a reduction in colloid content of the follicles. En-

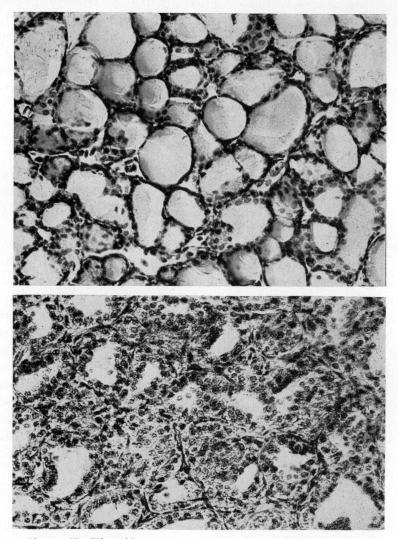

Figure 87. Thyroid gland of a normal chick showing colloid-filled follicles (upper) and thyroid of a chick administered thiouracil (lower).

Increase in size and number of follicular cells and absence of colloid are apparent in the lower figure. (From Larson *et al., Endocrinol.,* 1945a.)

larged thyroids may reflect either a hyper- or hypofunctioning gland. TSH stimulates the thyroid and produces both hypertrophy and hyperplasia, together with accelerated formation or secretion of thyroxine (Rawson and Salter, 1940; Larson *et al.*, 1945). Thiouracil, thiourea, and methimazole (goitrogens) produce the same histological picture but suppress the formation of thyroxine. Hypophysectomy causes a decrease in thyroid size, since production of TSH is abolished.

THYROTROPHIC HORMONE (TSH)

A decrease in the size of the thyroid following hypophysectomy (Mitchell, 1929; Nalbandov and Card, 1943) indicates that the bird pituitary elaborates a thyroid-stimulating hormone (TSH). Two types of beta-basophil cells exist in the anterior pituitary of the chicken, differing in size and shape but having similar secretory granule size. Both stain positive with the periodic acid–Schiff procedure. Thyrotrophic hormone is produced by the large beta cells of polygonal shape, in contrast to the small, regularly shaped cells reported to be gonadotrophic (Perek, Eckstein, and Sobel, 1957). Brown and Knigge (1958) showed that TSH is produced by beta-basophil cells and that the gonadotrophins are produced by △-basophils, since only beta cells stain positive for aldehyde fuchsin, and it is these cells that increase in number after propylthiouracil treatment. The beta basophils are found exclusively in the cephalic lobe, according to Mikami (1958), and produce TSH. Assays of TSH potency of the cephalic and caudal lobes showed high potency of the cephalic lobe and none for the caudal lobe.

Martindale (1941) demonstrated the presence of a thyrotrophic hormone in the 11-day chick embryo by transplanting chick embryo pituitaries into the hypophysectomized chick, which restored the thyroid to normal size. Tixier-Vidal (1956), using chick pituitaries, was unable to detect TSH in *in vitro* cultures prior to the 7th day of incubation but was able to show its presence at 7 days. There is an increase in aldehyde fuchsin (AF) positive cells in the pituitary of the chick embryo on the 7th day of incubation, together with an accumulation of periodic acid–Schiff (PAS) staining material indicative of mucoprotein (Phillips, 1962). A decrease in basophilia occurs at mid-incubation (Rahn, 1939). At the 13th day of incubation, degranulation of AF-positive material occurs in the pituitary cells. PAS- and AF-positive material appears in the veins near the pituitary (Philips, 1962), and may indicate the start of pituitary control over the thyroid, which is responsible for the rapid increase in radioactive iodide accumulation in the 13-day chick embryo thyroid (see review by Waterman, 1959).

The TSH output of the day-old chick is very low (Frey and Flock, 1958). Administration of triiodothyronine or thyroxine to chicks decreased I^{131} uptake by the thyroid (Shellabarger and Godwin, 1954), indicating that the chick's pituitary normally produces minute quantities of TSH and that this quantity can be inhibited by exogenous thyroid hormones.

The amount of TSH in circulation in the pigeon is 0.09 Junkmann-Schoeller units/100 ml. of plasma (D'Angelo and Gordon, 1950). A Junkmann-Schoeller unit equals about 10 international units (activity of 20 mg. of USP reference substance = 1 I.U.).

Payne (1944a; 1957) reported that the chicken pituitary developed "T" cells following thyroidectomy, in a manner similar to cytological changes in mammals. It has been suggested that the cells which produce TSH, called thyrotrophs, may lose their identity and become the thyroidectomy cells seen upon ablation of the thyroid gland. Thyrotrophs lose their receptivity to AF stain before thyroidectomy cells develop PAS-positive granules. Positive identification of thyroidectomy cells as former thyrotrophs thus becomes difficult, although the Golgi apparatus of these two cells appears to be similar to that in mammals (Elfman, 1958).

Administration of TSH mediates a response as early as one-half to two hours after injection (increased release of radioiodine and uptake of P^{32}), but the duration of response varies. In young chicks colloid droplets persist for 6 hours prior to diminishing. Thyroid follicular cell height response lasts for at least 24 hours after administration of TSH (Dvoskin, 1947). Olin-Lamberg and Lamberg (1953) injected 0.05 Junkmann-Schoeller units of TSH into chicks and observed a P^{32} uptake that increased linearly during the first few hours, remained at a plateau from the 8th to the

12th hour, and then declined. Maximum mean thyroid cell height was attained at 8 hours and then declined slightly. Thyroid weight increased slightly 6 hours after administration but not maximally until after 24 hours. Dosages exceeding 0.05 to 0.1 Junkmann-Schoeller units injected into day-old chicks appear excessive, and depress physiological parameters (P^{32} uptake and mean thyroid cell height) below that observed with smaller doses.

Assays

Fowl pituitary material stimulates thyroid growth in mammalian species, and conversely the chick and pigeon thyroid can be stimulated by pituitary extracts of mammalian origin. The chicken pituitary rates below that of the frog, rat, mouse, duck, and pig in potency of TSH (Adams, 1946). The chick has been used extensively in the assay for thyrotrophin.

The assay of TSH in the chick has employed the changes produced by injecting extracts of plasma and measuring the mitotic change in the thyroid epithelial cells, or the thyroid weight, or the intracellular droplets of colloid, or the uptake of radioactive iodine or phosphorus by the thyroid and the depletion of I^{131} from the thyroid. These assays vary in procedure with individual investigators. Some of the accepted methods are given below (for complete details see Turner, 1950, 1962; for a critical review see Brown, 1959).

Gravimetric method. Thyroid weight increase following TSH injection lacks sufficient sensitivity and thus has no application in assaying TSH in plasma or urine.

Histometric method. Histological techniques are 4 to 10 times more sensitive than gravimetric methods. Histometric techniques include the colloid droplet method and that of increased cell height.

    a. Colloid droplet method of Dvoskin (1947). Three-day-old cockerels are injected subcutaneously with 0.2 ml. of TSH solution and then killed 2 hours later. The thyroids are removed, weighed, and fixed in Carnoy's fluid. The thyroids are sectioned at 4 μ and stained with a modified Heidenhain's Azan stain. The colloid droplets of the thyroid epithelium of 25 cross sections of follicles are counted. This method is laborious and requires a large number of animals per assay in order to overcome individual differences of response to the dosage. An increase in intracellular colloid droplets is not specific for TSH, and therefore is questionable as an assay procedure.

b. Cell height method. Day-old cockerels are injected with a TSH solution at 12-hour intervals for a total of 5 injections. Twelve hours after the last injection the chick is killed, and the thyroid removed and fixed in Bouin's solution. Sections are cut at 4 to 6 μ and stained. Investigators have varied in the number of cells counted, but the majority have measured the height of 100 cells from different follicles. A standard TSH solution is used for comparison.

Chemical methods. Chemical determination of the reduction of iodine content of the thyroid following TSH injection has been used as an assay in chicks but is too tedious and laborious to be satisfactory.

Radiometric method. The use of radioisotope uptake or depletion has given researchers the most sensitive assay to date.

a. I^{131} Depletion method of Bates and Cornfield (1957). Day-old chicks given water but deprived of feed are injected subcutaneously with 2 to 3 microcuries of I^{131} solution. *In vivo* measurement of I^{131} uptake is made 24 hours later, using a scintillation counter. At this time a solution containing 8 mg. thyroxine and 0.5 mg. propylthiouracil is injected, both blocking endogenous TSH release and preventing recycling of I^{131}. Simultaneously 0.2 ml. of the TSH assay solution is injected (daily for 2 or 3 days), and daily I^{131} counts are made. The relative percent of I^{131} retained in the thyroid serves as an endpoint.

b. I^{131} uptake method of Shellabarger (1954b). Soon after hatching, cockerel chicks are injected subcutaneously, in the back of the neck, with 0.2 ml. of TSH (or saline control) solution. At 12-hour intervals the injections are repeated, for a total of 5 injections. Twelve hours after the last injection, 0.1 to 10 microcuries of I^{131} is injected; the chicks are killed 5 hours later, when the thyroids are removed and trimmed clean. They are then weighed, fixed in 3 cc. of Bouin's solution, and subjected to a radioactivity count in a well-type scintillation counter. The endpoint used is the uptake of I^{131} compared against standard TSH solutions.

c. P^{32} uptake method of Greenspan, Kriss, Moses, and Lew (1956). Day-old cockerels are kept without water and food. A 0.1 ml. solution of isotonic saline containing TSH is injected into the heart. Simultaneously a 0.5 ml. solution of saline containing 25 microcuries of P^{32} is injected intraperitoneally. After 6 hours the thyroids are dissected out, air dried, and given a P^{32} activity count with an end-window Geiger-Mueller counter. Assay solutions are compared to known TSH solutions.

The chick has also been used for the assay of urinary TSH; but the ultrafiltrate residue of human urine contains a factor or factors of other than hypophysial origin that stimulated P^{32} uptake by the chick thyroid and interfered with I^{131} depletion (Greenspan and Lew, 1959).

Thyroid hormones given in combination with TSH diminish the increase in cell height and thyroid weight brought about by TSH alone. Thus, thyroid hormones can act directly on the thyroid to inhibit its response to TSH (Shellabarger and Godwin, 1954). Testosterone propionate diminishes the thyrotrophin content of the pituitary of canaries, whereas estrone has no effect (Kobayashi, 1955).

THYROID CONTROL

Thyroid-Pituitary Balance

Within certain limits the function of the thyroid is governed by the concentration of the circulating thyroid hormones and their effects upon the pituitary release of TSH. A decrease in the amount of circulating thyroid hormones to a level below metabolic requirements prompts the anterior pituitary to increase the release of thyrotrophic hormone. An exogenous injection of thyroxine lends to a decrease in production of the thyrotrophic hormone. Thus the thyroid-pituitary feedback mechanism is constantly in a state of balance and counterbalance between the hormones.

Administration of TSH to chicks causes a rapid response of the thyroid as measured by an increase in size, an increase in the height of the follicular epithelial cells, and the formation of colloid droplets (Smelser, 1938; Adams and Beeman, 1942; Dvoskin, 1947). Marked increases (100 to 300 percent) in cell height have been reported following one injection of TSH (Smelser, 1938;

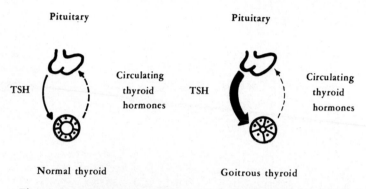

Figure 88. Diagram of pituitary thyroid feedback mechanism.

Adams and Beeman, 1942; Shellabarger, 1954a). TSH increases the formation and release of thyroxine (Rawson and Salter, 1940; Larson *et al.*, 1945; Frey and Flock, 1958), and causes an increase in iodine uptake (Keating *et al.* 1945; Shellabarger and Godwin, 1954). TSH also increases the thyroid uptake of P^{32} and increases the depletion rate of I^{131} from the thyroid (Piotrowski, Steelman, and Koch, 1953; Bates and Cornfield, 1957; Greenspan, Kriss, Moses, and Lew, 1956). Both the synthesis of thyroid hormone within the gland and its release from the gland are under the control of TSH. The mode of action of TSH on the follicular cells is unknown.

Hypothalamic-Pituitary-Thyroid Control

There is little doubt that the hypothalamus plays a role in the secretion of anterior pituitary TSH in mammals, since anterior pituitary transplants outside of the hypothalamic area (beneath the kidney capsule), or hypothalamic lesions, result in less thyroid activity than in intact animals. The degree of TSH depression is limited but quantitative. Indications are that the major feedback system controlling TSH secretion is the level of circulating hormones reaching the pituitary directly, and that the hypothalamus acts as a modulator for quantitative adjustments in the output of

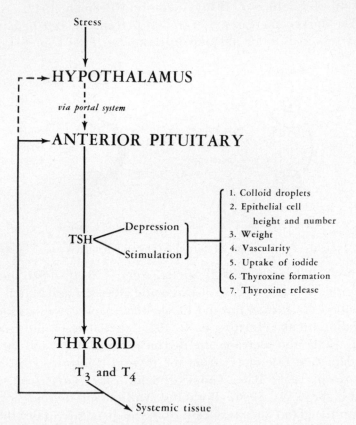

Figure 89. Hypothalamic-pituitary-thyroid interrelationship.

TSH. Damage to the hypothalamic-hypophysial portal vessels is followed by decreased thyroid activity, thus suggesting that the hypothalamic influence is mediated via the portal vessels.

By comparing anterior pituitary autotransplants with normal and hypophysectomized cockerels, Ma (1963) reported that thyroid weight was maintained in autotransplants but not in hypophysectomized birds. He indicated that the birds with autotransplanted pituitaries had an I^{131} uptake 89 percent of normal, and that the feedback mechanism was normal since exogenous thyroxine decreased both thyroid weight and radioiodine uptake. It appears that the hypothalamus is not necessary for the feedback mechanism to function.

THYROID HORMONES

Formation of Thyroxine and Triiodothyronine

Little or no information is available on thyroid hormone synthesis in birds; but it is assumed to occur in the same manner as in mammals, where iodide is concentrated within the thyroid, the so-called iodide trap, by the maintenance of a gradient over that of blood. The iodide is converted to I_2 and then to I^+, which is the iodinating substance. The thyroid proteins are then iodinated. It is necessary to couple mono- and diiodotyrosine together before the synthesis of triiodothyronine (T_3) and thyroxine (T_4) is complete. Taurog, Tong, and Chaikoff (1950) demonstrated that the thyroid of chickens contained monoiodotyrosine. Both monoiodotyrosine and diiodotyrosine have been shown chromatographically to be present in the chick (Frey and Flock, 1958) and in the adult (Vlijm, 1958).

In the chick embryo, Trunnell and Wade (1955) reported that at 7.5 days of incubation only iodide appears after I^{131} injection; it is followed at 8.5 days by monoiodotyrosine, at 9.25 days by diiodotyrosine, and at 9.75 days by thyroxine. This sequence indicates that the mechanisms of synthesis come into play at various stages of embryonic development.

The composition of iodinated compounds varies with age in the fowl (see Table 68).

TSH probably stimulates the conversion of tyrosine to thyroxine, since in 24 hours one large dose of TSH depletes from 70 to 90 percent of the I^{131} taken up by the thyroid of day-old chicks that have been given thiouracil in order to block the formation of new hormones (Frey and Flock, 1958). Only a small portion of the radioiodine is in the form of thyroxine (see table); thus the tyrosines must convert to thyroxine and triiodothyronine for release. Evidently only thyroxine and triiodothyronine ever leave the gland, since tyrosines are never seen in the blood.

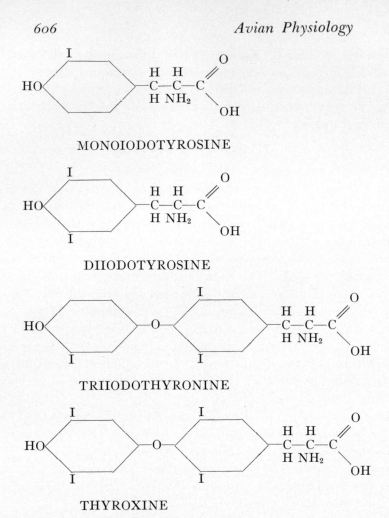

MONOIODOTYROSINE

DIIODOTYROSINE

TRIIODOTHYRONINE

THYROXINE

Figure 90. Iodinated compounds of the thyroid.

The Circulating Hormones

Early investigations indicated that the major thyroid hormone found in the blood plasma was thyroxine, and that triiodothyronine was present in only limited amounts. Both L-triiodothyronine and L-thyroxine have been isolated radiochromatographically from both plasma (Mellen and Wentworth, 1959a) and thyroid extracts (Shellabarger and Pitt-Rivers, 1958; Mellen and Wentworth, 1959a) from chickens. Recently it has been shown by

Table 68. Percentage of radioiodinated compounds in the thyroid 24 hours after injection of I[131]

Compound	Percent of compound in thyroid after 24 hrs.	
	Adult chicken (Vlijm, 1958)	Day-old chick (Frey & Flock, 1958)
Monoiodotyrosine	28	18
Diiodotyrosine	40	53
Thyroxine	20	5 to 18
Triiodothyronine	3	0.9
Iodide	7	5

The values given in this table do not necessarily represent the absolute amounts of iodinated compounds within the thyroid, but do indicate the rate of labeling and turnover rate of these compounds after injection of I[131].

Wentworth and Mellen (1961b) that both triidothyronine and thyroxine are found in the blood of chickens, turkeys, and ducks at the ratio of 60 percent thyroxine to 40 percent triiodothyronine.

The thyroid hormones are released from the thyroid as the amino acids thyroxine and triiodothyronine. Once in the blood they are again bound to protein. In man an alpha-globulin is considered an important carrier of thyroxine, whereas serum albumin plays a lesser role as a carrier (Robbins *et al.*, 1961). Electrophoretic studies of chicken and duck serum show no alpha-globulinlike, thyroxine-binding protein corresponding to that in mammals. Both thyroxine and triiodothyronine are bound to serum albumin, and the binding affinity of albumin for T_3 and T_4 is the same (Tata and Shellabarger, 1959). Farer, Robbins, Blumberg, and Rall (1962) found chickens, turkeys, and pigeons to have thyroxine-binding prealbumins as well as albumins but no thyroxine-binding globulins.

Binding of I[131]-labeled thyroxine to duck and fowl albumin is evidently poor compared to that in man since labeled thyroxine will bind rapidly with the proteins in human blood when they are mixed together with avian blood.

The biological half-lives of T_3 and T_4 are identical in birds, whereas T_3 has a much shorter half-life in mammals (Tata and Shellabarger, 1959). The rate of degradation of thyroid hormones depends partially on the general metabolic state of the animal. Cold, for example, calls for greater utilization, and leads to a shorter half-life of the thyroid hormones.

In the rat, triiodothyronine has been shown to be 3 to 7 times more potent than thyroxine in preventing goiter. Triiodothyronine is a potent thyroid hormone in chicks, but no more potent than thyroxine in preventing goiter (Shellabarger, 1955). Thyroxine is more potent than triiodothyronine as an antigoitrogenic substance in the chicken (Newcomer, 1957; Mellen and Wentworth, 1959b), and is apparently also more potent in reducing thyrotrophic hormone secretion. The last-named workers reported that the blocking doses for thyroid secretion were 0.0064 μ. mol./ 100 gm. body weight/day for L-triiodothyronine, and 0.0052 μ. mol./100 gm./day for L-thyroxine. L-thyroxine and L-triiodothyronine are equally potent in influencing oxygen consumption, heart rate, suffocation time, and feather length in thiouracil-treated chicks (Newcomer, 1957). The explanation of the difference in mammalian and avian response to these thyroidal hormones may be partly that in man the thyroxine-binding globulin has a four fold affinity for T_4 as compared to T_3, whereas in birds the protein-binding affinity is equal. Thus the rates of disappearance from blood of T_3 and T_4 are equal in birds, and the two hormones diffuse into the tissues at a similar rate (Shellabarger and Tata, 1961).

The L form of the circulating hormone is the physiologically active one. Reineke and Turner (1945a) reported that the D,L form of thyroxine possessed only half the physiological activity of L-thyroxine in rats and chickens by the antigoiter method, and in tadpoles and guinea pigs by metabolic rate method. Recent mammalian studies indicate that D-thyroxine might have some activity based on different criteria (see Turner and Premachandra, 1962).

GOITROGENIC (ANTITHYROID) COMPOUNDS

Compounds which when administered cause enlargement of the thyroid (goiter) and suppress thyroxine formation are termed goitrogens or antithyroid substances. Since hormone formation is suppressed, the pituitary becomes hyperactive and secretes abnormally high amounts of TSH, which lead to an enlarged thyroid. The action of these goitrogenic compounds may be through inhibition of thyroid hormone synthesis by interfering with iodide concentration within the thyroid, or they may inhibit iodination of thyroglobulin. A compound that produces the former goitrogenic action is thiocyanate, while thiourea and thiouracil are iodination-inhibiting compounds. It appears that in the chick, thiouracil produces a block in thyroxine synthesis between monoiodotyrosine (MIT) and diiodotyrosine (DIT), since the MIT/DIT ratio of the thyroid is greater at 48 hours after administration of thiouracil than at 6 hours, indicating accumulation of MIT (Kobayashi and Gorbman, 1960). A third kind of goitrogen, such as resorcinol, forms a complex with thyroglobulin. Interference with iodide concentration can be counteracted by feeding high levels of iodine; however, the action of thiourea and thiouracil cannot.

Thiourea, thiouracil, and more recently methimazole (1-methyl-2-mercaptoimidazole) have had wide usage in avian studies. Thiourea, because of its toxicity, is rarely used today. Feeding thiouracil at the 0.1 percent level to chicks for as short a period as 10 days will enlarge thyroids to 5 to 7 times normal size. Feeding for 10 weeks may enlarge the glands to 45 times the normal size (Astwood, Bissell, and Hughes, 1944). Methimazole at the level of 1.5 gms./pound of feed for 5 and 7 weeks to 10-day-old chicks increased thyroid weight by 3 and 4 times the normal weight respectively (Haynes and Glick, 1960). Feeding 80 to 120 mg. of methimazole per pound of ration from 1 day to 4 weeks of age caused an 18- to 25-fold increase in thyroid weight. The higher level of methimazole causes less thyroid hypertrophy with more hyperplasia, especially in the interfollicular regions, than does 0.075 percent thiouracil.

Large dosages of potassium iodide can act as a goitrogen in embryos, chicks, and hens (Wheeler and Hoffman, 1949, 1950).

Goitrogens and Embryo Development

The effects of antithyroid compounds on embryonic development include retardation of hatching, reduction in embryo size, lack of retraction of yolk sac, enlarged thyroids with hyperplasia and hypertrophy, and decreased limb growth.

When thiouracil is fed to laying hens, the chicks hatched from their eggs have enlarged thyroid glands (Andrews and Schnetzler, 1945). Thyroprotein given in the feed to layers has the same effect (Wheeler and Hoffman, 1948a, 1948b; McCartney and Shaffner, 1949), as does diiodotyrosine (Huston and Wheeler, 1961). The last-named workers propose that the goitrogenicity of thyroprotein may be due to one of its major components, diiodotyrosine, and that the liberation of iodide from the metabolism of diiodotyrosine indirectly leads to the goitrous thyroids through inhibiting the production of thyroxine. Iodine deficiency of chicken dams produces goiters in embryos from eggs laid by these hens. The thyroidal epithelium is hypertrophied, and the follicles lack colloid (Rogler, Parker, Andrews, and Carrick, 1959b).

Thyroid involution in developing chicks follows injection of thyroxine into fertile eggs (Booker and Sturkie, 1949). Hatching time is not influenced by thyroxine injection (Rogler, Parker, Andrews, and Carrick, 1959c). Thyroids of chicks hatched following injection of thiouracil into the embryonating egg are goitrous (Adams and Bull, 1949; Adams and Buss, 1952; Rogler, Parker, Andrews, and Carrick, 1959c).

THYROID AND METABOLIC RATE (MR)

Thyroid hormones play a major role in regulating oxidative metabolism of birds. Any pronounced alteration in thyroid function, i.e. hyperthyroidism or hypothyroidism, is reflected in an altered metabolic rate. A depression in metabolic rate following thyroidectomy occurs in geese (Lee and Lee, 1937), chickens (Winchester, 1939; Mellen and Wentworth, 1962), and pigeons (Marvin and Smith, 1943). Any physiological or environmental factor known to shift the metabolic rate of the bird may effect a change in the thyroid secretion rate (see Chapter 9).

Thiouracil, which renders an animal hypothyroidal, reduces the metabolic rate (Sulman and Perek, 1947; Romijn, 1950; McCartney and Shaffner, 1950; Mellen, 1958), whereas thyroprotein stimulates the metabolic rate (McCartney and Shaffner, 1950; Singh and Shaffner, 1950; Mellen, 1958) for as long as supplementation is maintained. Variations in the response of the metabolic rate to goitrogens and administration of thyroprotein are influenced by the length of the withdrawal of the drug prior to metabolic rate determinations. Thiouracil depresses MR for less than 24 hours after the drug is withdrawn, but withdrawal for a longer time results in MR values identical to control values (Mellen, 1958); thyroprotein stimulates MR for only a few hours after withdrawal, and as a result the bird is hypothyroid from the 13th to 38th hour. The short duration of thyroprotein stimulation is at variance with prolonged stimulation in the mammal following a single injection of thyroxine.

THYROXINE SECRETION RATE (TSR)

Much information about the role of the thyroid in physiology can be gathered from studies on hypo- or hyperthyroid conditions, thyroidectomy, hypophysectomy, and basal metabolic rate; but for accurate measurement of physiological changes within the normal range of thyroid function, more precise measures are necessary. A large step forward in the accurate determination of individual thyroid secretion rates came with the advent of radioisotope detection and the use of I^{131}, radioactive iodine. Individual determinations *in vivo* are now possible, whereas the goiter-prevention method requires sacrifice of the animal. In addition, tests of protein-bound iodine and protein-bound-iodine[131] have been used as a criterion of secretion rate. Each of these methods merits discussion.

Goiter-Prevention Method

The method of Dempsey and Astwood (1943) for rats was first applied to chickens by Mixner, Reineke, and Turner (1944). The method assumes that the dosage of injected exogenous thyroxine necessary to reduce TSH secretion by the pituitary of goitrogen-fed animals to that of control animals represents the normal secretion rate. Since the circulating hormone and TSH release by the pituitary are in "equilibrium," any feeding of a goitrogenic substance will be compensated for by a greater release of hypophysial thyrotrophin. Increased TSH causes the thyroid to enlarge, and injection of exogenous thyroxine will not reduce the release of TSH to that of control animals until it meets the metabolic needs of the body and is equivalent to the normal thyroxine secretion rate.

Several groups of birds must be used for the assay. One group is maintained on the basal ration throughout the test; a second large group receives the basal plus 0.1 percent thiouracil or another goitrogen of adequate dosage to prevent production of thyroxine. The level of 0.1 percent thiouracil is a surplus amount, and higher levels are unnecessary. Depending upon the precision desired, several subgroups receiving the basal diet plus thiouracil are injected with graded dosages of thyroxine. The assay duration is from 2 to 5 weeks, depending upon breed of chickens used. At the end of this period the thyroids are removed, trimmed clean of extraneous tissue, and weighed accurately. Relative thyroid weights, i.e. thyroid weights in milligrams per 100 grams of body weight, are used rather than absolute values. The values are then plotted. The level of thyroxine, injected daily, that gives thyroid weights equal to those of chicks on the basal ration is considered the secretion rate (see Figure 91). Individual TSR values cannot be measured by the goiter-prevention method; only group averages can be obtained. This being so, the statistical significance of differences cannot be evaluated unless duplicate assays are used, such as have been reported by Mellen and Wentworth (1960).

Mean thyroxine secretion rates obtained by this method are considerably lower than values obtained by use of I^{131} (see Table 69).

Radioiodine Assays

Since the advent of radioactive iodine a great deal of progress has been made, both in elucidating some of the steps involved in the synthesis of thyroid hormone by the thyroid and in describing the kinetics of iodine turnover by this gland. The thyroid normally has a very high affinity for iodide, maintaining a ratio of thyroid to plasma iodide of about 30:1. Following a single injection of I^{131}, this element is collected rapidly by the thyroid, reaching maximal concentrations in one to three days. The iodine combines with tyrosine contained within the thyroglobulin molecule of the thyroid colloid to form monoiodotyrosine and diiodotyrosine. These, in turn, undergo an oxidative coupling reaction to form the thyroactive compounds, triiodothyronine and thyroxine. Under the influence of TSH from the pituitary, these iodinated compounds

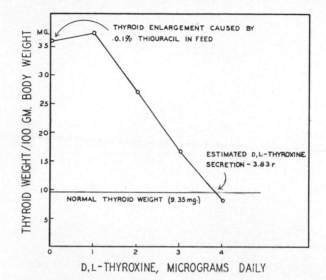

Figure 91. Method of plotting data to determine thyroxine secretion rate of the fowl.

Data are for 4-week-old White Leghorn cockerels. (From Schultze and Turner, *Mo. Agric. Exp. Sta. Res. Bull.* 392, 1945.)

are released from peptide combination in the thyroglobulin through the mediation of a proteolytic enzyme. Thus, the iodine released to the circulation is principally in the form of the thyroactive compounds, thyroxine and triiodothyronine.

Both the uptake and the output rate of thyroidal I[131] have been employed rather widely in animals and man as comparative indices of thyroid function. However, such parameters yield meaningful data over a very broad area of thyroid functions, such as would be encountered in distinguishing a hypo- or hyperthyroid individual from the normal. Both the uptake and the output rate of I[131] are influenced very markedly by the relative supply of die-

Table 69. Range of average thyroxine secretion rates as reported by various investigators

Reference	Exptl. bird	Ambient temp. (°F.)	Type of assay	Form of thyroxine	Aver. L-thyroxine secr. rates* (mcg./100 g./day)	
					Lowest	Highest
Schultze & Turner (1945)	Chick	82–90	Goiter-prevention	DL	0.72	1.38
Mixner & Upp (1947)	Chick	84–92	Goiter-prevention	DL	0.93	1.81
Kleinpeter & Mixner (1947)	Chick	84–96	Goiter-prevention	DL	1.04	1.18
Hoffman (1950)	Duckling	80	Goiter-prevention	DL		1.90
Boone *et al.* (1950)	Chick	80–88	Goiter-prevention	DL	0.74	0.81
Biellier & Turner (1950)	Duckling	62–96	Goiter-prevention	DL	1.28	1.70
Smyth & Fox (1951)	Turkey poult	?	Goiter-prevention	DL	1.31	1.49
Odell (1952)	Chick	?	Goiter-prevention	DL	1.30	1.40
Biellier & Turner (1955)	Turkey poult	77–84	Goiter-prevention	DL	0.76	1.33
Premachandra *et al.* (1958)	Chicken (adult)	?	Radioiodine	L	1.02	2.98
Mellen & Wentworth (1958)	Chicken (young)	65–70	Radioiodine	L	3.02	4.47
Mueller & Amezcua (1959)	Chicken (adult)	85	Radioiodine	L	2.29	2.59
Mueller & Amezcua (1959)	Chicken (adult)	55	Radioiodine	L		3.47
Grosvenor & Turner (1960)	Pigeon	77–79	Radioiodine	L		1.94

* Values originally reported in terms of DL-thyroxine have been halved for presentation here. According to Reineke and Turner (1945a), the L-isomer has twice the antigoitrogenic potency of the racemic mixture. (From Mellen & Wentworth, *Poultry Sci.,* 1960)

tary I^{127}. In an iodine deficiency these values are greatly increased. If an excess of I^{127} is present, the specific activity of the I^{131} is reduced to the point that its accumulation in the thyroid is very low. For these reasons, and perhaps others as yet undetermined, the uptake or output rate of simple I^{131} is not a sufficiently sensitive measure to differentiate the small differences in thyroid activity that are usually found in normal mammals and birds.

In the radioiodine assay of thyroid secretion rate the assumption is made that the level of exogenous thyroxine required to block completely the TSH output by the pituitary is the thyroid secretion rate. The basic procedure, designed for the determination of thyroid secretion rate in individual intact animals, was reported first by Henneman *et al.* (1952) for the sheep, and by Reineke and Singh (1955) for the rat. Carrier-free Na I^{131} is injected either subcutaneously, intraperitoneally, or intravenously into the animal. Thyroid radioactivity is determined at intervals with a scintillation counter, maintained at a fixed and repeatable geometry in apposition to the thyroid region. Body background counts are taken at similar geometry to estimate the nonthyroidal radioactivity, and these are subtracted from the thyroid count. After peak thyroid radioactivity has been reached, a base thyroid count is taken and a small dose of L-thyroxine is injected on 2 successive days, followed by another thyroid count. The thyroxine dose is then increased by a small increment, and counts are taken after 2 days' exposure to the increased dosage. Thyroxine dosage is increased progressively in this manner, with counts being taken on alternate days until the thyroidal output of radioactivity is substantially suppressed. The thyroxine dose that produces maximal inhibition of thyroid output can be determined by visual inspection of a plot of thyroid count vs. thyroxine dose (Figure 92) or, more effectively, by expressing each thyroid count as a percentage of the preceding count and then plotting these values against thyroxine dosage (Figure 93). By this method, 100 percent of the preceding count would indicate complete inhibition of thyroid output. This method has been applied to such diverse species as the mouse, mink, and goat with little modification (Reineke, 1959).

Lewis *et al.* (1955) reported that in cattle the I^{131} output slope

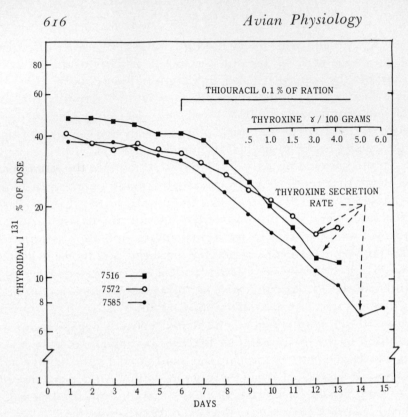

Figure 92. Visual method of plotting data to determine thyroxine secretion rate of the fowl (radioiodine method)

Arrows indicate the dosage of L-thyroxine that blocked the secretion of thyrotrophic hormone and, consequently, the release of radiothyroxine from the gland as shown by the measurement on the following day. (Redrawn from Pipes *et al., Poultry Sci.* 37:36, 1958.)

was too flat for effective application of this procedure. Therefore, after maximal accumulation of I[131] by the thyroid had occurred, these workers administered thiouracil twice daily to cause a faster output rate and then applied the thyroxine substitution procedure essentially as already described. The true goitrogens (thiouracil, propylthiouracil, methylthiouracil, methimazole) block the formation of iodinated compounds in the thyroid and thus prevent recycling of I[131] from the thyroid hormone that was previously released and metabolized; they also prevent the normal combination with nonradioactive I[127]. Though thyroxine synthesis is blocked, release of preformed thyroxine is not impeded. The result is a much faster rate of release because the output is from a smaller and constantly diminishing pool of thyroxine in the thyroid.

Pipes, Premachandra, and Turner (1958), and Mellen and Wentworth (1958), adapted the thyroid secretion rate procedure for use in chickens, and in most cases have employed a goitrogen to accelerate the I^{131} output rate. However, a few results have been reported without use of a goitrogen, and the values thus obtained are usually somewhat lower (Himeno and Turner, 1961; Tanabe and Komiyama, 1962).

In an alternative procedure, reported by Biellier and Turner (1957), the effect of graded thyroxine injections on the release of radioactivity from the thyroid, as determined by radioactivity counts on serial blood samples, was used as an endpoint. The procedure is laborious; thus, little further work has been reported on this method.

The literature on thyroid secretion rates is rather confusing, in part because of the different endpoints employed by the several laboratories working in this field. In the work with normal rats and sheep, cited earlier, thyroid secretion rate was taken as the daily thyroxine dose that would maintain the thyroid count at 100 percent of the previous count. In thiouracil-treated rats (Reineke and Singh, 1955), however, thyroxine suppressed output to only 92 percent of the preceding count, and therefore the thyroid secretion rate was read at this point. In work with chickens (Himeno and Turner, 1961) the endpoint was taken as at least 95 percent of previous reading. A higher TSR was recorded in tapazole-treated than in normal birds. Tanabe and Komiyama (1962) suggested as an endpoint for thyroid secretion rate the thyroxine dose that would return the thyroidal I^{131} output rate of goitrogen-treated birds merely to the output rate of normal birds not receiving a goitrogen. Although this computation yielded values that agreed rather closely with those obtained by the earlier goitrogen procedure, the physiologic basis for the computation is not clear, since such birds are still releasing labeled products from the thyroid at a rate equivalent to the normal one.

Most comparisons of normal and goitrogen-treated animals by

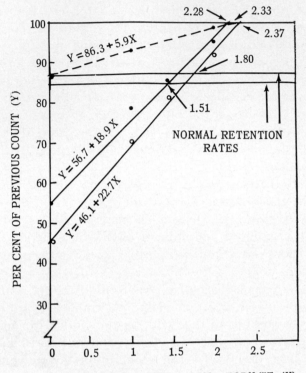

Figure 93. Plotting thyroid count as a percentage of the preceding count and then plotting these values against thyroxine dosage (radioiodine assay).

Estimation of group averages of thyroxine secretion rate from regression of average thyroidal I^{131} retention rate (Y) on thyroxine dose (X). ● — — — ● represents the average retention of the non-thiouracil-treated cockerels receiving thyroxine. ●————● represents the average retention of first 4 days of experiment with thiouracil-treated birds. o————o represents the average retention of all data with thiouracil-treated birds. Regression equations were solved for X with Y set equal to average normal retention rate of control birds without thiouracil or thyroxine for the thiouracil-treated groups, or to 100% for all groups. (Modified from Tanabe & Komiyama, *Endocrinol.* 70:142, 1962.)

the tracer method have shown a higher estimated thyroid secretion rate for those receiving a goitrogen. This may be, at least in part, because some goitrogenic drugs affect the peripheral metabolism of thyroxine and appear to increase the level of thyroxine needed to supply the normal metabolic requirement (Van Middlesworth *et al.*, 1959; Escobar and Escobar, 1961).

None of the methods thus far available has been shown to measure the absolute level of thyroid secretion rate. However, when conducted under suitably controlled conditions they all yield comparative values that provide a reliable index of thyroid function.

Mellen and Wentworth (1960), using RIR x WL chickens about 5 weeks old, injected I^{131} at zero hours; thiouracil feeding was started at 24 hours, and thyroxine (T_4) was first injected at 48 hours and again at 72 and 96 hours. Radioactivity was counted at the time of the first thyroxine injection, 48 hours, to indicate the level before there was any T_4 effect, and again at 120 hours or 24 hours following the last T_4 injection. In this procedure the investigators collected only group data; they compared the results of the radioiodine method with a simultaneous goiter-prevention assay, and found a significant difference in the TSR values (see Table 70).

Careful examination of the two procedures will readily reveal that they are not measuring exactly the same endpoint. Whereas with the goiter-prevention assay the assumption is made that the dosage of exogenous T_4 necessary to suppress the output of TSH

Table 70. "Mean" thyroxine secretion rates (µg./100 gm./day)
(From Mellen & Wentworth, *Poultry Sci.*, 1960)

	Goiter-prevention assay		Radioiodine assay	
	Female	Male	Female	Male
"Means"	1.35	1.40	1.95	2.29
Method "means"	1.37		2.12	

to that of control animals is the TSR value, the radioiodine assay assumes that TSH output is completely blocked. This in part accounts for some of the differences in TSR reported in the literature concerning the use of the two methods (personal communication, Reineke and Mellen). In addition, the application of a goitrogen in the procedure may interfere with T_4 utilization and add to the variation.

Protein-Bound Iodine

In this method the iodine-containing hormones, thyroxine and triiodothyronine, are precipitated with the serum proteins from the blood by tungstic acid or another suitable compound. The quantity of protein-bound iodine may be chemically analyzed (PBI), or if I^{131} was injected prior to the blood sampling, detection can be made by radioisotope (PBI[131]).

Using 4-week-old New Hampshire chicks of two lines differing in response to thiouracil, Bumgardner and Shaffner (1957) reported a mean value of 1.12 mcg. percent for protein-bound iodine, with no line differences. Mellen and Hardy (1957) could not alter PBI levels in 8- and 20-month-old chickens (1.13–1.22 mcg. percent) by either cold stress or thiouracil treatment, both known to change thyroid activity. These workers reported similar values for Pekin ducks ranging from 1.17 to 1.49 mcg. percent. These values are far below those for rats or man. The absence of a specific thyroxine-binding globulin in avian blood may contribute to this difference. The method is not sensitive enough to measure thyroid secretion rates in chickens since 40 mcg. of D,L-thyroxine are required to elicit a response in the presence of thiouracil.

PBI[131] determinations can be used to measure the level of the thyroid circulating hormone (Wentworth and Mellen, 1961a), whereas chemically determined PBI cannot (Mellen and Hardy, 1957; Bumgardner and Shaffner, 1957). The turkey (Biellier and Turner, 1957) and the duck (Wentworth, 1960) show differences in the ratio of PBI[131] to total plasma iodine. Determination of PBI[131], as is true of PBI, does not constitute a sensitive assay technique.

Effect of Season and Reproduction on TSR

Two principles are thought to influence thyroxine secretion rate: the inherited genetic potential for thyroxine secretion, and environmental variations. Booker and Sturkie (1950) studied the effect of rate of egg production on secretion rate. Pullets laying 2-egg sequences averaged 10.85 micrograms of D,L-thyroxine per day, whereas those laying 4-egg sequences produced 13.75 micrograms per day. Egg production for 13 days after I^{131} injection was correlated with the I^{131} secretion rate, but total egg production was not (Mueller and Amezcua, 1959). Individual variation is evident under similar environmental conditions, and is dependent upon inherited endocrine potentials. Reineke and Turner (1945b) showed that in young chicks (2 weeks of age) the thyroxine secretion rate in summer was one-half that in winter. A select line of high thyroxine-secreting chickens had mean secretion rates of 2.98 mcg./100 grams body weight in winter; in summer the rate was 1.24 mcg./100 grams body weight for these same birds (Stahl and Turner, 1961). This was a 58.3 percent decrease in hot weather.

Turner (1948b), who measured the thyroxine secretion rate of 2-year-old hens, observed that the secretion rate was greatest in the fall and winter and lowest during the warm months. Similar decreases in thyroid secretion with high environmental temperatures have been reported by others (Mueller and Amezcua, 1959; Huston, Edwards, and Williams, 1962). Thus, the maximum genetic-endocrine potential for thyroid secretion can be achieved only in cold environments. This fact may account for variations in response to the feeding of thyroprotein for stimulated growth (to be discussed later). Many of the reports showing growth gains were from areas of warm climate where the chicken was not operating at its full genetic-endocrine potential and was stimulated. Cooler climates give less consistent results.

Normally, temperatures change slowly from winter to spring; therefore the thyroxine secretion rate would be altered gradually. Sudden exposure to low temperatures in mammals alters the pituitary-thyroid feedback mechanism in a matter of hours (Bottari, 1957). Stahl, Pipes, and Turner (1961) demonstrated in New Hampshire chickens that only a slight alteration in thyroidal-I[131] release rate occurred within 10 days after a sudden exposure to cold. Maximum thyroxine secretion rate was reached, in most birds, 32 to 54 days after exposure, with several chickens showing increased secretion rate levels for 190 days.

Winchester (1940) has shown that the TSH content of the hen pituitary is higher in winter than in summer. At high environ-

Table 71. New Hampshire chickens selected for high and low thyroxine secretion rates (Stahl & Turner, *Poultry Sci.*, 1961)

Season	Strain	Sex	Thyroxine secretion rate (mcg./100 grams body weight)
Winter (Sept.–Apr.)	High	M	2.89
	"	F	3.08
	Low	M	1.01
	"	F	1.03
Summer (May–Sept.)	High	M	1.17
	"	F	1.30
	Low	M	0.54
	"	F	0.65

mental temperatures (105°F.) the thyroid response to TSH may be diminished (Heninger, Newcomer, and Thayer, 1960), demonstrating that the anterior pituitary must mediate the environmental influence on the thyroid. Acclimatization should be taken into account when measuring thyroid secretion rates.

Age may influence the seasonal response in thyroid function. In growing birds, from the age of 6 weeks to sexual maturity, the drop in thyroxine secretion rate in the summer was less than that in mature chickens (Stahl, Pipes, and Turner, 1961). Kobayashi and Gorbman (1960) reported a seasonal variation in the quantitative radioiodine thyroidal uptake of chicks (15-fold) greater than that due to TSH injection (7- or 8-fold).

Strain Differences in TSR

El-Ibiary and Shaffner (1950) selected two lines of New Hampshire chickens for three generations that differed markedly in their thyroid response to the administration of thiouracil. The two strains were propagated from breeders which showed the greatest and least enlargement of their thyroid glands after feeding with goitrogens. The first-generation progeny of selected high-response and low-response dams and sires yielded offspring with thyroids weighing 161.8 and 95.7 mg. respectively. Premachandra, Pipes, and Turner (1958) showed that the line with the greatest response to thyroid enlargement had a mean TSR of 1.01 ± 0.47 mcg. L-thyroxine/100 gm. body weight/day, whereas the line with the least enlargement caused by thiouracil had a mean TSR of 2.97 ± 1.43 mcg./100 gm. body weight/day. Selection for goitrogenic response does not mean selection for secretion rate or thyroid function.

Stahl *et al.* (1962) studied the heritability of TSR (radioiodine assay) of growing chicks, and reported that TSR could be rapidly changed by selection since the heritability estimates (from dam's components, 0.68; and intra-sire correlation, 0.59) were high. Smyth and Fox (1951), using the goiter-prevention method, showed that the progeny of a cross between two varieties of turkeys had a higher TSR than either parent, as follows:

	D,L-*Thyroxine, micrograms per 100 gm. body weight (males and females)*
Crossbred poults	2.98
Jersey Buff poults	2.76
Bronze poults	2.72

Slow- and rapid-growing strains of chickens exhibit differences in thyroid secretion rate during the periods of greatest growth (Glazener, Shaffner, and Jull, 1949).

Genetically determined slow- and rapid-feathering strains of Rhode Island Red chicks did not differ in TSR (Boone, Davidson, and Reineke, 1950); however, administration of thyroprotein to the slow-feathering group increased the rate of feathering.

Hale and Flipse (1958) could not show differences in thyroid activity related to the fighting ability of cocks. In interbreed contests the winning New Hampshire cocks and the losing Barred Plymouth Rock cocks had comparable thyroxine secretion rates.

Influence of Other Factors on TSR

In measurements of thyroidal I^{131} uptake by chicks, the dietary iodine of the chick or of its mother may alter thyroid function (Kobayashi and Gorbman, 1960).

Starvation lowers thyroid function, presumably through depressing the production of thyrotrophin. Restricting the feed intake also lowers TSR. Restricting the feed intake of the pigeon to 66 percent of the control intake depressed TSR by 27 percent; at restrictions of 67 percent and 80 percent the thyroid secretion rate was depressed by 37 percent and 54 percent, respectively (Premachandra and Turner, 1960).

The quantity of light received alters the thyroid activity of chicks (Kleinpeter and Mixner, 1947). Twenty-four hours of light increased the secretion rate over that at 12 hours of light. The quality of light had little or no effect on the thyroid. Pekin ducks placed in total darkness in autumn had decreased thyroid secretion based on lower values for PBI determinations (Tixier-Vidal and Assenmacher, 1961b).

Body weight was not correlated with TSR in pigeons but the biological half-life of thyroidal I^{131} was negatively correlated with body weight. (Grosvenor and Turner, 1960).

THYROID AND MOLT

Molting, a complex mechanism in birds, is known to be under the influence of several factors, one of which is the thyroid hormone. The feather papilla is stimulated by feeding or injection of thyroid material. The administration of high dosages of thyroxine or desiccated thyroid produces a molt within seven or eight days (Van der Meulen, 1939). The mallard duck molts after thyroidectomy (Höhn, 1949), whereas thyroidectomy in the domestic fowl prevents subsequent molting. During the normal molting period it is easier to induce molt by administering thyroxine than in other periods of the year (Van der Meulen, 1939). During the same molting period the metabolic rate increases (Perek and Sulman, 1945); but whether this increase is the result of increased TSH production by the pituitary followed by greater thyroxine secretion or the secondary effect of feather depletion, remains unsettled (see Chapter 9).

The feeding of thiouracil to laying hens retarded the molt but did not prevent it (Glazener and Jull, 1946b). Shaffner (1954, 1955) showed that progesterone stimulated the feather papilla to grow a new feather but that the number of wing primaries molted depended upon the progesterone level and thyroidal activity. Thiouracil lessens, whereas thyroprotein enhances the molt associated with progesterone injections (Harris and Shaffner, 1957). The idea that surges of thyroidal activity initiate the events characteristic of molt must be re-evaluated, upon the basis of the part played by progesterone (Juhn and Harris, 1955). Prolactin may also initiate molt, and may be the immediate stimulator of new feather growth following a disruption of ovarian activity (Juhn and Harris, 1958).

Further evidence that molt is not the consequence of changes in thyroidal functions has been presented by Tanabe, Himeno, and Nozaki (1957). These workers studied the rate of release of I^{131} and thyroidal uptake of I^{131} in yearling hens injected with 40 mg. of progesterone to induce molt. They concluded that there was no increase in the rate of relase of thyroid hormone in either the premolting or the molting period as compared to the laying period. There was also no difference in I^{131} thyroidal uptake as between molting and laying hens. Thus it would appear that natural molts are independent of increases in thyroid activity.

HYPOTHYROIDISM

Methods of Thyroidectomy

An important tool in endocrine research is a study of the physiological parameters following complete ablation of the gland under study. Thyroidectomy has been successfully performed on birds, but not without some difficulty. Its anatomical location and its proximity to the parathyroid glands in certain species (see Chapter 20) make removal of the thyroid without the parathyroids a difficult operation.

Procedures for thyroidectomy in the duck are described by Benoit and Aron (1934), in the goose by Lee and Lee (1937), in the chicken by Parkes and Selye (1937) and by Winchester (1939), and in the pigeon by Marvin and Smith (1943).

Destruction of the chick thyroid by the injection of large doses of radioactive iodine (I^{131}), called "radio-thyroid-ecrexis" or "radiothyroidectomy," has been described by Winchester, Comar and Davis (1949). The procedure involves the injection of 6 millicuries of radioactive iodine per 100 grams of body weight. This dosage of I^{131} is excessive and may cause destruction of tissues other than that of the thyroid, which is completely destroyed. Lower dosages (1.2 and 1.5 mc. I^{131} per 100 gms. of body weight) have been successfully used in parakeets and chickens (Schlumberger, 1958; Mellen and Wentworth, 1962) to destroy thyroids without causing extensive damage to other tissues. Whether all thyroid tissue is destroyed by radiothyroidectomy has been questioned by Mellen and Wentworth (1962), since subsequent injection with I^{131} yielded I^{131}-thyroxine and triiodothyronine.

Effects of Thyroidectomy and Hypothyroidism on Growth

That the thyroid is necessary for normal growth and development is evident in that growth is markedly retarded following thyroidectomy (Blivaiss and Domm, 1942; Blivaiss, 1947b; Winchester, Comar, and Davis, 1949; Winchester and Davis, 1952; Clegg, Ericson, and Hein, 1959). Thyroidectomy of female chicks at 10 days of age reduced growth rate to the extent that adult body size was reduced by 30 to 50 percent (Blivaiss, 1947b). Thyroidectomized hens in maturity appear dwarf like and obese, having excessive fat deposits in the neck, back, breast, and viscera. The long bones of the body are shortened, as is the skeleton generally.

Radiothyroidectomized chickens show growth rates comparable to birds that have undergone surgical ablation of the thyroid (Winchester and Davis, 1952). The growth rate of radiothyroidectomized chicks could be stimulated to 91 to 99 percent of control body weights by replacement therapy using either 2 or 4 micrograms of D,L-thyroxine daily per 100 grams of body weight. Clegg, Ericson, and Hein (1959) were able to accelerate growth by using 2 mcg. of D,L-thyroxine/100 grams of body weight/day following

Table 72. Body weight in grams of (1) control chickens; (2) radiothyroid-ectomized chickens receiving thyroxine injections; and (3) radiothyroid-ectomized chickens (From Clegg *et al. Poultry Sci.*, 1959)

Group	Age of chickens in weeks				
	0	2	4	6	8
(1)	40	109 ± 14	296 ± 31	637 ± 56	926 ± 59
(2)	40	90 ± 6	193 ± 36	400 ± 93	505 ± 138
(3)	40	79 ± 9	143 ± 18	226 ± 40	280 ± 47

radioiodine destruction of the thyroid, but could not reach near-normal growth (Table 72).

According to the current theory, the thyroid hormone's stimulus to growth consists either of a direct action on enzymes, or of an interaction with metal ions, or of an effect on the permeability of membranes or on the release of somatotrophic hormone.

Considerable interest has been shown in the use of goitrogens, such as thiouracil and methimazole, to increase growth or improve carcass quality through increased deposition of fat. Depressed thyroid activity is reflected in a reduced metabolic rate, which in turn could produce a gain in weight.

Conflicting results on growth have been observed after the feeding of thiouracil. Glazener and Jull (1946a), using the chicken, and Mountney *et al.* (1957), using the turkey, have reported decreases in growth rate. Hebert and Brunson (1957) fed 0.2 percent thiouracil to chickens from the ages of 5 to 9 weeks, and noted a decrease in feed consumption and gains in body weight as a result; the differences, however, were not statistically significant. Combining diethylstilbestrol with thiouracil improves weight gains (Andrews and Bohren, 1947). The effect of thiouracil on carcass quality and fat deposition is clearly established. Feeding thiouracil to broilers increases fat deposition and market quality (Kempster and Turner, 1945; Andrews and Schnetzler, 1946; Andrews and Bohren, 1947; Detwiler, Andrews, and Bohren, 1950; Hebert and Brunson, 1957); however, the protein, moisture, and ash content of the carcass is reduced (Hebert and Brunson, 1957).

Methimazole, when fed at levels above 0.001 percent of the ration, depresses growth (Wilson and MacLaury, 1961). Sell and Balloun (1960) fed 20 mg. of methimazole to cockerels from 6 to 10 weeks of age; they reported decreased weight gains and no effect on carcass. Diethylstilbestrol combined with methimazole did not depress growth in chickens, but this combination did improve carcass finish and growth in turkey broilers (Miner, Marsden, and Denton, 1959).

Effect on Reproduction

Hypothyroidism and its effect on egg production have been studied extensively. Winchester (1939), and Taylor and Burmester (1940), thyroidectomized pullets at or near the age of sexual maturity. Egg production was sustained at 10 to 29 percent of that of the normal controls. Blivaiss (1947b) thyroidectomized female chicks and observed the course of their reproductive development. The female reproductive organs remained juvenile up to 2 years of age; comb and wattle size was markedly decreased, but could be restored by administration of exogenous thyroxine. Radiothyroidectomized New Hampshire chicks do not produce eggs at the normal age of sexual maturity. Egg production can be restored to normal or even above normal levels by injections of 4 to 32 mcg. of D,L-thyroxine/100 gm. of body weight daily.

Thyroidectomy decreased egg weight and shell thickness (Taylor and Burmester, 1940).

Thiouracil fed to laying hens at 0.3 percent of the ration reduces egg production and fertility. Berg and Bearse (1951) reported that 0.1 percent thiouracil fed to hens decreased egg production and egg weight but had no effect on the shell. Feeding 0.1 percent thiouracil to ducks at various ages up to 12 weeks of age (3 week periods of feeding) depressed ovarian weight.

Thyroidectomy of White Leghorn cockerels (Benoit and Aron, 1934) reduced testes size by 80 to 90 percent, respectively, 11 and 20 days after the operation. Similarly, the drake showed a reduction in testis size (Benoit, 1936) and an even greater inhibition of penis development (Benoit, 1937). Spermatogenesis is arrested following thyroidectomy (Greenwood and Chu, 1939; Payne, 1944b; Blivaiss and Domm, 1942), and does not proceed beyond the secondary spermatocyte stage up to 22 months of age (Blivaiss, 1947a). Chicks thyroidectomized at 4 to 20 days of age have combs 62 to 68 percent below control size at 8 months of age (Blivaiss and Domm, 1942).

In the male, dosage, duration of treatment, and age influence the response of the gonads to thiouracil (Andrews and Schnetzler, 1946; Schultze and Turner, 1945; Kumaran and Turner, 1949). The latter workers fed thiouracil at different levels from one day to 16 weeks of age and reported a slight depression of testis size up to 8 weeks of age; but at 14 weeks of age the testis size of the experimental group was 10 times that of the control group. The Leydig cells did not develop, as reflected by the small size of the comb. Feeding 0.1 percent thiouracil to ducks was reported to increase the testis weight (Biellier and Turner, 1950). Even though testis and comb weights and the size of seminiferous tubules were all decreased by thiouracil, Shaffner and Andrews (1948) found no decrease in sperm concentration or semen volume; however, fertilizing capacity was reduced. The feeding of 0.02 percent and 0.04 percent thyroprotein to cocks restored the semen volume that had been slightly depressed by thiouracil feeding (Wilwerth, Martínez-Campos, and Reineke, 1954). Excessive thyroprotein doses depressed spermatogenesis in normal birds.

Effect on Feathers

Following thyroidectomy the feathers of both the male and female become fringed and elongated with a loss of barbules (see Figure 94), an effect that is sometimes described as "lacy." This change of structure occurs in chickens, pigeons, and ducks. Thyroidectomy retards feather growth. The feathers of Brown Leghorns made hypothyroid by thyroidectomy or thiouracil show a loss of the black, brown, and yellow melanins, which are replaced by a deposition of light reddish-brown pigment (Juhn, 1946; Blivaiss, 1947b). Injection of thyroxine restores the feathers to normal (Chu, 1940; Emmens and Parkes, 1940; Blivaiss, 1941).

Figure 94. Saddle feathers (the two at left) and wing coverts (the two at right) of Brown Leghorn females.
The first and third are those of a normal hen, the second and fourth of a thyroidectomized hen. (From Blivaiss, *J. Exp. Zool.,* 1947.)

Effect on Blood Constituents

Destruction of the thyroid by I[131] produces lipemic blood, high in cholesterol, phosphorus, or phosphorus-containing lipids, and an increase in alpha and beta globulins (Clegg, Ericson, and Hein, 1959). Thyroxine injections will prevent these changes but will not correct the lowered protein (see also Chapter 2). Similar increases in fatty acids, plasma cholesterol, and phospholipids have been observed in the duck (Benoit and Bogdanovitch, 1937). Thiouracil fed to turkeys also increased the plasma lipids (Reineke, Davidson, Wolterink, and Barrett, 1946).

HYPERTHYROIDISM

The possibility that slow-growing birds and poor egg-layers might respond favorably when a mild state of hyperthyroidism was induced has been tested by many investigators, who added thyroid substances to the diet of birds. The studies were stimulated by the synthesis (Reineke, Williamson and Turner, 1943) of iodinated casein (thyroprotein), which has a 1 percent thyroxine content and is relatively inexpensive.

The early literature on thyroprotein dosages employed in avian and mammalian experiments is confusing because of the variable thyroxine content reported for these preparations. Early products were reported by Reineke *et al.* (1945) to contain about 3 percent thyroxine as determined by a procedure involving hydrolysis and extraction with N-butanol. Subsequent investigation (Reineke, 1954) showed that the N-butanol extraction procedures yielded erroneously high values owing to the inclusion of thyroxinelike products in this fraction. The true thyroxine content of preparations now available, determined by a highly specific isotope dilution procedure, is about 1 percent. Thyroxine occurs in thyroprotein as the physiologically active L-form (Reineke and Turner, 1943). In addition to L-thyroxine, thyroprotein contains an unknown but limited quantity of L-triiodothyronine (Reineke and Mellen, personal communication).

Hyperthyroidism can also be produced by administering pituitary extract, thyroid-stimulating hormone, raw or desiccated thyroid, and T_4 or T_3 hormones. Dosage, season of the year, temperature, and inheritance all play an important role in evaluating present experimental results.

Complete reviews of hyperthyroidism and its effect on birds are given by Biellier and Turner (1957), and by Turner (1959).

Effect on Growth

The level of thyroprotein administered is most important, since the optimum level may stimulate growth whereas a level above or below optimum may have no effect or may retard growth.

Iodinated casein (200 mg. per pound of feed) does not stimulate growth in pheasants up to 4 weeks of age, but does enhance feather growth (Scott, Holm, and Reynolds, 1954). Iodinated casein improves growth in ducks. White Pekin ducks fed a basal ration supplemented with low levels of iodinated casein, 50 to 150 grams per ton of feed, showed increased growth, improved feathering, and decreased carcass fat when compared to controls (Scott, Baker, and Dougherty, 1959).

Slight improvement in growth was observed in Rhode Island Red chickens receiving levels of 0.025 to 0.2 percent thyroprotein (Parker, 1943). White Plymouth Rocks fed less than 0.1 percent thyroprotein (Irwin, Reineke, and Turner, 1943) showed an improvement in growth up to 6 weeks of age but not at 12 weeks. No growth improvement resulted from the feeding of thyroprotein in experiments conducted by Boone, Davidson, and Reineke (1950), by Ackerson, Borchers, Temper, and Mussehl (1950), or by Hebert and Brunson (1957). Depressed growth has also been observed as a result of feeding thyroprotein (Turner, Irwin, and Reineke, 1944; Glazener, Shaffner, and Jull, 1949; Oloufa, 1955).

Response to thyroprotein may be influenced by genetic make-up of the strain studied, since a rapid-growing strain of New Hampshire chickens was depressed in growth rate whereas a slow-growing New Hampshire and a rapid-growing Barred Plymouth Rock strain showed an improved growth rate after being fed thyroprotein (Glazener, Shaffner, and Jull, 1949). Premachandra, Pipes, and Turner (1959) reported that progeny from high x high thyroxine secretion rate lines had greater body weights at 20 weeks of age than progeny from low x low TSR lines.

Effect on Reproduction

Since laying declines during the summer months and coincides with the decline in thyroid secretion rate during the warm weather, it has been presumed that the addition of low levels of thyroprotein might stimulate egg production. Turner, Irwin, and Reineke (1945) demonstrated that 10 grams of thyroprotein per 100 pounds of feed was about the optimum dosage to maintain egg production in yearling White Leghorn hens. Twenty grams per 100 pounds of feed was excessive, and caused loss of weight as well as a higher mortality than the lower level. Only 40 percent egg production was attained at the 10-gram level, which was considered optimum and the increase occurred during the hot weather. Even this level of production is below expected rates.

Using Egyptian hens, Oloufa (1953) reported a decrease in egg production with 10 grams of thyroprotein per 100 pounds of feed. These results were obtained during the summer months, and agree with those of Hutt and Gowe (1948), of Godfrey (1949), and of Berg and Bearse (1951). Dropping the level of thyroprotein to 5 grams per 100 pounds of feed stimulated summer egg production (Oloufa, 1954).

Egg weight has shown varied responses to the administration of thyroprotein. Decreased egg weight was observed by Oloufa (1953), but not by Berg and Bearse (1951), among others. Eggshell deposition improved with the feeding of thyroprotein (see Gabuten and Shaffner, 1954).

There is considerable disagreement regarding the influence of hyperthyroidism on testicular development and spermatogenesis in the male fowl. It is generally agreed that feeding moderate to heavy dosages of thyroidal material to chickens under 12 weeks of age depresses the development of testes, and that this effect may be reversed after that age (see review by Wilwerth, Martínez-Campos, and Reineke, 1954). Feeding 0.04 percent thyroprotein to Rhode Island Red cocks increased the concentration of sperm but did not influence semen volume (Wilwerth *et al.*, 1954), and higher dosages were detrimental.

Effect on Blood Constituents

Thyroxine, when injected simultaneously with estrogen, inhibits some of the usual responses to estrogen. Thyroxine given at 1 mg./day inhibits the rise in hemoglobin and iron produced by estrogen (Campbell, 1960). Serum calcium and phosphorus do not rise when thyroxine is administered with estrogen. Total serum protein increases with the feeding of estrogen, but is inhibited by thyroxine (Sturkie, 1951; Campbell, 1960; see also chapter 2).

Thyroxine alone causes a lowering of serum protein (Sturkie, 1951). Thyroxine increases, and thiouracil decreases, the blood level of vitamin C (Thornton and Deeb, 1961).

ACKNOWLEDGMENT

The author wishes to acknowledge his gratitude to Dr. E. Paul Reineke for his consultation on many technical points, and to Dr. William J. Mellen for his critical review of the manuscript and his many suggestions.

REFERENCES

Ackerson, C. W., R. L. Borchers, J. E. Temper, and F. E. Mussehl
1950 The utilization of food elements of growing chicks. Poultry Sci. 29:640.

Adams, A. E. 1946 Variations in the potency of thyrotrophic hormone of the pituitary in animals. Quart. Rev. Biol. 21:1.

Adams, A. E., and E. A. Beeman 1942 The reaction of the chick thyroid to frog and mouse anterior pituitaries. Endocrinol. 31:128.

Adams, A. E., and A. R. Bull 1949 The effects of anti-thyroid drugs on chick embryos. Anat. Rec. 104:421.

Adams, A. E., and J. M. Buss 1952 The effect of a single injection of an anti-thyroid drug on hyperplasia in the thyroid of the chick embryo. Endocrinol. 50:234.

Andrews, F. N., and B. B. Bohren 1947 Influence of thiouracil and stilbestrol on growth, fattening and feed efficiency in broilers. Poultry Sci. 26:447.

Andrews, F. N., and E. E. Schnetzler 1945 The effect of feeding thiouracil to hens upon the thyroid gland of chicks. Endocrinol. 37:382.

Andrews, F. N., and E. E. Schnetzler 1946 Influence of thiouracil on growth and fattening in broilers. Poultry Sci. 25:124.

Astwood, E. B., A. Bissell, and A. M. Hughes 1944 Inhibition of the endocrine function of the chick thyroid. Fed. Proc. 3:2.

Bates, R. W., and J. Cornfield 1957 An improved assay method for thyrotrophin using depletion of I^{131} from the thyroid of day-old chicks. Endocrinol. 60:225.

Benoit, J. 1936 Rôle de la thyroïde dans la gonado-stimulation par la lumière artificielle chez le canard domestique. Comp. Rend. Soc. Biol. 123:243.

Benoit, J. 1937 Thyroïde et croissance du pénis chez le canard domestique. Comp. Rend. Soc. Biol. 125:461.

Benoit, J. 1950 Traité de Zoologie, edited by P. P. Grassé. Tome XV: Oiseaux, p. 290. Masson & Co., Paris.

Benoit, J., and M. Aron 1934 Sur le conditionnement hormonique du développement testiculaire, chez les oiseaux, résultats de la thyroidectomie. Comp. Rend. Soc. Biol. 116:221.

Benoit, J., and S. B. Bogdanovitch 1937 Sur la teneur du sang en acides gras, phosphore lipidique, et cholesterol chez le canard domestique, après l'injection d'extraits préhypophysaires et après thyroïdectomie. Comp. Rend. Soc. Biol. 125:891.

Berg, L. R., and G. E. Bearse 1951 Effect of iodinated casein and thiouracil on the performance of laying birds. Poultry Sci. 30:21.

Biellier, H. V., and C. W. Turner 1950 The thyroxine secretion rate of growing White Pekin ducks. Poultry Sci. 29:248.

Biellier, H. V., and C. W. Turner   1955   The thyroxine secretion rate of growing turkey poults. Poultry Sci. 34:1158.

Biellier, H. V., and C. W. Turner   1957   The thyroid hormone secretion rate of domestic fowls as determined by radio-iodine techniques. Mo. Agr. Exp. Sta. Bull. 622.

Blivaiss, B. B.   1941   Response of comb and plumage in thyroid-ectomized Brown Leghorn hens to hormone administration. Am. J. Anat. 89:381.

Blivaiss, B. B.   1947a   Interrelation of thyroid and gonad in the development of plumage and other sex characters in Brown Leghorn roosters. Physiol. Zool. 20:67.

Blivaiss, B. B.   1947b   Development of secondary sexual characters in the thyroidectomized Brown Leghorn hen. J. Exp. Zool. 104:267.

Blivaiss, B. B., and L. V. Domm   1942   Relation of thyroid gland to plumage pattern and gonad function in the Brown Leghorn male. Anat. Rec. 84:529.

Booker, E. E., and P. D. Sturkie   1949   The effect of thyroxine and iodinated casein on the development of the chick thyroid. Poultry Sci. 28:147.

Booker, E. E., and P. D. Sturkie   1950   Relation of rate of thyroxine secretion to rate of egg production in the domestic fowl. Poultry Sci. 29:240.

Boone, M. A., J. A. Davidson, and E. P. Reineke   1950   Thyroid studies in fast and slow-feathering Rhode Island Red chicks. Poultry Sci. 29:195.

Bottari, P. M.   1957   The concentration of thyrotrophic hormone in the blood of the rabbit under different environmental conditions: Ciba Colloq. Endocrinol. 11:52.

Breneman, W. R.   1954   The growth of thyroids and adrenals in the chick. Endocrinol. 55:54.

Brown, J. R.   1959   The measurement of thyroid-stimulating hormone (TSH) in body fluids: A critical review. Acta Endocrinol. 32:289.

Brown, L. T., and K. M. Knigge   1958   Cytology of the pars distalis in the pituitary gland of the chicken. Anat. Rec. 130:395.

Bumgardner, H. L., and C. S. Shaffner   1957   Protein-bound iodine levels of the chick. Poultry Sci. 36:207.

Burger, R. E., F. W. Lorenz, and M. T. Clegg   1962   The effect of estrogen on the pituitary-thyroid axis in the immature domestic fowl. Poultry Sci. 41:1703.

Campbell, E. A. 1960 Changes in plasma iron, haemoglobin and plasma proteins in mature pullets, resulting from simultaneous administration of (A) oestrogen and thyroxine, (B) oestrogen and sulphamethazine. Poultry Sci. 39:140.

Chu, J. P. 1940 The endocrine system and plumage types. III: Further experiments on the relation between the thyroid gland and plumage patterns in domestic fowls and ducks. J. Genetics 39:493.

Clegg, R. E., A. T. Ericson, and R. E. Hein 1959 Distribution of phosphorus in the electrophoretic components of the blood serum of radio-thyroid-ecrecticized chickens. Poultry Sci. 38:77.

Cruickshank, E. M. 1929 The iodine content of the thyroid and ovary of the fowl during growth, laying and molting periods. Biochem. J. 23:1044.

D'Angelo, S. A., and A. S. Gordon 1950 The simultaneous detection of thyroid and thyrotrophic hormones in vertebrae sera. Endocrinol. 46:39.

Dempsey, E. W., and E. P. Astwood 1943 Determination of the rate of thyroid hormone secretion at various environmental temperatures. Endocrinol. 32:509.

Detwiler, R. W., F. N. Andrews, and B. B. Bohren 1950 The influence of thiouracil and stilbestrol on broiler quality. Poultry Sci. 29:513.

Draper, H. H., and J. A. Firth 1957 The regression of thyroid weight on body weight in the growing chick and the influence of penicillin. Poultry Sci. 36:42.

Dvoskin, S. 1947 The spontaneous formation of intracellular colloid droplets in surviving chick thyroid tissue. Endocrinol. 41:403.

Elfman, H. 1958 Origin of thyroidectomy cells. Anat. Rec. 131:119.

El-Ibiary, H. M., and C. S. Shaffner 1950 Genetic responses to induced goiter in chickens. J. Heredity 41:246.

Emmens, C. W., and A. S. Parkes 1940 The endocrine system and plumage types. II: The effects of thyroxine injections to normal, caponized and thyroidectomized caponized birds. J. Genetics 39:485.

Escobar del Rey, F., and G. Morreale de Escobar 1961 The effect of propylthiouracil, methylthiouracil and thiouracil on peripheral metabolism of 1-thyroxine in thyroidectomized, 1-thyroxine maintained rats. Endocrinol. 69:456.

Farer, L. S., J. Robbins, B. S. Blumberg, and J. E. Rall 1962 Thyroxine-serum protein complexes in various animals. Endocrinol. 70:686.

Frey, H., and E. V. Flock 1958 The production of thyroid hormone in the day-old chick, with notes on the effect of thyrotrophin on the chick thyroid. Acta Endocrinol. 29:550.

Gabuten, A. R., and C. S. Shaffner 1954 A study of the physiological mechanisms affecting specific gravity of chicken eggs. Poultry Sci. 33:47.

Galpin, N. 1938 Factors affecting the hatching weight of Brown Leghorn chickens. Proc. Roy. Soc. Edinburgh 58:98.

Glazener, E. W., and M. A. Jull 1946a Effects of thiouracil, desiccated thyroid, and stilbestrol derivatives on various glands, body weight, and dressing appearance in the chicken. Poultry Sci. 25:236.

Glazener, E. W., and M. A. Jull 1946b Effect of thiouracil on naturally occurring molt in the hen. Poultry Sci. 25:533.

Glazener, E. W., C. S. Shaffner, and M. A. Jull 1949 Thyroid activity as related to strain differences on growing chickens. Poultry Sci. 28:834.

Godfrey, G. F. 1949 The effect of feeding thyroprotein on egg shell quality and hatchability. Poultry Sci. 28:867.

Greenspan, F. S., J. P. Kriss, L. E. Moses, and W. Lew 1956 An improved bioassay method for thyrotrophic hormone using thyroid uptake of radiophosphorus. Endocrinol. 58:767.

Greenspan, F. S., and W. Lew 1959 Limitations of the chick radiophosphorus uptake assay and the chick radioiodine depletion assay for thyrotropic hormone when applied to blood and urine. Endocrinol. 64:160.

Greenwood, A. W., and J. C. Chu 1939 On the relation between thyroid and sex gland functioning in the Brown Leghorn fowl. Quart. J. Exp. Physiol. 29:111.

Grosvenor, C. E., and C. W. Turner 1960 Measurement of thyroid secretion rate of individual pigeons. Am. J. Physiol. 198:1.

Hale, E. B., and R. J. Flipse 1958 Thyroid activity as measured with radioactive iodine and fighting behavior in cocks. Poultry Sci. 37:187.

Hansborough, A. L., and M. Khan 1951 The initial function of the chick thyroid gland with the use of radio-iodine (I^{131}). J. Exp. Zool. 116:447.

Harris, P. C., and C. S. Shaffner 1957 Effect of season and thyroidal activity on the molt response to progesterone in chickens. Poultry Sci. 36:1186.

Haynes, R., and B. Glick 1960 The effect of methimazole on the white blood cells, bursa Fabricius, thyroid gland and body weight of young chickens. Poultry Sci. 39:1495.

Hebert, B. A., and C. C. Brunson 1957 The effects of diethylstilbestrol, testosterone, thiouracil, and thyroprotein on the chemical composition of broiler carcasses. Poultry Sci. 36:898.

Heninger, R. W., W. S. Newcomer, and R. H. Thayer 1960 The effect of elevated ambient temperatures on the thyroxine secretion rate of chickens. Poultry Sci. 39:1332.

Henneman, H. A., S. A. Griffin, and E. P. Reineke 1952 A determination of thyroid secretion rate in intact individual sheep. J. Animal Sci. 11:794.

Himeno, K., and C. W. Turner 1961 Influence of goitrogen (tapazole) in feed on thyroid secretion rate of cockerels. Proc. Soc. Exp. Biol. & Med. 108:627.

Höhn, E. 1949 Seasonal changes in the thyroid gland and effects of thyroidectomy in the mallard in relation to molt. Am. J. Physiol. 158:337.

Hoffman, E. 1950 Thyroxine secretion rate and growth in the White Pekin duck. Poultry Sci. 29:109.

Huston, T. M., H. M. Edwards, and J. J. Williams 1962 The effects of high environmental temperature on thyroid secretion rate of domestic fowl. Poultry Sci. 41:640.

Huston, T. M., and R. S. Wheeler 1961 Anti-thyroidal influence of diiodotyrosine. Poultry Sci. 40:440.

Hutt, F. B., and R. S. Gowe 1948 On the supposed effect of iodocasein upon egg production. Poulty Sci. 27:286.

Irwin, M. R., E. P. Reineke, and C. W. Turner 1943 Effect of feeding thyroactive iodocasein on growth, feathering, and weights of glands of young chicks. Poultry Sci. 22:374.

Juhn, M. 1946 Effect of thiouracil on the juvenile plumages of Brown Leghorn fowl. Endocrinol. 39:14.

Juhn, M., and P. C. Harris 1955 Local effects on the feather papilla of thyroxine and of progesterone. Proc. Soc. Exp. Biol. & Med. 90:202.

Juhn, M., and P. C. Harris 1958 Molt of capon feathering with prolactin. Proc. Soc. Exper. Biol. & Med. 98:669.

Keating, F. R., Jr., R. W. Rawson, W. Peacock, and R. D. Evans 1945

The collection and loss of radioactive iodine compared with the anatomic changes induced in the thyroid of the chick by the injection of thyrotrophic hormone. Endocrinol. 36:137.

Kempster, H. L. and C. W. Turner 1945 The effect of feeding thiouracil on the fleshing of New Hampshire broilers. Poultry Sci. 24:94.

Kleinpeter, M. E., and J. P. Mixner 1947 The effect of the quantity and quality of light on the thyroid activity of the baby chick. Poultry Sci. 26:494.

Kneeling, A. D., C. H. Hill, H. W. Garren, and J. W. Kelley 1955 Effect of chlortetracycline and fish meal on the growth and thyroids of chickens. Poultry Sci. 34:1453.

Kobayashi, H. 1955 Thyrotrophin content of the pituitary body of canaries receiving implants of sex steroids. Ann. Zool. Jap. 27:138.

Kobayashi, H., and A. Gorbman 1960 Radioiodine utilization in the chick. Endocrinol. 66:795.

Kraicziczek, M. 1956 Histogenese und Funktionszustand der embryonalen Hühnerthyreoiden. Z. Zellforschung Mikr. Anat. 43:421.

Kumaran, J. D. S., and C. W. Turner 1949 The endocrinology of spermatogenesis in birds. III: Effect of hypo- and hyperthyroidism. Poultry Sci. 28:653.

Larson, R. A., F. R. Keating, Jr., W. Peacock, and R. W. Rawson 1945 A comparison of the effects of thiouracil and of injected thyrotrophic hormone on the collection of radioactive iodine and the anatomic changes induced in the thyroid of the chick. Endocrinol. 36:149.

Latimer, H. R. 1924 Postnatal growth of the body, systems, and organs of the Single-Comb White Leghorn. J. Agr. Res. 29:363.

Lee, M., and R. C. Lee 1937 Effect of thyroidectomy and thyroid feeding in geese on the basal metabolism at different temperatures. Endocrinol. 21:790.

Lewis, R. C., E. P. Reineke, and J. R. Lodge 1955 A technique for estimating the thyroxine secretion rate of dairy cattle. J. Animal Sci. 14:1250.

Libby, D. A., and J. Meites 1954 Negative effects of antibiotics on thyroid gland. Science 120:354.

Ma, R. C-S. 1963 The feedback mechanism of thyroid hormone in hypophysectomized cockerels with adenohypophyseal autotransplants. Poultry Sci. 42:240.

McCartney, M. G., and C. S. Shaffner 1949 Chick thyroid size and incubation period as influenced by thyroxine, thiouracil and thyroprotein. Poultry Sci. 28:223.

McCartney, M. G., and C. S. Shaffner 1950 The influence of altered metabolism upon fertility and hatchability in the female fowl. Poultry Sci. 29:67.

Maghrabi, M. H., and C. W. Turner 1953 Nutritional requirements in hyperthyroidism of growing chicks. Mo. Agr. Exp. Sta. Res. Bul. 523.

March, B. E., and J. Biely 1957 The effect of dietary fat level on thyroid activity in the growing chick. Poultry Sci. 36:1270.

Martindale, F. M. 1941 Initiation and early development of thyrotrophic function in the incubating chick. Anat. Rec. 79:373.

Marvin, H. N., and G. C. Smith 1943 Technique for thyroidectomy in the pigeon and early effect of thyroid removal on heat production. Endocrinol. 32:87.

Mellen, W. J. 1958 Duration of effect of thyroxine and thiouracil in young chickens. Poultry Sci. 37:672.

Mellen, W. J., and L. B. Hardy 1957 Blood protein-bound iodine in the fowl. Endocrinol. 60:547.

Mellen, W. J., F. W. Hill, and H. H. Dukes 1954 Studies of the energy requirements of chickens. 2: Effect of dietary energy level on the basal metabolism of growing chickens. Poultry Sci. 33:791.

Mellen, W. J., and E. F. Waller 1954 Antibiotics and thyroid size in growing chickens. Poultry Sci. 33:1036.

Mellen, W. J., and B. C. Wentworth 1958 Studies with thyroxine and triiodothyronine in chickens. Poultry Sci. 37:1226.

Mellen, W. J., and B. C. Wentworth 1959a Thyroid studies in the domestic fowl utilizing radioiodine. U. S. Atomic Energy Commission Pub. TID-7578:77.

Mellen, W. J., and B. C. Wentworth 1959b Thyroxine vs. triiodothyronine in the fowl. Poultry Sci. 38:228.

Mellen, W. J., and B. C. Wentworth 1960 Comparison of methods for estimating thyroid secretion rate in chickens. Poultry Sci. 39:678.

Mellen, W. J., and B. C. Wentworth 1962 Observations on radiothyroidectomized chickens. Poultry Sci. 41:134.

Menge, H., and M. H. Conner 1955 Effect of chlortetracycline on chick thyroid size. Proc. Soc. Exp. Biol. & Med. 88:216.

Mikami, S. I. 1958 The cytological significance of regional patterns in the adenohypophysis of the fowl. J. Fac. Agr., Iwate Univ. (Japan) 3:473.

Miner, J. J., S. J. Marsden, and C. A. Denton 1959 The effect of diethylstilbestrol-methimazole and dienestrol diacetate on turkey broilers. Poultry Sci. 38:750.

Mitchell, J. B. 1929 Experimental studies of the bird hypophysis. I: Effects of hypophysectomy in the Brown Leghorn fowl. Physiol. Zool. 2:411.

Mixner, J. P., E. P. Reineke, and C. W. Turner 1944 Effect of thiouracil and thiourea on the thyroid gland of the chick. Endocrinol. 34:168.

Mixner, J. P., and C. W. Upp 1947 Increased rate of thyroxine secretion by hybrid chicks as a factor in heterosis. Poultry Sci. 26:389.

Mountney, F. J., L. A. Atkinson, D. B. Mellor, and J. H. Quisenberry 1957 The influence of diethylstilbestrol, thiouracil and fat on the growth and quality of turkeys. Poultry Sci. 36:1144 (Abs.).

Mueller, W. J., and A. Amezcua 1959 The relationship between certain thyroid characteristics of pullets and their egg production, body weight and environment. Poultry Sci. 38:620.

Nalbandov, A., and L. E. Card 1943 Effect of hypophysectomy of growing chicks. J. Exp. Zool. 94:387.

Newcomer, W. S. 1957 Relative potencies of thyroxine and triiodothyronine based on various criteria in thiouracil-treated chickens. Am. J. Physiol. 190:413.

Nonidez, J. R., and H. D. Goodale 1927 Histological studies on the endocrines of chickens deprived of ultraviolet light. Am. J. Anat. 38:319.

Odell, T. T., Jr. 1952 Secretion rate of thyroid hormone in White Leghorn castrates. Endocrinol. 51:265.

Okonski, J., F. W. Lengemann, and C. L. Comar 1960 The utilization of egg iodine by the chicken embryo. J. Exp. Zool. 45:263.

Okonski, J., F. W. Lengemann, and C. L. Comar 1961 Incorporation of I^{131} into chicken eggs. Health Physics 6:27.

Olin-Lamberg, C., and B. A. Lamberg 1953 Relationship between the uptake of P^{32}, the histological changes and the change in thyroid weight after thyrotrophin treatment. Acta Endocrinol. 14:83.

Oloufa, M. M. 1953 Effect of thyroprotein on egg production, egg weight and body weight of chickens during summer. Poultry Sci. 32:391.

Oloufa, M. M.   1954   Influence of thyroprotein and darkness on Egyptian chicken during summer. Poultry Sci. 33:649.

Oloufa, M. M.   1955   Effect of thyroprotein on the growth of Egyptian baby chickens. Poultry Sci. 34:1292.

Parker, J. E.   1943   Influence of thyroactive iodocasein on growth of chicks. Proc. Soc. Exp. Biol. & Med. 52:234.

Parkes, A. S., and H. Selye   1937   The endocrine system and plumage types. I: Some effects of hypothyroidism. J. Genetics 34:298.

Patton, A. R., H. S. Wilgus, and G. S. Harshfield   1939   The production of goiter in chickens. Science 89:162.

Payne, F.   1944a   Pituitary changes in aging capons. Anat. Rec. 89:563.

Payne, F.   1944b   Anterior pituitary thyroid relationship in fowl. Anat. Rec. 88:337.

Payne, F.   1957   A cytological study of the thyroid glands of normal and experimental fowl including interrelationships with the pituitary, gonads and adrenals. J. Morph. 101:89.

Perek, M., B. Eckstein, and H. Sobel   1957   Histological observations on the anterior lobe of the pituitary gland in moulting and laying hens. Poultry Sci. 36:954.

Perek, M., and F. Sulman   1945   The basal metabolic rate in molting and laying hens. Endocrinol. 36:240.

Phillips, J.   1962   Evidence of early pituitary function in the White Leghorn chick. Anat. Rec. 144:69.

Piotrowski, L. J., S. L. Steelman, and F. C. Koch   1953   Thyrotrophin assay based on the depletion of iodine in chick thyroids. Endocrinol. 52:489.

Pipes, G. W., B. N. Premachandra, and C. W. Turner   1958   Measurement of the thyroid hormone secretion rate of individual fowls. Poultry Sci. 37:36.

Premachandra, B. N.   1962   Radioiodine (I^{131}) and thyroid function in the fowl. Proc. XII World's Poultry Congress, p. 131.

Premachandra, B. N., G. W. Pipes, and C. W. Turner   1958   Thyroxine secretion rates of two strains of New Hampshire chickens selected for high and low response to thiouracil. Poultry Sci. 37:399.

Premachandra, B. N., G. W. Pipes, and C. W. Turner   1959   Studies of growth in New Hampshire chickens with varying thyroid status. Poultry Sci. 38:795.

Premachandra, B. N., and C. W. Turner   1960   Reserpine and thyroid activity in fowls. Proc. Soc. Exp. Biol. & Med. 104:306.

Rahn, H. 1939 The development of the chick pituitary with special reference to the cellular differentiation of the par buccalis. J. Morph. 64:483.

Rawson, R. W., and W. T. Salter 1940 Microhistometric assay of thyrotrophic hormone in day-old chicks. Endocrinol. 27:155.

Reineke, E. P. 1954 The thyroxine content of thyroactive iodinated proteins as determined by a radioactive isotope dilution technique. J. Dairy Sci. 37:1227.

Reineke, E. P. 1959 Thyroid function in several species of animals with special reference to environment and body size. U. S. Atomic Energy Commission Pub. TID-7578:87.

Reineke, E. P., J. A. Davidson, L. F. Wolterink, and F. N. Barrett 1946 The effect of thiouracil on fattening turkeys. Poultry Sci. 25:410.

Reineke, E. P., and O. N. Singh 1955 Estimation of thyroid hormone secretion rate in intact rat. Proc. Soc. Exp. Biol. & Med. 88:203.

Reineke, E. P., and C. W. Turner 1943 Recovery of L-thyroxine from iodinated casein by direct hydrolysis with acid. J. Biol. Chem. 149:563.

Reineke, E. P., and C. W. Turner 1945a The relative thyroidal potency of L and D,L-thyroxine. Endocrinol. 36:200.

Reineke, E. P., and C. W. Turner 1945b Seasonal rhythm in the thyroid hormone secretion of the chick. Poultry Sci. 24:499.

Reineke, E. P., C. W. Turner, G. O. Kohler, R. D. Hoover, and M. B. Beezley 1945 The quantitative determination of thyroxine in iodinated casein having thyroidal activity. J. Biol. dhem. 161:599.

Reineke, E. P., M. B. Williamson, and C. W. Turner 1943 The effect of progressive iodination followed by incubation at high temperature on the thyroidal activity of iodinated proteins. J. Biol. Chem. 147:115.

Riddle, O. 1927 Studies on thyroids. Endocrinol. 11:161.

Riddle, O. 1947 Endocrines and constitution in doves and pigeons. Carnegie Inst. Wash., Pub. 572.

Robbins, J., J. E. Rall, and P. G. Condliffe 1961 The thyroid stimulating hormone and iodine-containing hormones. in Hormones in Blood, p. 49. Academic Press, New York.

Roche, J., R. Michel, and E. Volpert 1956 Concentration des hormones thyroïdennes par les ovocyte de la poule. Comp. Rend. Soc. Biol. 150:2149.

Rogler, J. C., H. E. Parker, F. N. Andrews, and C. W. Carrick 1959a

The effect of an iodine deficiency on embryo development and hatchability. Poultry Sci. 38:398.

Rogler, J. C., H. E. Parker, F. N. Andrews, and C. W. Carrick 1959b Various factors affecting the iodine-131 uptake of embryonic thyroids. Poultry Sci. 38:405.

Rogler, J. C., H. E. Parker, F. N. Andrews, and C. W. Carrick 1959c Effects of thiouracil and thyroxine on chick embryo development. Poultry Sci. 38:1027.

Romanoff, A. L. 1960 The Avian Embryo, The Macmillan Co., New York.

Romijn, C. 1950 Stofwisselingsonderzoek bij de kip. Proeven met Noord-Hollandse Blauwen. 3: De invloed van anti schildklierstoffen op de stofwisseling. Tijdschr. Diergeneesk 75:839.

Schlumberger, H. G. 1958 Effect of radiothyroidectomy in the parakeet. A.M.A. Arch. Pathol. 66:747.

Schultze, A. B., and C. W. Turner 1945 The determination of the rate of thyroxine secretion by certain domestic animals. Mo. Agr. Exp. Sta. Res. Bul. 392.

Scott, M. L., R. C. Baker, and E. Dougherty 1959 Iodinated casein in duck feed: preliminary findings. Feeds Illustrated, Aug., p. 53.

Scott, M. L., E. R. Holm, and R. E. Reynolds 1954 Studies on pheasant nutrition. 3: Effect of antibiotics, arsenicals and thyroactive compounds upon growth and feathering in pheasant chicks. Poultry Sci. 33:1261.

Sell, J. L., and S. L. Balloun 1960 The effects of methimazole on weight gains, carcass composition, thyroid gland weight and blood components of cockerels. Poultry Sci. 39:930.

Shaffner, C. S. 1954 Feather papilla stimulation by progesterone. Science 120:345.

Shaffner, C. S. 1955 Progesterone induced molt. Poultry Sci. 34:840.

Shaffner, C. S., and F. N. Andrews 1948 The influence of thiouracil on semen quality in the fowl. Poultry Sci. 27:91.

Shaklee, W. E., and C. W. Knox 1956 Selection for thyroid weight in New Hampshire chickens. J. Hered. 47:211.

Shellabarger, C. J. 1954a Effects of cortisone on thyroid function in White Leghorn cockerels. Endocrinol. 55:100.

Shellabarger, C. J. 1954b Detection of thyroid stimulating hormone by I^{131} uptake in chicks. J. Appl. Physiol. 6:721.

Shellabarger, C. J. 1955 A comparison of triiodothyronine and thyroxine in the chick goiter-prevention test. Poultry Sci. 34:1437.

Shellabarger, C. J., and J. T. Godwin 1954 Effects of thyroxine or triiodothyronine on the chick thyroid in the presence or absence of exogenous TSH. Am. J. Physiol. 176:371.

Shellabarger, C. J., and R. Pitt-Rivers 1958 Presence of triiodothyronine in fowl. Nature 181:546.

Shellabarger, C. J., and J. R. Tata 1961 Effect of administration of human serum thyroxine-binding globulin on the disappearance rates of thyroid hormones in the chicken. Endocrinol. 68:1056.

Singh, H., and C. S. Shaffner 1950 Effect of thyroprotein and caloric level of diet on metabolic rate of chickens. Poultry Sci. 29:575.

Smelser, G. K. 1938 Chick thyroid responses as a basis for thyrotrophic hormone assay. Endocrinol. 23:429.

Smyth, J. R., Jr., and T. W. Fox 1951 The thyroxine secretion rate of turkey poults. Poultry Sci. 30:607.

Stahl, P., G. W. Pipes, and C. W. Turner 1961 Time required for low temperature to influence thyroxine secretion rate in fowls. Poultry Sci. 40:646.

Stahl, P., G. W. Pipes, C. W. Turner, and A. B. Stephenson 1962 Mode of inheritance of thyroxine secretion rate in lines of New Hampshire chickens. Poultry Sci. 41:570.

Stahl, P., and C. W. Turner 1961 Seasonal variation in thyroxine secretion rates in two strains of New Hampshire chickens. Poultry Sci. 40:239.

Stoll, R., and P. Blanquet 1953 Sur l'activité des thyroïdes de l'embryon de poulet, provenant d'oeufs "marqués" par l'administration de I^{131} à la poule. Ann. Endocrinol. 14:1.

Sturkie, P. D. 1951 Effects of estrogen and thyroxine upon plasma proteins and blood volume in the fowl. Endocrinol. 49:565.

Sulman, F., and M. Perek 1947 Influence of thiouracil on the basal metabolic rate and on molting in hens. Endocrinol. 41:514.

Tanabe, Y., K. Himeno, and H. Nozaki 1957 Thyroid and ovarian function in relation to molting in the hen. Endocrinol. 61:661.

Tanabe, Y., and T. Komiyama 1962 A new procedure for estimating thyroxine secretion rate with radioiodine. Endocrinol. 70:142.

Tata, J. R., and C. J. Shellabarger 1959 An explanation for the difference between the responses of mammals and birds to thyroxine and triiodothyronine. Biochem. J. 72:608.

Taurog, A., W. Tong, and I. L. Chaikoff 1950 The monoiodotyrosine content of the thyroid gland. J. Biol. Chem. 184:83.

Taylor, L. W., and B. R. Burmester 1940 Effect of thyroidectomy on production, quality and composition of chicken eggs. Poultry Sci. 19:326.

Thommes, R. C.   1958   Vasculogenesis in selected endocrine glands of normal and hypophysectomized chick embryos. I: The thyroid. Growth 22:243.

Thornton, P. A., and S. S. Deeb   1961   The influence of thyroid regulators on blood ascorbic acid levels in the chicken. Poultry Sci. 40:1063.

Tixier-Vidal, A.   1956   Étude chronologique in vivo et in vitro des correlations hypophyse-thyroïde chez l'embryon de poulet. Arch. Anat. Microsc. Morph. Exp. 45:236.

Tixier-Vidal, A.   1957   Influence d'un abaissement de la température d'incubation sur la thyroïde de l'embryon de poulet en fin d'incubation. Comp. Rend. Acad. Sci. 246:1463.

Tixier-Vidal, A., and I. Assenmacher   1961a   Étude comparée de l'activité thyroïdenne chez le canard normal, castré, ou maintenu a l'obscurité permanente. I: Période de l'activité sexual saisonnière. Comp. Rend. Soc. Biol. 155:215.

Tixier-Vidal, A., and I. Assenmacher   1961b   Étude comparée de l'activité thyroïdenne chez le canard normal, castré, ou mis à l'obscurité permanente. II: Période du repos sexuelèle saisonnire. Comp. Rend. Soc. Biol. 155:286.

Trunnell, J. B., and P. Wade   1955   Factors governing the differentiation of the chick embryo thyroid. II: Chronology of the synthesis of iodinated compounds studied by chromatographic analysis. J. Clin. Endocrinol. & Metab. 15:107.

Turner, C. W.   1948a   Effect of age and season on the thyroxine secretion rate of White Leghorn hens. Poultry Sci. 27:146.

Turner, C. W.   1948b   Effect of thyroprotein-feeding on the gland and organ weights of two-year-old White Leghorn hens. Poultry Sci. 27:155.

Turner, C. W.   1950   Thyrotrophic hormone, in Hormone Assay, ed. C. W. Emmens. Academic Press, New York.

Turner, C. W.   1959   Role of thyroid, adrenal and posterior pituitary hormones in reproductive processes; Chapter 5, Reproduction in Domestic Animals, ed. H. H. Cole and P. T. Cupps. Academic Press, New York.

Turner, C. W.   1962   Thyrotrophic hormone, in Methods in Hormone Research, ed. R. I. Dorfman, Vol. 2. Academic Press, New York.

Turner, C. W., M. R. Irwin, and E. P. Reineke 1944 Effect of feeding thyroactive iodocasein to Barred Rock cockerels. Poultry Sci. 23:242.

Turner, C. W., M. R. Irwin, and E. P. Reineke 1945 Effect of the thyroid hormone on egg production of White Leghorn hens. Poultry Sci. 24:471.

Turner, C. W., and B. N. Premachandra 1962 Thyroidal substances, in Methods in Hormone Research, ed. R. I. Dorfman, Vol. 2. Academic Press, New York.

Van der Meulen, J. B. 1939 Hormonal regulation of molt and ovulation. Proc. VII World's Poultry Congr., p. 109.

Van Middlesworth, L., G. Jagiello, and W. P. Vanderlaan 1959 Observations on the production of goiter in rats with propyl-thiouracil and on goiter prevention. Endocrinol. 64:186.

Van Tienhoven, A., H. C. Thomas, and L. J. Dressen 1956 The effect of sulfamethazine feeding on thyroids, combs and testes of Single Comb White Leghorn cockerels. Poultry Sci. 35:179.

Vlijm, L. 1958 On the production of hormones in the thyroid glands of birds: A quantitative study with the help of radio-iodine and antithyroid drugs. Arch. Neerl. Zool. 12:467.

Waterman, A. J. 1959 Development of the thyroid-pituitary system in warm-blooded aminotes, in Comparative Endocrinology, ed. A. Gorbman. John Wiley & Sons, New York.

Wentworth, B. C. 1960 A radiochromatographic study of thyroxine and triiodothyronine in the thyroid gland and circulation of domestic birds. M. S. Thesis, University of Massachusetts.

Wentworth, B. C., and W. J. Mellen 1961a Effect of thiouracil on plasma PBI[131] in the fowl. Poultry Sci. 40:1022.

Wentworth, B. C., and W. J. Mellen 1961b Circulating thyroid hormones in domestic birds. Poultry Sci. 40:1275.

Wheeler, R. S., and E. Hoffman 1948a Goitrous chicks from thyroprotein-fed hens. Endocrinol. 42:326.

Wheeler, R. S., and E. Hoffman 1948b The value of thyroprotein in starting, growing and laying rations. Poultry Sci. 27:509.

Wheeler, R. S., and E. Hoffman 1949 Goitrogenic action of iodide and the etiology of goiter in chicks from thyroprotein-fed hens. Proc. Soc. Exp. Biol. & Med. 72:250.

Wheeler, R. S., and E. Hoffman 1950 The etiology of goiter in chicks from thyroprotein-fed hens; negative role of inorganic iodide. Poultry Sci. 29:306.

Wilgus, H. S., Jr., F. X. Gassner, A. R. Patton, and R. G. Gustavson 1941 The goitrogenicity of soybeans. J. Nutrition 22:43.

Wilson, H. R., and D. W. MacLaury 1961 The effect of tapazole on growth of hybrid cockerels. Poultry Sci. 40:890.

Wilwerth, A. M., C. Martínez-Campos, and E. P. Reineke 1954 Influence of the thyroid status on volume and concentration of cock semen. Poultry Sci. 33:729.

Winchester, C. F. 1939 Influence of thyroid on egg production. Endocrinol. 24:697.

Winchester, C. F. 1940 Growth and development. II: Seasonal metabolic and endocrine rhythm in the domestic fowl. Mo. Agr. Exp. Sta. Res. Bul. 315.

Winchester, C. F., C. L. Comar, and G. K. Davis 1949 Thyroid destruction by I[131] and replacement therapy. Science 110:302.

Winchester, C. F., and G. K. Davis 1952 Influence of thyroxine on growth of chicks. Poultry Sci. 31:31.

Wollman, S. H., and E. Zwilling 1953 Radioiodine metabolism in the chick embryo. Endocrinol. 52:526.

CHAPTER 20

Parathyroids, Thymus, Pineal, and Pancreas

PARATHYROIDS

Anatomy

THERE are usually four parathyroid glands in the chicken, pigeon and duck—two on each side, attached to or near the posterior pole of the thyroid gland. In the chicken, the pair on each side consists of a larger lobe, parathyroid three, which is developed from the third visceral pouch, and a smaller one, parathyroid four, which is developed from the fourth visceral pouch (Schrier and Hamilton, 1952). The two lobes are usually fused, and the larger lobe is usually attached to, but sometimes separated from, the posterior pole of the thyroid. In some instances, the smaller lobe may be in contact with the thyroid, with the larger lobe behind the smaller one (Nonidez and Goodale, 1927). See Figure 86, Chapter 19.

In the pigeon, the two parathyroids on each side are located outside of the thyroid and are entirely separated from it, and they may be separated from each other (Smith, 1945). The glands make contact with the jugular veins and carotid arteries and receive branches from these vessels.

Nonidez and Goodale (1927) reported accessory parathyroid tissue in the chicken, which was found in the caudal lobe of the thymus and in the thymus tissue under the thyroid, as well as in the ultimobranchial bodies. Campbell and Turner (1942), who serially sectioned thyroids of 7-day-old chicks, found no traces of parathyroid tissue. Smith (1945) sectioned and studied the thyroids of a number of pigeons and found no accessory parathyroid tissue.

Histology and Size

The chief cells of the parathyroids of birds are arranged in cords, like those of mammals, but there are no oxyphiles, according to Benoit (1950) and Benoit, Clavert, and Cabannes (1944a, b). The cords of the chief cells are elongated in the duck (Benoit) but may be somewhat irregular and may anastomose freely in the chicken (Nonidez and Goodale). The cords are separated by a thin stroma of connective tissue, abounding in capillaries. The appearance of the cord cells varies with the physiological state of the gland, according to Benoit (1950). The nucleus may stain very lightly and the cytoplasm may be vacuolated with relatively few granules, or the nucleus may be more chromatic and the cytoplasm may be granular and relatively free of vacuoles, indicating a more active condition of the cells.

In chickens, ducks, and pigeons deprived of ultraviolet light or vitamin D, or fed rations deficient in calcium, the parathyroids undergo hypertrophy and hyperplasia, more than doubling in size in many cases; but this is usually followed by regression in size (Higgins and Sheard, 1928; Marine, 1924; Oberling and Guerin, 1933; Nonidez and Goodale, 1927; and Hurwitz and Griminger, 1961). Ducks kept in darkness for several months exhibit parathyroids 10 times the normal size (Benoit, 1950).

Benoit, Clavert, and Cabannes (1944a) reported that hypophysectomy in the duck caused regression in size and an arrest of mitosis in the parathyroids, but that this condition was not permanent, since the cells might later show signs of activity.

Administration of estrogen to ducks (Benoit, Clavert, and Cabannes, 1944b) and of estrogen to cockerels (Landauer, 1954) caused hypertrophy of the parathyroids.

The weights of the parathyroids show considerable variation (Table 73). The data of Turner (1948) suggest that seasonal changes may also influence size of parathyroids apart from amount of light.

Table 73. Weights of parathyroids of birds

Species, age, sex, treatment	Body wt. gm.	Parathyroid weight, mg.	Parathyroid weight in mg. per kg. of body wt.	Author
Chicken				
White Leghorn, male, normal	642	4.0	6.2	Kumaran & Turner, 1949b
White Leghorn, male, normal	957	5.8	6.0	Kumaran & Turner, 1949b
White Leghorn, male, normal	1339	8.4	6.2	Kumaran & Turner, 1949b
White Leghorn, male, normal	2000	16.3	8.15	Kumaran & Turner, 1949a
White Leghorn, 6 wks., no sunlight, no vitamin D	—	50.0	—	Nonidez & Goodale, 1927
White Leghorn, 6 wks., sunlight	—	22.0	—	Nonidez & Goodale, 1927
White Leghorn, laying hen (Sept.)	1883	14.5	7.7	Turner, 1948
White Leghorn, laying hen (Nov.)	1861	15.9	8.5	Turner, 1948
White Leghorn, laying hen (Jan.)	2043	19.2	9.4	Turner, 1948
White Leghorn, laying hen (March)	2007	27.2	13.6	Turner, 1948
White Leghorn, laying hen (May)	2043	33.5	16.4	Turner, 1948
White Leghorn, laying hen (July)	1725	54.5	31.4	Turner, 1948
Pigeon				
2 months, male and female, sunlight	321	3.4	10.3	Hollander & Riddle, 1945
23 months, male and female, sunlight	390	3.7	9.4	Hollander & Riddle, 1945
3 months, rickets	239	28.5	118.0	Hollander & Riddle, 1945
Duck				
Rouen, male	—	—	9.4	Benoit, 1950
Rouen, female	—	—	10.7	Benoit, 1950

PARATHYROIDECTOMY

Parathyroidectomy has been performed in the chicken, pigeon, and duck. The operation has been successfully performed in the chicken by Nonidez and Goodale (1927), Polin and Sturkie (1957), Tilgner-Peter (1957), and Urist *et al.* (1960). Typical symptoms of tetany are not observed in the chicken following the operation, but blood calcium drops within 5 to 24 hours and mortality is usually highest during this period. Urist *et al.* reported a 60 percent mortality within 8 to 48 hours after surgery. Survival after 48 hours probably depends upon the development of accessory parathyroid tissue, or incomplete removal (Polin and Sturkie; Urist *et al.*). Tilgner-Peter determined blood calcium in parathyroidectomized chickens at varying intervals after the operation; he found the values lowest at 5 hours and 1 day, and noted that they began to rise on the second day after the operation. Unlike the chicken, the duck and pigeon develop symptoms of tetany after parathyroidectomy. The mortality in the duck is high 20 to 30 hours after the operation unless replacement therapy is used (Benoit, Fabiani, Grangaud, and Clavert, 1941; Mandel, Clavert, and Mandel, 1953).

Smith (1945) described a technique for parathyroidectomy in pigeons. She, and likewise Riddle, Rauch, and Smith (1945), Riddle and McDonald (1945), and McDonald and Riddle (1945), have reported on the effects of the operation. They showed that the pigeon develops tetany, but that this can be prevented by the administration of calcium or aluminum hydroxide.

EFFECTS OF PARATHYROID HORMONE

On Blood Calcium

There is a pronounced drop in blood calcium after parathyroidectomy, particularly in the filterable or ionic calcium, though the nondiffusible or bound calcium also drops under certain conditions, particularly as a result of starvation. Withholding food for 24 hours decreases nondiffusible calcium more than the diffusible (Polin and Sturkie, 1957), and the effect is greater in females than males because the amount of nondiffusible calcium in relation to the total calcium is greater in laying females. Parathyroidectomy depresses food consumption considerably up to 4 days after surgery; hence much of the drop in bound calcium after the operation is the result of lowered calcium intake.

The effects of parathyroidectomy (P) and sham parathyroidectomy (SP) upon blood calcium of chickens 18 to 24 hours after surgery are as follows (Polin and Sturkie, 1957, 1958):

Ca. (mg/100 ml.)	*Cocks*		*Capons*		*Laying Hens*	
	SP	*P*	*SP*	*P*	*SP*	*P*
Diffusible	6.43	4.59	6.88	5.19	5.7	4.3
Non diffusible	5.55	3.88	5.02	4.03	10.7	7.3
Total	11.98	8.47	11.90	9.22	16.4	11.6

Similar results have been reported in the duck by Benoit *et al.* (1941) and by Mandel, Clavert, and Mandel (1953).

Inorganic phosphorus usually rises following parathyroidectomy, although the extent of the rise varies and appears to depend in part on the level before the surgery. Benoit *et al.* (1941) reported an increase of 300 percent in the duck after the operation, but the level before the operation appeared to be unusually low.

The increase of phosphorus in chicken blood after parathyroidectomy (about 2 mg. percent) is considerably less (Polin, 1955). The increased blood phosphorus following parathyroidectomy is the result of decreased renal excretion, and the parathyroid hormone is believed to regulate the excretion or reabsorption of phosphorus by the kidney tubule (Munson, 1960). That the kidney tubules of chickens excrete phosphorus was reported in Chapter 13.

Parathyroid extracts administered to normal male and female chickens had no consistent effect on inorganic phosphorus (Urist, Deutsch, Pomerantz, and McLean, 1960).

The data concerning the effects of mammalian parathyroid extracts on the blood calcium of birds are inconsistent and often conflicting. Positive effects have been reported in the pigeon by Riddle and Dotti (1934), and in the chicken by Deobald *et al.* (1936), Knowles *et al.* (1935), Polin, Sturkie, and Hunsaker (1957), and Urist *et al.* (1960).

A larger number of investigators have reported negative results. Polin *et al.* (1957) demonstrated that the effects of the hormone administered subcutaneously to chickens persisted for only 6 to 8 hours. Most of the investigators took blood samples for calcium determinations 18 to 24 hours after administration of the hormone, and this may account for their negative results.

Polin *et al.* (1957) reported that the chicken was quite sensitive to parathyroid extracts and responded maximally 3 to 4 hours after the administration of the hormone. The laying hen, with an initially higher level of blood calcium, responded more than the cock or capon to a given dosage (see also Urist *et al.*, 1960). The increases in blood calcium following subcutaneous injection of 100 units of Parathormone (Lilly) were 7.6 mg./100 ml. for laying hens and 2.1 for cocks. The same workers showed that chicks 5 to 7 weeks old made suitable assay animals for the hormone, and that the log dose response was linear over the range of 50 to 200 units. Urist *et al.* (1960), who injected 500 and 1,000 units, reported a maximum effect with 500 units. Whether or not the diet is deficient in vitamin D does not influence the action of parathyroid extract on blood calcium (Hertelendy and Taylor, 1960).

Whether or not the avian parathyroid gland produces a hormone that lowers blood calcium, as has been reported for the dog (Copp *et al.*, 1962), remains to be determined.

Estrogen and Parathyroid Hormone

It was demonstrated in Chapters 2 and 18 that estrogen increases blood calcium of normal males and females, or castrates. In parathyroidectomized male or female pigeons, Riddle and co-workers have reported that estrogen elicits the same rise in blood calcium and phosphorus as when the parathyroids are present. Most of their experiments were on immature males or females, and their birds received calcium or aluminum hydroxide to prevent tetany. The blood calcium response to estrogen in hypophysectomized pigeons was the same as for intact animals, and neither of these operations affected the increased endosteal bone formation induced by estrogens.

In the parathyroidectomized duck, estrogen does not elevate

blood calcium appreciably (Benoit, Fabiani, Grangaud, and Clavert, 1941; Benoit, Stricker, and Fabiani, 1941; Mandel, Clavert, and Mandel, 1953). This is demonstrated graphically in Figure 95. When estrogen is injected intramuscularly in the intact duck, blood calcium is elevated over 5 times within 2 days. Ablation of

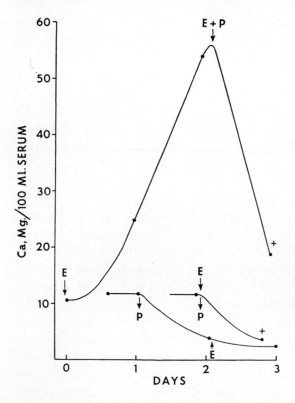

Figure 95. Effects of estrogen (E) and parathyroidectomy (P) on blood calcium of the duck.

Estrogen (10 mg. estradiol) increases calcium of normal duck (upper curve, E). The duck was parathyroidectomized and given 5 mg. of estrogen (E and P at peak of curve), and calcium dropped. The lower curves show that blood calcium drops after parathyroidectomy even when estrogen is administered. (From Benoit, Fabiani, Grangaud, and Clavert, *Comp. Rend. Soc. Biol.,* 1941, slightly modified.)

the parathyroids at this point causes a marked drop in calcium within the next 24 hours, even if the estrogen is again injected.

These results led Polin and Sturkie (1957, 1958) to suggest that the ability of estrogen to augment plasma calcium (particularly nondiffusible Ca) appeared to be dependent on the action of parathyroid hormone in regulating diffusible calcium levels. They postulated that parathyroid hormone regulates the diffusible calcium level, which in turn governs the response to estrogen; they demonstrated this (1958) in the chicken, and the result has been

confirmed by Urist *et al.* (1960). When the diffusible Ca level fell
below 4 mg. percent in the chicken following parathyroidectomy,
estrogen did not increase the total calcium or nondiffusible calcium, but at levels above 4 mg. it did so.

*Effects of Estrogen and Parathyroid Hormone on Bone and Shell
Formation*

This subject is discussed in detail in Chapter 15. It is sufficient
to state here that parathyroid hormone influences the transfer of
calcium from bone to blood; it increases osteoclastic activity and
detaches intramedullary bone from cortical bone (Urist and
Deutsch, 1960). Estrogen causes the formation of medullary or
spongy bone, particularly in the long bones (Urist *et al.,* 1960).

THYMUS

Structure

The thymus is at its maximum in the young chick, where it exists in the form of lobulated bodies which extend the entire length
of the neck. It diminishes in size with age, so that in adult birds
only remnants of it may be found, or it may be entirely absent.
The pattern of distribution of thymus in passerine birds is somewhat different (Höhn, 1956); the number of lobes is smaller, and
the lobes do not extend down to the thyroid gland. The main portion of the thymus is derived from the entodermal lining of the
third visceral pouch. In the chick this thickening elongates to form
an epithelial cord extending along the jugular vein. A small portion, thymus four, is derived from a corresponding part of the
fourth pouch and fuses with thymus three. The gland in the
chicken is similar histologically to that in mammals. It consists of a
connective tissue capsule and is divided into lobules by septa of
connective tissue. The entodermal cells of the solid epithelial
cords become changed into a stellate reticulum, and in this reticulum appear small cells, the thymocytes, which resemble small lymphocytes. These cells are probably true lymphocytes of mesenchy-
mal origin which invade the entodermal epithelium.

Function

The thymus is sometimes classified as an endocrine organ, although this classification is not justified.

Removal of the thymus in chickens has no ill effects. Maughan (1938) showed that thymectomy in the chicken had no effect on growth, blood calcium, bone formation, egg production, egg size, or shell thickness. Morgan and Grierson (1930) also found that removal of the gland had no effect on egg production or size of egg laid. Riddle and Krizenecky (1931), who thymectomized pigeons, observed no ill effects.

The thymus and bursa of Fabricius in the bird tend to involute or degenerate with age. It has been shown that involution and changes in the size of the bursa are associated with stress and the elaboration of cortical hormones (see Chapter 21). Cortical hormones also cause a regression in the size of the thymus (Garren and Satterfield, 1957; Huble, 1958; Höhn, 1959), as do testosterone and a mixture of estrogen and progesterone (Huble, 1958). Höhn (1959), however, was unable to influence the weight of the thymus in adult chickens or ducks with testosterone. Prolonged administration of thyroxine increased thymus weight, according to Höhn.

PINEAL

The literature on the pineal gland and its function is voluminous and controversial. In the last score of years, many experiments have been conducted on the pineal, chiefly in Europe and in Japan. The evidence as reviewed by Kitay and Altschule (1954), and by Kelly (1962), definitely indicates that the pineal produces a substance which has antigonadotrophic effects in a number of mammals, and also in the chicken. The evidence for some of the other reported effects is less convincing.

PANCREAS

The pancreas of the bird, like that of the mammal, has both endocrine and exocrine functions. It produces the hormones insulin and glucagon, as well as pancreatic juice. The role of the hormones in the regulation of carbohydrate metabolism in the bird has been discussed in Chapter 12. The function of pancreatic juice in digestion was discussed in Chapter 11.

Anatomy and Histology

The pancreas of the bird is an elongated, lobulated gland located in the loop of the duodenum. The gland in the chicken has three lobes, according to most investigators (see Calhoun, 1933, for review). These are the dorsal and ventral lobes, and a third, smaller lobe extending toward the spleen, called the splenic lobe. The dorsal and ventral lobes have one and two excretory ducts, respectively, which open into the intestine at the junction of the duodenum and jejunum, beside the two bile ducts (see Figure 36, Chapter 10). Most observers state that the splenic lobe has no excretory duct. Mikami and Ono (1962) designate a portion of the ventral lobe as the third lobe of the pancreas.

The pancreas is supplied with arterial blood from the anterior and posterior pancreaticoduodenal arteries, which run along the duodenal loop, supplying the duodenum and pancreas. The anterior artery is a branch from the hepatoduodenal, which arises beyond the splenic artery. The posterior pancreatic artery is a branch of the right gastric. The pancreas is drained by the pancreaticoduodenal vein, which courses in the duodenal loop and collects blood from the duodenum as well as the pancreas. The pancreatic vein empties into the gastroduodenal, which in turn empties into the hepatic portal (Hyman, 1932). The abdominal viscera, and probably the pancreas, receive parasympathetic fibers from the vagus and sympathetic fibers from the celiac ganglion.

Weights of the pancreas of the fowl are as follows:

Species and sex	Body weight gm.	Weight of pancreas gm.	Pancreas wt. as % body wt.	Author
White Plymouth Rock, males	420	1.553	0.37	Kumaran & Turner (1949c)
"	906	2.455	0.27	"
"	2,005	3.400	0.17	Kumaran & Turner (1949d)
White Leghorn, adult females	1,520–2,159	2.76–4.58	0.13–0.22	Oakberg & Lucas (1949)

The gland is larger per unit of body weight in small birds than in large ones. Within a given age and weight group the weights of the pancreas are fairly constant and show less variation than the other endocrine organs. Hypophysectomy causes a decrease in the weight of the pancreas in pigeons, and likewise in the intestine and other nonendocrine organs (Schooley, Riddle, and Bates, 1941), and probably is not a specific effect. Starvation also decreases the size of the pancreas, and hypophysectomy reduces considerably feed consumption and body weight.

The pancreas is divided into lobes and lobules, but interlobular septa are indistinct, and little intralobular connective tissue is present in the gland of the chicken (Calhoun, 1933; Batt, 1940). The lobules are composed of short tubles or acini, as in the mammal. The acinar cells are low-columnar and have a granular cytoplasm. The acinar cells, the exocrine portion of the pancreas, produce pancreatic juice containing enzymes. Batt has described zymogen granules in the acinar cells of chickens like those present in mammals. Distributed irregularly among the acini are the islet cells of Langerhans, which produce insulin and glucagon (Figure 96).

There are three cell types in the pigeon gland, according to Miller (1942), who described them as follows: The alpha cells of the pigeon have oval or round nuclei, and many large red cytoplasmic granules (stained with Heidenhains Azan). The beta cells, the largest, have spherical nuclei, showing diffuse scant chromatin and small cytoplasmic granules which stain yellow. The delta cells, the smallest of the three types, are variously shaped and their nuclei stain rather densely, with the small cytoplasmic granules staining blue. The beta cells are believed to produce insulin. The distribution of cells in an islet is such that the delta and alpha cells form one islet, and the beta and delta another.

More recent work by Hellman (1961), by Hellerström (1963), and by Hellman and Hellerström (1960), employing improved staining and histochemical techniques, indicates that in the chicken and duck there are cells of two main types, alpha and beta. There are probably two types of alpha cells, A_1 and A_2, or it may be that the same cell type exhibits different staining reactions under different conditions. The A_1 cells are markedly argyrophilic

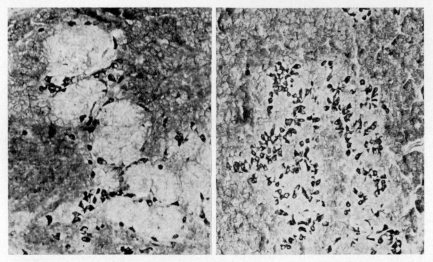

Figure 96. Silver-impregnated paraffin sections from the pancreas of the duck (x 215).

(*Left*) B cell islets (light) with occasional distinctly silver-staining A_1 cells (black) at the periphery.

(*Right*) In the lower central part of the picture there is an A cell islet containing cords of silver-positive A_1 cells as well as silver-negative A_2 cells (light). (Courtesy Dr. C. Hellerström.)

(silver-staining), and the A_2 cells are not (Figure 96). The A_1 cells in the duck are characteristically localized around capillaries, and have larger nuclei than A_2 cells. It is believed that the A_1 cells are more active than the A_2 cells, and that the A_2 cells produce glucagon; the function of the A_1 cells remains obscure. The beta cells produce insulin. Histochemical studies of these cell types (Hellerström, 1963) revealed important differences in enzyme content of the alpha and beta cells. The A_1 and A_2 cells exhibited a strong acid phosphatase activity, and the beta cells a strong alkaline phosphatase activity. There were also other differences.

Hypophysectomy in the pigeon leads to an increase in size of the alpha cells; but the beta cells become smaller and less well granulated, and many degenerate. The number of delta cells is also decreased. It was shown that these changes are due to starvation rather than to the operation, since when the operated birds were forcefed, no cell changes occurred.

Miller (1942) also demonstrated that the beta cells could be stimulated by overfeeding of normal birds, as well as by prolactin, partial pancreatectomy, and corticotrophin, whereas gonadotrophins and thyrotrophin had no effect. By contrast, large doses of insulin caused a marked atrophy of the beta cells. Atrophy of the beta cells follows fasting of normal birds. Castration in chickens and ducks increases the number and size of the islet cells (Schultz, 1940). Alloxan administered to mammals causes necrosis of the islet cells, but does not have this effect in birds (see Chapter 12).

The distribution of the alpha and beta islet cells in chickens of various ages has been studied by Oakberg (1949). In the pancreas of the day-old chick the numbers of alpha and beta cells average 150 and 3,500 respectively, and at 100 days of age they average 2,000 and 29,000 respectively. The number of alpha cells then remains fairly constant up to 300 days, but the number of beta cells increases to 40,000. The alpha cells are most numerous in the proximal part of the gland, but the beta cells are distributed throughout the gland. Lucas (1947) reported inclusion bodies in the beta cells of most chickens more than 40 days of age, but none in birds less than 30 days. The significance of these bodies is unknown.

Pancreatectomy

The pancreas is supplied by blood vessels which also supply the adjacent parts of the intestines. Sprague and Ivy (1936) have shown that destruction of these vessels in the duck leads to gangrene of the duodenum and death. Thus, in removing the pancreas, one must avoid impairing the blood supply to the duodenum. Some workers have attempted to remove the pancreas without disturbing the intestine, but it is difficult to remove all fragments of pancreatic tissue. Others, realizing this difficulty, have removed the pancreas and duodenum en masse, and then anastomosed the intestinal ends. The latter is a difficult operation and involves possible complications as a result of removing about 20 percent of the small intestine. Either kind of operation deprives the bird of pancreatic juice, and the result may be inanition and ultimate death.

Pancreatectomy has been performed in the duck by Minkowski (1893), Kausch (1896 and 1897), Paton (1905), Fleming (1919), and Weintraud (1894); in the goose by Sprague and Ivy (1936), Seitz and Ivy (1929), Mirsky, Nelson, Grayman, and Korenberg (1941), and Mirsky and Gitelson (1958); in the pigeon by Minkowski and by Riddle (1937); in the chicken by Koppanyi, Ivy, Tatum, and Jung (1926), Giaja (1912), Batt (1940), and Lepkovsky *et al.*, (1964); and in the owl by Nelson, Elgart, and Mirsky (1942). The operation appears to be least successful in the pigeon, but it has been performed only on a few birds.

Most birds recover rapidly following the operation and remain in a fair state of health for several days; then they begin to lose weight and most of them (ducks) die within anywhere from 6 weeks to 4 months (Seitz, 1930). The weight loss in depancreatized chickens, 7 weeks after the operation, is 27 percent despite normal food consumption (Batt, 1940). Ultimate death is attributed to impaired digestion as a result of the loss of pancreatic juice. The weight loss can be prevented in pancreatectomized ducks by feeding pancreatin or raw pancreas (Mirsky *et al.*, 1941), but not in the depancreatized owl (Nelson *et al.*, 1942). Other workers have demonstrated that ligation of the pancreatic ducts of birds produces the same effects on health and body weight as removing the pancreas. The effects of pancreatectomy on carbohydrate regulation are discussed in Chapter 12.

Mikami and Ono (1962), who asserted that the alpha cells in the chicken were located in or restricted to the third and splenic lobes of the pancreas, removed these areas of the pancreas surgically. They reported severe hypoglycemia, an effect they attributed to lack of glucagon, which is produced by the alpha cells only.

More recent work by Lepkovsky *et al.* (1964) indicates that when chickens are depancreatized they lose weight, and that the gonads tend to atrophy unless the birds are fed raw pancreas.

REFERENCES

Batt, H. T. 1940 The pancreas of the fowl. Thesis, University of Toronto.

Benoit, J. 1950 Traité de Zoologie, edited by P. P. Grassé. Tome XV; Oiseaux, p. 297. Masson & Co., Paris.

Benoit, J., J. Clavert, and R. Cabannes 1944a Étude histo-physiologique de la parathyroïde du canard domestique. I: Conditionnement partiel de son activité par la préhypophyse. Comp. Rend. Soc. Biol. 138:1071.

Benoit, J., J. Clavert, and R. Cabannes 1944b Étude histo-physiologique de la parathyroïde du canard domestique. 2: Modifications histologiques déterminées par le traitement à la folliculine. Comp. Rend. Soc. Biol. 138:1074.

Benoit, J., G. Fabiani, R. Grangaud, and J. Clavert 1941 Suppression par la parathyroïdectomie de l'action hypercalcémiante du dipropionate d'oestradiol chez le canard domestique. Comp. Rend. Soc. Biol. 135:1606.

Benoit, J., P. Stricker, and G. Fabiani 1941 Technique et résultats de la parathyroïdectomie chez le canard domestique. Comp. Rend. Soc. Biol. 136:1600.

Calhoun, M. L. 1933 The microscopic anatomy of the digestive tract of Gallus domesticus. Iowa State Coll. J. Sci. 7:261.

Campbell, I. L., and C. W. Turner 1942 The relation of the endocrine system to the regulation of calcium metabolism. Univ. Mo. Res. Bul. 352.

Copp, D. H., E. C. Cameron, B. A. Cheney, A. George, F. Davidson, and K. G. Henze 1962 Evidence for calcitonin—a new hormone from the parathyroid that lowers blood calcium. Endocrinol. 70:638.

Deobald, H. J., E. J. Lease, E. P. Hart, and J. G. Halpin 1936 Studies on the calcium metabolism of laying hens. Poultry Sci. 15:179.

Fleming, G. B. 1919 Carbohydrate metabolism in ducks. J. Physiol. 53:236.

Garren, H. W., and G. H. Satterfield 1957 Attempt to stimulate lymphatic gland changes of fowl typhoid with adrenal cortex extract. Proc. Soc. Exp. Biol. & Med. 95:716.

Giaja, J. 1912 Sur la glycémie chez le poulet. Comp. Rend. Soc. Biol. 73:102.

Hellerström, C. 1963 Enzyme histochemistry of the pancreatic islets in the duck with special reference to the two types of A cells. Z. f. Zellforschung 60:688.

Hellman, B. 1961 Nuclear differences between the argyrophil (A_1) and non-argyrophil (A_2) pancreatic A cells in the duck. Acta Endocrinol. 36:603.

Hellman, B., and C. Hellerström 1960 The islets of Langerhans in ducks and chickens with special reference to the argyrophil reaction. Z. f. Zellforschung 52:278.

Hertelendy, F., and T. G. Taylor 1960 On the interaction between vitamin D and parathyroid hormone in the domestic fowl. Biochim. Biophys. Acta 44:200.

Higgins, G. M., and C. Sheard 1928 The effects of selective solar irradiation on the parathyroid glands of chickens. Amer. J. Physiol. 85:299.

Höhn, E. O. 1956 Seasonal recrudescence of the thymus in adult birds. Canadian J. Biochem. & Physiol. 34:90.

Höhn, E. O. 1959 Action of certain hormones on the thymus of the domestic hen. J. Endocrinol. 19:282.

Hollander, W. F., and O. Riddle 1945 On partial mechanism associated with parathyroid enlargement in pigeons. Am. Nat. 79:451.

Huble, J. 1958 Effects of hormones on endocrine and lympho-epithelial glands in young fowl. Poultry Sci. 37:297.

Hurwitz, S., and P. Griminger 1961 The response of plasma alkaline phosphatase, parathyroids and blood and bone minerals to calcium intake in the fowl. J. Nutr. 73:177.

Hyman, L. H. 1932 A Laboratory Manual for Comparative Vertebrate Anatomy. University of Chicago Press.

Kausch, W. 1896 Über den Diabetes Mellitus der Vögel nach Pankreasexstirpation. Arch. f. Exp. Path. u. Pharm. 37:274.

Kausch, W. 1897 Der Zuckerverbrauch im Diabetes Mellitus des Vogels nach Pankreasexstirpation. Arch. f. Exp. Path. u. Pharm. 39:219.

Kelly, D. E. 1962 Pineal organs: Photoreception, secretion and development. Am. Scientist 50:597.

Kitay, J. I., and M. D. Altschule 1954 The Pineal Gland—A Review of the Physiologic Literature. Harvard University Press, Cambridge.

Knowles, H. T., E. B. Hart, and J. G. Halpin 1935 The variations in the calcium level of the blood of the domestic fowl. Poultry Sci. 14:83.

Koppanyi, T., A. C. Ivy, A. L. Tatum, and F. T. Jung 1926 Absence of permanent diabetes following pancreatectomy in the domestic fowl. Am. J. Physiol. 76:212.

Kumaran, J. D. S., and C. W. Turner 1949a The endocrinology

of spermatogenesis in birds. I: Effects of estrogen and androgen. Poultry Sci. 28:593.

Kumaran, J. D. S., and C. W. Turner 1949b The endocrinology of spermatogenesis in birds. II: Effects of androgens. Poultry Sci. 28:739.

Kumaran, J. D. S., and C. W. Turner 1949c The normal development of the testes in the White Plymouth Rock. Poultry Sci. 28:511.

Kumaran, J. D. S., and C. W. Turner 1949d The endocrinology of spermatogenesis in birds. III: Effect of hypo- and hyperthyroidism. Poultry Sci. 28:653.

Landauer, W. 1954 The effect of estradiol benzoate and corn oil on bone structure of growing cockerels exposed to vitamin D deficiency. Endocrinol. 55:686.

Lepkovsky, S., A. V. Nalbandov, M. K. Dimick, L. Z. McFarland, and R. Pencharz 1964 Growth and reproduction of depancreatized chickens. Endocrinol. 74:207.

Lucas, A. M. 1947 Intranuclear inclusions in the islands of Langerhans in chickens. Am. J. Path. 23:1005.

McDonald, M. R., and O. Riddle 1945 The effect of reproduction and estrogen administration on the partition of calcium, phosphorus and nitrogen in pigeon plasma. J. Biol. Chem. 159:445.

Mandel, L., J. Clavert, and P. Mandel 1953 Action de la parathyroïdectomie sur l'hypercalcémie d'origine folliculinique. Chez le canard: calcium ultrafiltrable. Comp. Rend. Soc. Biol. 146:1805.

Marine, P. 1924 Parathyroid hypertrophy and hyperplasia in fowls. Proc. Soc. Exp. Biol. & Med. 11:117.

Maughan, G. H. 1938 Some effects of thymus removal in chickens. Am. J. Physiol. 123:319.

Mikami, S., and K. Ono 1962 Glucagon deficiency induced by extirpation of alpha islets of the fowl pancreas. Endocrinol. 71:464.

Miller, R. A. 1942 Effects of anterior pituitary preparations and insulin on islet cells of pigeon pancreas. Endocrinol. 31:835.

Minkowski, O. 1893 Untersuchungen über den Diabetes Mellitus nach Exstirpation des Pankreas. Arch. Exp. Path. Pharm. 31:85.

Mirsky, A., and S. Gitelson 1958 The diabetic response of geese to pancreatectomy. Endocrinol. 63:345.

Mirsky, A., N. Nelson, I. Grayman, and M. Korenberg 1941 Studies on normal and depancreatized domestic ducks. Am. J. Physiol. 135:223.

Morgan, A., and M. Grierson   1930   Effects of thymectomy on young fowls. Anat. Rec. 47:101.

Munson, P. L.   1960   Recent advances in parathyroid hormone research. Fed. Proc. 19:593.

Nelson, N., S. Elgart, and I. A. Mirsky   1942   Pancreatic diabetes in the owl. Endocrinol. 31:119.

Nonidez, F. J., and H. D. Goodale   1927   Histological studies on the endocrine of chickens deprived of ultraviolet light. I: Parathyroids. Am. J. Anat. 38:319.

Oakberg, E. F.   1949   Quantitative studies of pancreas and islands of Langerhans in relation to age, sex and body weight in White Leghorn chickens. Am. J. Anat. 84:279.

Oakberg, E. F., and A. M. Lucas   1949   Variations in body weight and organ: Body weight ratios of inbred lines of White Leghorn chickens in relation to mortality, especially from lymphomatosis. Growth 13:319.

Oberling, C., and M. Guérin   1933   Les modifications des parathyroïdes dans les ostéites par carence chez la poule. Comp. Rend. Assoc. Anat. 28:489.

Paton, W.   1905   The effect of adrenaline on sugar and nitrogen excretion in urine of birds. J. Physiol. 32:59.

Polin, D.   1955   Mobilization of blood calcium and phosphorus in Gallus domesticus. Thesis, Rutgers University.

Polin, D., and P. D. Sturkie   1957   The influence of the parathyroids on blood calcium levels and shell deposition in laying hens. Endocrinol. 60:778.

Polin, D., and P. D. Sturkie   1958   Parathyroid and gonad relationship in regulating blood calcium fractions in chickens. Endocrinol. 63:177.

Polin, D., P. D. Sturkie, and W. Hunsaker   1957   The blood calcium response of the chicken to parathyroid extracts. Endocrinol. 60:1.

Riddle, O.   1937   Carbohydrate metabolism in pigeons. Cold Spring Harbor Symposia on Quantitative Biol. 5:362.

Riddle, O., and L. B. Dotti   1934   Action of parathyroid hormone in normal and hypophysectomized pigeons. Proc. Soc. Exp. Biol. & Med. 32:507.

Riddle, O., and J. Krizenecky   1931   Failure of thymectomy to reveal thymus function. Am. J. Physiol. 97:343.

Riddle, O., and M. R. McDonald   1945   The partition of plasma calcium and inorganic phosphorus in estrogen-treated normal and parathyroidectomized birds. Endocrinol. 36:48.

Riddle, O., V. M. Rauch, and G. C. Smith 1945 Action of estrogen on plasma calcium and endosteal bone formation in parathyroidectomized pigeons. Endocrinol. 36:41.

Schooley, J. P., O. Riddle, and R. W. Bates 1941 Replacement therapy in hypophysectomized juvenile pigeons. Am. J. Anat. 69:123.

Schrier, J. E., and H. L. Hamilton 1952 An experimental study of the origin of the parathyroids and thymus glands in the chick. J. Exp. Zool. 119:165.

Schultz, H. 1940 Das Pankreas im Geschlechtszyklus der Taube. Endokr. 22:319.

Seitz, I. J. 1930 On the respiratory quotient of depancreatized ducks. Am. J. Physiol. 93:686 (Abs.).

Seitz, I. J., and A. C. Ivy 1929 The effects of pancreatectomy in ducks. Proc. Soc. Exp. Biol. & Med. 26:463.

Smith, G. C. 1945 Technique for parathyroidectomy in pigeons. Anat. Rec. 92:81.

Sprague, R., and A. C. Ivy 1936 Studies in avian carbohydrate metabolism. Am. J. Physiol. 115:389.

Tilgner-Peter, A. 1957 Die Folgen der Parathyreoidektomie bei Hühnern. Arch. ges. Physiol. (Pflügers) 265:187.

Turner, C. W. 1948 Effects of thyroprotein on the gland and organ weights of two-year-old White Leghorn hens. Poultry Sci. 27:155.

Urist, M. R., and N. M. Deutsch 1960 Effects of cortisone upon blood adrenal cortex, gonads and development of osteoporosis. Endocrinol. 66:805.

Urist, M. R., N. M. Deutsch, G. Pomerantz, and F. C. McLean 1960 Interrelations between actions of parathyroid hormone and estrogens on bone and blood in avian species. Am. J. Physiol. 199:851.

Weintraud, W. 1894 Über den Pankreas-Diabetes der Vögel. Arch Exp. Path. Pharm. 34:303.

CHAPTER 21

Adrenals

ANATOMY

THE adrenals of birds are paired, oval-shaped organs whose location is anterior and medial to the cephalic lobe of the kidneys, and just anterior to the bifurcation of the posterior vena cava. In mammals the glands are divided into distinct zones, the outer cortex and the inner medulla (chromaffin tissue): these tissues have different origins, as they do in birds. In most birds the chromaffin tissue is not located in the center of the gland but is intermingled with the interrenal tissue, which does not form a true cortex as in mammals. Hence the use concerning birds of the term "interrenal" instead of "cortex" (Hartman and Brownell, 1949).

The interrenal cells arise from the peritoneal epithelium (mesothelium) ventral and medial to the mesonephros and dorsal to the hind gut. Their origin is mesodermal. The chromaffin cells arise from the sympathetic trunks on each side of the embryonic aorta, and migrate into the gland (Hays, 1914); they can be recognized histochemically in the 6th-day chick embryo 24 hours prior to the appearance of the adrenal cortex (Dawson, 1953). The chromaffin cells stain very darkly with iron hematoxylin or osmic acid. With chromic acid the granules of these cells stain brown; this is known as the chromium reaction.

Eranko (1957) and Schümann (1957) have shown that over one-half of the total catecholamines of the chicken adrenal consist of epinephrine and the remainder of norepinephrine. Chromatographic separation of granular fractions of the chicken adrenal revealed that certain fractions contained mainly epinephrine, while

another contained mainly norepinephrine. This evidence and histological studies suggest that there are at least two types of secretory granules in the chromaffin tissue.

Ghosh (1962) studied cytochemically the relative proportions of
epinephrine and norepinephrine in 9 different species of adult
males, including the chicken. He reported, contrary to the work of
Eranko and Schümann, a higher proportion of norepinephrine in
the adrenals of chicken, and in most of the other avian species.

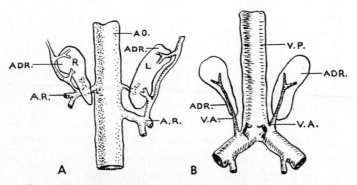

Figure 97. Diagram of arteries (A) and veins (B) of the
adrenals of the fowl.

AO., aorta; ADR., R and L, right and left adrenals; A.R.,
renal artery with branches (adrenal arteries) shown entering
the glands; V.P., posterior vena cava; V.A., adrenal vein.
(From Hays, *Anat. Rec.,* 1914, slightly modified.)

Ghosh and Ghosh (1963) reported that administration of reserpine to pigeons caused a rapid depletion of adrenal norepinephrine, and had less effect on adrenaline.

The blood supply of the fowl adrenal is shown in Figure 97.
The left gland receives arterial blood from the adrenal artery and
the arteries branching from the renal artery; the right gland is
supplied by branches of the renal artery. The adrenals are drained
by two veins, one from each gland, which empty into the posterior
vena cava (Hays).

Many nerve fibers penetrate the adrenals of birds, and most of
them are unmyelinated, according to Giacomini (quoted by Hartman and Brownell). Some of the nerve trunks located in the capsule give off fibers which run between the chromaffin cells near

the periphery and then penetrate the interior. The nerve fibers never enter the interrenal, but do enter the chromaffin tissue.

HISTOLOGY

Histological studies have been made on the adrenals of chickens (Uotila, 1939; Nalbandov and Card, 1943; Kar, 1947a and 1947b); of pigeons (Miller and Riddle, 1942); ducks (Benoit, 1950); and of many wild species of birds (Hartman, Knouff, McNutt, and Carver, 1947; Hartman and Brownell, 1949; Knouff and Hartman, 1951; and Fujita, 1961). The adrenals are enclosed by a thin capsule containing blood vessels and nerves. The interrenal tissue of all birds studied thus far, including many wild species, is not zonated, except in the brown pelican, where the interrenal tissue is organized into three zones which correspond in position and general appearance, but not in relative proportions, to the three zones of the mammalian adrenal (Knouff and Hartman). In all other species, the interrenal tissue may extend from the periphery far into the gland, but the relative distribution of the chromaffin and cortical tissues varies with the species (Hartman *et al.,* 1947).

The interrenal cells are arranged in cords or strands, and are less chromatic than the chromaffin cells. The cytoplasm of the cortical cells contains mitochondria and lipid droplets, the relative proportions of which vary under different conditions of activity of the gland (Figure 98). Fujita (1961) made an electron-microscopic study of the chicken adrenal cortex. He reported that all of the cortical cells had a larger proportion of the cytoplasm made up of mitochondria and vacuoles. Most of the mitochondria were round or oval and less than 1.5 microns in diameter, irrespective of the age of the bird. Most of the vacuoles were likewise round and less than 1.5 microns in diameter. Fujita reported that lipid droplets are found only in the cortical cells of adult hens, and not in chicks or embryos. He suggested that the cortical lipid implicated in the cortical hormones was produced "within the cytoplasmic vacuoles as endoplasmic reticulum; presumably this takes place with the aid of mitochondria which are usually near them. Osmiophilic droplets elaborated from mitochondria, accumulated within or around the cytoplasmic vacuoles and seen in the hen but not the chick are considered to be a substance related to aging."

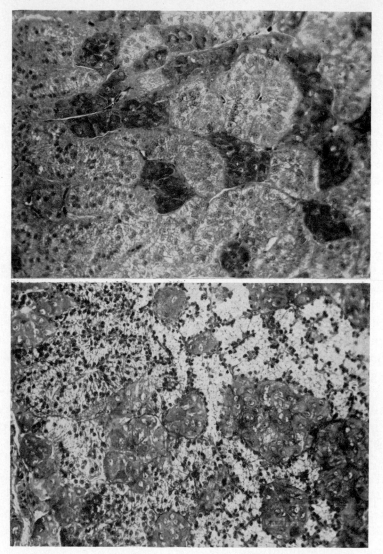

Figure 98. Cross sections of the adrenals of normal (upper) and hypophysectomized (lower) ducks.

In the upper figure are shown the prominent cortical or inter-renal cells (light staining) and the chromaffin cells (darker staining) arranged in islets, as well as blood vessels. In the lower figure, the adrenal of the duck, 47 days after hypophysectomy shows signs of involution and degeneration of the interrenal cells, which are filled with lipids. (From Benoit, in *Traité de Zoologie,* edited by P. P. Grassé, Tome XV, Figures 249 and 250, Masson & Co., Paris, 1950.)

A recent electron-microscopic study of the adrenal of the brown pelican has been conducted by Sheridan, Belt, and Hartman (1963). From a study of the outer half of the gland there appears to be only one interrenal cell type, regardless of zone. The authors state that the variations presented by the lipid droplets in this study from what has been reported by others may be due to differences in fixation or in the contained lipid itself because of the secretory or synthetic activity of the cell.

Following hypophysectomy the interrenal tissue atrophies, exhibiting shrunken lipid-filled cells and golgi bodies with a decrease in mitochondria (Miller and Riddle, 1942; Benoit, 1950).

The cortex of the male chicken adrenal comprises 40 percent of the gland, according to Kar (1947a), or 44.2 percent, according to Sauer and Latimer (1931). The interrenal tissue of the female gland amounts to 71 percent, according to Kar. In proportion to body weight, females have 30 percent more cortical tissue than males (Sauer and Latimer). In immature chickens there is slightly more chromaffin than interrenal tissue (Elliot and Tuckett, 1906). More extensive studies involving three different lines of White Leghorn males and four line of females, 120 days of age (Oakberg, 1951), reveal that the amounts of interrenal and chromaffin tissue in males are approximately the same but that there is slightly more interrenal tissue (52 percent) in the female gland. The interrenal tissue in percentage of body weight averaged 0.0043 for the males and 0.005 for the females. Some of the individual lines exhibited considerable variation in the relative proportions of interrenal and chromaffin tissues. Approximately 65 percent of the adrenal of male and female pigeons (Miller and Riddle, 1939), and 85 to 90 percent of the gland of pelicans, is composed of interrenal tissue (Knouff and Hartman, 1951).

FACTORS AFFECTING SIZE

The size of the adrenals of birds varies considerably within and between species, according to age, sex, state of health, and other factors. Hartman and Brownell (1949), reporting the adrenal weights of 20 species of birds (exclusive of chicken, pigeon, and duck), showed that the adrenal weights in percentage of body weight ranged from 0.0085 percent for the downy woodpecker to

0.0405 for the brown pelican. Among these species there was no sex difference in size. The variation within individuals of some of the same species was great. The adrenal weights of some species of birds are shown in Figure 99 and Table 74.

In proportion to body weight, the size of the adrenals is larger in embryos and young birds. Crile and Quiring (1940) and others

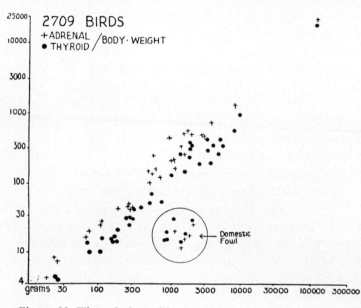

Figure 99. The relation of body weight to adrenal and thyroid weights of birds.

Ordinates represent adrenal and thyroid weights in milligrams, and abscissae, body weight in grams. (From Quiring, Growth, 1951.)

have shown that in chicks weighing 40 to 50 grams the adrenals are approximately twice as large, in proportion to body weight, as in chicks weighing 300 grams. There is no difference in the size of the right and left adrenals in chickens, according to Sauer and Latimer (1931). Breneman (1954), who studied adrenal weights of White Leghorn chickens from 2 to 140 days of age, reported that adrenal weights of cockerels were greater than those of females, as early as 30 days of age. The glands of cockerels were also larger than those of capons after 100 days of age.

Riddle (1923) claimed that the male pigeon adrenal was slightly heavier than that of the nonlaying female, but that the glands of the females enlarged preceding and during ovulation, and regressed in size following ovulation (see table). Data from a number of sources on the chicken show that on a body-weight basis there is no real difference in adrenal size in males and females. The relation between adrenal size and reproductive cycle in the chicken has received scant attention, but there are few data to show that circulating estrogens or androgens in the sexes under different conditions, or injections of these hormones, affect adrenal size (Breneman, 1954; Conner and Shaffner, 1954).

Effects of Stress, Hormones, and Chemicals on Adrenal Size

Various stress reactions in mammals cause adrenal hypertrophy and an outpouring of cortical hormones.

Adrenal hypertrophy can be induced with thyroxine in the intact and hypophysectomized pigeon (Miller and Riddle, 1939 and 1942). Bates, Riddle, and Miller (1940) reported no change in adrenal weights of chickens injected for 5 days with thyroxine. Later work by Irwin and co-workers, and by Turner (see Chapter 19) reveals that dosage is an important factor in the response of the adrenal. Mild hyperthyroidism induced by small doses in chickens does not affect adrenal size (also see Conner and Shaffner, 1954), but large doses do cause enlargement. Hypothyroidism resulting from the administration of 0.1 percent thiouracil or thyroidectomy causes adrenal hypertrophy in the chicken, according to Morris (1953). The results of Conner and Shaffner (1954) do not confirm this.

Repeated injections of ACTH, or restraint for extended periods of time, caused an increase in adrenal size (Newcomer, 1960; Zarrow *et al.,* 1962) and a decrease in size of the bursa of Fabricius; regression of the latter is believed to be a good indicator of chronic stress. The effects of stress, ACTH, and cortical hormones on leucocytes of blood are discussed in Chapter 1.

Marine birds that are able to secrete salt through the nasal glands have larger adrenals than freshwater birds. Holmes, Butler, and Phillips (1961), reported the adrenal weights of birds living in

Table 74. Adrenal weights of chickens and pigeons

Species, sex, and age	Body weight gm.	Adrenal weight gm.	Adrenal wt. as percentage of body wt.	Author
Chicken, embryo, 10 days	—	—	0.040	Venzke (1943)
Chicken, embryo, 21 days	—	—	0.024	
White Leghorn, male, 4 weeks	272.3	—	0.0127	Breneman (1942)
White Leghorn, male 8 weeks	642.0	0.071	0.0110	Kumaran & Turner (1949)
White Leghorn, male, 14 weeks	1339.0	0.123	0.0090	
White Leghorn, male	2079.0	0.106	0.0051	Sauer & Latimer (1931)
White Leghorn, female	1641.0	0.094	0.0057	
White Leghorn, male 3 months	—	0.086	0.0082	Kar (1947a, b)
White Leghorn, male, 3 months, castrate	—	0.1146	0.0112	
White Leghorn, male, 4 months	—	0.1756	0.0107	Oakberg (1951)
White Leghorn, female, 4 months	—	0.1280	0.0102	
Brown Leghorn, male, 11 months	—	—	0.0177	Juhn & Mitchell (1929)
Brown Leghorn, male, 11 months, castrate	—	—	0.0154	
Brown Leghorn, female, 11 months	—	—	0.0182	
Black Minorca, female, 3 years	2400.0	0.142	0.0060	Elliott & Tuckett (1906)
Black Minorca, male, 3 years	3570.0	0.101	0.0030	
Pigeon, male, adult	344.0	0.0199	—	Riddle (1923)
Pigeon, female, 108 hrs. before ovulation	308.0	0.0163	—	
Pigeon, female, during ovulation	341.0	0.0358	—	
Pigeon, female, 108 hrs. after ovulation	317.0	0.0162	—	

marine, brackish, and freshwater environments as follows:

	Adrenal wt. (mg. percent of body weight
Marine birds	23.8
Brackish water	14.4
Terrestrial and freshwater	9.9

The larger adrenals of marine birds are believed to be related to stimulation of ACTH and the release of cortical hormone following the ingestion of sea water (see also Chapter 13).

Depriving laying hens of calcium and vitamin D in the diet increased adrenal weights from 105 to 220 mg. The increased weight was probably the result of the increased secretion of ACTH (Urist, 1959).

Insulin injections given to pigeons for 4 days (60 units per day) increased adrenal size of 100 percent in intact birds and to a lesser extent in hypophysectomized ones (Miller and Riddle, 1941).

Formaldehyde, ACTH, and other anterior pituitary hormones increase adrenal size in the pigeon, whereas DCA decreases it and causes a marked atrophy of the interrenal tissue (Miller and Riddle, 1942).

Pigeons infested with ascarids or infected with tuberculosis (Riddle, 1923), and chicks parasitized by *Plasmodium gallinaceum* (Taylor *et al.*, 1956), have enlarged adrenals. Avian leucosis in the chicken causes hypertrophy and hyperplasia of the adrenals and thyroids, and the change in the adrenal is mainly in the interrenal tissue (Arvy and Gabe, 1951).

Adrenal enlargement resulting from vitamin B_1 deficiency has been reported in pigeons (Beznak, 1923) and in chickens. Fasting also causes enlargement of the adrenals (Sure, 1938).

Adrenal cortical hormones such as cortisone, corticosterone, and hydrocortisone depress adrenal weight of chickens (Dulin, 1956), and cortisol is much more effective than cortisone (Zarrow *et al.,* 1962).

The effects of hypophysectomy and lack of ACTH upon adrenal weights vary. In pigeons, Schooley, Riddle, and Bates (1941) reported a 27 percent decrease in adrenal weight following hypophysectomy.

Similar changes were reported in the duck by Benoit (1950), and in the chicken by Nalbandov and Card (1943). The latter workers reported initial degeneration soon after the operation, but partial recovery later on.

Newcomer (1959) reported only an insignificantly slight decrease in adrenal weights of cockerels 25 to 58 days after hypophysectomy, and no change in adrenal ascorbic acid or cortocosteroids. Brown *et al.* (1958a) likewise reported a modest decrease in adrenal weight after hypophysectomy (see also Chapter 17).

Substances which in mammals usually cause the alarm reaction and an outpouring of cortical hormones and hypertrophy of the adrenals have little effect in the young chick, according to Bates, Riddle, and Miller (1940). More recent work by Jailer and Boas (1950) and others, indicates however, that the chick adrenal does respond to ACTH and epinephrine, characterized by hypertrophy. Conner and Shaffner (1954) demonstrated that chickens fatigued by being made to walk on a treadmill for several times over a period of 10 days developed enlarged adrenals. Exposure to cold also increased adrenal weights of chickens (Garren and Shaffner, 1956).

HORMONES OF THE ADRENAL

It has been known for many years that extracts from the mammalian adrenal cortex will maintain life in adrenalectomized birds, but only in recent years has knowledge concerning the identity of the cortical hormones in birds been obtained (Phillips and Jones, 1957, and Jones *et al.*, 1958). These workers determined the content of venous blood from the adrenal vein of the chicken (capon) and reported concentrations of the hormones as follows:

| | *Normal capon* | | | *ACTH treated capon, 25 I.U. (3 days)* | | | |
	Cortico-sterone	Hydro-corti-sone	Cortisone	Cortico-sterone	Hydro-cortico-sterone	Corti-sone	Aldo-sterone
Adrenal venous blood, µg./100 ml.	312	3	Trace	65.5	3.5	2.5	1.0
Peripheral whole blood (estimates) µg./100 ml.	31.2	0.3	—	6.5	0.3	0.2	0.1

Jones *et al.* (1958) found no aldosterone in vertebrates lower than birds, and among birds only in the ACTH-treated capon; it was present in small amounts in the rat and in man. Cortico-sterone appears to be the principal cortical hormone in birds and reptiles and in some mammals.

Levels of corticosterone in the blood of chickens, pheasants, and turkeys as reported by Nagra, Baum, and Meyer (1960) are as fol-lows, in μg./100 ml. of plasma:

Species	Age & sex	No.	Adrenal blood	Peripheral blood
Chickens (males):	10–20 wks.			
Wisco white		8	44.3	7.3
New Hampshire		8	48.8	12.3
Pheasants	5–12 months	19	34.8	8.6
" (castrate)		5	33.1	7.8
Turkeys	6 months	6	42.4	7.8

The administration of 8 I.U. of ACTH to the pheasant in-creased corticosterone in adrenal venous blood by 186 percent, 30 minutes after injection, and by 253 percent, 60 minutes after in-jection. The same workers showed that the rate of withdrawal of blood from the adrenal vein directly influenced the concentration of corticosterone. For example, if 0.8 ml. of blood per minute was withdrawn from the adrenal vein of the turkey, the concentration of corticosterone was 31 μg./100 ml., but it was only 4.5 when blood was withdrawn at the rate of 6.0 ml. per minute. The difference in the method of collection and withdrawal of venous blood may account in part for the differences in concentration re-ported by different investigators.

Newcomer (1962), who determined free corticosterone in the adrenals and blood of normal chickens (by a fluorometric tech-nique, a modification of the Silber method), reported values of 7.16 micrograms per 100 ml. of peripheral plasma. Similar figures were reported by Urist and Deutsch (1960a). After injection of re-serpine, the value increased significantly (Newcomer). DeRoos 1960 studied the adrenal secretory pattern in 3 species of birds (chicken, pigeon, and gull) by *in vitro* incubation of adrenal tissue. Adrenal cortical activity was similar in all species. Corticosterone is the principal hormone, with aldosterone present in much smaller quantities. The ratio of corticosterone to aldosterone is between 5:1 and 15:1 when the adrenals are incubated in the presence of mammalian ACTH.

DeRoos and DeRoos (1963) found that ACTH considerably increased the steroid production of chicken adrenal tissue incubated *in vitro,* as follows:

ACTH	Corticosterone	Aldosterone
	(micrograms per 100 mg. of tissue)	
1 I.U.	6.64	1.39
None	0.23	0.33

Angiotensin II, added to the adrenal tissue, did not increase the output of the hormones, as it has been reported to do for the bovine adrenal.

Corticosterone (glucocorticoid) is concerned in the metabolism of carbohydrates and fats (see Chapter 12), and aldosterone (mineralocorticoid) is the principal corticoid which regulates sodium, potassium, and water balance in mammals and also in birds.

The structural formulas of corticosterone and aldosterone are as follows:

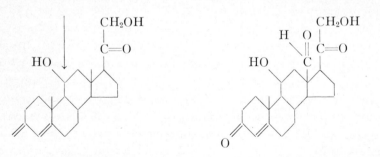

CORTICOSTERONE   ALDOSTERONE

Progesterone is a very important precursor of corticosteroids in chicken and duck adrenals, and pregnenolone less so. From 10 to 13 percent of the 18-oxygenated steroids formed in chickens and ducks are derived from pregnenolone without the intermediary of progesterone (Sandor *et al.,* 1963). Although their results do not settle the exact origin of aldosterone and 18-hydroxycorticosterone in birds, Sandor *et al.* have little doubt that both have corticosterone as a very near precursor. Whether these hormones are formed in parallel fashion from corticosterone, or whether 18-hydroxycorticosterone is a precursor of aldosterone, is not known.

EFFECTS OF ADRENAL HORMONES

Although it is known that corticosterone and aldosterone are the principal cortical hormones of birds, little work has been done concerning the metabolic effects of these hormones, particularly on salt and water metabolism. Most of the work has been done with adrenal cortical extracts of mammalian origin. The older work was reviewed by Sturkie (1954).

The meager data of Holmes, Phillips, and Butler (1961) on salt-loaded birds indicate that aldosterone decreases the volume of urine and the total renal output of sodium considerably more than does cortisol or cortexone, and that the same is true of the concentration of sodium in the urine (see also Chapter 13). Thus it appears that aldosterone is very potent in causing sodium retention in the bird, as it is in the mammal. The effects of total and subtotal adrenalectomy on the renal output of sodium in the salt-loaded duck are difficult to evaluate from the data of Phillips, Holmes, and Butler 1961). Both the volume of urine excreted and the period of diuresis were increased and extended in the adrenalectomized ducks. The authors also state that the output of sodium in the urine was increased, as might be expected, although this increase is not clear from the data. Cortisol markedly increased the retention of sodium in the adrenalectomized duck. Brown, Meyer, and Brown (1958b) reported that adrenalectomy in chicks decreased sodium excretion but had no effect on K excretion, contrary to results on adrenalectomized mammals.

Brown *et al.* (1958a) studied the effects of cortisone and DCA on daily excretion values and water intake in cockerels. The values for a 24-hour period are as follows:

	Urine (ml.)	H₂O (ml.)	Na excreted (mg.)	K excreted (mg.)	Uric acid nitrogen (mg.)	Total nitrogen (mg.)
Controls	57.5	158.6	118.5	218	478	582
DCA, 4 mg./day	105.0	338.5	99.9	146	—	—
Cortisone, 15 mg./day	95.5	153.5	180.2	323	850	1076

Both DCA and cortisone increased the flow of urine over that of the controls, and DCA increased water consumption markedly. Excretion of sodium and potassium were significantly decreased (indicating retention) following injection of DCA, but were increased with cortisone.

Neither hormone influenced the serum concentrations of Na, K, uric acid, and glucose, 24 hours after the injections. Liver glycogen, however, was increased markedly after cortisone and ACTH (see also Chapter 12).

Possible reasons for the differences in the effects of DCA and cortisone are discussed by Brown *et al.*

Other effects. Cortisone, hydrocortisone, and desoxycorticosterone acetate (DCA), when injected into chick embryos, cause a marked reduction in growth and development, and the effect of cortisone is more pronounced than that of hydrocortisone (Karnofsky, Stock, and Rhoads, 1950; Sames and Leathem, 1951; Moscona and Karnofsky, 1960; see also Chapter 12). Since certain other chemicals, as well as viruses, also decrease embryonic growth, the effect of cortical hormones is probably not a specific one.

Selye and Friedman 1941 reported that a number of steroid hormones, and particularly desoxycorticosterone acetate (DCA) cause testicular atrophy in the chick, possibly by suppression of pituitary gonadotrophins. DCA also causes hypoplasia of the developing gonads of the chick embryo (Vanninni, 1947).

Hooker and Collins (1940) reported that DCA increased comb growth slightly, but was considerably less effective than testosterone in the capon. Paschkis (1941), however, reported negative results, as did Dulin (1953). Likewise, Boas (1958) found DCA to have only slight androgenic activity based upon comb size, but to increase testis size considerably.

Adrenaline or epinephrine injected into the sparrow (Perry, 1941) or the chicken (Wheeler *et al.,* 1942) causes atrophy of the testes, probably in the same manner as DCA.

Large doses of DCA produce nephrosclerosis in chicks (Selye, 1942) as well as cardiac hypertrophy and hypertension (Stamler, Pick, and Katz, 1951). Adrenal cortical extract (ACE) injected into the adult chicken, or the release of cortical hormones as a result of stress (Newcomer, 1962) produces lymphopenia and leucocytosis, with the increase occurring mainly in the heterophils (see Chapter I). Cortical hormones and ACTH cause a reduction in eosinophils in certain mammals, but apparently have no effect upon the eosinophils of birds (Chapter 1).

Cortical extracts (hydrocortisone), but not cortisone, produce marked hyperglycemia in normal or depancreatized chicks, and increase the lipemia induced by cholesterol, according to Stamler (1952); see also Chapter 12.

Hydrocortisone and corticosterone caused an increase in liver, visceral, and carcass fat in the chicken, but cortisone had no effect. The three corticoids, at the levels administered, depressed growth in the chick (Dulin, 1956). ACTH also had a depressing effect on body weight (Dulin, 1953).

Cortisone acetate markedly inhibited chondrogenesis in the proximal and distal ends of the long bones of the cockerel's leg (Huble, 1957).

Urist and Deutsch (1960b) have proposed the term osteoporosis for a condition occurring in laying hens, in which there is resorption of bone, influenced by estrogen and parathyroid hormones. These investigators demonstrated that cortisone also influenced bone resorption, but in a manner different from the action of parathyroid hormone. Parathyroid hormone, which invokes osteoclastic activity, detaches intramedullary bone from the bone cortex, but cortisone produces resorption without formation of osteoclasts, and does not detach intramedullary bone from the cortex (see also Chapters 15 and 20). Cortisone produces hypercalcemia in the cockerel or capon, but the increase is in the filterable fraction, whereas estrogen increases the nonfilterable fraction. Cortisone also increases the blood lipids of cockerels, but has no appreciable effect on other blood chemical constituents.

Cortisone acetate (3 mg./lb. body weight) depressed egg production significantly in chickens (Kudzia and Champion, 1963).

Cortisone inhibits the uptake of radio iodine by the chicken thyroid, and the effects appear to be directly on the thyroid (Shellabarger, 1954).

Adrenaline. Adrenaline, or epinephrine, affects the bird much as it does mammals. It increases heart rate and blood pressure (Chapters 3 and 4), and mobilizes blood sugar (Chapter 12). Its effects upon respiration, upon motility of the digestive tract, and upon other organs are discussed in the chapters concerned.

ADRENALECTOMY

Adrenalectomy has been performed in the pigeon (Miller and Riddle, 1943), the duck (Bulbring, 1940; Benoit, 1950 and earlier; Parkes and Selye, 1936), and in the chicken (Parkins, 1931; Parkes and Selye, 1936; Herrick and Torstveit, 1938; Herrick and Finerty, 1941; Hewitt, 1947; Taber *et al.,* 1956; and Brown *et al.,* 1958b). The operation is difficult because of the close connection of the gland with the friable vena cava. It is best performed in males or immature females. The highly vascular ovary of the adult female makes for unusual difficulty in removing the left adrenal without fatal hemorrhage.

The glands may be removed by splitting the capsule and removing the tissue with a cannula attached to a suction pump. The remaining fragments may be destroyed by applying ferric chloride solution (Selye, 1949). Parkins (1931), after clamping and dissecting away as much of the gland as possible, used an electric cautery to destroy the remaining portion of the gland. Herrick *et al.* (1938, 1941) removed both glands in two different operations. Other workers have removed both at one time.

Completely adrenalectomized ducks and chickens usually die 6 to 60 hours after the operation unless given replacement therapy. Such birds can be maintained with 4 mg. of DCA/kg./day or 10 mg. cortisone kg./day (Brown *et al.,* 1958b).

Taber *et al.* (1956) reported that among 205 adrenalectomized poulards, 156 died within 2 weeks, and that they could not be kept alive on drinking water containing 0.9 or 1.6 percent NaCl. Among the 44 birds that did not die without replacement therapy, most exhibited regenerated adrenal tissue, or all tissue had not been removed.

Bulbring (1940) showed that life could be maintained in the duck with cortical extracts or DCA. The requirement of cortical extract to maintain life was higher in the spring when the testes were growing, and lower in castrates. When testosterone was administered to castrates, however, their survival time was not changed, suggesting that androgen is not a factor. Cortical extracts in oil, 0.05 to 3.0 cc., had to be injected at 4-hour intervals to maintain life, whereas daily injections of 5 mg. DCA were sufficient. NaCl was not used.

Herrick and Torstveit (1938) reported that typical signs of adrenal insufficiency as observed in mammals do not appear in the chicken immediately after the operation. The birds appear normal until shortly before death, when muscle weakness is the principal symptom observed. Parkins, who claims to have completely adrenalectomized chickens, reported an average survival time of 80 days without replacement therapy. During the acute stages following the operation, uric acid in the blood increased from a normal of about 3 to 11.8 mg./100 ml. There was also a slight decrease in blood sugar (Chapter 12).

The adrenalectomized pigeon can be maintained for 9 days on NaCl. Cortical extracts or DCA not only maintain life but also restore feed consumption and body weight to normal levels (Miller and Riddle, 1943).

The effects of adrenalectomy and cortical hormones on salt and water metabolism have already been discussed.

Effects on Gonads

Adrenalectomy causes a marked reduction in the size of the testes and combs of chickens within 2 to 4 days after the operation. Histological studies show the seminiferous tubules reduced in size and the cells in a state of degeneration. Herrick and Finerty (1941) demonstrated that adrenalectomy causes pronounced changes in the pituitary. Within 30 to 50 days after the operation (birds maintained on cortical extracts and salt), the testes were one-half normal size and the pituitary revealed a significant increase in the number of degenerating basophils. The pituitaries of castrates with intact adrenals revealed few degenerating basophils. The same workers concluded that adrenalectomy caused degeneration of the testes indirectly, by decreasing the production of gonadotrophins from the pituitary.

Hewitt (1947) demonstrated also that adrenalectomy decreases testis size in the male fowl, and that in the female it prevents the hypertrophy of the rudimentary right gonad or development of an ovotestis, as well as the production of androgen, which normally occurs in the ovariectomized fowl with intact adrenals.

In ovariectomized chickens (poulards) the rudimentary right gonad usually develops, but this development is greatly retarded following adrenalectomy (Taber *et al.*, 1936). The effect may be due to general systemic disturbances resulting from adrenal insufficiency; there is no evidence to support a specific adrenocortical gonadotrophism.

Tumors of the suprarenal cortex of female mammals may bring about the production of androgen and consequent virilism. The same thing has also been reported in chickens by McGowen (1936).

ADRENOCORTICOTROPHIC HORMONE (ACTH)

ACTH stimulates the growth and development of cortical tissue and the elaboration of cortical hormones of the adrenal. The bird pituitary, like that of mammals, contains ACTH, but exact amounts or potencies have not been established. ACTH is present in the hypophysis of the chick embryo by the 16th day of development, and increases thereafter up to hatching time. Pituitary extracts from 16- to 18-day chick embryos, injected into rabbits, increased adrenal size (Moszkowski, 1949). Decapitation of chick embryos in the early stages has no appreciable effect upon adrenal size prior to 16 days of age, but thereafter a pronounced decrease occurs in adrenal size and cortical tissue. That the changes in the adrenal are caused by the lack of ACTH was demonstrated by injections of ACTH, which partially restored adrenal size in the decapitated embryos (Case, 1951). The depressed adrenal weight of hypophysectomized rats can be restored to normal with fresh chicken pituitary (500 mg.) or extracts (Herbert, 1939). Early death from hypophysectomy in chickens and pigeons can be prevented by injections containing ACTH or adrenal cortical extracts (Hill and Parkes, 1934; Nalbandov and Card, 1943; Schooley, Riddle, and Bates, 1941).

In some mammals, administering epinephrine and exposure to stress, both of which cause the pituitary to release ACTH, result in the stimulation of the adrenal cortex, which in turn elaborates cortical hormones. One of the usual effects of such stimulation is a depletion of adrenal ascorbic acid and cholesterol; but this, on the basis of early work, appeared not to be true in birds. It was shown that injections of ACTH and epinephrine in chicks (Jailer and Boas, 1950; Howard and Constable, 1958; Breitenbach, 1962) and in quails (Baldini and Zarrow, 1951), and of epinephrine in ducks (Zarrow and Zarrow, 1950) did not deplete the adrenals of ascorbic acid, but might deplete adrenal cholesterol and increase adrenal size. Thus, it appeared that the decrease of adrenal ascorbic acid was not a necessary concomitant to the release of corticosteroids. The work mentioned above was based upon the use of immature chickens.

Recent work by Perek, Eckstein, and Eshkol (1959) has demonstrated conclusively that the adrenals of adult birds are depleted of adrenal ascorbic acid following release of ACTH, as in mammals, but that those of young chicks or sexually immature chickens are not. The results in laying hens and 3-month-old pullets are as follows:

	Mean adrenal wt. (mg.)	Total mean ascorbic acid content (mg.)	Mean ascorbic acid content (mg./percent)
Laying hens (control)	138	222	161
Laying hens ACTH	135	95	77
Pullets (control)	91	305	335
Pullets ACTH	94	309	329

Perek and Eckstein (1959) also showed that molting hens have much less adrenal ascorbic acid than normal laying hens, and concluded that molting may cause a release of ACTH. It was further shown by Perek and Eilat (1960) that the bursa of Fabricius (lymphoid tissue), which is prominent in immature chickens and becomes degenerate or involuted at sexual maturity, is concerned in the adrenal ascorbic acid response. When the bursa of Fabricius was surgically removed from chicks, their response to ACTH was a depletion of adrenal ascorbic acid.

The function of the bursa in adrenal response is not clear, but there is evidence that it is concerned in the response to stress and the release of cortical hormones. Cortical hormones and testosterone administered to chicks causes an involution of the bursa (Glick, 1955; Breitenbach, 1962), as does ACTH (Glick, 1957, and others).

The change in size of the bursa of Fabricius can be utilized in young birds as a criterion of stress and ACTH release, according to Newcomer (1960), and to Perek and Bedrak (1962). The latter investigators induced stress in 7-week-old cockerels by immersing them in cold water, and then determined adrenal ascorbic acid. Bursectomized birds subjected to stress showed a 21.8 percent greater depletion rate for adrenal ascorbic acid than those with the bursa intact. Likewise, the depletion of adrenal cholesterol was greater in the bursectomized chicks.

Although the bursa of Fabricius is related to the ascorbic acid response of the adrenal, the lack of ascorbic acid depletion in chicks subjected to stress or treated with ACTH (with bursa intact) does not mean that adrenal cortical hormones are not released. Breitenbach (1962) has demonstrated that there is a significant increase in the amount of plasma glucocorticoids in cockerels after administration of ACTH, but that the change in adrenal ascorbic acid was not significant.

The bursa of Fabricius contains ascorbic acid, for which it probably serves as a reservoir (Perek and Eilat, 1960), but there are other body sources of adrenal ascorbic acid. Roy and Guha (1958) reported that certain species of birds, including the chicken, pigeon, and owl, can synthesize ascorbic acid in kidney homogenates, whereas the Passeriformes synthesize it in the liver, as do certain mammals.

Blood citric acid increases in chickens following exposure to certain stresses, and is presumably related to the release of ACTH and cortical hormones (Hill, Warren, Garren, and Baker, 1961). Administration of ACTH likewise increased blood citric acid. Hill *et al.* suggest that stress and ACTH partially blocks the citric acid cycle.

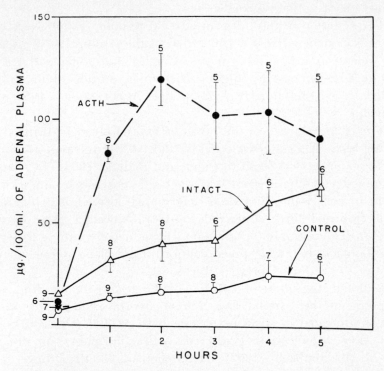

Figure 100. Corticosterone levels in adrenal venous plasma of intact and hypophysectomized chickens.

The intact and control hypophysectomized birds were serially bled only. The cold stress group of hypophysectomized chickens was partially defeathered after 0-time and placed at –8°C until rectal temperatures were depressed about 10°C. The ACTH group received 10 I.U. of ACTH intravenously after removal of a 0-time sample of blood. Each point on the curves is a mean and is accompanied by the standard error (vertical deflections) and sample size. Occasionally, no standard errors are visible because the vertical deflections depicting the variation do not exceed the size of the symbols representing the means. (From Nagra *et al., Gen. & Comp. Endocrinol.* 3:274, 1963.)

Hypophysectomy in chickens may not cause a decrease in the weight of the adrenal as it does in mammals, and some investigators have reported little or no change in adrenal size after administration of ACTH. This has led some to conclude that the avian adrenal is relatively autonomous. More recent data show, however, that hypophysectomy does decrease the secretion of cortical steroids (Nagra, Birnie, Baum, and Meyer, 1963) and that the administration of proper dosages of ACTH causes adrenal enlargement and release of adrenal cortical hormones, as it does in mammals.

Nagra *et al.* demonstrated that administration of ACTH to pheasants and chickens (both intact and hypophysectomized) increased the amount of corticosterone released from the adrenals (Figure 100). Hypophysectomy did not decrease adrenal size in chickens appreciably; this is in agreement with the work of Newcomer (1959). In pheasants, however, the operation decreased adrenal size by 29 percent. Moreover, stressful stimuli such as withdrawing blood caused the release of cortical hormones of chickens with intact pituitaries, and of lesser but still appreciable amounts even in hypophysectomized ones (Figure 100).

REFERENCES

Arvy, L., and M. Gabe 1951 État des glandes endocrincs au cours de l'érythroblastose aviaire transmissible (leucose aviaire). Comp. Rend. Acad. Sci., Paris 232:260.

Baldini, J. T., and M. X. Zarrow 1951 Ascorbic acid in the adrenal gland of the bobwhite quail. Poultry Sci. 30:906 (Abs.).

Bates, R. W., O. Riddle, and R. A. Miller 1940 Preparation of adrenotrophic extracts and their assay on two-day chicks. Endocrinol. 24:781.

Benoit, J. 1950 Traite dé Zoologie, edited by P. P. Grassé. Tome XV: Oiseaux, p. 305. Masson & Co., Paris.

Beznak, A. 1923 Die Rolle der Nebennieren bei Mangel an Vitamin B. Biochem. Z. 141:1.

Boas, N. F. 1958 The effects of desoxycorticosterone acetate on testis size and function in the cockerel. Endocrinol. 63:323.

Breitenbach, R. P. 1962 The effect of ACTH on adrenocortical secretion and ascorbic acid depletion in normal and testosterone treated cockerels. Poultry Sci. 41:1318.

Breneman, W. R.   1942   Action of diethylstilbestrol in the chick. Endocrinol. 31:179.

Breneman, W. R.   1954   The growth of thyroids and adrenals in the chick. Endocrinol. 55:54.

Brown, K. I., D. J. Brown, and R. K. Meyer   1958a   Effect of surgical trauma, ACTH and adrenal cortical hormones on electrolytes, water balance and gluconeogenesis in male chickens. Am. J. Physiol. 192:43.

Brown, K. I., R. K. Meyer, and D. J. Brown   1958b   A study of adrenalectomized male chickens with and without adrenal hormone treatment. Poultry Sci. 37:680.

Bulbring, E.   1940   The relation between cortical hormone and the size of the testis in the drake, with some observations on the effect of different oils as solvents and on DCA. J. Pharm. & Exp. Thera. 69:52.

Case, J. F.   1951   Adrenal cortical-anterior pituitary relationships during embryonic life. Presented to N.Y. Acad. of Sci.

Conner, M. H., and C. S. Shaffner   1954   Effect of altered thyroidal and gonadal activity on size of endocrine glands and resistance to stress in the chick. Endocrinol. 55:45.

Crile, G., and D. P. Quiring   1940   A record of body weight and certain organ and gland weights of 3690 animals. Ohio J. Sci. 40:219.

Dawson, A. B.   1953   Histochemical evidence of early differentiation of the suprarenal gland of the chick. J. Morph. 92:579.

DeRoos, R., and C. C. DeRoos   1963   Angiotensin II: Its effects on corticoid production by chicken adrenals in vitro. Science 141:1284.

DeRoos, R.   1960   The corticosteroids of bird adrenals investigated by in vitro incubation. Anat. Rec. 138:343.

Dulin, W. F.   1953   The effects of adrenocorticotrophin on the White Leghorn cockerel and capon. Endocrinol. 53:233.

Dulin, W. F.   1956   Effects of corticosterone, cortisone and hydrocortisone on fat metabolism. Proc. Soc. Ex. Biol. & Med. 92:253.

Elliott, T. R., and I. Tuckett   1906   Cortex and medulla in the suprarenal glands. J. Physiol. 34:322.

Eranko, O.   1957   Distribution of adrenaline and noradrenaline in the hen adrenal gland. Nature 179:417.

Fujita, H.   1961   An electron microscopic study of the adrenal cortical tissue of the domestic fowl. Z. f. Zellforschung 55:80.

Garren, H. W., and C. S. Shaffner 1956 How the period of exposure to different stress stimuli affects the endocrine and lymphatic gland weights of young chickens. Poultry Sci. 35:266.

Ghosh, A. 1962 A comparative study of the histochemistry of the avian adrenals, in General and Comparative Endocrinology, Supplement I, p. 75. Academic Press, New York.

Ghosh, I., and A. Ghosh 1963 The effect of reserpine on adrenal medulla of the pigeon—A cytochemical investigation. Cytologia 28:146.

Glick, B. 1955 Growth and function of the bursa of Fabricius. Poultry Sci. 34:1196.

Glick, B. 1957 Experimental modification of the growth of the bursa of Fabricius. Poultry Sci. 36:18.

Hartman, F. A., and K. A. Brownell 1949 The Adrenal Gland. Lea & Febiger, Philadelphia.

Hartman, F. A., R. A. Knouff, A. W. McNutt, and J. E. Carver 1947 Chromaffin patterns in bird adrenals. Anat. Rec. 97:211.

Hays, V. J. 1914 The development of the adrenals in the bird. Anat. Rec. 8:451.

Herbert, S. K. 1939 The gonadotrophic and adrenotrophic hormones of the chicken hypophysis. J. Pharm. & Exp. Thera. 65:104.

Herrick, E. H., and J. C. Finerty 1941 The effect of adrenalectomy on the anterior pituitaries of fowls. Endocrinol. 27:279.

Herrick, E. H., and O. Torstveit 1938 Some effects of adrenalectomy in fowls. Endocrinol. 22:469.

Hewitt, W. F. 1947 The essential role of the adrenal cortex in the hypertrophy of the ovotestis following ovariectomy in the hen. Anat. Rec. 98:159.

Hill, C. H., M. K. Warren, H. W. Garren, and V. C. Baker 1961 Blood citric acid concentration as affected by heat and cold stress and adrenocorticotrophic hormone. Poultry Sci. 40:422.

Hill, R. T., and A. S. Parkes 1934 Hypophysectomy of birds. I: Technique, with a note on results. Proc. Roy. Soc. London, B, 115:402.

Holmes, W. N., D. G. Butler, and J. G. Phillips 1961 Observations on the effect of maintaining glaucous winged gulls on fresh water and sea water for long periods. J. Endocrinol. 23:53.

Holmes, W. N., J. G. Phillips, and D. G. Butler 1961 The effect of adrenocortical steroids on the renal and extra-renal responses of the domestic duck after hypertonic saline loading. Endocrinol. 69:483.

Hooker, C. W., and V. J. Collins 1940 Androgenic action of DCA. Endocrinol. 26:269.

Howard, A. N., and B. J. Constable 1958 The metabolism of adrenocorticotrophic hormone and ascorbic acid in the chick. Biochem. J. 69:501.

Huble, J. 1957 Effects of cortisone acetate on chondrogenesis and ossification in cockerels. Acta Endocrinol. 25:59.

Jailer, J. W., and N. F. Boas 1950 The inability of epinephrine or adrenocorticotrophic hormone to deplete the ascorbic acid content of the chick adrenal. Endocrinol. 45:312.

Jones, I. Chester, J. G. Phillips, and W. N. Holmes 1958 Comparative physiology of the adrenal cortex, in Comparative Endocrinology, ed. A. Gorbman. John Wiley & Sons, Inc., New York.

Juhn, M., and J. B. Mitchell, Jr. 1929 On endocrine weights in Brown Leghorns. Am. J. Physiol. 88:177.

Kar, A. B. 1947a The adrenal cortex, testicular reactions in the fowl: The effect of castration and replacement therapy on the adrenal cortex. Anat. Rec. 99:177.

Kar, A. B. 1947b The action of male and female sex hormones on the adrenals in the fowl. Anat. Rec. 97:551.

Karnofsky, D. A., C. C. Stock, and C. P. Rhoads 1950 The effect of adrenal steroids on growth of chick embryo. Fed. Proc. 9:290.

Knouff, R. A., and F. A. Hartman 1951 A microscopic study of the adrenal of the brown pelican. Anat. Rec. 109:161.

Kudzia, J., and L. R. Champion 1963 Investigations concerning the effect of cortisone in the domestic fowl. Poultry Sci. 34:1357.

Kumaran, J. D. S., and C. W. Turner 1949 The endocrinology of spermatogenesis in birds. II: Effect of androgens. Poultry Sci. 28:739.

McGowen, J. P. 1936 Suprarenal virilism in a domestic hen; its possible significance. J. Exp. Biol. 13:377.

Miller, R. A., and O. Riddle 1939 Stimulation of adrenal cortex of pigeons by anterior pituitary hormones. Proc. Soc. Exp. Biol. & Med. 41:518.

Miller, R. A., and O. Riddle 1941 Cellular response to insulin in suprarenals of pigeons. Proc. Soc. Exp. Biol. & Med. 47:449.

Miller, R. A., and O. Riddle 1942 The cytology of the adrenal cortex of normal pigeons and in experimentally induced atrophy and hypertrophy. Am. J. Anat. 71:311.

Miller, R. A., and O. Riddle 1943 Effects of prolactin and cortical hormones on body weight and food intake of adrenalectomized pigeons. Proc. Soc. Exp. Biol. & Med. 52:231.

Morris, D. M. 1953 Adrenal hypertrophy in the White Leghorn cockerel after treatment with thiouracil and thyroidectomy. Science 117:61.

Moscona, M. H., and D. A. Karnofsky 1960 Cortisone induced modifications in the development of the chick embryo. Endocrinol. 66:533.

Moszkowski, A. 1949 Pouvoir corticotrope et gonadotrope de l'hypophyse de l'embryon de poulet. Comp. Rend. Soc. Biol. 143:1332.

Nagra, C. L., G. J. Baum, and R. K. Meyer 1960 Corticosterone levels in adrenal effluent blood of some gallinaceous birds. Proc. Soc. Exp. Biol. & Med. 105:68.

Nagra, C. L., J. B. Birnie, J. Baum, and R. K. Meyer 1963 The role of the pituitary in regulating steroid secretion by the avian adrenal. Gen. & Comp. Endocrinol. 3:274.

Nalbandov, A. V., and L. E. Card 1943 Effect of hypophysectomy of growing chicks. J. Exp. Zool. 94:387.

Newcomer, W. S. 1959 Effects of hypophysectomy on some functional aspects of the adrenal gland of the chicken. Endocrinol. 65:133.

Newcomer, W. S. 1960 The bursa of Fabricius as an indicator of chronic stress in immature chickens. Endocrinol. 67:264.

Newcomer, W. W. 1962 Reserpine and adrenocortical function in chickens. Am. J. Physiol. 202:337.

Oakberg, E. F. 1951 Genetic differences in quantitative histology of the adrenal organ weights, and inter-organ correlations in White Leghorn chickens. Growth 15:57.

Parkes, A. S., and H. Selye 1936 Adrenalectomy of birds. J. Physiol. 86:35 (Proc.).

Parkins, W. M. 1931 An experimental study of bilateral adrenalectomy in the fowl. Anat. Rec. 51:39.

Paschkis, K. E. 1941 Androgenic action of DCA. Proc. Soc. Exp. Biol. & Med. 46:366.

Perek, M., and E. Bedrak 1962 The effect of cold and debeaking upon the adrenal ascorbic acid concentration of chickens fed aureomycin supplement. Poultry Sci. 41:1149.

Perek, M., and B. Eckstein 1959 The adrenal ascorbic acid content of molting hens and the effect of ACTH on adrenal ascorbic content of laying hens. Poultry Sci. 38:996.

Perek, M., B. Eckstein, and Z. Eshkol 1959 The effect of ACTH on adrenal ascorbic acid in laying hens. Endocrinol. 64:831.

Perek, M., and A. Eilat 1960 Effect of removal of bursa Fabricii on depletion of adrenal ascorbic acid in ACTH treated chicks. Endocrinol. 66:304.

Perry, J. C. 1941 The antagonistic action of adrenaline on the reproductive cycle of the English sparrow, Passer domesticus. Anat. Rec. 79:57.

Phillips, J. G., W. N. Holmes, and D. G. Butler 1961 The effect of total and subtotal adrenalectomy on the renal and extra-renal response of the domestic duck (Anas platyrhynchus) to saline loading. Endocrinol. 69:958.

Phillips, J. G., and I. Chester Jones 1957 The identity of adrenocortical secretions in lower vertebrates. J. Endocrinol. 16:111.

Quiring, D. P. 1951 Studies on the comparative anatomy of the endocrine system. Growth 15:121.

Riddle, O. 1923 Studies on the physiology of reproduction in birds. XIV: Suprarenal hypertrophy coincident with ovulation. Am. J. Physiol. 66:322.

Roy, R. N., and Guha, B. C. 1958 Species differences in regard to biosynthesis of ascorbic acid. Nature 182:319.

Sames, G. L., and J. H. Leathem 1951 Influence of ICA and cortisone acetate on body weight of chick embryos. Proc. Soc. Exp. Biol. & Med. 78:231.

Sandor, T., J. Lamoreux, and A. Lanthier 1963 Adrenocortical function in birds: In vitro biosynthesis of radioactive corticosteroids from pregnenolone-7-H[3] and progesterone-4-C[14] by adrenal glands of the domestic duck and chicken. Endocrinol. 73:629.

Sauer, F. C., and H. B. Latimer 1931 Sex differences in the proportion of cortex and medulla in the chicken suprarenal. Anat. Rec. 50:289.

Schooley, J. P., O. Riddle, and R. W. Bates 1941 Replacement therapy in hypophysectomized juvenile pigeons. Am. J. Anat. 69:123.

Schümann, H. J. 1957 The distribution of adrenaline and noradrenaline in chromaffin granules from the chicken. J. Physiol. 137:318.

Selye, H. 1942 Production of nephrosclerosis by overdosage with desoxycorticosterone acetate. Canadian Med. Assoc. J. 47:515.

Selye, H. 1949 Textbook of Endocrinology. 2nd ed. Acta Endocrinologica, Inc., Montreal.

Selye, H., and S. Friedman 1941 The action of various steroid hormones on the testis. Endocrinol. 28:229.

Shellabarger, C. G. 1954 Effects of cortisone on thyroid function in White Leghorn cockerels. Endocrinol. 55:100.

Sheridan, M. N., W. D. Belt, and F. A. Hartman 1963 The fine structure of the interrenal cells of the brown pelican. Acta Anat. 53:55.

Stamler, J. 1952 Effects of adrenal steroid F in depancreatized, cholesterol-fed cockerels. Fed. Proc. 11:153.

Stamler, J., R. Pick, and L. N. Katz 1951 Effects of corticoids and ACTH on fluid exchange, blood pressure, glycemia, cholesterolemia and atherogenesis in chicks. Fed. Proc. 10:131.

Sturkie, P. D. Avian Physiology (1st ed., 1954) Cornell University Press, Ithaca, N.Y.

Sure, B. 1938 Influence of avitaminosis on weights of endocrine glands. Endocrinol. 23:575.

Taber, E., K. W. Salley, and J. S. Knight 1956 The effects of hypoadrenalism and chronic inanition on the development of the rudimentary gonad in sinistrally ovariectomized fowl. Anat. Rec. 126:177.

Taylor, D. J., J. Greenberg, E. S. Josephson, and E. M. Nadel 1956 Histochemical sudanophilia and cholesterol concentration in the adrenal glands of chicks parasitized with plasmodium gallinaceum. Acta Endocrinol. 22:173.

Uotila, U. U. 1939 On the fuchsinophile and pale cells in the adrenal cortex tissue of the fowl. Anat. Rec. 75:439.

Urist, M. R. 1959 The effects of calcium deprivation upon the blood, adrenal cortex, ovary and skeleton in domestic fowl. Rec. Prog. in Hormone Res., Vol. 15. Academic Press, New York.

Urist, M. R., and N. M. Deutsch 1960a Influence of ACTH upon avian species and osteoporosis. Proc. Soc. Exp. Biol. & Med. 104:35.

Urist, M. R., and N. M. Deutsch 1960b Effects of cortisone upon blood, adrenal cortex, gonads, and the development of osteoporosis in birds. Endocrinol. 66:805.

Vannini, E. 1947 The effects of desoxycorticosterone acetate on the development of the gonads of the chick embryo. Bol. Soc. Biol. Sper. 23:240 (English abstract, Animal Breeding Abs. 18[1950]: 104.).

Venzke, W. G. 1943 Endocrine gland weights of chick embryos. Growth 7:265.

Wheeler, N. C., G. L. Search, and F. N. Andrews 1942 The effect of epinephrine upon semen production in the domestic fowl. Endocrinol. 30:369.

Zarrow, M. X., D. L. Greenman, J. Kollius, and D. Dalrymple 1962 The pituitary adrenal axis in the bird. Gen. & Comp. Endocrinol. 2:177.

Zarrow, M. W., and I. G. Zarrow 1950 Ascorbic acid in the adrenal gland of the duck. Anat. Rec. 108 (Abs.).

CHAPTER 22

The Nervous System of Birds

BY JASPER TEN CATE

INTRODUCTION

THE nervous system of birds and all other vertebrates consists of nerve cells and their branches (processes), the neuroglial cells and fibers. The nerve cells and their processes are the important active elements; the later are primarily supporting structures. Nerve cells are present in the brain, in the spinal cord, and also in the outlying ganglia of the autonomic system.

The nerve cell or neuron consists of three parts: the cell body with its branches, called dendrites, and one axon or axis cylinder which forms the nerve fiber. The dendrites branch out through surrounding tissue, so as to give the neuron a large surface for the reception of nervous impulses from other neurons and also for the exchange with the blood and the lymph of the products of metabolism. Each nerve cell contains a nucleus, embedded in the cytoplasm. The nerve cell is distinguished from all other cells by very fine filaments—the neurofibrils—which enter it from the dendrites and run toward the axon. Some investigators have considered these neurofibrils to be artifacts produced by the staining of microscopic specimens, but others claim to have seen them in the living cells of lower animals (Figures 101 and 102).

Another characteristic structure of the nerve cell is the aggregation of fine basophilic granules, first described by Nissl and called the Nissl bodies, which appear in the cytoplasm of the cell body after staining with toluidine blue. These granules can be regarded as stored food or fuel, since fatigue, asphyxia, and various poisons

697

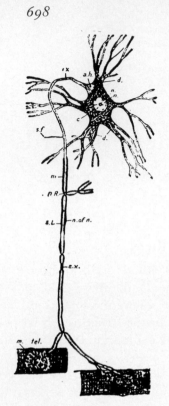

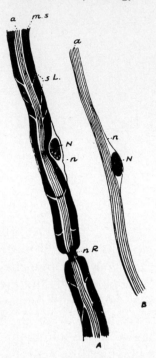

Figure 101. Diagram of a motor nerve cell with its nerve fiber and two motor end plates (after Bakker).

a.h., axon hillock; *d,* dendrites; *a. x.,* axis cylinder; *m,* medullary sheath; *n R.,* node of Ranvier.

Figure 102. A, portion of a medullated nerve fiber; *B,* portion of a nonmedullated nerve fiber.

a, the axis-cylinder containing neurofibrils; *m.s.,* the medullary sheath; *n,* the neurolemma; *N,* a nucleus; *n R,* a node of Ranvier.

cause a breakdown of the substance in the cell known as chromatolysis. These granules are not found in the axons (Figure 103).

In cross section the axon shows a central bundle of fibers, the axis cylinder, surrounded by a membrane, the neurilemma, and often by a fatty covering, the myelin sheath, which lies between the axis cylinder and the neurilemma. Axons which have a myelin sheath are called myelinated nerve fibers. The myelin sheath is interrupted at regular intervals, giving the appearance of constrictions at these points, which are called the nodes of Ranvier. The myelinated nerve fibers form the white substance of the nervous system, whereas dendrites, cell bodies, and nonmyelinated axons form the gray matter.

The axons end in arborizations known as the terminal boutons of Cajal. These have only a functional connection with the dendrites of other cells or the cell bodies themselves. Neighboring cells—neurons—do not anastomose with each other; however, the impulses of one neuron may come into close contiguity with the

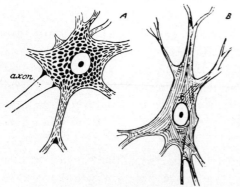

Figure 103. A, Nerve cell after coloring with toluidine-blue: the Nissl bodies.

B, nerve cell after coloring with the silver method of Golgi: the neurofibrils.

cell body or processes of another. The place where the nervous impulses actually pass from one neuron to another is called the synapse.

Nerve Centers

The nerve cells in the gray matter of the spinal cord and brain are mostly arranged in groups, which have a more or less similar configuration and a common function. These groups of cells form the centers. Formerly the central nervous system was believed to be composed of a series of separate and circumscribed divisions of cells with definite functions, namely the centers. More recent investigations have shown that the aggregations of cells with the same function need not be anatomically definable since they often comprise several closely coordinated groups, which may be at considerable distances from each other. The identity is one of function rather than of location. One group of cells—the higher centers —may be of predominant importance, and may control the subordinate centers of secondary importance.

Degeneration and regeneration. When the axon is cut across, the part so cut off from the cell undergoes degenerative changes. The acute changes on each side of the cut are known as traumatic degeneration. The distal portion of the axon shows what is known as secondary or Wallerian degeneration. The myelin sheath of the medullated nerves breaks up into irregular droplets of myelin, and the neurofibrils swell and fuse. Later the axis cylinder itself breaks up. Meanwhile the cells of the neurilemma proliferate, and excitability is lost.

If the nerve fibers of a peripheral nerve have been cut across, the function may be restored by axis cylinders which sprout from the proximal cut nerve stump. These enter and grow down into the degenerated distal stump. In this way some restoration of continuity may be obtained. The nerve fibers of the central nervous system, which have no neurilemma, have only a limited capacity for such new growth after damage. In the adult brain no such regeneration is possible.

Metabolism of the nerve tissue. Like every other tissue, nervous tissues continually take up oxygen and give off carbon dioxide. When a nerve is stimulated, the consumption of O_2 and production of CO_2 are increased. Its glucose requirement and its metabolism increase also. There is a breakdown of adenosine diphosphate (ADP) and of creatine phosphate. Hill (1933), and others since, have shown that the heat production is increased when impulses pass along the nerve. These facts indicate that the ionic balance and the conductivity depend on metabolic activity in the nerve.

Function of the nerve fibers. The functions of the nervous fibers can best be investigated in a nerve-muscle preparation using the gastrocnemius muscle of a frog with its attached sciatic nerve. Stimulation of the nerve in this preparation is followed after a very short delay (latent period) by a contraction of the muscle. This shows that the principal properties of the nerve fibers, and so of the nervous tissue in general, are its excitability and conductivity. A visible contraction of the muscle is shown when the nervous impulse reaches it. Under normal conditions a direct excitation of the nerve fibers very seldom takes place. The principal function of the nerve fibers is the conduction of impulses or the propagation of an excitatory state along the nerve.

Stimulation of the nerve fibers. When a stimulus is applied to a nerve, chemical and electrical changes appear along the whole nerve fiber; these are completely independent of the nature of the primary stimulus, which may be electrical, mechanical, thermal, or chemical. In physiological experiments the stimuli most used are weak electrical currents, because these do not damage the nerves.

Membrane potentials and the nerve impulse. It is generally believed that the nerve impulse is a self-propagating electrical charge known as the action potential, which passes along the nerve. This important finding was made by Adrian (1935); further details were established by Katz (1939), Bodian (1942), Hodgkin and Huxley (1945), and Huxley (1954).

The electrical charge depends on the existence of a resting potential in the nerve, maintained by vital ion pumps, which keep up a high concentration of potassium inside the nerve and a low concentration of sodium as compared to the surrounding medium. In consequence, the interior of the nerve is electrically negative as compared to its exterior, a fact which was established in the large nerves of the squid (*Loligo*) by Hodgkin and Huxley (1945), who placed one electrode inside the axon and the other outside it and then connected them through an amplifier with an oscillograph. In this way they registered the resting potential. When the nerve is stimulated the action potential generated thereby will usually be much greater than the resting potential (Bullock and Hagiwara, 1957; Brock and Eccles, 1958). The action potential represents an alteration of the resting potential, or depolarization (Figure 104).

Erlanger and Gasser (1937) contributed much to our knowledge of the electric phenomena in nerves during the conduction of stimuli. They showed that under identical conditions, the action potentials propagated along the nerve always have a characteristic and constant value. The action potentials are propagated at the same speed as the impulse and are present in every part of the nerve during conduction. The conduction of the impulse and also

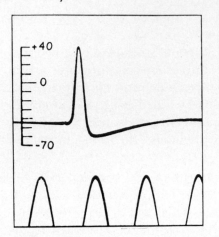

Figure 104. Action potential recorded between inside and outside of squid giant axon. The vertical scale indicates the potential of the internal electrode in mV, the seawater outside being taken as zero potential. Time marker 500 cyc./sec. (After Hodgkin and Huxley, *J. Phys.* 104:176, 1945.)

of the action potential is depressed by cold.

Nature of the nerve impulse. On the basis of the foregoing, the explanation of the nervous impulse is as follows: A wave of depolarization moves rapidly over the polarized membranes of the surface of the nerve fibers and produces the action potential.

It is apparent that in myelinated nerves the impulse does not pass steadily along the nerve but jumps from one node of Ranvier to the next, so that the intensity at one node is just sufficient to depolarize the next node. This phenomenon is known as the saltatory nature of the nervous impulse. It has been shown by Huxley and Stämpfli (1949) that the nerve is much more excitable at the nodes, and that the action potentials there are greater, than elsewhere.

Humoral transmission. Loewi (1921) found that stimulation of the vagus nerve caused a liberation of acetylcholine in the heart. Later Brown (1937) showed that acetylcholine is the essential transmitter, not only in the parasympathetic nerves but also in those that innervate skeletal muscles. It was shown that during the stimulation of the nerve the acetylcholine acts not directly on the muscle fibers themselves but on the end-plate in the muscle (Dale, 1937; Dale, Feldberg, and Vogt, 1936; Castillo and Katz, 1956).

According to the present view there is an activity in the nerve which leads primarily to the liberation of acetylcholine and the establishment of an end-plate potential by depolarization, an effect which in turn causes the excitation of the muscle fibers.

The role of acetylcholine in the propagation of the impulse along the nerve fibers is not yet fully understood. Nachmansohn (1955) supposed the depolarization that accompanies the passage of the impulse along the nerve fiber to be the result of an increased permeability of the membrane, owing to the sudden appearance of acetylcholine. According to him, the production and destruction of acetylcholine by cholinesterase (an enzyme which can very quickly neutralize acetylcholine) is an essential factor in the conduction of nerve impulses.

Direction and velocity of the nerve impulse. Although it has been demonstrated experimentally that an isolated nerve fiber can conduct impulses in both directions, under normal circumstances in the body the nerve impulses most likely are conducted in one direction only, since the impulse can only pass in one direction across a synapse and thence to the axon via the dendrites and cell body. In consequence there is a differentiation of function between various nerve fibers in the body. In afferent nerves the impulses are normally conducted in the direction of the nerve centers; in efferent nerves the impulses travel in the opposite direction.

The velocity of propagation along a nerve was first measured by Helmholtz (1850). The velocity of the impulse can be determined with precision by stimulating a nerve at two different points and recording the time taken for the monophasic potential spike to arrive at a distant point, or, less accurately, by the time taken for the occurrence of a muscular response (Figure 105).

At room temperature the impulse velocity in the motor nerves of a cold-blooded animal (e.g. the frog) averages 27 meters per second; in warm-blooded animals it is from to 90 to 120 meters per second. As a rule large fibers conduct more rapidly than small ones.

Erlanger and Gasser (1937) divided the nerve fibers of mammals into three groups. Group A consists of somatic medullated motor and sensory fibers, which carry impulses to and from the muscles and from the skin. The large motor fibers have the greatest propagation velocity—up to 120 m./sec.; the smaller sensory fibers have a conduction velocity of some 25 to 50 m./sec. Group B consists of fine autonomic medullated fibers in which the conduction velocity is from 3 to 14 m./sec. Group C consists of fine nonmedullated fibers in which the conduction velocities are 0.3–1.6 m./sec. for sympathetic fibers and 0.7–2.3 m./sec. for dorsal root fibers. Sensory afferent impulses travel at about a third the speed of efferent impulses in the same nerve (Gasser, 1950).

Compared with those of mammals, a preponderance of avian nerve fibers are small. This has been shown by Graf (1956), who

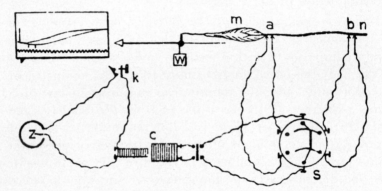

Figure 105. Diagram of arrangement of experiment according to Helmholtz (1850) for determining the velocity of an impulse transmitted down a nerve.

investigated microscopically the most representative parts of the peripheral nervous system in pigeons. The most prominent feature of the peripheral nerves is the relative absence of large fibers. In accordance with this fact, the conduction velocity of the nerve fibers should be less in birds than in mammals—at least in domestic birds, which move relatively slowly. The velocity of the impulse transmission in peripheral nerves was investigated by Carpenter and Bergland (1957), who measured the impulse velocity in chick embryos, young chicks, and adult chickens. The linear velocities in meters per second were 0.5 for 10-day-old embryos, 7 to 11 for the 21-day embryo or chick, and 50 for adult chickens.

In chickens the increase in conduction velocity during development was also concomitant with the deposition of myelin in the nerve fibers. A linear relation between fiber diameter and conduction velocity was observed also by Carpenter and Bergland, especially in adult chickens.

Reflexes. One of the fundamental functions of the central nervous system is reflex activity. This will be described in some detail (see Sherrington, 1906), because a thorough understanding of the theory of reflexes is necessary before the action of the central nervous system can be fully appreciated. According to Whytt (1755), the first investigations into the physiology of reflexes were carried out in 1730 by Stephen Hales but were not published. Hales dem-

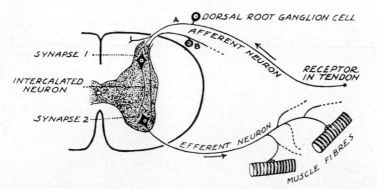

Figure 106. Diagram illustrating the reflex arc with all its subdivisions.

onstrated that the legs of a decapitated frog would withdraw when pinched, but that this reaction disappeared if the spinal cord was destroyed.

A reflex action is the simplest reaction of the nervous system, and is evoked by irritation of the sense organs. The impulse coming from an irritated sense organ is conducted to the cells of a center and thence along the axons of these cells (the efferent fibers) to the effector organs (muscles or glands; see Figure 106).

The reflex may be conscious, if the impulse is conducted also to the brain, or subconscious, if the impulse remains limited to the spinal cord.

The afferent sensory neuron, of which the cell is in the posterior root ganglion, and the motor neuron, whose cell is situated in the corresponding anterior horn of the gray matter of the spinal cord on the same side, form the monosynaptic reflex arc. This is the most simple reflex. One or more intermediate neurons can be interposed between the sensory and the motor neuron. In that event we have a multisynaptic reflex arc. An intermediate neuron can also be connected to an efferent neuron of the opposite side of the cord, to give a crossed reflex arc.

The junction between one neuron and another is formed by a synapse. The synaptic transmission of nerve impulses differs fundamentally from the conduction along the nerve fiber. When one nerve cell activates another, its impulse must pass across the synapse. This requires a certain interval of time, which for most synapses in warm-blooded animals amounts to 0.5-1.0 m./sec. The reflex latency depends on the number of synaptic delays at neurons successively activated by impulses on their way to the motor and neuron and the muscle. The anterior-horn cell and its axon, and the muscle fibers innervated by it, are called the motor unit.

Reflex arcs have characteristic properties which may be best studied in spinal animals, i.e. those in which the spinal cord has been isolated from the brain by transection. The most important aspects of impulse conduction in the reflex arc are:

1. *Forward conduction.* Conduction through a reflex arc is possible in one direction only, since the synapses transmit the excitatory process unidirectionally from one axon to the next dendrite.
2. *Facilitation.* If a stimulus is repeated frequently, but not rapidly enough so as to produce fatigue, the reflex becomes increasingly easy to elicit and the time becomes shorter.
3. *Fatigue.* When the stimuli follow each other rapidly, fatigue may readily be produced.
4. *Summation.* Repetition of a subliminal and therefore ineffective stimulus may produce a reflex response. If two or more subliminal stimuli are given at sufficiently short intervals, their effect is summated so that together they produce an excitation.
5. *Synaptic delay or resistance.* The time between the stimulation and the reflex response—the reaction time—is much longer than it would be if the pathways were continuous nerve fibers only.

By subtracting from the reflex time the time needed for the passage of an impulse along the nervous pathway, the synaptic delay can be calculated; it is found to be about 0.002 seconds per synapse.

6. *Inhibition.* One reflex can inhibit another. If, for instance, two different reflexes are initiated simultaneously, the one more important for the life of the animal inhibits—i.e. suppresses— the less important, if the latter has a contrary action.

7. *After-discharge.* One of the most peculiar properties of the reflex action is the phenomenon Sherrington has called the after-discharge. The contraction of muscle, or other action produced reflexively, does not cease immediately after cessation of the stimulus, but continues for a short while.

8. *Rebound.* If, during reflex contraction of a muscle, the stimulation is suddenly interrupted, after a short pause the muscle exhibits an after-discharge. Sherrington called this phenomenon the rebound.

Reflexes can be classified in two distinct groups according to the receptors whose stimulation gives rise to the reflex action. The *exteroceptive reflexes* are provoked by irritation of 1) the cutaneous receptors, the sense organs of the skin for perception of pain, touch, cold, and warmth; 2) the chemoreceptors involved in taste and smell; and 3) the distance receptors, used in vision and hearing.

To the second group belong the *interoceptive reflexes* which are evoked by irritation of 1) the visceroceptors, the sense organs in the various parts of the intestine, and 2) the proprioceptors, the sense organs that are stimulated by actions of the body itself. These are in the muscle spindles and tendons, and also in the organs of equilibrium.

Physiology of the Nervous System of Birds

The central nervous system of normal living animals acts as one complete system serving all organs; but anatomically and physiologically its various parts present such great individual differences that it is necessary to treat them separately.

THE SPINAL CORD

The spinal cord of birds may be divided into several segments with a pair of roots on each side, namely the anterior or ventral and posterior or dorsal roots. The anterior roots originate from the motor cells of the anterior horn of the gray matter. Efferent in

←⦗⦗⦗⦗

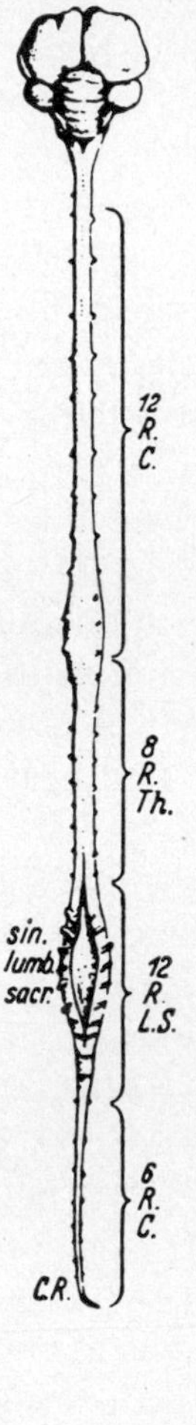

Figure 107. The spinal cord of the pigeon (after Ariens Kappers).

R.C. cervical roots; *R.Th.,* thoracic roots; *R.L.S.,* lumbosacral roots; *C.R.,* coccygeal roots; *sin. lumb. sacr.,* sinus lumbosacralis.

function, they conduct impulses from the spinal cord to the muscles and glands. The posterior roots are characterized by the presence of a ganglion. They are afferent or sensory, and conduct impulses from the periphery to the spinal cord.

The spinal cord of birds is distinguished by the great number of segments in the cervical cord and by the lumbosacral sinus, which is located between the posterior strands of the lumbosacral cord (Figure 107).

In birds the sensory innervation of the skin is arranged segmentally. And one sensory area of the skin— the dermatome—is supplied by a single dorsal root, which always widens towards the ventral midline. Each dermatome is partly overlapped by adjacent dermatomes. Therefore transection of a single nerve root does not produce any local anesthesia of the skin, but the transection of two or more adjacent roots does result in fairly extensive loss of sensation, (see ten Cate, 1936).

Not much is known about the innervation of the skeletal muscles in birds, or of its segmental arrangement. Quednau (1926) investigated the segmental innervation of some muscles in pigeons, using the isometric registration of muscle contraction. He found that the sum of the muscular tensions in M. extensor metacarpi ulnaris produced by successive stimulations of the first and second nerve roots of the brachial plexus was equal to the tension produced by the simultaneous stimulation of both nerve roots. These experiments confirmed the segmental arrangement of the innervation of the musculature in pigeons, but do not account for a double innervation of muscle fibers in birds, as was supposed by some investigators.

Whereas the innervation of the muscles in birds has been somewhat sketchily studied, the reflex activity of the spinal cord has been the subject of numerous studies.

Many investigations of the functions of the spinal cord and other parts of the central nervous system have been made by transecting the nervous axis at different levels or by the removal of some part of it. Separation of a lower part of the central nervous system from a higher part causes a loss of certain functions in consequence of the interruption of the pathways by which the lower centers are affected by the higher ones. After transection of the dorsal or lumbar cord birds and other animals may survive for months or even years, and the reactions in the spinal cord can be studied without interfering influences from higher centers of the central nervous system.

An animal with a transected spinal cord is called a spinal animal. It shows loss of motility and sensation on both sides in the areas of the body supplied by the nerves below the transection for the initial period of what is called spinal shock, during which all reflexes are absent. After a certain time typical protective spinal reflexes appear; later other reflexes of the limbs and of the trunk may take place.

As early as 1858 Schiff had drawn attention to the great reflex capacity of spinal birds. After transection of the spinal cord at the level of the thoracic segments it is possible, by passively bending and stretching one foot of the bird, to produce antagonistic stretching and bending reflexes of the opposite foot. Later, when reflex activity has further increased, lifting the pigeon causes rapid rhythmical motions of both feet, similar to the alternating movements of the hind legs of transected dogs, first described by Freusberg (1874).

In birds with a transected spinal cord various reflex movements of the tail may be provoked. If a pigeon with head and body extended vertically is suddenly raised upward to the horizontal position, there is a fanlike spreading of the main tail feathers. If the pigeon is pushed back to its original position, there is only a brief upward flick of the tail. These reflexes normally serve to maintain the bird's balance. According to Clementi (1914), the tail reflexes arise in the uropygial articulation as a result of proprioceptive stimuli which are independent of the higher centers.

Although alternating movements of the hind limbs are an essential element in the walking movements, no true locomotor movements of the hind limbs have been elicited in the spinal bird. Tarchanoff (1895) described a kind of walking movement in decapitated ducks, but this was observed only immediately after decapitation and was of very short duration. The walking movements of the legs were accompanied by violent beating of the wings. These phenomena, caused by the strong excitation of the spinal cord in decerebration, certainly do not have the character of normal walking movements.

Under normal circumstances a spinal bird is unable to walk, since owing to the absence of the control of the higher centers, it can no longer maintain the upright posture. It was thought probable that locomotor movements of the hind limbs would occur if the birds were placed in such a position that their legs could maintain contact with the ground (Figures 108 and 109). To this end a small 4-wheeled carriage was constructed, in which a pigeon could be fixed in a normal position and in such a way that its extended legs could reach the ground. When a spinal pigeon was so fixed in this carriage a true walking movement in the hind limbs could be evoked by applying painful stimuli to the hind part of the body. In this way the pigeon could move over relatively great distances. The lumbosacral cord of birds shows a high degree of autonomy of the lower centers in the coordination of walking movements. The

Figure 108. Spinal pigeon resting on belly. The tone of the muscles of the hind limbs is very low.

Figure 109. Walking movements of the spinal pigeon fixed to the carriage.

higher centers initiate and regulate these movements (ten Cate, 1960).

Unlike the leg reflexes of a spinal bird, which tend to alternate, the reflex movements of the wings are generally identical and simultaneous. A weak stimulus causes only a slight movement of the irritated wing; a somewhat stronger irritation of one of the wings or of other parts of the body causes identical, simultaneous, and well-coordinated movements of both wings. Both wings are rhythmically fanned and raised, as in normal flight. A single stimulus

can cause one or more of such wing movements. Unlike the leg
reflexes, the reflex movements of the wings in spinal birds are very
monotonous (ten Cate, 1936, and ten Cate *et al.*, 1937).

Trendelenburg (1910) gave us a deeper insight into the action
of the spinal centers which govern the movements of the wings.
After unilateral transection of the dorsal roots of the wings he
found that the position in which the wings were held was identical
on the two sides, even when the pigeon was suspended with its
head downward. Artificially induced abnormal positions of the
wings were corrected only in the normal innervated wing. The capacity for flight and even for performing turns was retained. If a
spinal pigeon is held by the tail, it beats both wings normally.
After complete transection of the dorsal roots which innervate the
wings, flying capacity quite naturally is lost.

After unilateral denervation of one wing, the loss of centripetal
afferent stimuli from the one side is amply replaced by those of the
other side. Therefore such pigeons can fly well and maintain their
balance. Movements in which both wings participate show no abnormalities; unilateral control of motion impulses suffices for both
sides. When the pigeon is forced into a position in which only one
wing is normally used, then abnormalities arise if the wing needed
for correction is the denervated one. Rhythmical beating of the
wings originates in the spinal cord itself, and depends on the reflex
stimulus exerted on each wingbeat by the preceding one.

Experiments in which the dorsal roots of one leg were divided
showed that centripetal stimuli from the normal side could not
compensate, as occurred in the wings! The explanation must be
found in the differing innervation of the extremities, simultaneous in the former, alternating in the latter.

The famous experiments by Goltz and Evald with dogs (1896)
were repeated with pigeons by Sammartino (1933), who extirpated
the entire lumbar cord. Sensation and movement in the caudal
part of the body were lost. The cloacal sphincter lost its tone completely after the operation; but some time later it was regained
and the feces once again were voided spontaneously at regular intervals. Thus, there is a distinct difference between the innervation of smooth and skeletal muscle.

Regeneration in the Spinal Cord

It is important to know how far the process of regeneration of the nerve fibers can take place in the cord following transection. Experiments for determining this on birds have been carried out only by Katherine Clearwaters (1954). She demonstrated that complete structural restitution after transection of the cord occurred only in chick embryos after 2 to 5 days of incubation. Many of the nerve fibers crossed the point of transection and passed into the distal part of the cord. Where there were lesions in the chick, Clearwaters found a few indications of regeneration, but the nerve fibers did not traverse the level of the transection.

In our experiments with adult pigeons (ten Cate, 1960 and earlier) we have made microscopical preparations of the spinal cord to establish the anatomical alterations at the place of transection. A regeneration of the whole spinal cord has not been observed, but we have found some growth of nerve fibers in the proximal as well as in the distal part of the cord. These abortive attempts at regeneration appear as fine fibers growing in various directions.

This disorientation is caused by the growth of connective tissue and the glia, which grow more rapidly than the nervous tissue and form a barrier that impedes the slower-growing nerve fibers from bridging the gap between the two parts of the cut spinal cord. It seems that the failure of the restoration of the connections between the two parts of the cord must be due not so much to a lack of possibility of regeneration of the nerve fibers as to the presence of insurmountable obstacles on their way.

Hamburger (1955) reports that in numerous investigations of reflexes and other problems of neurophysiology, involving transection of the central nervous system of adult birds, the regeneration and restoration of the functional activity has never been observed.

Regeneration of spinal cord in adult mammals (cats and dogs) is likewise very limited (Campbell *et al.*, 1957).

In fetal and newborn mammals, experiments on cord regeneration were more successful. In marked contrast to the lack of functional regeneration reported by Windle and Chambers (1950) in adult cats and dogs, Sugar and Gerard (1940) and Freemen (1952) have found a functional regeneration in newborn and young animals, especially rats, following cord transection. Perhaps this can be explained by the more plastic nature of the central nervous system of the young animals, and the less dense scars of glial and mesodermal elements (Windle and Chambers, 1950). It is not known whether the glial barrier is the most important hindrance to a functional connection of regenerating neurons or the mesodermal connective tissue.

Complete regeneration of the spinal cord can take place apparently only in fishes and urodeles. Regeneration of excised brain parts seems to occur only to a very limited extent in any of the vertebrates (Piat, 1955).

Transmission in the spinal cord

Each separate segment of the spinal cord, as has already been said, is connected to the sensory organs by nerve fibers which enter the dorsal roots, and to muscles and glands by efferent fibers which come from the ventral roots. In addition to these connections, there are those linking each segment to other segments of the cord and to the higher centers of the central nervous system.

The fibers which connect different segments and form the short or association tracts usually lie deep in the white matter. Fibers connecting the spinal segments and the higher centers form long tracts which are of two main kinds: the ascending tracts, which convey impulses upward (centripetally) to the higher centers, and the descending tracts, which convey impulses in the reverse direction (centrifugally).

As a transmission organ the spinal cord of birds has been little investigated. The ascending sensory tracts are relatively poorly developed, and few dorsal fibers run upward to the medulla oblongata. Perhaps this explains the low peripheral sensitivity in birds, whose dorsal roots are relatively smaller than in other animals. According to Ariens-Kappers (1947), this anatomical peculiarity indicates that birds are pre-eminently reflex animals.

The spinal cord of birds contains other long ascending tracts, which proceed ventrolaterally and transmit perception of pain and temperature, and probably muscular perceptions also. These tracts run upward to the tegmentum and tectum opticum of the mid-brain, and are in close association with the centers of balance and vision.

A still longer ascending tract—the tractus spinocerebellaris—originates at the level of the lumbar segments and runs up to the cerebellum. Medial to this is the tractus cerebellospinalis, which conveys impulses in the opposite direction.

Birds have other well-developed descending tracts coming from the root of the optic tectum and from the vestibular nuclei. According to Ariens-Kappers, these connections of the spinal cord with the cerebellum, the vestibular apparatus, and the optic system are thought to be related to the excellent equilibrium known to be possessed by birds.

Experiments with dissected tracts of the spinal cord are generally inconclusive. After complete transection of the thoracic cord, pigeons lay passively with their legs drawn up toward the body. When starting an attempt at flight they beat their wings violently (ten Cate, 1960).

If only one side of the spinal cord is dissected the ipsilateral leg is paralyzed and the tail is twisted toward the intact side. Sensation is only slightly reduced. All these phenomena gradually diminish, and after one or two weeks the pigeons can both stand and walk. Only a slight weakness of the paralyzed leg remains (ten Cate, 1960).

THE AUTONOMIC NERVOUS SYSTEM

The somatic or cerebrospinal part of the central nervous system controls the voluntary striated muscles, which are responsible for the movements of the body in space and for maintaining posture in opposition to gravity and external forces. The involuntary or autonomic nervous system is responsible for the innervation of the viscera: intestines, blood vessels, glands, and in general the organs with nonstriated or smooth muscles. Both systems are coordinated segmentally in the brain stem and in the spinal cord. The control centers for the autonomic system are situated in the hypothalamus.

The involuntary neurons, and also the visceral organs which

they control, possess a certain power of self-government or autonomy; Langley (1903 and 1921) accordingly called them the autonomic nervous system. The organs formed of smooth muscles—and likewise the heart, which is also innervated by autonomic nerves—show a relatively high degree of self-regulation. Whereas the striated muscles of the skeleton degenerate quickly after transection of the motor nerve, the visceral organs, for example the intestine, heart, and oviduct, continue to function for a long time after section of their nerves (denervation); the denervated heart continues to beat and the intestine to show peristaltic waves, and so on. Anatomically the autonomic nervous system of birds show little specialization in comparison with that of other Amniota. It can be divided into two parts, the sympathetic and the parasympathetic systems, which are anatomically, physiologically, and pharmacologically quite different.

The sympathetic nervous system originates in the lateral horns of the gray matter of the spinal cord, the nuclei intermediolaterales. The axons of the cells of these centers leave the thoracic and lumbar segments of the spinal cord by way of the anterior (ventral) roots and reach a chain of ganglia, joined to each other by connecting fibers, which form the pair of lateral sympathetic chains situated one on each side of the vertebral column.

Although it has been generally supposed that these two chains merge to form a single chain and an unpaired ganglion in the cloacal region of birds (ganglion impar), more recent studies on the chicken do not support this belief. Hseih (see Grahame, 1953) reported that the chicken has no impar ganglion; and Freedman (unpublished) likewise did not observe it.

At the cranial end of each chain is a large upper cervical ganglion, from which nerve fibers run to the head. The cervical part of the lateral chain consists of two tracts. The deeper one runs in a channel formed by the transverse processes of the cervical vertebrae. The superficial tract follows the vagus nerve in its course and reaches the thoracolumbar chain at the end of the cervical region. In birds, the abdominal part of the chain is more prominent than the thoracic part. These are the most important peculiarities of the structure of the sympathetic system in birds (Figure 110).

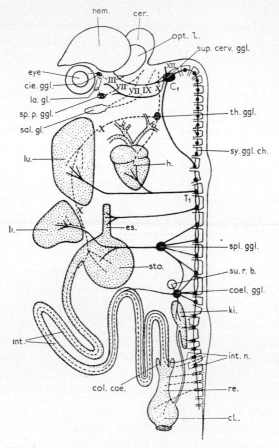

Figure 110. Diagram of sympathetic fibers (drawn outlines) and para-sympathetic fibers (broken lines) showing their course from the central nervous system to the viscera.

I–XII, brain nerves; C₁ first cervical nerve; T₁, first thoraci nerve; cer., cerebellum; cie.ggl., ciliary ganglion; cL., cloaca; coel. gg., coeliac ganglion; int., intestine; int.n., intestinal nerves; ki., kidney; la. gl., lachrymal gland; li., liver; lu., lung; opt., optic lobe; re., rectum; sal.gl., salivary gland; sp.p. ggl., sphenopalatine ganglion; spl.ggl., mesenteric ganglion and splanchnic nerves; sto., stomach; su.r.b., suprarenal body; sup.cer.ggl., superior cervical ganglion; sy.ggl.ch., sympathetic ganglion chain; th.ggl., thoracic ganglion. (After Ariens-Kappers.)

The sympathetic fibers which run from the spinal cord to the ganglia of the lateral chain, and there make synapses with the cells of the ganglia, are called preganglionic fibers (first neuron). The second neuron, consisting of the postganglionic fibers, begins at the nerve cells of the ganglia and runs to the peripheral tissues.

The postganglionic sympathetic fibers run with the spinal nerves to the blood vessels, the smooth muscles which move the feathers, and to the glands of the skin. The postganglionic fibers whose cell bodies are in the upper cervical ganglion also run to the viscera of the thorax. Other preganglionic sympathetic fibers bypass the ganglia of the lateral chain and terminate in the splanchnic prevertebral ganglia (Cannon and Rosenbluth, 1937; Ariens-Kappers). Some of the sympathetic fibers bypass the lateral chain to end directly in the local network of the visceral organs— namely the interconnected nerve plexuses together with parasympathetic fibers.

According to Langley (1904), the sympathetic nervous system of birds resembles in general the sympathetic system of mammals. Of those features applying especially to birds it may be noted that the feathers are supplied with a complicated system of smooth muscles, some of which cause the depression and others the erection of the feathers, and that either movement may be accompanied by more or less rotation. Both erector and depressor muscles are supplied with sympathetic nerve fibers and can be caused to contract separately. The depressor muscles are larger than the erector muscles, and upon nerve stimulation depression of the feather usually occurs.

It has been observed by Langley and other investigators that stimulation of the cervical sympathetic nerves causes a slight retraction of the eyelids, pallor of the mucous membrane of the mouth, contraction of the cutaneous blood vessels of the neck, and usually depression of the feathers of the neck, though occasionally the feathers may be erected.

Section of the preganglionic or postganglionic sympathetic fibers causes erection of feathers and dilation of cutaneous blood vessels.

The other part of the autonomic nervous system is formed by

neurons, with centers in the mesencephalon and the medulla oblongata, and in the sacral section of the spinal cord. Together they form the parasympathetic system.

The cranial part of the parasympathetic system is connected with the cranial nerves: the oculomotor, facial, glossopharyngeal, and vagus nerves. The vagi are the main parasympathetic nerves. They give branches to the thoracic organs and to the abdomen (the intestinal nerves). Most parasympathetic nerves run in association with sympathetic nerves, thus providing a joint supply to the visceral organs. Sympathetic and parasympathetic innervations of the chicken's uterus are derived from separate pathways (Freedman and Sturkie, 1963). An unpaired sympathetic nerve (the hypogastric) supplies the rostral portion of the gland, and the pelvic nerves supply the more caudal parts (see Chapter 15 for further details).

Microscopic examination shows that the postganglionic nerves contain many more fibers than do the preganglionic. As a consequence, the spreading of the stimuli, conducted to the effectors, may be considerably increased. Perhaps this is part of the functional significance of the ganglia. Another function of the sympathetic ganglia is to prolong the effect of preganglionic stimuli in a state of excitation. This is possibly due to the presence of re-excitation circuits (Bronk, 1939). The reflex centers of the autonomic nervous system are situated in the cerebral trunk and in the spinal cord, as has already been mentioned. The sympathetic ganglia do not have the function of reflex centers. But a certain reflex activity can take place in the autonomic nervous system in the ramifications of the axons, outside the central nervous system. This was first described by Langley and Anderson (1893) as axon or pseudo-reflexes. Such phenomena have not been specifically investigated in birds, but pseudo-reflexes are peculiar to the vertebrates.

Together with the somatic nerves, the afferent part of the reflex arc of the autonomic system, which is composed of sensory pathways from the receptors of the visceral organs, runs along the dorsal roots to the centers in the spinal cord. Anatomically the autonomic nervous system is closely related to the somatic nervous system, although its functions are independent of it.

Functionally the autonomic nervous system is very different from the somatic, which innervates the skeleton muscles. Generally speaking the nerves of the autonomic system have less irritability than the somatic nerves. The autonomic nerves are more sensitive to stimuli of long duration than to the rapid alterations of electrical current that act so powerfully on the somatic nerves. In the autonomic nerves the conduction of electrical potentials, and consequently of stimuli, is slow.

The autonomic nerves regulate the functions of those visceral organs which show a relatively complete autonomy. Thus the automatic mechanisms of these organs can be subjected to the central nervous system, which in the general interest has to be able to regulate the activity of all the visceral organs, adapting their activity to the needs of the body as a whole, and so contribute to homeostasis.

The visceral organs are mostly innervated by both sympathetic and parasympathetic nerves, which usually have an antagonistic influence. The parasympathetic vagi, for example, exert a stimulatory effect on the intestinal canal, while the effect of the splanchnic sympathetic is inhibitory. The effects on the heart of these nerves are exactly opposite. An explanation of the antagonistic action of the sympathetic and parasympathetic nerves can be found in the experiments of Loewi (1921), and of Cannon and Rosenbluth (1937). These investigators were able to demonstrate that by stimulating the parasympathetic nerves a chemical substance (acetylcholine) could be liberated at the ends of these nerves. Acetylcholine is also liberated in the preganglionic fibers of the parasympathetic and sympathetic fibers, and is probably liberated also at the synapses of somatic nerves and in the central nervous system. Acetylcholine may well be the mediator in all these systems.

The transmitter in the sympathetic postganglionic nerve fibers is believed to be identical with noradrenaline. Accordingly, Dale (1937) suggested "cholinergic" to characterize the nerves that play a role in the production of acetylcholine, and "adrenergic" for those that liberate noradrenaline (see also Rosenbluth, 1950).

All these phenomena have been found in mammals and frogs, and it is almost certain that they are also present in birds.

THE BRAIN

Medulla Oblongata: The Bulb

The medulla oblongata is the most important part of the central nervous system. Whereas an animal without forebrain, without cerebellum, or with extensive damage to the spinal cord can survive, it cannot do so without the medulla oblongata. The importance of the bulb can be deduced from the fact that 8 of the 12 cerebral nerves originate in this part of the cerebrum. Dorsal and Ventral views of a typical avian brain are shown in Figure 111.

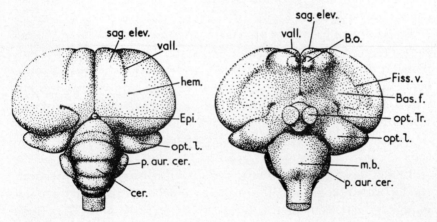

Figure 111. Brain of *Merops apiaster,* a typical avian brain; dorsal and ventral views. (After Portmann and Stingelin, 1961.)

Bas.f., basal field; B.o., bulbus olfactorius; cer., cerebellum; Epi., epiphysis; Fiss.v., fissura ventralis; hem., hemisphere; m.b., medullary bulb; opt. l., optic lobe; opt. tr., optic tract; p.aur.cer., pars auricularis cerebelli; sag.elev., sagittal elevation; vall., vallecula. (After Portmann and Stingelen, in Marshall, *Biology and Comparative Physiology of Birds,* 1961.)

The medulla oblongata is a direct continuation of the spinal cord. It includes the fourth ventricle, an expansion of the central canal of the spinal cord. Anteriorly it continues in the midbrain. According to Buddenbrock (1953), the bulb is one of the most conservative parts of the central nervous system, and varies little, either anatomically or physiologically, throughout the whole range of the vertebrates. In birds the bulb is well developed and contains many reflex centers important for life.

The medulla oblongata as the seat of the respiratory center has been extensively investigated following Flourens' discovery (1824) that in birds and mammals, damage to the posterior tip of the floor of the fourth ventricle, the so-called "knot of life," caused an immediate arrest of respiration (see also Chapter 6 for further details on respiratory centers).

It has since been established that in mammals there are not one but several centers for maintaining and regulating respiration, by sending rhythmic impulses to the motor cells of the respiratory muscles. There are sound reasons for believing that this is also true of birds.

The problem has not yet been solved as to whether these centers work by reflex action or perhaps by controlling the chemical composition of the blood. However, the assumption of a purely automatic action by the motor cells themselves, whereby impulses are sent to the respiratory organs, cannot be excluded. If the assumption should be correct, then the rhythmic activity of the respiratory centers would be based on the individual metabolism of these cells.

Besides the typical automatic centers for controlling respiration, the medulla oblongata contains many reflex centers which play an important part in the maintenance and regulation of the functions of visceral organs, such as the organs of digestion and the blood vessels. The action of the heart is also regulated by the vagus nerves, whose centers are in the bulb. Under normal conditions the activity of all these centers is regulated by reflex action from different parts of the body. The chemical composition of the blood, especially the concentration of CO_2, also has a great influence on the activity of the centers of the medulla oblongata.

Of the centers that influence the animal functions of the body the most important are those in the vestibular part of the medulla oblongata. The vestibular fibers of the 8th cranial nerve end around one of the 4 different cell groups which form the vestibular ganglia of the bulb. Fibers originating in these nerve cells form pathways, which convey impulses for the movements of the eyes, neck, and trunk. These pathways are (1) the posterior longitudinal bundle, going to the oculomotor nuclei which coordinate the movements of the eye muscles and (2) the vestibulospinal tract descending to the spinal motorneurons in the ventral horns of the gray matter.

Also important are the vestibulocerebellar tracts, whose fibers convey impulses from the vestibular nuclei, especially from Dieters' nucleus to the cortex of the cerebellum, chiefly to the posterior lobe.

The vestibular nuclei are reflex centers for movements of the external eye muscles as well as for the musculature of the rest of the body. They are concerned with the maintenance and recovery of the normal attitude of the head and body, as well as of the position of the eyes. Birds are particularly suitable for the study of these reflex movements.

The importance of the vestibular centers of the bulb, and especially of the balancing mechanism for spatial orientation, was explored in pigeons by Groebbels (1928). He was able to demonstrate the importance of the vestibular nuclei, which are in close contact with the labyrinths, in the tonic positional reflexes of the head, wings, legs, and tail as well as in the reflexes that provoke these movements in normal birds.

Unilateral damage to the vestibular part of the medulla oblongata in pigeons (and still more noticeably in ducks) led to deviation of the eyes, rotation and lateral flexion of the head, and spiral rotation of the neck and trunk toward the side of the lesion. A diminution in the tone of the limbs on the damaged side and an increase on the opposite side were produced. Frequently rolling movements were observed. It can easily be understood that birds behave normally after bilateral labyrinth extirpation as well as after symmetrical lesions of both vestibular parts of the bulb.

Benjamins and Huizinga (1927) investigated the influence of the vestibular nuclei, and thus of the labyrinths, on the tone and contractions of the external eye muscles. All changes in movements of the body are accompanied by so-called compensatory movements of the eyes. The latter disappear after a lesion of the vestibular nuclei. These reflexes play an important part in the spatial orientation of birds.

Various chapters of this book discuss the innervation of different organs of the body by nerves whose centers are in the medulla oblongata; therefore it is sufficient to give only a short review here of the most important general properties of this structure.

Cerebellum

In birds the cerebellum is well developed and is composed of a large central mass—the corpus cerebelli or vermis—and two lateral lobes. The vermis can be divided into three main parts, namely the anterior, middle, and posterior lobes, which are separated by deep fissures. The middle lobe is separated from the posterior lobe by the fissura praepyramidalis and from the anterior lobe by the sulcus primarius. This part exhibits a great variability in the size and number of its lamellae.

Extirpation. The functions of the cerebellum can be studied by extirpation either of selected areas or of the organ in its entirety. The phenomena that follow such extirpation can be divided into those that appear immediately and have a dynamic character, and those that are permanent in their effects.

After extirpation of the whole organ, walking and flight are impossible at first because the muscles of the neck and the legs are subject to spasm. The legs are stretched forward stiffly, the head is drawn backward and toward the body (opisthotonus; see Figure 112). Occasionally there is a definite increase in the tone of the tail muscles. The wing muscles remain practically unchanged. The head sways in various directions. Feeding is hindered by the constant retraction of the head as it approaches the food, so that the bird can only get at it in jerks. Stiffness is more pronounced and extensive when more of the tissue is extirpated. Unilateral extirpation produces only a stiffness of the ipsilateral leg and a slight bending of the head in the same direction (Lange, 1891; ten Cate, 1923).

Some weeks after the operation all these signs diminish, and only the permanent deficiency phenomena remain. Walking continues to be unsteady, the body wobbling in all directions. Not long after removal of part of cerebellum, a pigeon is able to fly if it is thrown into the air, but it is unable to take off from the ground unaided. Only very extensive lesions of the cerebellum lead to complete loss of the ability to fly. A bird so affected can maintain its balance erect and can stand on its legs. The head can be held steady so long as the bird sits quietly; with excitement it develops a very slight swaying tremor. Disturbances identical to

Figure 112. Pigeon after extirpation of the anterior lobe of the cerebellum. The legs are stretched forward, the head is drawn backward (opistotonus).

those following extirpation of the cerebellum in its entirety have been described by Bremer and Ley (1927) and ten Cate (1923) following lesions of the anterior lobe only. It is noteworthy that after superficial lesions of the anterior lobe the disturbances were far more pronounced than after lesions of the other lobes. The explanation is that spinocerebellar tracts lead in the main to areas of the anterior lobe in which most of the sensory areas of the limbs and the tail are located.

Deficiency phenomena are most readily apparent in the legs. After the extirpation of one-half of the cerebellum, the ipsilateral leg is extended further than the other when the bird stands.

The wings exhibited less obvious differences after unilateral extirpation. If a pigeon so treated is held with the head downward, the normal wing is held close against the body, whereas the wing of the operated side hangs more or less loose. This difference in position of the wings indicates a lack of tone in the wing muscles on the operated side. The lack of tone could also be seen during flight and in various postural reactions in maintaining balance. Groebbels (1929) also noted a transitory or permanent lowering of tone in the wing muscles after lesions of the cerebellum. In none of these cases was there any disturbance of coordination, but only a difference in the effective strength of the wing muscles. However, after unilateral extirpation of the middle lobe a slight decrease in muscle tone became evident in the leg and wing of the same side (ten Cate, 1926; Manni, 1951).

Stimulation. Bremer and Ley (1927) conducted experiments in which, using very weak currents, they stimulated the cortex of the anterior lobe in pigeons whose extensor muscles were spastic in consequence of decerebration (removal of the forebrain). During this electrical stimulation there was inhibition of the ipsilateral extensor tone of the neck and leg muscles. These experiments indicate that the anterior lobe of the cerebellum contains an inhibitory mechanism concerned with maintaining normal muscle tone. That the inhibitory effect is related only to the extensor muscles indicates that this mechanism is primarily concerned with the maintenance of posture.

The various reflex movements of the tail are also under the control of the cerebellum. Several birds with a lesion of the posterior segments of the cerebellum showed definite abnormalities of the tail movements; extension of the tail was not as pronounced as usual.

The experiments of Bremer were further extended by Raymond (1958), who applied electrical stimulation by electrodes implanted in the cerebellum of chickens and pigeons, which were not anesthetized and which were held in various positions. Raymond observed that various postures caused different responses, but that the movements obtained by stimulation also varied with the position of the electrodes in the cerebellar cortex. The strength and duration of the stimulating current also influenced all these phenomena. According to Raymond, the responses of the birds to the stimulation can be divided into two general categories, namely those obviously related and those not related to the act of balancing. Every bird stimulated by strong currents responded by swaying or rotating and squatting and so lost its balance.

Stimulation of certain points of the cerebellar cortex with weak currents caused well-defined movements of the beak, tongue, and nictitating membranes of the eyes, and even vocalization. Wing, leg and tail movements could also be evoked, some of which were, and some were not, associated with equilibrium. In this way Raymond established a certain correlation between the points of the cerebellar cortex stimulated and the movements of different parts of the body.

In view of the above experiments the following conclusions can be drawn: The cerebellum of birds, like that of mammals, controls the tone of muscles in various parts of the body. To some extent this controlling influence is localized in the cerebellar cortex, as has been demonstrated in experimental lesions and by electrical stimulation of the different lobes.

In a study of the development and subdivision of the cerebellum of birds, which gives a new and more detailed subdivision of the cerebellar cortex, Larsell (1948) suggested a functional arrangement in this organ. Folium I (lingula in the old nomenclature) may be associated with the tail muscles, and folia II and III (central lobule) with the legs; folia IV and V (culmen) and folium VIa are associated with the wing muscles (see Figure 113).

Whitlock (1952) examined the same problem experimentally in pigeons, ducks, and owls. The localization of evoked electrical activity in the cerebellar cortex was found by using a recording method which registered the differences in electrical potentials. Whitlock first examined the electrical activity of different parts of the cerebellum evoked by the stimulation of various regional nerves with a single electrical shock. He was able to establish a definite somatotopic arrangement of the responding sites into areas. It must be noted that the responding loci were distributed ipsilaterally, and that the borders of the areas overlapped. The responses recorded from the cerebellar cortex during stimulation of a nerve were used to map out the receiving zones of the cerebellar cortex. The area associated with the tail region is located most rostrally; then, in sequence backward, come the leg, wing, and face areas.

In other experiments Whitlock (1952) examined the action of

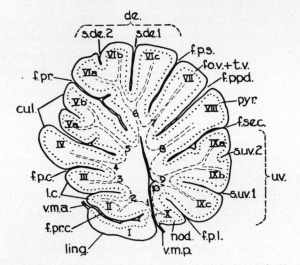

Figure 113. Schematic representation in sagittal section of the division of the cerebellum of a pigeon according to Larsell (1948), in 10 primary folia numbered I to X.

Folium I can be shown as homologous to the lingula (ling) of mammals; folia II and III correspond to the central lobule (l.c.); folia IV and V correspond to the culmen (cul.); folia VIa,b,c correspond to the decliva (de.); folium VII is a combined folium corresponding to vermis and tuber vermis of the mammals; folium VIII is homologous to the mammalian pyramis (pyr.); folium IXa,b,c, corresponds to the uvula (uv); folium X corresponds to the nodulus nod.); f.pr., fissura prima of Brouber-Ingvar; f.p.p.d., the fissura pyramidalis of the same authors. (From *J. Comp. Neurol.* 89:123.)

tactile, visual, and sound stimuli on the so-called spontaneous electrical activity of the cerebellar cortex. Tactile stimulation was produced by touching one or more feathers. In this way it was possible to establish that tactile receiving areas are present in the avian cerebellum. These correspond with the areas responding to nerve stimulation and show a similar somatotopic arrangement.

Stimulation of the eye was produced by a flash of light falling on a dark-adapted eye. The stimulus used in studying the relation between the auditory organs and the cerebellum consisted of a simple click. Auditory and visual receiving areas lie close to each other in the avian cerebellar cortex. The areas are found in folium VIc (caudal decliva), folium VII (tuber), and folium VIII (pyramis). The latent period of these responses is comparable with that of similar responses described in the mammalian cerebellum. The investigations of Whitlock confirm in more detailed manner the results of the former experiments (Bremer; ten Cate) with partial extirpation of some parts of pigeon cerebellum, and with Raymond's electrical stimulation.

Cerebellar nuclei. Besides the cortex, other very important structures are the cerebellar nuclei, n. laterales and n. tecti, which lie deep in the white matter of the cerebellum.

Groebbels (1929) made an extensive study of the positional and the motion reflexes of pigeons following lesions of the cerebellar nuclei. He found that the cerebellar nuclei exerted a reflex inhibitory control over the stimuli acting on the vestibular centers in the medulla oblongata for the muscles which turn and raise the neck. If, for example, the right lateral nucleus is injured, the same stimuli are freed from this inhibitory control so that the right vestibular center in the medulla is then stimulated; the tone of the muscles which turn the neck toward the left becomes augmented, and so the neck becomes bent toward the left. When both lateral nuclei are destroyed the same augmentation is present equally on the two sides, so that there is no displacement of the neck. The lateral nuclei are also important for the spreading of the tail. If both lateral nuclei are destroyed, the ability to fan the tail is lost on both sides.

An inhibitory mechanism is also present in the cortex of the posterior lobe and the nuclei tecti; these act on the vestibular centers for the muscles that raise the neck and the tail. If this system is damaged retroversion appears in the neck and tail, causing the bird to fall over backwards.

Mesencephalon (Midbrain)

Structure. Anatomically there is no clearly defined separation between the mesencephalon from the diencephalon. As centers of the sensory and motor systems they stand in close relation to each other and sometimes are even connected by the same nerve tracts to other parts of the brain. Nevertheless, it seems preferable to give a separate description of the physiological characteristics of the midbrain and interbrain. A stereotaxic atlas of the chicken tel-encephalon, diencephalon, and mesencephalon has been prepared by Van Tienhoven and Juhasz (1962).

The dorsal part of the midbrain is formed by the tectum opti-cum, which in birds consists of two very conspicuous lateral emi-nences, the lobi optici. These, as might be expected in view of the relatively greater development of the eyes and their importance in reflex activities, are relatively larger than they are in other ani-

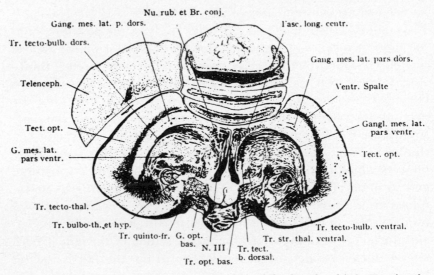

Figure 114. A cross section through the midbrain of a bird (*Pratincola rubicola*).

N.III, nucleus oculomotorius; Gang. mes. lat. pars dors., nucleus mesen-cephalicus lerali pars dorsalis; Gang. mes. lat. pars ventr., nucleus mesen-cephalicus lerali pars ventralis; G. opt. bas., nucleus opticus basalis; Tect. opt., tectum opticum; Nu. rub., nucleus ruber; Br. conj., brachium con-junctivum; Ventr., ventricle. (After Ariens-Kappers.)

mals. Some of the optic nerve fibers end, after crossing, in the lobi optici which are also important centers for the integration of afferent stimuli coming from peripheral sources (especially from along the tectospinal tract). The principal efferent connections of the midbrain are (1) the tecto-oculomotor fibers to the nuclei of the oculomotor nerves; (2) the tectobulbar fibers which form the descending system of fibers going to the medulla oblongata and perhaps further caudally also. The ventral part of the mesencephalon is formed by the tegmentum, which contains some important nerve centers. Prominent among these are the nuclei of the oculomotor and trochlear nerves, the reticular centers and the red nucleus; the latter consists of large cells situated near the midline at the level of the oculomotor roots. The tectum has no connections with the optic nerves, but does connect with the auditory (8th) cranial nerves. Like the thalamus, the tectum opticum is an area for coordinating different sensory impressions.

Destruction of optic lobes. The famous French physiologist Flourens (1824) was the first to find that after destruction of one optic lobe in pigeons and fowls, blindness arose in the contralateral eye. When both optic lobes were damaged blindness was complete. These experiments of Flourens were later confirmed by many other investigators. More recent experiments have demonstrated that the blindness is not complete after removal of only the upper layers of the optic lobes. After such an operation pigeons could avoid obstacles when walking, but the fright reactions were lost and the birds no longer pecked at grain. These disturbances resemble those seen after removal of the forebrain. Only psychic blindness is induced.

The reaction of the pupils to light remains intact bilaterally if only the cortex of the optic lobes has been damaged. Noll (1927) gave an explanation for this phenomenon. He established that the fibers responsible for the pupillary light reflex lie relatively deep and do not reach the surface of the lobes with the visual fibers. All other sensory organs remain more or less normal after destruction of the cortex of the lobi optici. After formation of deep lesions of the lobi optici blindness is complete, and the pupillary response to light is lost. In all vertebrates, disturbances in the equilibrium and attitude of the body appear after damage to the midbrain. Both the tectum and the tegmentum have numerous connections with the adjacent parts of the brain: the thalamus, the cerebellum, the medulla oblongata, and the spinal cord. Therefore it is easily understood that lesions of the mesencephalon give rise to motor disorders in birds also.

Motor disturbances following lesions of the optic lobes in birds were described by Groebbels (1929). He found that removal of the right optic lobe led to a turning of the neck and circular movements on the floor toward the side of the lesion. Damage to the left optic lobe gave rise to precisely opposite effects. These findings are ascribed to the damage to the connections between the tectum, the thalamus, and the corpus striatum. The optic lobes have also an influence on the carrying of the tail; spreading and turning appear changed when these are damaged. Groebbels demonstrated clearly that removal of the optic lobes in birds also affected the landing reaction of the legs.

Stimulation of optic lobes. Martino (1926) stimulated the optic lobes of pigeons and fowls chemically with strychnine. He placed small pieces of filter paper, about 1 mm. in diameter, that had been soaked in a 1 percent strychnine solution, upon the exposed surface of the lobe and then let the birds run loose. This stimulation of the lobes usually led to convulsive movements of the legs and wings, and of the tail on the side corresponding to the lobe irritated. Martino was able to locate a few places whose stimulation caused quite definite movements. One such spot, in the lower anterior section of the lobe, was found to induce withdrawal of the ipsilateral foot. The stimulation of a more caudally located point provoked a raising, and that of a point still farther down a dipping, of the ipsilateral wing. An even lower irritation provoked movements of the tail. The sensitivity of the skin of the stimulated extremities was increased. Stimulation of the surface of the forebrain with strychnine had no effect on motor phenomena. According to Martino, the motor centers on the surface of the optic lobes have a function analogous to the motor zone of the forebrain in mammals.

The experiments of Martino were confirmed by Popa and Popa

(1933). They provoked movements of definite parts of the body by both electrical and mechanical stimulation of the surface of the anterior portions of the optic lobes. Stimulation of the lower pole of the optic lobe caused movements of the neck; stimulation of an area lying somewhat more dorsally caused movements of neck and wing; stimulation of another area caused movements of the legs and wings; stimulation of the upper pole of the optic lobe caused movements of the tail. All these movements started on the ipsilateral side of the body. The motor centers for the movements of the beak and the larynx are more ventrally situated. They appear also to lie further internally, since responses are also obtained when the stimulating electrodes are inserted more deeply into the lobes. Here also a voice center seems to be located. In connection with the former experiments of Martino, Vorgas-Pena (1932) tried to determine the relation between the sensitivity of the skin and the function of the optic lobes in pigeons. A small piece of strychnine-soaked filter paper was placed on the lateral surface of the optic lobe and on the spot where Martino had found a center for the raising and retraction of the ipsilateral wing. Vorgas-Pena likewise evoked a raising and adduction of the ipsilateral and sometimes also of the contralateral wing, and various movements of the tail. By stimulation of several areas of the skin with a needle or an electric current, intensification of the wing movements was obtained. Vorgas-Pena found a reflex generating zone for the raising of the wing on the dorsal surface and for the adductors on the ventral surface. These experiments show that the functioning of the optic lobes can be influenced by reflexes from the skin surface.

Among the tegmental centers of the mesencephalon, the red nucleus plays an important role in the regulation of the muscle tone in mammals. This nucleus is well developed in birds. According to Ariens-Kappers (1947), it consists of large nerve cells situated near the midline of the tectum. From these cells runs a rubrobulbar and possible a rubrospinal pathway. This nucleus receives afferent fibers from the tectum opticum and the cerebellum. The nucleus ruber must also have a certain influence on the muscles in birds, as Bremer had supposed. Unfortunately an experimental approach to this problem has not yet been undertaken. Hamdi and Whitteridge (1954) demonstrated that in pigeons there was a point-to-point representation of the retina on the optic tectum. Earlier the same thing had been found in fishes by Buser and Dusardier (1953). A representation of the retina on the superior colliculus of mammals, which is homologous to the optic tectum in lower vertebrates, has been reported by Apter (1945), and by Hamdi and Whitteridge (1953); the latter have registered the electical activity of the optic tectum with microelectrodes put on different places of the exposed optic tectum of decerebrated pigeons. The microelectrode and the indifferent electrode were connected with a cathode-ray tube with amplifier. A neon flash lamp was used for visual stimuli. The excitation of the retina was caused by a flash lasting about one second. In these experiments Hamdi and Whitteridge have found that the deeper layers of the optic lobes give visual responses which can be evoked from whole quadrants of the visual field. They have thus proved the existence of the point-to-point representation of the retina on the optic tectum.

The Diencephalon or Interbrain

The diencephalon or interbrain, which includes the third ventricle, consists mainly of the thalamus and the hypothalamus. In birds the thalamus is distinguished by pronounced connections with the cortex of the forebrain. The nuclei of the thalamus are the chief relay stations between the forebrain and sensory systems of the whole body. Several afferent tracts coming from the periphery terminate in the cells of the thalamic nuclei. The most important afferent tracts are the optic, auditory, spinothalamic, and trigeminal tracts and the cerebellar projections (Figure 115).

From the nerve cells of the thalamic nuclei, tracts run to different parts of the forebrain. At the same time the thalamus receives several pathways from the forebrain. In this way there is a kind of circuit between the thalamus and the forebrain. Besides the nuclei mentioned, which communicate with the forebrain, there are also nuclei in the thalamus which have connections with different subcortical systems of the brain stem, as well as nuclei which connect the different parts of the thalamus. All these ana-

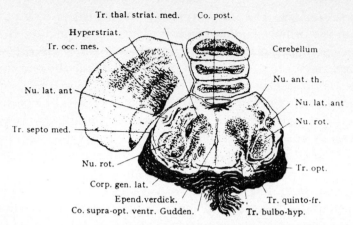

Figure 115. A cross section through the diencephalon of *Pratincola rubicola,* passing dorsally through the posterior commissure (Co. post.) and ventrally through the optic chiasma.

Nu.ant.th., nucleus anterior thalami; Nu.lat.ant., nucleus lateralis anterior; Nu.rot., nucleus rotundus; Corp.gen.lat., corpus geniculatum laterale; Co.supra-opt.ventr., commissura supraoptica ventralis; Tr.opt., tractus opticus. (After Ariens-Kappers)

tomical details are well known in mammals, but in birds the matter has not been investigated sufficiently.

Function of thalamus. The functions of the thalamus can only be determined by comparing the behavior of birds whose forebrain has been carefully extirpated with those in which the extirpation of the forebrain was accompanied by damage to or total removal of the thalamus. A great many experiments on the removal of the forebrain of birds have been reported; but in only one case could it be established with certainty that the forebrain had been removed with negligible damage to the thalamus. These experiments were carried out by Thauer and Peters (1938), who examined in detail the behavior of several pigeons which had survived up to 2 years after complete extirpation of the forebrain. Later the same authors made a histological study of the remaining parts of the brain. Nearly all the pigeons showed to some degree a lack of spontaneity and of reaction to food, as had been described by earlier investigators. The one exception was a pigeon, also a 2-year survivor, in which a remarkable restitution of function had occurred. Spontaneous reactions were very good, and the pigeon had acquired the ability to peck and eat its food. Only by exact observation was it possible to detect slight changes in the psychical functions of the bird, among others a degree of optical agnosia (inability to recognize complicated objects). It is a pity that only one such case is known; nevertheless, in my opinion this one observation is of great value, since it shows the important role of the thalamus in the behavior of birds. For mammals this role is already a well-known fact. The reticular formation, which lies in between the nuclei, also has great influence on the behavior of mammals. No experimental approach to this problem in birds has been made. Only two investigations into the role of the diencephalon in the motor functions of birds are worth quoting here.

Langworthy (1926), who investigated the motor and postural functions after extirpation of both the diencephalon and the forebrain, found that as a result of increased flexor tone in the legs the birds could no longer stand. The pigeons lay on one side with their legs strongly flexed. Bremer and Lay (1927) also described a marked tone in the flexor muscles of the legs after damage to the diencephalon in pigeons. Whereas Langworthy believed that the flexor tone in the legs was caused by damage to the thalamus, Bremer supposed that, as in mammals, the tone in birds was disturbed only if the centers of the midbrain, especially the red nucleus, were also injured. This very interesting assumption has not yet been experimentally confirmed. It should be noted that in mammals, damaging the red nucleus provokes an increase of tone in the extensor muscles, whereas in birds after damage to the diencephalon the tone is increased in the flexor muscles.

Electrical stimulation. Electrical stimulation of the more frontal surface of the thalamus in birds caused chewing movements and weak muscular contractions of the neck, and led to secondary circular movements by the bird. The same stimulation to the lower parts of the thalamus caused strong flexion of the neck, wings, and legs; this too gave rise to circular movements (Rogers, 1928). The lower part of the thalamus, and probably also the adjacent parts of the hypothalamus, have a somatic-muscular effect on different parts of the body.

Hypothalamus. The hypothalamus lies at the base of the diencephalon, below the thalamus. The nerve cells of the hypothalamus are grouped in different nuclei just as in the thalamus. These nuclei and their connections can be very well distinguished in birds as an anterior, middle, and posterior group. There are many short connections between the various nuclei, and also long afferent and efferent paths. The hypothalamus is connected by afferent nerve fibers to the olfactory tract, the thalamus, and the forebrain. The hypothalamus receives impulses from various parts of the body via ascending tracts from the medulla oblongata and the spinal cord. The efferent connections pass from the hypothalamus to the anterior thalamus, to the forebrain via the thalamus, and to the autonomic nuclei of the brain stem and the spinal cord. The connections of the hypothalamus with the hypophysis are most important. In birds the hypothalamus plays an important part in the regulation of the body temperature (Rogers, 1919). After removal of the diencephalon together with the forebrain, the control of body temperature is lost and the body temperature then varies with the ambient temperature. After removal of the forebrain only the control over body temperature is maintained. If the hypothalamus is injured to any extent the body temperature falls. The degree of reflex activity varies with the body temperature. Rogers (1928) also showed that the hypothalamus has an influence on the vasomotor centers in the medulla oblongata. Hypothalamic injury is followed by a distinct fall in the blood pressure. Weak electrical stimulation produced shiverings over the entire body, contraction of the blood vessels of the skin, and a rise in temperature; there was a simultaneous erection of the feathers. This activity together with the contractions of the body muscles may be considered to be the main reason for the increase in temperature. After destruction of the hypothalamus a marked diuresis and a consequent great loss of water by the organism was observed. Feldman *et al.* (1957) reported aphagia in chicks following lesions of hypothalamus.

It is well known that the hypothalamus is closely connected to the hypophysis (see Chapter 17). The hypophysis can be divided into two principal parts (lobes). The posterior lobe—the neurohypophysis—is embryologically and functionally a part of the brain and is under the nervous control of the hypothalamus by way of a bundle of nerve fibers—the supraoptico-hypophysial tract, which acts as an efferent pathway for the hypothalamus. One result of stimulation of this tract is that diuresis is inhibited, because of the release of an antidiuretic hormone into the circulation. The anterior lobe of the hypophysis—the adenohypophysis—has a vascular link with the hypothalamus and the posterior lobe; the anterior lobe has no controlling nervous mechanism. It is believed that the activities of this lobe are controlled by humoral influences (see Chapter 17).

It is commonly assumed that the hormones oxytocin and vasopressin in mammals, and oxytocin and vasotocin in birds, are formed in the nerve cells of the supraoptic and paraventricular nuclei of the hypothalamus (see Chapters 13 and 17). These cells produce the so-called neurohormones. The neurosecretory cells may be defined as nerve cells which receive nervous impulses but do not pass them on to other neurons or effector organs. The results of electron microscope studies confirm that these cells secrete microscopically detectable granules which are transferred into the blood of the posterior lobe of the hypophysis via the axons of the cells. These basic facts about the neurosecretion in the hypothalamus of vertebrates are now well known. That the same mechanism obtains in birds has been demonstrated by Wingstrand (1951) and many others (see Chapter 17). It is now quite certain that the hypothalamic neurosecretory system in birds has much more extensive functions than was formerly supposed. It controls the gonadotropic activity of the adenohypophysis (Chapters 15, 16 and 17); furthermore, it is closely related to the control of the adenocorticotrophic activity of the adenohypophysis (see Chapter 21).

Forebrain

The forebrain of birds is distinguished by the powerful development of the striatum, whereas the cortex is relatively thin. Anatomically the striatum of birds can be divided into the

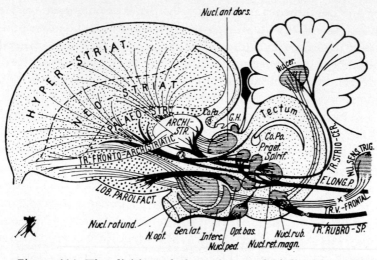

Figure 116. The division of the striatum of birds and its most important connections.

Nuc.ant.dors., nucleus anterodorsalis thalami; *Praet.,* nucleus praetectalis; *Spirif.,* nucleus spiriformis; *Nucl.rotund.,* nucleus rotundum thalami; *N.opt.,* nervus opticus; *Gen.lat.,* geniculatum laterale; *Interc.,* nucleus intercalatus hypothalami; *Nucl.ped.,* nucleus pedunculi; *Opt.bas.,* nucleus opticus tegmenti; *Nucl.ret.-magn.,* nucleus reticularis; *Nucl.rub.* nucleus ruber. (From Ariens-Kappers, *Anatomie du système neiveux,* 1947.)

paleostriatum, the archistriatum, the neostriatum, and the hyper-striatum (see Figure 116). The existence of afferent and efferent connections between the forebrain and the diencephalon, the mesencephalon, the medulla oblongata, and the spinal cord has been established anatomically.

Effects of extirpation of cortex. In most studies the importance of the forebrain in the behavior of birds has been investigated by extirpating the organ and observing the resulting alterations in behavior. Since the work of the Italian physiologist Roland in 1809, numerous investigations have been made; but in most of these anatomical control was lacking, and they are therefore unconvincing. Good research on the behavior of forebrainless pigeons was done by Schrader (1889), and later by Visser and Rademaker (1934).

Schrader tried to determine whether forebrainless pigeons could carry out spontaneous movements. In his experiments the pigeons were in a sleeplike state during the first days after the operation, as was first described by Flourens (1824). Later the birds invariably became more and more active. The visual ability was preserved to the degree that all obstacles were avoided. The movements guided by the sense of touch remained normal. The pigeons deprived of the forebrain responded normally to change in equilibrium. A loud noise, such as that of a shot, caused the pigeon to flinch. Less intense sounds or noises did not usually provoke spontaneous movements. When movements did occur it was shown that they were appropriate to the sensory organ stimulated.

According to Schrader, the apparently spontaneous movements depend on a normal irritability in the remaining parts of the central nervous system, and are provoked by stimuli which for the most part emanate from the higher centers. But stimuli can also arise from vegetative organs (hunger and thirst). According to Visser and Rademaker (1934), light and hunger favor the movements of forebrainless pigeons. Such pigeons run or fly toward moderately illuminated objects; strong light sources as well as dark areas are avoided. Sudden darkening of the room leads to an immediate cessation of all motion. In a forebrainless pigeon, flight and the appreciation of direction and distance are influenced by light. Vision is not appreciably impaired. A forebrainless pigeon pecks frequently at seeds and spots that stand out in strong contrast with the floor, but does not feed itself. Schrader gives a solution to this remarkable problem in his experiments with falcons. After removal of the forebrains falcons exhibited a peculiar reaction to a mouse. A hungry falcon pounced on the mouse and held it, but the captured animal was not killed and devoured; it was only retained in the claws for as long as it continued to move. If the mouse was crushed to death, the falcon would drop it. The visual perception of a running mouse set in motion the whole reflex action of pursuit and capture. Any moving object is attacked in the same fashion as the mouse. Accordingly, the forebrain must govern the ability to discriminate between such objects.

According to Essen (1931), the act of feeding consists of the following components: the visual-sensory perception of the food, the motor reaction to this and a further correlation between "seeing" and "doing." We are thus forced to assume the existence of sensory-motor association centers. In forebrainless birds sensory and motor reactions are present, but the associative component has vanished.

Pigeons in which small fragments of the corpus striatum still remain connected to the rest of the central nervous system exhibit pecking movements when they are hungry. Under normal circumstances the pecking actions are evoked by the sense impression of light and are based on a recognition of the grain on the basis of previous experience. In a normal pigeon the sighting of food is accompanied by accommodation of the eyes, pupillary unrest, and specific expressive movements. All these phenomena disappear when the forebrain has been extirpated. The inability to feed is due to the loss of psychic vision, "the sensor agnosia" (Essen).

The expressive psychical aspects of behavior (usually the result of endocrine activity), such as that of courtship during the nuptial season or the particular movements of a hen preparing to lay an egg, are not lost in forebrainless birds. But it has been shown that they differ from the behavior of normal birds in one important aspect: in the former, all these motions proceed without reference to the objects of the external world. The sexually excited male pigeon is wholly indifferent to the female, and the hen ignores the egg she has just laid. In view of the experiments quoted above it can be concluded that psychic functions of the birds must be centered in the forebrain.

The importance of the cortex and of the striatum had been investigated by a few physiologists in experiments with removal or electrical stimulation of only one of these two areas of the forebrain. The removal of the cortex alone, which was done by some investigators, did not produce clear results. Particular alterations in behavior were not observed.

Rogers (1922a) established the importance of the corpus striatum for instinctive reactions, such as feeding, drinking, nesting, and the nurture of the young. After removal of the cortex, no characteristic changes in the behavior of the operated pigeons could be found. But if the cortex was removed together with the hyperstriatum, although after a certain period of helplessness the pigeon could feed spontaneously again, the capacity for pairing and nesting was permanently lost. The presence of ecto-, epi-, and mesostriatum are sufficient for feeding, drinking, and courtship. These reactions are brought under the control of visual stimulation by the epistriatum. The hyperstriatum is essential for the more complicated reactions of pairing, nesting, and nurture of the young. The epistriatum has the function of a coordinating visual center, whereas the ecto- and the mesostriatum are centers for the movements of the muscles.

Electrical stimulation. There have been many experiments with electrical excitation on the forebrain of birds, but over a long period there has been no consistency in the findings related to the excitability of the cortex. The interpretation of such experiments is often difficult because of the possibility of a misleading spread of current in the striatum.

Rogers (1922b), working on pigeons and using weak electrical currents, found only two movements that were irrefutably of cortical origin, namely myosis of the contralateral eye and depression of the feathers of the throat. He interpreted all other movements as being due to a spread of the current to the corpus striatum. According to Bickel (1898), all these movements must be attributed to stimulation of the striatum. The most complete investigations were those of Kalischer (1905), who studied very carefully the electrical excitability of the cerebral cortex in various birds, particularly in parrots. In this last species, in which the cerebral cortex is particularly well developed, Kalischer found evidence for true motor centers. Proceeding from the rostral toward the caudal area, a focus was detected for tongue and jaw movements, as well as a phonetic center and foci for movements of the feet and wings. In the occipital region a zone was present that evoked movements of the eyes.

Bremer, Dow, and Moruzzi (1939) similarly found that the cerebral cortex of pigeons is electrically excitable by weak currents. The reactions to unilateral stimulation consist of a combined deviation of the head and eyes toward the opposite side, accompanied by the opening of the palpebral fissure. This response is evidently the expression of the excitation of the neurons of the cortical layers, since it is abolished almost instantaneously by superficial cocainization of the excited region. The simultaneous excitation of two symmetrical points on the right and the left cortex with currents of equal intensity produces rhythmic movements of the head in the vertical plane, resembling the pecking movements in the intact bird. The conclusion from these experiments is that motor reactions depend at least partly on the cerebral cortex.

Electroencephalograms. According to Bremer and his collaborators (1939), the spontaneous electrical activity derived from the cerebral cortex of the nonanesthetized pigeon is not fundamentally different from that of a rabbit. The irregular alternation of the slow alpha waves with the frequent small waves of the beta type, as found in rabbits, is seen in pigeons also, but the amplitude of the waves is smaller. That this spontaneous activity was not abolished by superficial cocainization permits the conclusion that, under normal circumstances, subcortical as well as cortical potentials are being recorded. In consequence, in normal pigeons we derive from the cerebral cortex an electroencephalogram and not an electrocorticogram as in mammals. The forebrain of the pigeon reacts to illumination of one eye by a large and typical reaction in the electrical potentials in the contralateral cortex. From an anlysis of the excitability and electrical activity of the cerebral cortex of the pigeon, Bremer drew the conclusion that in birds at least the superficial layer of neurons covering the striatum dorsally and posteriorly has physiological properties and a functional significance— the latter being essentially optokinetic, much as is the neopallium of mammals.

The electrical activity of the forebrain was also explored by Eulkar (1955) to determine areas of response to clicks and to light tactile stimuli. Potentials evoked by light tactile stimuli to the face and beak were recorded from a small region of the caudal neostriatum. Potentials evoked by auditory stimuli were recorded from another small region of the neostriatum.

The phenomenon of spreading depression of the spontaneous EEG activity in the cerebral cortex to electrical, mechanical, and chemical stimuli was first described by Leao in 1944. This remarkable reaction of the cortex develops in the stimulated region and spreads slowly, at a rate of 3 to 6 mm./min., in all directions across the cortex. The front of the spreading depression-wave is accompanied by a slow potential variation—a negativity attaining 10 mv. on amplitude, followed after to 1 to 2 minutes by lower and longer-lasting positivity.

In birds spreading depression was first elicited by Leao; later Bures, Fifova, and Marsala (1960) made extensive experiments with pigeons. They were able to show that spreading depression of the EEG activity could be evoked in all the accessible parts of the cortex in spite of important anatomical difference in the structure.

With capillary electrodes introduced in the neostriatum, Bures and others were able to register the slow potential-waves of this part of the brain. They thus established that the spreading depression of the electrical activity in the neostriatum had approximately the same character as on the surface of the hemispheres, if this phenomenon were registered simultaneously in both parts of the brain.

Conditioned reflexes. The conditioned reflexes, which can be considered the basis of the different forms of training, belong to one of the most important functions of the forebrain. Conditioned reflexes, or responses, are established when a neutral stimulus, which normally does not evoke a response in the animal, is repeatedly associated with another stimulus which does elicit a reflex response. For instance, if a current of air blown on the face of a pigeon (unconditioned stimulus) is accompanied by a sound (conditioned stimulus), the effect of the combined stimulus is a reactive movement of the head, After a number of such combined stimulations have been given the pigeon will respond by making the same head movement when stimulated by sound only. A conditioned reflex to the sound—a neutral stimulus—will then have been acquired by the pigeon.

In the course of the animal's life, conditioned reflexes are acquired as the result of adaptation to changes in the surroundings. The formation of these reflexes depends on the conditions under which the individual animal lives. In contrast to those that are common or unconditioned, conditioned reflexes are not inborn but are acquired by an individual animal during its life. They disappear more or less quickly when the conditions change, whereas the unconditioned reflex has a permanent and stable character and but a slight dependence upon surrounding conditions. A conditioned reflex never originates spontaneously, but only in association with another, previously established reflex, usually an inborn, unconditioned reflex.

The method of conditioning reflexes was introduced by the Russian physiologist Pavlov in his investigation of the functions of the forebrain cortex in dogs. It can be used with completely normal animals, gives an objective insight into the functions of the cerebral cortex, and is a very useful tool in the study of the effects and interacti on of sensory stimuli. The experimental study of conditioned reflexes is based on the forming of associations between a stimulus of a neutral character and an unconditioned common reflex action; the hitherto neutral stimulus is transformed into a conditioned stimulus and acquires the properties of an ordinary stimulus. Experiments in pigeons designed to produce conditioned reflexes to various neutral stimuli were carried out by ten Cate (1923). These experiments showed that, in normal pigeons, conditioned reflexes to different stimuli could be established in the same way as the conditioned salivation reflexes in dogs had been established by Pavlov. The formation of these conditioned reflexes in pigeons agrees completely with the laws that Pavlov laid down for the salivation reflexes in dogs.

If a conditioned reflex to a given musical tone has been formed, it can be demonstrated that all other sounds produce no such effect on the pigeon. It was possible for the pigeon to differentiate visual as well as auditory stimuli. They could be trained to distinguish circular, ellipsoid, and rectangular figures. Hence the contention of behaviorists, that birds can distinguish between outlines, is confirmed.

Popov (1926) succeeded in forming conditioned defensive reflexes to visual, acoustic, and tactile stimuli after extirpation of the forebrain cortex only. In view of these experiments it seems probable that the achievement of conditioned reflexes in birds must also be localized in the striatum.

Action of the Forebrain on the Visceral Organs

The question of whether the forebrain exerts any influence on the functions of the visceral organs in birds has scarcely been examined. Rogers (see Chapter 10) found that in hungry pigeons, both with and without a forebrain, there was hypermotility of the crop. In normal pigeons this hypermotility is inhibited by food or water, but also by fear or surprise. In hungry pigeons lacking a forebrain, hypermotility of the crop is inhibited by food and water, and also by painful stimuli, but not by fear or other psychical stimuli. These experiments show that the forebrain has some influence on the functions of autonomic-innervated visceral organs. Because of the psychological mechanism should be localized in the forebrain. Walter (see Chapter 11), using ducks with a fistula in the pars glandularis of their stomachs, tried to condition their secretion of gastric juice to the acoustic stimulus of an electric bell. Once the bell had been rung, food was offered while the ringing continued. After the ducks had experienced such combined events for some time their reaction to the sound alone became very pronounced. When the conditioned stimulus—the sound—was given and no food was offered, the secretion of the gastric juice from the fistula began immediately. These experiments also confirm the importance of the forebrain in its relation to the function of a visceral organ, in this instance the stomach.

REFERENCES

Adrian, E. D.   1935   The Mechanism of Nervous Action. University of Pennsylvania Press, Philadelphia.

Apter, J.   1945   Projection of the retina on superior colliculus of cats. J. Neurophysiol. 8:123.

Ariens-Kappers, C. U.   1947   Anatomie du système nerveux. Erven Bohn, Haarlem; Masson & Co., Paris.

Benjamins, C. E., and E. Huizinga   1927   Untersuchungen über die Funktion des Vestibularapparates der Taube. Arch. ges. Physiol. (Pflügers) 217:105.

Bickel, A.   1898   Zur vergleichender Physiologie des Grosshirns. Arch. ges. Physiol. (Pflügers) 72:190.

Bodian, D.   1942   Cytological aspects of synaptic function. Physiol. Rev. 22:241.

Bremer, F., R. S. Dow, and G. Moruzzi 1939 Physiological analysis of the general cortex in reptiles and birds. J. Neurophysiol. 2:473.

Bremer, F., and R. Ley 1927 Recherches sur la physiologie du cervelet chez le pigeon. Arch. Int. Physiol. 28:58.

Brock, L. G., and R. M. Eccles 1958 The membrane potentials during rest and activity of the ray electroplate. J. Physiol. 142:251.

Bronk, D. W. 1939 Synaptic mechanism in sympathetic ganglia. J. Neurophysiol. 2:380.

Brown, G. L. 1937 Transmission at nerve endings by acetylcholine. Physiol. Rev. 17:485.

Buddenbrock, W. von 1953 Vergleichende Physiologie. Bd. II: Neurophysiologie. Verl. Birkhäuser, Basel.

Bullock, T. H., and S. Hagiwara 1957 Intracellular recording from the giant synapse of the squid. J. Gen. Physiol. 40:565.

Bures, J. E., E. Fifova, and J. Marsala 1960 Leão's spreading depression in pigeons. J. Comp. Neurol. 114:1.

Buser, P., and M. Dusardier 1953 Organisation des projections de la rétine sur les lobes optiques chez quelques theleostéens. J. Physiol., Paris 45:57.

Campbell, J. B., C. A. L. Basset, J. Husby, and C. R. Nobuck 1957 Regeneration of adult mammalian spinal cord. Science 126:929.

Cannon, W. B., and A. Rosenbluth 1937 Anatomic Neuro-effector System. The Macmillan Co., New York.

Carpenter, F. G., and R. M. Bergland 1957 Excitation and conduction in immature nerve fibers of the developing chick. Am. J. Physiol. 190:371.

Castillo, J. del, and B. Katz 1956 Biophysical aspects of neuromuscular transmission. Progr. of Biophys. 6:122.

Clearwaters, K. 1954 Regeneration of the spinal cord of the chick. J. Comp. Neurol. 101:317.

Clementi, A. 1914 Beitrag zum Studium der autonomen Functionen des Rückenmarks. Experimentelle Untersuchungen über das Lendenmark der Vögel. Arch. ges. Physiol. (Pflügers) 157:13.

Dale, H. H. 1937 The transmission of nervous effects by acetylcholine. Harvey Lecture 32:229.

Dale, H. H., W. Feldberg, and M. Vogt 1936 Release of acetylcholine at voluntary motor nerve endings. J. Physiol. 86:353.

Erlanger, J., and H. S. Gasser 1937 Electrical Signs of Nervous Activity. Oxford University Press, London.

Essen, J. van 1931 Einiges über das Verhalten der Tauben nach einseitiger Hemisphärenabtragung. Z. f. Neurologie 135:510.

Eulkar, S. D.   1955   Tactile and auditory areas in the brain of the pigeon. J. Comp. Neurol. 103:421.

Feldberg, W.   1945   Present views on the mode of action of acetylcholine in the central nervous system. Physiol. Rev. 25:596.

Feldman, S. E., S. Larsson, M. K. Dimick, and S. Lepkovsky   1957   Aphagia in chickens. Am. J. Physiol. 191:259.

Flourens, W. H.   1824   Recherches expérimentales sur les propriétés et les fonctions du système nerveux dans les animaux vertébrés. Paris.

Freedman, S. L., and P. D. Sturkie   1963   Extrinsic nerves of chicken's uterus. Anat. Rec. 147:431.

Freemen, L.   1952   Return of function after complete transection of the spinal cord of the rat, cat and dog. Ann. of Surgery 136:193.

Freusberg, A.   1874   Reflexbewegungen beim Hunde. Arch. ges. Physiol. (Pflügers) 9:358.

Gasser, H. S.   1950   Unmedullated fibers originating in dorsal root ganglia. J. Gen. Physiol. 33:651.

Goltz, F., and J. R. Evald   1896   Der Hund mit verkürzten Rückenmark. Arch. ges. Physiol. (Pflügers) 63:362.

Graf, W.   1956   Caliber spectra of nerve fibers in the pigeon. J. Comp. Neurol. 105:355.

Grahame, T.   1953   The sympathetic and parasympathetic nervous systems of the fowl. Brit. Vet. J. 109:481.

Groebbels, F.   1928a   Die Lage- und Bewegungsreflexe der Vögel. VII Mitt.: Die Lage- und Bewegungsreflexe der Haustaube nach Läsionen des Rückenmarks und der Oblongata. Arch. ges. Physiol. (Pflügers) 218:198.

Groebbels, F.   1928b   Die Wirkung zweiseitiger Labyrinth-Operationen auf die Lage- und Bewegungsreflexe der Haustaube. Arch. ges. Physiol. (Pflügers) 218:408.

Groebbels, F.   1929   Die Wirkung von Kleinhirnläsionen und die anatomisch-physiologische Analyse. Arch. ges. Physiol. (Pflügers) 221:15.

Hamburger, V.   1955   Regeneration in the ventral nervous system of Reptiles and Birds, Chapter 3, Regeneration in the Central Nervous System, ed. W. F. Windle. C. C. Thomas, Springfield, Ill.

Hamdi, F. A., and D. Whitteridge   1953   The representation of the retina on the optic lobe of the pigeon and the superior colliculus of the rabbit and goat. J. Physiol. 121:44P.

Hamdi, F. A., and D. Whitteridge   1954   The representation of the retina on the optic tectum of the pigeon. Quart. J. Exp. Physiol. 39:111.

Helmholtz, H. von 1850 Messungen über die Fortpflanzungsgeschwindigkeit der Reizung in den Nerven. Arch. f. Anat. u. Physiol., Jahrgang 1850,71.

Hill, A. V. 1933 The three phases of nerve heat production. Proc. Roy. Soc. 113B:345.

Hodgkin, A. L., and A. F. Huxley 1945 Resting and action potentials in single nerve fibers. J. Physiol. 104:176.

Huxley, A. F. 1954 Electrical Processes in Nerve Conduction. Academic Press, New York.

Huxley, A. F., and R. Stämpfli 1949 Evidence for saltatory conduction in peripheral myelinated nerve fibers. J. Physiol. 108:315.

Kalischer, O. 1905 Über Grosshirnexstirpation bei Papageien. Sitzungsber. Kgl. Preuss. Acad. der Wissensch., Berlin.

Katz, B. 1939 Electrical Excitation in Nerve. Oxford University Press, London.

Lange, B. 1891 In wieweit sind die Symptome, welche nach Zerstörung des Kleinhirns beobachtet werden auf Verletzung des Acusticus zuruckzuführen. Arch. ges. Physiol. (Pflügers) 50:615.

Langley, J. N. 1903 The autonomic nervous system. Brain 26:1.

Langley, J. N. 1904 On the sympathetic system of birds and on the muscles which move the feathers. J. Physiol. 30:221.

Langley, J. N. 1921 The Autonomic Nervous System. W. Heffer & Sons, Ltd., Cambridge.

Langley, J. N., and H. Anderson 1893 On the arrangement of the sympathetic nervous system. J. Physiol. 16:410.

Langworthy, O. R. 1926 Abnormalities of posture and progression on the pigeon following experimental lesions of the brain. Am. J. Physiol. 78:34.

Larsell, O. 1948 The development and subdivision of the cerebellum of birds. J. Comp. Neurol. 89:123.

Loewi, O. 1921 Über humorale Übertragbarkeit der Herznervenwirkung Arch. ges. Physiol. (Pflügers) 189:239.

Manni, N. 1951 Sulla funzione del lobo medio cerebellare degli uccelli. Archivio di Scienze Biol. 35:504.

Martino, G. 1926 Contributo alla conoscenza della funzione dei lobi ottici nel columbo. Arch. di Fysiol. 24:282.

Nachmansohn, D. 1955 Chapter 10, Textbook of Physiology, 17th ed., J. F. Fulton, ed., W. B. Saunders, Philadelphia.

Noll, A. 1927 Die Lidbewegungen und die Tätigkeit der Lidzentren bei normalen und grosshirnlosen Tauben. Arch. ges. Physiol. (Pflügers) 218:331.

Piat, J. 1955 Regeneration in Central Nervous System of Amphibia. W. F. Windle, Springfield, Ill.

Popa, G., and F. Popa 1933 The sympathetic innervation of the skeletal muscles in the wing of the pigeon. Proc. Roy. Soc. London, B, 113:191.

Popov, N. A. 1926 Zur Physiologie der höheren Nerventätigkeit der Vögel. Arb. des 2 Kongress f. Physiol., Leningrad, U.S.S.R.

Portmann, A., and W. Stingelin 1961 The central nervous system, in Biology and Comparative Physiology of Birds, ed. A. J. Marshall. Academic Press, New York.

Quednau, W. 1926 Plurisegmentale Innervation. Arch. ges. Physiol. (Pflügers) 212:541.

Raymond, M. 1958 Responses to electrical stimulation of the cerebellum of unanesthetised birds. J. Comp. Neurol. 110:299.

Rogers, F. T. 1919 Regulation of body temperature in the pigeon and its relation to certain cerebral lesions. Am. J. Physiol. 49:271.

Rogers, F. T. 1922-1923a An experimental study of the corpus striatum of pigeon as related to various instinctive types of behaviour. J. Comp. Neurol. 35:24.

Rogers, F. T. 1922-1923b A note on the excitable areas of the cerebral hemispheres of the pigeon. J. Comp. Neurol. 35:61.

Rogers, F. T. 1928 The effects of artificial stimulation and traumatism of the avian thalamus. Am. J. Physiol. 86:639.

Rosenbluth, A. 1950 The transmission of nerve impulse at neuroeffector junctions and peripheral synapses. John Wiley & Sons, New York.

Sammartino, U. 1933 Sugli animali a midolla spinale accrociato. Arch. di Farmacologia Sper. 55:219.

Schrader, M. E. G. 1889 Zur Physiologie des Vogelgehirns. Arch. ges. Physiol. (Pflügers) 44:175.

Sherrington, E. S. 1906 The Integrative Action of the Nervous System. Constable & Co., Ltd., London.

Sugar, O., and R. W. Gerard 1940 Spinal cord regeneration in the rat. J. Neurophysiol. 3:1.

Tarchanoff, J. 1895 Mouvements forcés des canards décapités. Compt. Rend. Soc. Biol., Paris 47:454.

Ten Cate, J. 1923 Essai d'étude des fonctions de l'écorce cérébrale de pigeons par la méthode des réflexes conditionnels. Arch. Néerl. Physiol. 8:234.

Ten Cate, J. 1926 Contributions à la physiologie comparée du cervelet. I: Le cervelet du pigeon. Arch. Neerl. Physiol. 11:1.

Ten Cate, J. 1936 Uni-und-plurisegmentale Reflexen bei Tauben. Arch. Neerl. Physiol. 21:161.

Ten Cate, J. 1960 Locomotor movements in the spinal pigeon. J. Exp. Biol. 37:609.

Ten Cate, J., J. A. Stommel, and W. G. Walter 1937 Pflügelreflexen bei Rückenmarkstauben. Arch. Neerl. Physiol. 22:332.

Thauer, R., and G. Peters 1938 Sensibilität und Motorik bei lange überlebende Zwischen- und Mittelhirn-tauben. Arch. ges. Physiol. (Pflügers) 240:503.

Trendelenburg, W. 1910 Vergleichende Physiologie des Rückenmarks. Ergebnisse der Physiologie 10:454.

Van Tienhoven, A., and L. P. Juhasz 1962 The chicken telencephalon, diencephalon, and mesencephalon in sterotaxic coordinates. J. Comp. Neurol. 118:185.

Visser, J. A., and G. G. J. Rademaker 1934 Die optische Reaktionen der grosshirnloser Taube. Arch. Neerl. de Physiol. 19:482.

Vorgas-Pena, B. 1932 Contributo alla conoscenza dei rapporti tra sensibilita cutanea ed attivita dei lobbi ottici nal colombo. Boll. Soc. Ital. Biol. Sper. 7:762.

Whitlock, D. G. 1952 A neurohistological and neurophysiological study of afferent fiber tracts and receptive areas of the avian cerebellum. J. Comp. Neurol. 97:567.

Whytt, R. 1755 An Essay on the Vital and Other Involuntary Motions of Animals. Hamilton & Neill, Edinburgh.

Windle, W. F., and W. Chambers 1950 Regeneration in the spinal cord in the cat and the dog. J. Comp. Neurol. 93:241.

Wingstrand, K. G. 1951 The structure and development of the avian pituitary. C. W. K. Gleerup, Lund, Sweden.

Index

753